Les Routiers
FRANCE
1995

food and accommodation
RECOMMENDED
for Quality and Value

IN
ASSOCIATION
WITH

First published in the United Kingdom in 1995
Routiers Ltd.
25 Vanston Place
London SW6 1AZ

ISBN 1-85733-142-7

Les Routiers inspectors visit each establishment anonymously and settle their bill before revealing their identity. Complimentary meals and/or accommodation are not accepted.

Les Routiers, 25 Vanston Place, London SW6 1AZ

Tel. 0171 385 6644
Fax: 0171 385 7136

Editor: Malcolm Morris
Assistant Editor: Stephanie Willbond

Design, Typesetting & Map Editing: Castle House Press, Llantrisant
                                          Mid Glamorgan, Wales, UK

Digital Cartography: European Map Graphics Ltd.
                                          Finchampstead, Berkshire, UK

Cover Design: William Stone & Associates, London, UK

Production, Marketing & Distribution: Kuperard (London) Ltd.
                                          No. 9 Hampstead West, 224 Iverson Road
                                          West Hampstead, London NW6 2HL, UK
                                          Tel: 0171 372 4722 / Fax: 0171 372 4599

Printed in Great Britain by: The Bath Press, Bath, Avon, UK

CONTENTS

See Why Our Members Prefer Us

BRITANNIA RESCUE

We Offer You the Choice

Road Rescue – What price peace of mind?
Answer –
Less than you'd think!

For twelve years Britannia Rescue has been providing a fast, efficient breakdown and recovery service, originally exclusively for members of the CMSA. But now, this excellent service is offered to buyers of the Les Routiers Guides to Britain and France. Britain's leading consumer testing magazine in their April 1992 issue, voted Britannia Rescue as their 'Best Buy' with an average callout time of 34 minutes, well ahead of the AA, RAC and National Breakdown.

What services can you have?

Superstart – a home start-up service from £26.50 per year

An economically priced service, ideal for drivers who use their cars infrequently or for shorter journeys. If your car will not start at home, or if you break down within half a mile of home, our agent will come to your assistance. If the car cannot be started you can be taken to a single destination of your choice (within 10 miles) while your car is transported to a local garage.

Rescue Plus – roadside assistance and local recovery service from £30.00 per year

Designed to offer protection against minor breakdowns away from your home. If your problem can't be solved at

BRITANNIA RESCUE

the roadside we will transport you, your vehicle and up to five passengers to a nearby garage. We will also reimburse you up to £12 towards the cost of a taxi or other alternative transport.

Standard Cover – roadside assistance and recovery to nearby garage or home or to an onward destination from £57.25 per year or £5.75 per month*

Cover offers protection from every breakdown situation while away from the vicinity of your home, both for your car and for you. We will endeavour to fix any minor problems on the spot as quickly as possible. If, however, this is not possible, our agent will transport you, your vehicle and up to five passengers home or to the destination of your choice.

Comprehensive Cover– roadside assistance, recovery, attendance at home from £75.70 per year or £7.60 per month*

This cover gives you complete peace of mind. We cater for annoying non-start problems such as flat batteries and damp engines to roadside breakdowns and accident recovery. We also include Housecall, covering you at home or within a half a mile radius of home. It should be noted that Housecall is not intended as a home maintenance service and we would not expect to attend recurring faults.

Deluxe Cover – roadside assistance, recovery, attendance at home, free car hire or hotel accommodation from £92.50 per year or £9.25 per month*

As the name suggest, this is the highest level of cover. You and your vehicle are not only catered for both at home and on the road, but if your car cannot be repaired the same day you can choose between a free replacement car (for up to 48 hours), or assistance with overnight hotel accommodation. Please note that car hire is subject to the terms and conditions of Britannia Rescue's car companies, minimum age of drivers must be 23 years.

Personal Cover – £18.50 per year or £1.85 per month*

Whichever Britannia Rescue cover you choose, for just £18.50 we will extend the cover to include any car you or your spouse/domestic partner may drive.

* Monthly Premiums

Monthly premiums are available on the top three levels of service – Standard, Comprehensive and DeLuxe – when paying by Direct Debit.

All Part of Our Service

Legal advice and defence

We offer every member a 24 hour legal advice service. We can also provide representation in magistrates' courts.

Assistance after theft and vandalism

In the case of vehicle immobilization, we will provide roadside repair or transport to a local garage or on to your destination.

Relief driver

Britannia Rescue will arrange a relief driver to assist you in case of illness, injury or severe mental distress.

Tyres and windscreens

We assist on less serious, but often annoying occasions, such as punctures, shattered windscreens, lack of fuel or even locking your keys in the car.

BRITANNIA RESCUE

Caravans and trailers

These are covered free of charge (excluding Housecall).

Why choose Britannia Rescue?

■ Dedicated to providing every member with a fast, caring road rescue service

■ 34 minutes average callout time

■ Over 3,000 trained personnel on call 24 hours a day 365 days a year

■ A BSI registered firm committed to consistent service quality

■ Value for money prices with easy payment methods

■ Recommended by Britain's leading consumer watchdog as 'Best Buy'

How to apply for Britannia Rescue membership

Near the back of the book you will find an application form and direct debit mandate. Or if you wish to join immediately by telephone, simply ring FREE on 0800 591563 and quote your credit card number!

Travelling abroad

Available to anyone, whether covered by Britannia Rescue in the UK or not, Britannia Continental is a superb emergency breakdown service, competitively priced, and designed to cover any mishap while travelling abroad. There are two types of cover, one for travel with a vehicle in Europe, and the other for travel anywhere in the world. Personal Insurance includes medical repatriation by air ambulance. For further details and a brochure, ring 01484 514848.

Motoring Peace of Mind in France

Britannia Continental offers you, in France and elsewhere in Europe, the standards of road rescue assistance achieved by Britannia Rescue in the UK. Backed up by a 24-hour emergency helpline, Britannia Continental provides a truly comprehensive breakdown package for car, motor cycle, trailer/caravan and motor caravans.

Real help just when you need it!

When an emergency arises abroad, the first thing you need is help from someone who will understand your problems. Our controllers will give you just that! They've met the problem before and they'll handle it with cool, calm efficiency so that the holiday you have looked forward to need not be spoiled.

Summary of protection provided:
Vehicle Cover

Roadside assistance, towing and emergency repairs	£250
Vehicle repatriation to the UK	vehicle market value
Car hire and continuation of journey	£800
Repatriation of driver and passengers	Unlimited
Alternative driver	Unlimited
Hotel expenses	£150 p.p.
Spare parts delivery	Unlimited
Legal defence and claims recovery following motor accident	£50,000
Advance for bail or Customs Duty	£1,000

Personal Cover

	Up to:
Medical and incidental expenses	*£2 million
Hospital inconvenience benefit	£300
Delayed departure	£120
Cancellation and curtailment	*£3,000
Personal accident	£20,000
Personal effects and baggage	*£1,500
Personal legal liability	£1,000,000
Replacement passport	£100
Hijack, kidnap and detention	£1,000
Missed departure	£500
Personal money and travellers cheques	*£500
Legal expenses	£10,000

*Under these sections the first £30 of each and every claim per person is excluded.

Premiums:
Vehicle Cover

Period not exceeding	Vehicles up to 6 years old	Vehicles 7 years to under 13 years	Vehicles 13 years and over
3 days	19.50	24.25	33.25
6 days	29.75	37.25	50.75
9 days	34.50	43.00	58.50
14 days	40.50	50.50	68.75
19 days	45.00	56.25	76.50
24 days	49.50	61.75	83.75
31 days	54.75	68.50	93.00
Extra weeks	9.25	11.50	16.00
Caravan/trailer	14.50	18.00	25.00
Annual cover*	99.00	124.00	168.00

Personal Cover

Period not exceeding	Each person 16 years and over	Children aged 4 to 15 years
3 days	9.00	4.50
6 days	13.75	7.00
9 days	16.50	8.25
14 days	18.75	9.50
19 days	22.50	11.25
24 days	25.00	12.50
31 days	29.50	14.75
Extra weeks	6.50	3.25
Annual Cover*	48.50	41.50

For full details and an application form ring 01484 514848 and ask for the Britannia Continental Department.

*Annual cover is available only to Britannia Rescue members.

Cover can be applied for by telephone quoting your credit card number.

The above prices apply to Britannia Rescue members. In other cases a supplement of £10.00 per policy applies.

LES ROUTIERS WELCOMES YOU!

**A personal introduction from Duncan Bradbury,
Managing Director of *Les Routiers* (Britain)**

Welcome to the *Les Routiers* guide to France, which lists an unrivalled choice of 1,600 carefully selected places where the traveller, businessman or holiday-maker can dine or spend the night in comfort, with excellent value for money.

Les Routiers establishments range from roadside cafés and local bars on the outskirts of fascinating little towns, to colourful brasseries and friendly, family-run hotels nestling in some of France's most picturesque countryside. More impor-tantly, though, they all provide outstanding food and drink, accommodation that is simply furnished but comfortable, and a warm, hearty welcome.

You'll find a world of difference when you stop off at a *Relais Routiers*. Whatever your tastes and requirements, and whether you prefer to remain totally inde-pendent or to immerse yourself in local life, you will find whatever you need.

At *Les Routiers* we feel that these qualities far exceed all other considerations when seeking great places at which to dine and stay in France. And after all, we have been recommending places there since 1934, so we should know what we are talking about. Come and see for yourself.

Bon voyage et bon appetit!

Duncan Bradbury

DISCOVER THE TRUE FLAVOUR OF FRANCE

The arrival of the autoroute café has not soured the infinite variety of Gallic regional cuisines, and in France you can enjoy a diversity of dishes, from a magnificent feast to a simple pâté or a piquant sausage, in the knowledge that, for the French, eating and drinking are more than just a means of satisfying hunger and thirst.

A French breakfast is simply croissant, brioche or bread and butter with coffee, tea, chocolate or fruit juice, but to the French, lunch can be as important as dinner. If you are unable to handle two large meals a day when travelling, then a baguette filled with pâté, ham or tuna and salad is a cheap and satisfying alternative.

THE SIMPLEST INGREDIENTS

The French have an enviable reputation for making an excellent meal out of the simplest ingredients, and it is often the plainest dishes that are the most successful. Once acquainted with this fact, you are ready to tackle the region's specialities.

From the fishing ports come fresh fish and seafood of all varieties . These might include shrimps, lobster and sole, perhaps served with *sauce hollandaise* (a miraculous blend of egg yolks, butter and lemon juice) – or an *assiette des fruits de mer* containing every available kind of shellfish. There are sausages from Lyon, goose from Le Mans, ham from Bayonne and endless other new culinary experiences including *bouillabaisse* (a celebrated fish stew from Marseille), jugged hare from Alsace, or lamprey eels from Bordeaux.

A WEALTH OF CHEESES

Cheeses brimming with flavour are available everywhere. Some, including the famous blue Roquefort and soft, white-crusted Camembert or Brie, are now familiar at home, but there are hundreds more to be explored, whether blue-veined, laden with nuts or made with strong goats' milk. Tempting desserts are likely to include a delicate mousse, a refreshing sorbet, the chef's own speciality, or a tasty array of fruit tarts in light pastry.

The best accompaniment to any meal will be a glass or two of one of the region's excellent wines. For the most complementary taste, choose your wine from the same region as your meal. Bordeaux produces light, easy-to-swallow, mature reds with a hint of tannin; from the Loire valley come crisp, dry white wines with a distinct flavour of fruit. The Rhône valley brings full-flavoured, sweet-tasting reds, elegant whites and excellent rosés, and the whites from Alsace are fruity and fragrant.

LES ROUTIERS IN FRANCE: THE SIGN OF QUALITY AND VALUE

Only after passing the test of recommendation and inspection is an establishment permitted to display the famous red and blue *Relais Routiers* sign – a sign which represents a recognized and reliable standard of achievement in all types of cuisine, and comfortable accommodation throughout France. Look out for it on your travels!

Although the majority of *Relais Routiers* are restaurants , many are also small hotels. In this guide, each establishment is clearly categorized by a symbol alongside its name. Symbols are explained overleaf.

FOOD

As well as the assurance of quality and value, you can be sure that all *Relais Routiers* will offer at least one fixed-price 3-course menu. Choosing this menu gives the traveller a first-class introduction to the specialities of the region without the need to pay the higher à la carte prices.

Certain entries in this guide also show a casserole symbol (🍲). This symbol is the *Les Routiers* "mark of excellence", awarded annually to those *Relais Routiers* where particular care is taken to offer 'above-average' meals. A complete list of *Casserole Relais Routiers* appears on pages 21–23.

ACCOMMODATION

Les Routiers-recommended accommodation is usually simply furnished but clean and comfortable, making it suitable for families and individuals alike. All the establishments have been personally recommended, and are inspected to ensure they observe the basic rules of hygiene in kitchens, bedrooms and bathrooms.

Whether you favour a pretty, country house hotel nestling in the lush pastures and colourful orchards of the Loire, or a lively town-centre hotel with an authentic French atmosphere, you can be sure that *Les Routiers'* standards apply.

Where a hotel has been officially classified by the French Tourist Board, its star-rating indicating level of comfort (on a scale from 1 to 4) appears in our entry. A full list of *Les Routiers* hotels with *Office de Tourisme* star-rating appears on pages 24–29.

REAL FRENCH HOSPITALITY

As most *Relais Routiers* are family-run, you can expect a warm, friendly French welcome, and personal care and attention from your hosts from the minute you arrive until the time comes for you to leave. Many may even give you the chance to dine *en famille*, and although your hosts will in most cases speak some English, you will probably be encouraged to practise your French.

HOW TO USE THIS GUIDE

Les Routiers establishments can be located quickly and easily using this guide.

- **REGIONAL SECTIONS**
  France has been divided into eight regional sections:

Paris and nearby	Central France
Northern France	The Loire Valley
North-West France	South-West France
North-East France	South-East France

- **ENTRIES LISTED ALPHABETICALLY**
  Within each regional section, individual establishments are listed alphabetically by **town name**. The *département* and the post code for each town are also given. Each entry gives details of the establishment, its cuisine and specialities, accommodation, prices, opening hours and facilities, as well as road numbers and directions.

- **COLOUR MAPS**
  Near the front of the book are detailed full-colour regional maps of France, which provide a useful basic touring guide. The maps show many of France's smaller towns, and can be used in conjunction with the directions given in the entry to help you as you drive. A complete map of France shows the location of all the *départements*.

- **INDEX**
  At the back of this guide there is an A–Z index of towns and villages in which there are *Les Routiers* establishments. If you know the name of a town but not its *département* or region, look in the index. If it is not shown, it has no *Relais Routiers*.

- **SYMBOLS USED IN THIS GUIDE**

  🏠 Establishment with accommodation (4 or more rooms, with bed and breakfast available)

  🏨 Establishment with accommodation and dining facilities

  🍴 Restaurant

  🍲 Establishment offering 'above-average' meals *(Relais Casserole)*

  🍸 Bar/café/snacks

  ☆ Official French Tourist Board star-rating

  ☎ Telephone   Fax Fax

  《〓 Sights and places of interest

For complete lists of *Relais Casserole* establishments and hotels with official French Tourist Board star-rating, see pages 21–23 and 24–29.

All prices are based on information supplied by the establishment. Although the prices quoted were correct as we went to press, they cannot be guaranteed.

WHEN IN FRANCE

- Always keep your *Les Routiers* guide with you when visiting restaurants or hotels, to let the owners know that you have chosen their establishment from the guide, and that you are expecting a high standard of food, service and hospitality.

- The French mostly take their holidays in either July or August, and you may find some hotels and restaurants closed. You should *book well in advance* if you intend to travel during this period. Try to avoid travelling on the summer public holidays (14th July or 15th August), or on the first and last day of July and August, when the roads are very crowded.

- **Public holidays** (*fêtes nationales*) in France are worth keeping in mind when you are planning your stay.

  - January 1   *le jour de l'an* (New Year's Day)
  - May 1   *la fête du travail* (Labour Day)
  - May 8   *la Libération* (VE Day)
  - July 14   *le quatorze juillet* (Bastille Day)
  - August 15   *l'Assomption* (Assumption)
  - November 1   *la Toussaint* (All Saints' Day)
  - November 11   *l'Armistice* (Armistice Day)
  - December 25   *Noël* (Christmas Day)

  Variable dates are:
  - Easter Monday   (*lundi de Pâques*)
  - Ascension   (*l'Ascension*) – 6th Thursday after Easter
  - Whit Monday   (*lundi de Pentecôte*) – 2nd Monday after Ascension

- **Smoking** is now banned, by law, in public places. Restaurants and cafés, however small, will have a designated no-smoking area, although smoking is still widespread. There is a total ban on smoking on all forms of public transport.

- **Tipping** presents less of a problem than it once did. By law, a sum is now included in your bill, and there is no need to tip separately in restaurants or hotels. Taxi-drivers will still expect at least 12 percent; and you should still expect to tip people that serve you personally, such as porters, hairdressers, lavatory and cloakroom attendants and tour guides.

- **Visitor information** of all kinds can be obtained in even quite small towns, from the *Office de Tourisme*, sometimes also called the *Syndicat d'Initiative*.

EN ROUTE

Traffic rules in France are very similar to those in Britain and Ireland, with the obvious exception that in France everyone drives on the right! Nevertheless, there are some exceptions, and you should study the points below carefully.

French roads are relatively empty most of the time, although during August, the southbound autoroutes are very crowded with French families heading to the coast for their holiday. If you equip yourself with a good map, driving in France can prove to be an enjoyable part of your holiday.

INSURANCE

Fully comprehensive cover is advisable when travelling abroad. A green card gives you better coverage than the minimum that otherwise applies in France.

Europ Assistance offer special schemes for motorists and passengers, and discounts can be obtained through membership of *Les Routiers' Club Bon Viveur* (turn to the page before the index for details of how to join).

SPEED LIMITS
Dry roads
■ Built-up areas / towns	50 km (30 miles) per hour
■ Main roads	90 km (56 miles) per hour
■ Dual carriageways / non-toll autoroutes	110 km (68 miles) per hour
■ Toll autoroutes (expressways)	130 km (80 miles) per hour

Wet roads
■ Built-up areas / towns	50 km (30 miles) per hour
■ Main roads	80 km (50 miles) per hour
■ Dual carriageways / non-toll autoroutes	100 km (60 miles) per hour
■ Toll autoroutes	110 km (68 miles) per hour

Autoroutes
■ A minimum speed limit of 80 km (50 miles) per hour applies on the outside lane of autoroutes when travelling on level ground, with good visibility, during dry daylight hours.

New drivers
■ New drivers must not exceed 90 km (56 miles) per hour in the first year after passing their test.

AUTOROUTES

France has over 3,000 miles of autoroutes, making it possible to cover large distances with considerable speed.

■ **Tolls** (*péages*) are charged on most autoroutes. Usually a ticket is issued and a toll paid when you leave the autoroute or at intermediate points during your journey.

Some autoroute stretches have automatic collection points where you throw the change into a basket. If you do not have the correct change, use the marked, separate lane. Travellers cheques are NOT accepted, but use a Visa card as an alternative. Toll charges vary according to route.

- **Free emergency telephones** are available every 2 km on autoroutes.
- **Parking and resting areas** (*aires de repos*) occur every 10 km; 24-hour services can be found at regular intervals of about 40 km.
- **Alternative routes** are signed, so you may choose to follow the 'Green Arrow' routes (*itinéraires bis*). This will help you escape the autoroute tolls and the most congested roads; there should be less traffic, and the routes provide a more scenic journey.

PETROL

Remember that *l'essence* is the word for petrol (*pétrole* means crude oil or paraffin). Diesel is considerably cheaper in France, and unleaded petrol is widely available. Ask as follows:

Please fill her up with . . . .   *le plein de . . . , s'il vous plaît.*
I'd like . . . litres of . . . .   *. . . litres de . . . , s'il vous plaît.*
super (4-star)   *de super*   unleaded   *de sans plomb*
ordinary (2-star)   *d'ordinaire*   diesel   *de gazole*

LAWS AND REGULATIONS

- **For speeding**, the minimum fine is 1,300 Frs.
- **Breath-test limits** are the same as in the United Kingdom (80 mg), but are *lower* than in the Republic of Ireland (100 mg). Tests are held at random. On-the-spot fines may be 2,000 to 3,000 Frs.
- **Minimum driving age** in France is 18 not 17.
- **Seat belts** are compulsory for the driver and all passengers. Failure to wear a seat-belt can result in a fine of between 450 and 1,000 Frs.
- **The use of car telephones** is prohibited, and you should affix a note to the telephone unit indicating the prohibition.
- **Documentation** is required. You must carry the original vehicle registration document, an International Driving Permit or your full national driving licence and current insurance certificate, plus a letter of authority from the owner if the vehicle is not registered in your name.
- **A red warning triangle** must be carried, unless the car has hazard flashers. Warning triangles are COMPULSORY when towing a caravan or trailer.
- **Headlights** must be altered for driving on the right, using beam deflectors. Yellow-tinted headlights are no longer compulsory.

OTHER POINTS TO REMEMBER

To avoid hefty, on-the-spot fines or worse, keep the following in mind:
- **No driving** on a provisional licence.
- **Seat belts** must be worn, by law, by the driver and front-seat passengers (rear passengers also, if belts are fitted).
- **Children under 12** must travel in the back.
- **STOP** signs mean STOP. Come to a complete halt.
- **No stopping** on an open road unless the car is completely OFF the road.
- **No overtaking** on an unbroken single white line. Heavy penalties can be imposed.
- **Sidelights** can only be used on their own when the car is stationary.
- **Spare bulbs** are essential. Take a full kit, or you may be fined if found driving with faulty lights.

USEFUL EXPRESSIONS *EN ROUTE*

Where is . . . ?

Where is . . . road / street?   *Où se trouve la rue . . .?*

How do I get to the bank?   *Comment aller à la banque?*

How do I get to the post office?   *Comment aller à la poste?*

Where can I find a post-box?   *Comment puis-je trouver une boîte aux lettres?*

Where is the police station?   *Où se trouve la gendarmerie?*

Getting to a garage

How far is the nearest garage?   *A quelle distance se trouve le garage le plus proche?*

Is it far?   *Est-ce loin?*

Do I go straight on?   *Faut-il aller tout droit?*

Turn around / do a U-turn?   *Faire demi-tour?*

Do I have to turn left / right?   *Dois-je tourner à gauche / à droite?*

At which traffic lights do I turn?   *Je tourne à quel feu?*

Fill her up please.   *Le plein, s'il vous plaît.*

In case of breakdown

I have broken down.   *Je suis en panne.*

I have a flat tyre.   *J'ai un pneu crevé.*

It's overheating.   *Cela surchauffe.*

The battery needs recharging.   *La batterie a besoin d'etre rechargeé.*

The . . . does not work.   *Le / la . . . ne marche pas.*

The . . . is broken.   *Le / la . . . est cassé(e).*

Will it take long?   *Ce sera vite fait?*

Vehicle part-names

axle	*essieu*	heating	*chauffage*
battery	*batterie*	horn	*avertisseur*
brake	*frein*	ignition	*allumage*
carburettor	*carburateur*	indicator	*(feu) clignotant*
choke	*starter*	oil	*huile*
clutch	*embrayage*	radiator	*radiateur*
distributor	*allumeur*	silencer	*silencieux*
door	*portière*	spark-plug	*bougie*
engine	*moteur*	steering	*direction*
exhaust-pipe	*tuyau d'échappement*	steering wheel	*volant*
		suspension	*suspension*
fan belt	*courroie*	tachograph	*contrôlographe*
fuel tank	*réservoir de carburant*	tyre	*pneu*
fuse	*fusible*	warning light	*voyant*
gearbox	*boîte de vitesses*	wheel	*roue*
hand brake	*frein à main*	windscreen	*pare-brise*
headlight	*phare*	windscreen wiper	*essuie-glace*

A L'HOTEL

- French *Hotels de Tourisme* are officially classified with one to four star-ratings according to the level of comfort. The stars are displayed on a blue plaque by the main entrance. There are also many unclassified hotels in France, where standards are equally acceptable.
- Accommodation prices are *for the room*, not the number of occupants. Only a small extra charge is usually made if more than two people share, which is helpful for families travelling on a budget. Room prices are, by law, displayed on a card on the back of the room door.
- It is normal to view the room before accepting it. This allows you to check the level of cleanliness and comfort. We recommend that all advance bookings should be made from our selection of approved *Relais Routiers Hôtels de Tourisme*.
- If you have booked a room, try to arrive before 6pm unless you have already advised the hotel otherwise. Without a reservation, your chances of finding a room after 6pm are slight.
- Many small hotels lock their doors quite early at night. Advise the proprietors if you are going out, so they can make arrangements for you.

USEFUL EXPRESSIONS *A L'HOTEL*

single room	*une chambre à un lit*	bathroom	*salle de bain*
double room	*une chambre pour*	shower	*douche*
	deux personnes avec un grand lit	breakfast	*petit déjeuner*
twin room	*une chambre avec*	half board	*demi-pension*
	deux lits	full board	*pension complète*

Do you have a room available? *Avez-vous une chambre libre?*
How much does that room cost? *Combien coûte la chambre?*
I would like to reserve a twin room with bathroom. *Je voudrais réserver une chambre à deux lits avec salle de bains.*
I'd like to reserve a table for 2 / 3 / 4. *Je voudrais réserver une table pour deux / trois / quatre personnes.*
I'd like to book / reserve . . . . *Je voudrais retenir / réserver . . . .*
At what time is dinner? *A quelle heure servez-vous le dîner?*
Can I have the menu please? *Voulez-vous me donner le menu?*
Do you have a set menu? *Avez-vous un menu du jour?*
Where are the toilets? *Où sont les toilettes?*
Could you prepare my bill please? *Pouvez-vous me préparer la note?*
How much do I owe you? *Combien vous dois-je?*
Does anyone here speak English? *Y-a-t-il quelqu'un ici qui parle anglais?*

AU RESTAURANT

MEALS
- A *repas complet* is a full meal served only at set mealtimes. A *casse-croûte* is a snack meal, often available at a bar or café. It might consist of an omelette, a sandwich or a selection of cold meats, and can be served at any time.
- A restaurant will usually offer two or three fixed-price three- or four-course meals (*menu prix-fixe*) at different prices, as well as the main list of dishes (*à la carte*), where each item is priced separately. The fixed-price menu is always the cheapest way to eat, and a meal ordered at lunchtime is often cheaper than the same meal in the evening.

TIPPING
- A service charge is now always included in the price of a meal (*service compris* or *SC*). Tips are rarely given, except to round up the price of a meal.

DRINKS
- *Vin compris* on a menu means that a *pichet* (jug) of ordinary or house wine is included in the price. *Boisson compris* (or *BC*) means that a drink is included. This can often vary, from a *pichet* of wine, a beer or a bottle of mineral water, so do check what is available.
- By law, free tap water (*l'eau du robinet*) must be provided if you are having a meal. If you prefer not to drink this, ask for *une bouteille d'eau minérale*; this is, of course, a chargeable item. Mineral water, both carbonated (*eau gazeuse*) and still (*eau non gazeuse*), is widely drunk, and a good variety will be found everywhere.
- Soft drinks and fruit juices are far more expensive in France than in Britain or Ireland. Try a brightly-coloured *sirop*, which is diluted with water like a sweet cordial. It is a much cheaper alternative to Coca Cola or lemonade.
- Prices in cafés must, by law, be clearly displayed. Drinks will be more expensive if taken sitting at a table as opposed to standing at the bar.

BON APPETIT!

UNDERSTANDING THE MENU

Meat (*les viandes*):

abats offal	*génisse* heifer
agneau lamb	*gésiers* (chicken) gizzards
andouille/tte chitterling sausage	*gigot* leg of mutton
boeuf beef	*grenouille* frog
boudin black pudding	*jambon* ham
charolais best cut	*jambon cru* raw smoked ham
chateaubriand double fillet steak	*langue* tongue
cochon piglet	*petit salé* pickled pork
contrefilet sirloin	*porc* pork
cuisses (de grenouille) (frogs') legs	*quenelle* meatball
daube stew	*rillettes* potted pork
entrecôte rib steak	*rillons* crackling
escargot snail	*ris* sweetbreads
faux filet sirloin steak	*rognons* kidneys
filet fillet	*sanglier* boar
foie liver	*tripes* tripe
foie gras goose liver	*veau* veal

Poultry / game (*la volaille / le gibier*):

caille quail	*gibelotte* hare/rabbit
canard duck	*lapin* rabbit
caneton duckling	*lievre* hare
cassoulet goose/pork/ bean casserole	*oie* goose
chevreuil venison	*perdrix* partridge
dindon turkey	*pintade* guinea fowl
faisan pheasant	*poulet* chicken

Fish / shellfish (*les poissons / les coquillages*):

anguille eel	*limande* lemon sole
cabillaud cod (fresh)	*lotte de mer* monkfish
calmar squid	*loup (de mer)* sea bass
coquille St-Jacques scallop	*maquereau* mackerel
crabe crab	*morue* cod (salt)
crevette rose/grise prawn/shrimp	*mouclade* mussels (in curry sauce)
daurade sea bream	*moule* mussel
écrevisse crayfish	*plie* plaice
espadon swordfish	*raie* skate
flétan halibut	*sandre* zander (freshwater fish)
fritures whitebait	*saumon* salmon
fruits de mer seafood	*seiche* cuttlefish
gamba large prawn	*Saint-Pierre* John Dory
homard lobster	*thon* tuna
huître oyster	*truite* trout
langouste crayfish	

Fruit / vegetables / herbs / spices
(*les fruits* / *les légumes* / *les herbes* / *les epices*):

ail	garlic	*fraise*	strawberry
ananas	pineapple	*framboise*	raspberry
aneth	dill	*gingembre*	ginger
abricot	apricot	*griotte*	morello cherry
artichaut	artichoke	*groseille*	gooseberry
asperge	asparagus	*haricot vert*	French bean
avocat	avocado	*laitue*	lettuce
banane	banana	*menthe*	mint
basilic	basil	*morille*	(flat) mushroom
cassis	blackcurrant	*mûre*	blackberry
cep	vine-stock	*muscade*	nutmeg
cep / cèpe	flat mushroom	*myrtille*	blueberry
		oignon	onion
cerise	cherry	*oseille*	sorrel
champignon	mushroom	*pamplemousse*	grapefruit
chou	cabbage	*pêche*	peach
choucroute	sauerkraut	*persil*	parsley
choufleur	cauliflower	*petit pois*	pea
ciboulette	chive	*poire*	pear
citron	lemon	*poireau*	leek
citron vert	lime	*poivre*	pepper
concombre	cucumber	*poivron*	green / red / yellow pepper
coriandre	coriander		
cornichon	gherkin	*pomme*	apple
courgette	courgette	*pomme de terre*	potato
couscous	North African semolina dish	*prune*	plum
		pruneau	prune
cresson	watercress	*radis*	radish
échalote	shallot	*raisin*	grape
endive	chicory	*romarin*	rosemary
épinards	spinach	*safran*	saffron
estragon	tarragon	*thym*	thyme
fenouil	fennel	*tomate*	tomato
fève	broad bean	*truffe*	truffle

USEFUL EXPRESSIONS *AU RESTAURANT*

Have you a table for . . . people? *Avez-vous une table pour . . . personnes?*
I'd like to reserve a table. *Je voudrais réserver une table.*
The menu / bill, please. *Le menu / l'addition, s'il vous plaît.*
I'll have the 80 Fr. (fixed-price) menu. *Le menu à 80 Fr. s'il vous plaît.*

OTHER USEFUL EXPRESSIONS

GREETINGS / GENERAL CONVERSATION

good morning / afternoon   *bonjour*
good evening   *bonsoir*
goodbye   *au revoir*
yes / no   *oui / non*
please / thank you   *s'il vous plaît /*
   merci
sorry / excuse me   *excusez-moi*
where / when / how   *où / quand /*
   comment
how much?   *combien?*

day / week / month   *jour /*
   semaine / mois
good / bad   *bon / mauvais*
big / small   *grand / petit*
cheap / expensive   *bon marché /*
   cher
hot / cold   *chaud / froid*
old / new   *vieux / neuf*
open / closed   *ouvert / fermé*
early / late   *tôt / tard*

ACCIDENT / ILLNESS

I have had an accident.   *J'ai en un accident.*
Call an ambulance.   *Appelez une ambulance.*
Where can I find a doctor?   *Où puis-je trouver un docteur?*
Where is the nearest chemist?   *Où est la pharmacie la plus proche?*
Do you have any aspirin?   *Avez-vous des aspirines?*

SIGHTS AND PLACES OF INTEREST

The vocabulary that follows may be useful as you consult the **sights and places
of interest** (◁⊱) in our entries.

barrage   dam
beffroi   belfry
blindé   tank (armoured)
bord   bank (of a river)
carrière   quarry
cascade   waterfall
cave   cellar
corderie   rope-making
   factory
corniche   coast / cliff-road
cristallerie   glass-works
croisière   cruise
dégustation   tasting
dentelle   lace
dolmen   megalithic tomb
église   church
environs   surroundings
étang   pond
fabrique   factory
faïencerie   earthenware factory /
   pottery
falaise   cliff
fouilles   excavations

gouffre   abyss, gulf
grotte   cave
guerre   war
haras   stud farm
hôtel de ville   town hall
marais   marsh
métier   trade, craft
mine d'argent   silver mine
moulin à vent   windmill
pêche   fishing
pierre sculptée   sculpted stone
plage du débarquement   landing
   beach
plage   beach
pont   bridge
poupée   doll
rapace   bird of prey
sabotier   clog maker
singe   monkey
souffleur de verre   glass-blower
tapisserie   tapestry
usine   factory
vieille ville   old town

FRANCE
KEY TO MAP PAGES

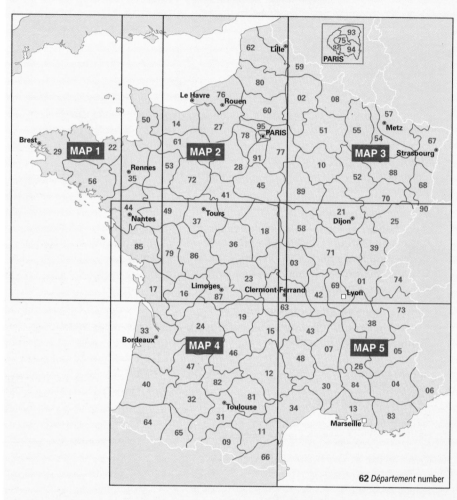

93
75
92 94
PARIS

62
Lille
59
80
Le Havre 76
Rouen
60
02
08
57
Metz
50
14
27
95
PARIS
51
55
54
67
Brest
29
MAP 1
22
61
78
MAP 2
77
MAP 3
Strasbourg
Rennes
53
28
91
10
52
88
56
35
72
45
89
70
68
44
Nantes
49
Tours
37
18
58
21
Dijon
25
90
85
79
86
36
71
39
17
Limoges
16
87
23
Clermont-Ferrand
42
03
69
01
Lyon
74
63
73
33
Bordeaux
24
15
43
38
MAP 4
46
48
07
MAP 5
05
47
12
26
40
82
30
84
04
06
32
81
Toulouse
34
13
83
64
31
Marseille
65
11
09
66

62 *Département* number

KEY TO MAP SYMBOLS

A26 — Autoroute

N1 — Route Nationale

— Route Départementale

— International boundary

Town	Population
▣ **PARIS**	over 1 million
☐ **MARSEILLE**	500,000–1 million
◉ **Nantes**	250,000–500,000
○ Cherbourg	100,000–250,000
● Beauvais	25,000–100,000
○ Amboise	10,000–25,000
●● Luz, Agay	less than 10,000

0   25   50   75 km
0   25   50 miles

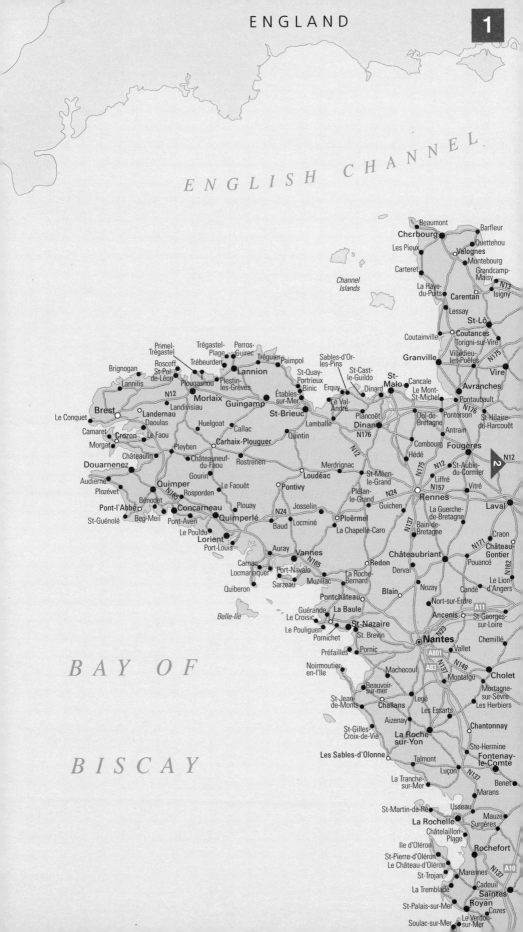

USEFUL ADDRESSES

EMBASSIES AND CONSULATES

N.B. : Paris / Ile-de-France telephone numbers should be preceded by **1** if dialling from outside Paris / Ile-de-France. Prefix also with **00-33** if dialling from the UK or Ireland.

- **UNITED KINGDOM** (Consulate)
  16 rue d'Anjou, 75008 Paris
  ☎ (1) 42.66.38.10

- **IRELAND** (Consulate)
  4 rue Rude, 75116 Paris
  ☎ (1) 45.00.20.87

- **USA** (Consulate)
  2 rue St-Florentin, 75001 Paris
  ☎ (1) 42.96.12.02

- **CANADA** (Consulate)
  35 av. Montaigne, 75008 Paris
  ☎ (1) 47.23.01.01

- **AUSTRALIA** (Embassy / Consulate)
  4 rue Jean-Rey,
  75015 Paris
  ☎ (1) 40.59.33.00

- **NEW ZEALAND** (Embassy / Chancellery)
  7 ter rue Léonard-de-Vinci,
  75016 Paris
  ☎ (1) 45.00.24.11

- **SOUTH AFRICA** (Chancellery / Consulate)
  59 quai d'Orsay, 75007 Paris
  ☎ (1) 45.55.92.37

TOURIST INFORMATION OFFICES

- **UNITED KINGDOM** (French Government Tourist Office / Maison de la France)
  178, Piccadilly, London W1V 0AL
  ☎ (0891) 244123 (calls charged at premium rate)

- **IRELAND** (French Government Tourist Office / Maison de la France)

  35, Lower Abbey Street, Dublin 1
  ☎ (01) 7034046

- **FRANCE** (Office du Tourisme de Paris)
  Enquiries handled covering all of France:
  127 av. des Champs-Elysées,
  75008 Paris
  ☎ (1) 47.23.61.72

ANNUAL KEY EVENTS IN FRANCE

Information on major events can be obtained from the three tourist information offices listed above.

CASSEROLE RELAIS ROUTIERS

Some *Les Routiers* establishments offer a more elaborate menu, still at a reasonable price. They are listed below according to their chapter in this guide, and a casserole symbol ⌒ appears with their entry.

TOWN	DEPARTEMENT	ESTABLISHMENT
PARIS AND NEARBY		
PIERREFITTE-SUR-SEINE	Seine-St-Denis, 93380	LE NORMANDIE
VOULX	Seine-et-Marne, 77940	LA BRUYERE
NORTHERN FRANCE		
MERLIMONT	Pas-de-Calais, 62155	LE CURACAO
NORTH-EAST FRANCE		
AUXERRE	Yonne, 89000	LE SAINTE NITASSE
BEAUMONT-SUR-VESLE	Marne, 51360	LA MAISON DU CHAMPAGNE
BOUXWILLER	Bas-Rhin, 67330	AU SOLEIL
CLUNY	Saône-et-Loire, 71250	AUBERGE DU CHEVAL BLANC
COSNE-SUR-LOIRE	Nièvre, 58200	LES 3 COULEURS
HYEVRE-PAROISSE	Doubs, 25110	RELAIS LA CREMAILLERE
NANCY	Meurthe-et-Moselle, 54000	RESTAURANT DU PORT
ORNANS	Doubs, 25290	LE PROGRES
LA TOUR-DU-MEIX	Jura, 39270	AUBERGE DU PONT DE LA PYLE
VENDENHEIM	Bas-Rhin, 67550	LE RELAIS DE LA MAISON ROUGE
NORTH-WEST FRANCE		
BALLEROY	Calvados, 14490	LE RELAIS DE LA FORET
BAYEUX	Calvados, 14400	LA COLOMBE
BEDEE	Ille-et-Vilaine, 35137	HOTEL DU COMMERCE
CABOURG	Calvados, 14490	L'AUBERGE DES VIVIERS
CAST	Finistère, 29150	LE RELAIS SAINT GILDAS
COUTANCES	Manche, 50202	LE RELAIS DU VIADUC
DINAN	Côtes-d'Armor, 22100	LA MARMITE
DINARD	Ille-et-Vilaine, 35800	L'EPICURIEN
DOL-DE-BRETAGNE	Ille-et-Vilaine, 35120	LE RELAIS DE BELLE LANDE
ELVEN	Morbihan, 56250	LE RELAIS DE L'ARGOUET
LA GUERCHE-DE-BRETAGNE	Ille-et-Vilaine, 35130	LE RELAIS DU PONT-D'ANJOU
LA HAYE-PESNEL	Manche, 50320	CHEZ ARMELLE
JALLAIS	Maine-et-Loire, 49510	LE VERT GALANT - La Croix Verte
LAMBALLE	Côtes-d'Armor, 22400	LA TOUR D'ARGENT

TOWN	DEPARTEMENT	ESTABLISHMENT
LANDEVANT	Morbihan, 56690	LE RELAIS DU PELICAN
LANDIVISIAU	Finistère, 29400	LE TERMINUS
MONTAUBAN-DE-BRETAGNE	Ille-et-Vilaine, 35360	HOTEL DE FRANCE
MOUZEUIL-SAINT-MARTIN	Vendée, 85370	CENTRAL ROUTIERS
PLOUER-SUR-RANCE	Côtes-d'Armor, 22490	LE BON ACCUEIL
PONT-AVEN	Finistère, 29930	CHEZ MELANIE ET MONIQUE
PONTCHATEAU	Loire-Atlantique, 44160	L'AUBERGE DU CALVAIRE
PONTCHATEAU	Loire-Atlantique, 44160	LE RELAIS DE BEAULIEU
RICHEVILLE	Eure, 27420	RESTAURANT LE BALTO
SAINT-GILDAS-DES-BOIS	Loire-Atlantique, 44530	RELAIS CASSEROLE LES ROUTIERS
SAINT-MARTIN-DES-BESACES	Calvados, 14350	LA RENAISSANCE
SAINT-SYMPHORIEN-DES-MONTS	Manche, 50640	LE RELAIS DU BOIS LEGER
SAINTE-LUCE-SUR-LOIRE	Loire-Atlantique, 44980	LA BOUGRIERE
SENE	Morbihan, 56860	RELAIS ROUTIERS
SIZUN	Finistère, 29450	HOTEL-RESTAURANT DES VOYAGEURS
VERNON	Eure, 27200	SARL DU HAMEAU FLEURI
VIRE	Calvados, 14500	HOTEL DE FRANCE
VIVY	Maine-et-Loire, 49680	RESTAURANT SAINT-PAUL

THE LOIRE

BARBEZIEUX-SAINT-HILAIRE	Charente, 16120	RELAIS DE LA BILLETTE
CHARTRES	Eure-et-Loir, 28000	RELAIS BEAUCERON
CHARTRES	Eure-et-Loir, 28000	RESTAURANT LE PALMIER
CHATEAUNEUF-SUR-LOIRE	Loiret, 45110	HOTEL DE LA PLACE
MAROLLES	Eure-et-Loir, 28260	AU RELAIS DE MAROLLES
NEUVY	Loir-et-Cher, 41250	LA CHEMINEE
SAINT-EUGENE	Charente-Maritime, 17520	LES DEUX CHARENTES
SECONDIGNY	Deux-Sèvres, 79130	LES ROUTIERS
SUEVRES	Loir-et-Cher, 41500	LE RELAIS DE LA PROVIDENCE
SURY-AUX-BOIS	Loiret, 45530	LE RELAIS DU PONT DES BEIGNERS
THEILLAY	Loir-et-Cher, 41300	RELAIS DE LA LOGE
LA TRIMOUILLE	Vienne, 86290	L'AUBERGE FLEURIE
VILLEDOMER	Indre-et-Loire, 37110	LES GRANDS VINS DE TOURAINE

CENTRAL FRANCE

BEAUNE-LES-MINES	Haute-Vienne, 87280	LA TERRASSE DE BEAUNE
COSTAROS	Haute-Loire, 43490	LES ROUTIERS
PONT-DE-MENAT	Puy-de-Dôme, 63560	CHEZ ROGER
SAINT-FLOUR	Cantal, 15100	LE PROGRES

TOWN	DEPARTEMENT	ESTABLISHMENT
SAINT-JUST-LE-MARTEL	Haute-Vienne, 87590	LE PETIT SALE
VARENNES-SUR-ALLIER	Allier, 03150	LES TOURISTES

SOUTH-WEST FRANCE

BERTHOLENE	Aveyron, 12310	HOTEL BANCAREL
CAMPSEGRET	Dordogne, 24140	LES TAMARIS
CENAC	Dordogne, 24250	LA PROMENADE
ESCOURCE	Landes, 40210	AU ROUTIER
GRAMAT	Lot, 46500	HOTEL DU CENTRE
LANGON	Gironde, 33210	HOTEL-RESTAURANT DARLOT
LAUSSEIGNAN-BARBASTE	Lot-et-Garonne, 47230	LES PALMIERS
MOISSAC	Tarn-et-Garonne, 82200	RELAIS AUVERGNAT
MUSSIDAN	Dordogne, 24400	LE PERIGORD
ONET-LE-CHATEAU	Aveyron, 12850	LA ROCADE
REMOULINS	Gard, 30210	AUBERGE LES PLATANES
ROUFFIGNAC-DE-SIGOULES	Dordogne, 24240	LA TAVERNE ALSACIENNE
SAINT-PAUL-DE-LOUBRESSAC	Lot, 46170	RELAIS DE LA MADELEINE
SAINTE-MARIE-DE-GOSSE	Landes, 40390	LES ROUTIERS
SAINTE-TERRE	Gironde, 33350	CHEZ REGIS

SOUTH-EAST FRANCE

CAZAN	Bouches-du-Rhône, 13116	L'ESCALIER
CORMORANCHE-SUR-SAONE	Ain, 01290	AUBERGE CHEZ LA MERE MARTINET
CORPS	Isère, 38970	RESTAURANT DU TILLEUL
EYGUIANS	Hautes Alpes, 05300	HOTEL DE LA GARE
GUILLESTRE	Hautes Alpes, 05600	HOTEL DE LA GARE
LIGNANE	Bouches-du-Rhône, 13540	LE RELAIS DE LIGNANE
MEGEVE	Haute-Savoie, 74120	CHALET DES FLEURS
PAJAY	Isère, 38260	MA PETITE AUBERGE
PIOLENC	Vaucluse, 84420	LE COMMERCE
ROCHETAILLEE	Isère, 38520	HOTEL BELLEDONNE
SAINT-JEAN-DE-MAURIENNE	Savoie, 73300	BAR-RESTAURANT RELAIS ROUTIERS
SAINT-RAPHAEL	Var, 83700	BEL AZUR
THONES	Haute-Savoie, 74230	L'HERMITAGE
LA TOUR-DU-PIN	Isère, 38110	CHEZ BABETH

HOTELS DE TOURISME

The following *Les Routiers* establishments are classified *Hôtels de Tourisme*. Fuller information on the French star-rating system is given on page 9.

STAR-RATING	TOWN	DEPARTEMENT	ESTABLISHMENT
PARIS AND NEARBY			
☆	CHAMARANDE	Essonne, 91730	RELAIS DE MONTFORT
☆	MONTLHERY	Essonne, 91310	LE SOLOGNE
NORTHERN FRANCE			
☆	BAILLEUL	Nord, 59270	AUBERGE DU SEAU
☆	BAPAUME	Pas-de-Calais, 62450	CHEZ BERNADETTE
☆	BRUAY-LA-BUISSIERE	Pas-de-Calais, 62700	LA LOUETTE
☆	FORMERIE	Oise, 60220	CAFE DE LA PAIX
NORTH-EAST FRANCE			
☆	ANCERVILLE	Meuse, 55170	LE RELAIS
☆	ARCES	Yonne, 89320	RELAIS DE LA FORET D'OTHE
☆ ☆	ARCHES	Vosges, 88380	LA TRUITE RENOMMEE
☆	AUXERRE	Yonne, 89000	LE SAINTE NITASSE
☆ ☆	BEAUMONT-SUR-VESLE	Marne, 51360	LA MAISON DU CHAMPAGNE
☆	BOUILLY	Aube, 10320	AU RELAIS MONTAIGU
☆ ☆	BOUXWILLER	Bas-Rhin, 67330	AU SOLEIL
☆	COSNE-SUR-LOIRE	Nièvre, 58200	LES 3 COULEURS
☆	FUMAY	Ardennes, 08170	HOTEL LION
☆ ☆ ☆	HYEVRE-PAROISSE	Doubs, 25110	RELAIS LA CREMAILLERE
☆	KOGENHEIM	Bas-Rhin, 67230	A L'ETOILE
☆	MERCUREY	Saône-et-Loire, 71640	LE MERCUREY
☆	ORNANS	Doubs, 25290	LE PROGRES
☆ ☆	OSTHEIM	Haut-Rhin, 68150	HOTEL-RESTAURANT BALTZINGER
☆	PLOMBIERES-LES-BAINS	Vosges, 88370	TOURING STRASBOUR-GEOIS
☆ ☆	RONCHAMP	Haute-Saône, 70250	A LA POMME D'OR

STAR-RATING	TOWN	DEPARTEMENT	ESTABLISHMENT
☆ ☆	SAINT-PIERREMONT	Vosges, 88700	LE RELAIS VOSGIEN
☆	SAINTE-MARGUERITE	Vosges, 88100	LE RELAIS DES AMIS
☆ ☆	TROYES	Aube, 10000	LE SPLENDID

NORTH-WEST FRANCE

STAR-RATING	TOWN	DEPARTEMENT	ESTABLISHMENT
☆	AIZENAY	Vendée, 85190	LE SAINT-BENOIST
☆	BALLEROY	Calvados, 14490	LE RELAIS DE LA FORET
☆	BEDEE	Ille-et-Vilaine, 35137	HOTEL DU COMMERCE
☆	BESSE-SUR-BRAYE	Sarthe, 72310	LES ROUTIERS
☆	BOSGUERARD-DE-MARCOUVILLE	Eure, 27520	LA TETE D'OR
☆ ☆	CABOURG	Calvados, 14490	L'AUBERGE DES VIVIERS
☆	CHATEAUBRIANT	Loire-Atlantique, 44110	SARL PARIS / OCEAN
☆ ☆	DOUE-LA-FONTAINE	Maine-et-Loire, 49700	CHEZ PAUL
☆	ELVEN	Morbihan, 56250	LE RELAIS DE L'ARGOUET
☆ ☆	ERBRAY	Loire-Atlantique, 44110	LE SAINT-HUBERT
☆	FOUGERES	Ille-et-Vilaine, 35300	AUX AMIS DE LA ROUTE
☆	LA GUERCHE-DE-BRETAGNE	Ille-et-Vilaine, 35130	LE RELAIS DU PONT D'ANJOU
☆	LES HERBIERS	Vendée, 85500	L'OREE DES BOIS VERTS
☆ ☆	JALLAIS	Maine-et-Loire, 49510	LE VERT GALANT – La Croix Verte
☆ ☆	LAMBALLE	Côtes-d'Armor, 22400	LA TOUR D'ARGENT
☆	LANDIVISIAU	Finistère, 29400	LE TERMINUS
☆	LANESTER	Morbihan, 56600	LA ROTONDE
☆	LOUDEAC	Côtes-d'Armor, 22600	LES ROUTIERS
☆	MALE	Orne, 61260	HOTEL DE LA BELLE RENCONTRE
☆ ☆	LE MONT-SAINT-MICHEL	Manche, 50116	HOTEL MOTEL VERT
☆ ☆	MONTAUBAN-DE-BRETAGNE	Ille-et-Vilaine, 35360	HOTEL DE FRANCE
☆ ☆	MONTAUBAN-DE-BRETAGNE	Ille-et-Vilaine, 35360	RELAIS DE LA HUCHERAIS
☆ ☆	MONTMARTIN-SUR-MER	Manche, 50590	HOTELLERIE DU BON VIEUX TEMPS

STAR-RATING	TOWN	DEPARTEMENT	ESTABLISHMENT
☆ ☆	MOREAC	Morbihan, 56500	LE RELAIS DU BARDERFF
☆	PIPRIAC	Ille-et-Vilaine, 35550	HOTEL DE LA TOUR D'AUVERGNE
☆ ☆	PLOUAGAT	Côtes-d'Armor, 22170	CHEZ PIERRETTE
☆ ☆	PONTCHATEAU	Loire-Atlantique, 44160	L'AUBERGE DU CALVAIRE
☆ ☆	LA ROCHE-SUR-YON	Vendée, 85000	HOTEL SULLY
☆ ☆	ROMAGNY	Manche, 50140	AUBERGE DES CLOSEAUX
☆ ☆	SAINT-BERTHEVIN	Mayenne, 53940	L'INTERNATIONAL
☆ ☆	SAINT-HILAIRE-DE-LOULAY	Vendée, 85600	LE RELAX
☆	SAINT-MARTIN-DES-BESACES	Calvados, 14350	LA RENAISSANCE
☆	SAINT-POL-DE-LEON	Finistère, 29250	LES ROUTIERS – Le Passiflore
☆	SAINT-VINCENT-STERLANGES	Vendée, 85110	A L'ACCUEIL VENDEEN – Chez Dudu
☆ ☆	SAUMUR	Maine-et-Loire, 49400	HOTEL-RESTAURANT DE LA GARE
☆	SENE	Morbihan, 56860	RELAIS ROUTIERS
☆ ☆	SIZUN	Finistère, 29450	HOTEL-RESTAURANT DES VOYAGEURS
☆ ☆	VANNES	Morbihan, 56190	L'AUBERGE VIEILLE FONTAINE
☆	VILLERS-SUR-MER	Calvados, 14640	LE NORMAND
☆ ☆	VIRE	Calvados, 14500	HOTEL DE FRANCE
☆	VIVY	Maine-et-Loire, 49680	RESTAURANT SAINT-PAUL

THE LOIRE

STAR-RATING	TOWN	DEPARTEMENT	ESTABLISHMENT
☆ ☆	AIGURANDE	Indre, 36140	LE RELAIS DE LA MARCHE
☆ ☆	CHARTRES	Eure-et-Loir, 28000	RELAIS BEAUCERON
☆ ☆	CHATEAU-LA-VALLIERE	Indre-et-Loire, 37330	LE GRAND CERF
☆	CHATILLON-SUR-INDRE	Indre, 36700	AUBERGE DE LA PROMENADE
☆	CHAUNAY-BOURG	Vienne, 86510	LE COMMERCE
☆	CORME-ROYAL	Charente-Maritime, 17600	L'AUBERGE CORNILLONNE
☆	MOULISMES	Vienne, 86500	LA TABLE OUVERTE

STAR-RATING	TOWN	DEPARTEMENT	ESTABLISHMENT
☆	LA ROCHELLE	Charente-Maritime, 17000	L'AQUARELLE
☆	ROMORANTIN-LANTHENAY	Loir-et-Cher, 41200	LES AUBIERS
☆	SAINT-GENIS-DE-SAINTONGE	Charente-Maritime, 17240	LE RELAIS DE SAINTONGE
☆	SAINTE-MAURE-DE-TOURAINE	Indre-et-Loire, 37800	L'ETOILE DU SUD
☆	SAUJON	Charente-Maritime, 17600	HOTEL DE LA GARE
☆	SULLY-SUR-LOIRE	Loiret, 45600	CHEZ LIONEL
☆	THEILLAY	Loir-et-Cher, 41300	RELAIS DE LA LOGE
☆	YMONVILLE	Eure-et-Loir, 28150	A L'ETOILE

CENTRAL FRANCE

STAR-RATING	TOWN	DEPARTEMENT	ESTABLISHMENT
☆ ☆	CLERMONT-FERRAND	Puy-de-Dôme, 63000	AUVERGNE PYRENEES – Les Routiers
☆	CREUZIER-LE-VIEUX	Allier, 03300	CHEZ LA MERE RIBOULIN (SARL)
☆ ☆	EYMOUTIERS	Haute-Vienne, 87120	LE SAINT-PSALMET
☆	LAPALISSE	Allier, 03120	LE CHAPON DORE
☆	MAURIAC	Cantal, 15200	LES ROUTIERS – Chez Brigitte
☆	PERIGNY	Allier, 03120	LE RELAIS DE PERIGNY
☆ ☆	SAINT-FLOUR	Cantal, 15100	LE PROGRES
☆	SAINT-JULIEN-CHAPTEUIL	Haute-Loire, 43260	AUBERGE DU MEYCAL
☆ ☆	SAINT-JUST-LE-MARTEL	Haute-Vienne, 87590	LE PETIT SALE
☆	SAUVIAT-SUR-VIGE	Haute-Vienne, 87400	HOTEL DE LA POSTE
☆ ☆	VIEILLE-BRIOUDE	Haute-Loire, 43100	LES GLYCINES

SOUTH-WEST FRANCE

STAR-RATING	TOWN	DEPARTEMENT	ESTABLISHMENT
☆	AIRE-SUR-L'ADOUR	Landes, 40800	LES ROUTIERS
☆	AMBRES	Tarn, 81500	AUBERGE DES POMMIERS
☆ ☆	AMOU	Landes, 40330	AU FEU DE BOIS
☆ ☆	BARAQUEVILLE	Aveyron, 12160	LE PALOUS
☆	BERTHOLENE	Aveyron, 12310	HOTEL BANCAREL
☆	CAMPSEGRET	Dordogne, 24140	LES TAMARIS
☆	CASTELSARRASIN	Tarn-et-Garonne, 82100	CHEZ MAURICE
☆	CHAUDEYRAC	Lozère, 48170	HOTEL DE FRANCE
☆ ☆	COLOMBIERS	Hérault, 34440	LA GRILLADE

STAR-RATING	TOWN	DEPARTEMENT	ESTABLISHMENT
☆ ☆	CUQ-TOULZA	Tarn, 81470	LE RELAIS CHEZ ALAIN
☆	ESPALION	Aveyron, 12500	RELAIS DES QUATRE ROUTES
☆ ☆	GRAMAT	Lot, 46500	HOTEL DU CENTRE
☆ ☆	ISSANKA	Hérault, 34540	LE GARRIGOU
☆	LAFOX	Lot-et-Garonne, 47270	LES ROUTIERS – Le Toulousain
☆	LALOUBERE	Hautes-Pyrénées, 65310	HOTEL DE PYRENEES
☆	LANGOGNE	Lozère, 48300	HOTEL DU LUXEMBOURG
☆	LIBOURNE	Gironde, 33500	LE MOULIN BLANC
☆ ☆	MILLAU-LARZAC	Aveyron, 12230	RELAIS ESPACE
☆ ☆	MIRAMONT-DE-GUYENNE	Lot-et-Garonne, 47800	LE RELAIS DE GUYENNE
☆	MOISSAC	Tarn-et-Garonne, 82200	RELAIS AUVERGNAT
☆	LE MONASTIER	Lozère, 48100	LES AJUSTONS
☆	MONDAVEZAN	Haute-Garonne, 31220	LA FERMIERE
☆ ☆	NARBONNE	Aude, 11100	LA CAILLE QUI CHANTE
☆	ONET-LE-CHATEAU	Aveyron, 12850	LA ROCADE
☆	PAUILLAC	Gironde, 33250	LE YACHTING
☆ ☆	REMOULINS	Gard, 30210	AUBERGES LES PLATANES
☆	RIEUPEYROUX	Aveyron, 12240	CHEZ PASCAL
☆	RISCLE	Gers, 32400	RELAIS DE L'AUBERGE
☆ ☆	ROUFFILLAC-DE-CARLUX	Dordogne, 24370	AUX POISSONS FRAIS
☆	SAINT-LON-LES-MINES	Landes, 40300	HOTEL DU FRONTON
☆	SAINT-NAZAIRE	Gard, 30200	LES TERAILLES
☆	SAINT-PAUL-DE-LOUBRESSAC	Lot, 46170	RELAIS DE LA MADELEINE
☆	SAINT-PERDON	Landes, 40090	LE RELAIS DE LA LANDE
☆	SAINTE-LIVRADE-SUR-LOT	Lot-et-Garonne, 47110	AU BON ACCUEIL
☆	SAINTE-MARIE-DE-GOSSE	Landes, 40390	LES ROUTIERS
☆	SAUVETERRE-DE-GUYENNE	Gironde, 33540	HOTEL DE GUYENNE

STAR-RATING	TOWN	DEPARTEMENT	ESTABLISHMENT
SOUTH-EAST FRANCE			
☆ ☆	ALIXAN	Drôme, 26300	HOTEL ALPES PROVENCE
☆ ☆	AVIGNON	Vaucluse, 84140	RELAIS D'AVIGNON
☆	BONSON	Loire, 42160	RESTAURANT DES SPORTS
☆	CHORGES	Hautes Alpes, 05230	HOTEL DES ALPES
☆ ☆	CORMORANCHE-SUR-SAONE	Ain, 01290	AUBERGE CHEZ LA MERE MARTINET
☆ ☆	CORPS	Isère, 38970	RESTAURANT DU TILLEUL
☆	DONZERE	Drôme, 26290	RELAIS LE BOLO
☆	EYGUIANS	Hautes Alpes, 05300	HOTEL DE LA GARE
☆	FOS-SUR-MER	Bouches-du-Rhône, 13270	LE RELAIS DE LA FOSSETTE
☆	FREJUS	Var, 83600	LES TROIS CHENES
☆	GENAY	Rhône, 69730	LA PETITE RIVE
☆ ☆	GUILLESTRE	Hautes Alpes, 05600	HOTEL DE LA GARE
☆	JOYEUSE	Ardèche, 07260	LES CEVENNES
☆	LALEVADE-D'ARDECHE	Ardèche, 07380	L'ESCHALLIER
☆ ☆	MEGEVE	Haute-Savoie, 74120	CHALET DES FLEURS
☆ ☆	MEGEVETTE	Haute-Savoie, 74490	AUBERGE DE MEGEVELLE
☆ ☆	MONTAUROUX	Var, 83440	LE RELAIS DU LAC
☆	MONTFAVET	Vaucluse, 84140	RELAIS DE BONPAS
☆	ORGON	Bouches-du-Rhône, 13660	RELAIS DE FUMADES
☆	ROCHETAILLEE	Isère, 38520	HOTEL BELLEDONNE
☆	SAINT-FIRMIN	Hautes Alpes, 05800	LA TRINITE
☆	SAINT-RAPHAEL	Var, 83700	BEL AZUR
☆	SEYNOD	Haute-Savoie, 74600	RELAIS SAINTE-CATHERINE
☆	THONES	Haute-Savoie, 74230	L'HERMITAGE
☆	VEYRINS-THUELLIN	Isère, 38630	L'OUSTRAL

PARIS AND NEARBY

☎ If you wish to telephone an establishment, the initial code **1**, given in this chapter as (1), needs to be used *only* if you are dialling from outside Paris / Ile-de-France.

This chapter covers the Ile-de-France and Paris itself, and includes the following *départements*:

Essonne (91)
Hauts-de-Seine (92)
Paris (75)
Seine-et-Marne (77)

Seine-St-Denis (93)
Val-de-Marne (94)
Val-d'Oise (95)
Yvelines (78)

ALFORTVILLE • Val-de-Marne, 94140

🍽 **LA TERRASSE**
(M. Boualem Belamri) 173 rue Etienne-Bolet
☎ (1) 43.75.17.02
Languages spoken: English.
Restaurant: dinner served until 20.00. Closed Sun, and in Sept.

ANTONY • Hauts-de-Seine, 92160

🍽 **LES ROUTIERS**
(Mme Ginette Laurence) 86 avenue de la Division-Leclerc ☎ (1) 46.66.02.62
Directions: RN 20.
Menu: 50 Frs.
Restaurant: breakfast from 7.30. Lunch from 12.00 until 14.00. Closed Sat and Sun.
Specialities: home-cooking.
Other points: bar, traditional decor, car/lorry parking.

AUBERVILLIERS
Seine-St-Denis, 93300

🍽 **AU RENDEZVOUS DES CAMIONNEURS**
(M. Akli Ayadi) 17 rue de la Haie-Coq
☎ (1) 43.52.09.15
Directions: Porte d'Aubervilliers.
Other points: bar.

AUFFERVILLE • Seine-et-Marne, 77570

🍽 **AUBERGE DE LA DILIGENCE**
(M. Bernard Vincent) 9 Route Nationale
☎ (1) 64.28.75.91
Directions: RD 403, between Nemours and Orléans.
Menu: 55 to 75 Frs.
Accommodation: 120 Frs.
Restaurant: breakfast from 7.00. Lunch from

11.00 until 15.00. Dinner from 18.00 until 21.00.
Specialities: couscous, paella, home-cooking.
Hotel: 2 rooms. Facilities: shower.
Other points: credit cards accepted, bar, children's menu, traditional decor, terrace, pets allowed, car/lorry parking.
◁ *Fontainebleau (23km); Château-Landon (11km); Nemours (9km); prehistory museum; forêt de Poligny.*

BANNOST • Seine-et-Marne, 77970

🍽 **LE RELAIS DE LA GARE**
(M. Georges Fontaine) La Gare, Route Nationale 4 ☎ (1) 64.01.02.07
Restaurant: closed Sat, Sun, and in Aug.
Other points: bar.

BERNES-SUR-OISE
Val-d'Oise, 95340

🍽 **LE BEL AIR**
(M. Hubert Ansevin) 1 rue de Creil
☎ (1) 34.70.04.00
Menu: 54 Frs (wine included).
Restaurant: breakfast from 5.00. Lunch from 12.00 until 14.00. Dinner from 20.00 until 21.00. Closed Sun.
Specialities: home-cooking.
Other points: credit cards accepted, bar, children's menu, car/lorry parking.

BLANC-MESNIL
Seine-St-Denis, 93150

🏨 **HOTEL DU PARC**
(Mohand and Abdellah Ayadi) avenue Charles-Floquet ☎ (1) 45.91.19.92
Directions: exit A1, towards Industrial Zone (Z.I.) at Molette.

Languages spoken: German and English.
Menu: 50 Frs.
Accommodation: 80 to 110 Frs.
Restaurant: breakfast from 5.30. Lunch from
11.30 until 15.00. Dinner from 19.00 until 23.00.
Closed Sun.
Specialities: couscous, paella, home-cooking.
Hotel: 9 rooms.
Other points: bar, children's menu, modern decor,
terrace, pets allowed, car/lorry parking.

☛ LE BON ACCUEIL
(M. André Seban) 58 avenue du 8 mai 1945
☎ (1) 48.67.19.88
Directions: RN 2, Le Bourget.
Languages spoken: English.
Restaurant: dinner served until 21.00. Closed Sun.
Specialities: home-cooking.
Other points: credit cards accepted, bar, modern
decor, pets allowed, car parking.
☙ Le Bourget: musée de l'air (aviation museum).

☛ LA TRAVERSEE DE L'ATLANTIQUE
(M. Blad Makkeb) 178 boulevard du 8 Mai
1945 ☎ (1) 48.67.25.97
Languages spoken: English, Italian and Portuguese.
Menu: 55 to 78 Frs.
Restaurant: lunch from 11.30 until 14.30. Dinner
from 18.30 until 22.00.
Other points: bar, lorry parking.

BOISSY-SOUS-ST-YON
Essonne, 91790

☛ LE RELAIS DE TORFOU
(M. Mohamed Toufahi) 52 avenue de Paris
☎ (1) 64.91.30.50
Directions: RN 20.
Languages spoken: English, German and Spanish.
Menu: 51 Frs.
Accommodation: 70 to 80 Frs.
Restaurant: breakfast from 6.30. Lunch from
12.00 until 15.00. Dinner from 19.00 until 22.30.
Closed Sat afternoon and Sun.
Specialities: home-cooking.
Other points: credit cards accepted, bar,
children's menu, à la carte menu, pets allowed,
car/lorry parking.
☙ Arpajon (3km); Saint-Sulpice (11thC church).

LE BOURGET • Seine-St-Denis, 93350

☛ LE SPOUTNICK
(M. Karim Ayadi) 70 rue de Verdun
☎ (1) 48.38.32.87
Menu: 59 Frs.
Restaurant: breakfast from 5.00. Lunch from
11.00 until 15.30. Dinner from 19.00 until 22.00.
Closed Sat afternoon and Sun.
Specialities: couscous, paella, home-cooking.
Other points: credit cards accepted, bar,
children's menu, modern decor, pets allowed,
car/lorry parking.
☙ Musée de l'air (aviation) at Le Bourget; Paris
sights.

BRIIS-SOUS-FORGES
Essonne, 91640

☛ CAFETERIA DE LIMOURS-JANVRY
(M. Stéphane Dupoty) A10, services at Limours-
Janvry (accessible Paris/Bordeaux directions)
☎ (1) 64.90.77.18 Fax 64.90.89.81
Restaurant: open 24 hours.
Other points: credit cards and foreign currency
accepted.

LA BROSSE-MONTCEAUX
Seine-et-Marne, 77940

☛ LE PETIT PERICHOIS
(M. Aimé Vollereau) 33 rue de la Vallée
☎ (1) 60.96.25.75 Fax 64.70.29.41
Directions: RN 6, between Fontainebleau and Sens.
Languages spoken: German and English.
Menu: 56 to 140 Frs.
Restaurant: breakfast from 5.00. Lunch from
11.00 until 15.00. Dinner from 19.00 until 23.00.
Specialities: regional menu, home-cooking.
Other points: credit cards accepted, bar,
children's menu, à la carte menu, modern decor,
terrace, pets allowed, car/lorry parking.
☙ Orvanne valley; chateau at Brie; pottery
museum at Montereau.

CHAMARANDE • Essonne, 91730

☖ RELAIS DE MONTFORT
(M. Daniel Cottin) Route Nationale 20
☎ (1) 60.82.20.80
Directions: RN 20, between Arpajon and Etampes.
Languages spoken: English.
Menu: 49 Frs (drink included).
Accommodation: 70 to 180 Frs.
Restaurant: breakfast from 3.30. Lunch from
12.00 until 15.00. Dinner from 19.30 until 23.00.
Closed Sat afternoon, Sun, in Aug and during the
last week of Dec.
Specialities: home-cooking.
Hotel: ☆ 34 rooms. Facilities: shower.
Other points: credit cards accepted, bar, modern
decor, car/lorry parking.

LA CHAPELLE-LA-REINE
Seine-et-Marne, 77760

☖ LA SALAMANDRE
(Mme Micheline Bourlier) 5 rue du
Docteur-Battesti ☎ (1) 64.24.30.03
Directions: RN 152, Fontainebleau/Orléans road.
Menu: 55 to 65 Frs.
Accommodation: 120 to 150 Frs.
Restaurant: breakfast from 6.30. Lunch from
11.30 until 14.30. Dinner from 19.00 until 21.00.
Closed Sat, Sun, and between Christmas Day and
New Year's Day.
Specialities: home-cooking.
Hotel: 6 rooms. Facilities: shower, private bathroom.
Other points: credit cards accepted, bar,

children's menu, traditional decor, pets allowed, car/lorry parking.
🍴 forêt de Fontainebleau; Saint-Pierre basilica; leisuretime base at Buthiers; glassworks at Noisy.

CHARENTON-LE-PONT
Val-de-Marne, 94220

🍴 L'ALLIANCE
(M. Albert Series) 121 rue de Paris
☎ (1) 43.68.03.71
Menu: 61 Frs.
Restaurant: breakfast from 6.30. Lunch from 12.00 until 14.30. Closed Wed, and in Aug.
Other points: credit cards accepted, bar, à la carte menu, traditional decor.

🍴 LE PARIS/LISBONNE
(M. Jacinto Duarte) 195 rue de Paris
☎ (1) 43.68.32.29
Languages spoken: Spanish and Portuguese.
Menu: 50 Frs.
Restaurant: breakfast from 10.00. Lunch 12.00–15.00. Dinner 19.00–23.00. Closed in Aug.
Specialities: Portuguese dishes, regional menu.
Other points: bar, à la carte menu, traditional decor.

CHAUFOUR-LES-BONNIERES
Yvelines, 78270

🛏 AU BON ACCUEIL
(M. Gérard Magne) Route Nationale 13
☎ (1) 34.76.11.29
Directions: RN 13, Paris/Deauville road.
Menu: 60 to 170 Frs.
Accommodation: 110 to 200 Frs.
Restaurant: breakfast from 5.30. Lunch from 11.30 until 14.30. Dinner from 19.55 until 22.00. Closed Sat, and from mid-July to mid-Aug.
Specialities: regional menu, home-cooking.
Hotel: 15 rooms. Facilities: shower, private bathroom.
Other points: credit cards accepted, bar, children's menu, à la carte menu, traditional decor, pets allowed, car/lorry parking.
🍴 Claude Monet's house at Giverny.

CHELLES • Seine-et-Marne, 77500

🛏 RELAIS DE LA PETITE VITESSE
(M. Michel Chef) 32 avenue du Marais
☎ (1) 64.21.09.47
Directions: RN 34.
Restaurant: closed Sunday.
Hotel: 7 rooms.
Other points: bar.

CHOISY-LE-ROI
Val-de-Marne, 94600

🛏 LE STADE
(M. Jean-Claude Villechenoux) 134 avenue de Villeneuve-Saint-Georges
☎ (1) 48.90.90.55

Restaurant: breakfast from 6.30. Closed Sat, Sun.
Specialities: home-cooking.
Other points: bar.

CLAYE-SOUILLY
Seine-et-Marne, 77410

🍴 LE RELAIS DE LA ROSEE
(Mme Claude Blom) Chemin Départemental 212 ☎ (1) 60.26.17.74 [Fax] 60.27.02.28
Directions: CD 212.
Menu: 57 Frs (wine included).
Restaurant: breakfast from 10.00. Dinner served until 22.00. Closed Sat, Sun.
Specialities: home-cooking.
Other points: credit cards accepted, bar, traditional decor, terrace, pets allowed, car/lorry parking.
🍴 EuroDisneyland; la Mer des Sables theme park at Ermenonville.

CLICHY • Hauts-de-Seine, 92100

🍴 AU SOLEIL
(M. Roger Queyraud) 105 boulevard Victor-Hugo ☎ (1) 47.37.15.45
Restaurant: closed Sun, and in Aug.
Other points: bar.

LA COURNEUVE
Seine-St-Denis, 93120

🛏 L'AUBERGE DES SEPT COEURS
(M. Khaled Naïet Liman) 27 avenue Jean-Jaurès ☎ (1) 48.36.43.78
Directions: Porte de la Villette exit.
Languages spoken: English, Italian and Arabic.
Menu: 55 Frs.
Restaurant: breakfast from 6.30. Lunch from 12.00 until 15.00. Dinner from 19.30 until 24.00. Closed Sun.
Specialities: couscous, pizzas, home-cooking.
Hotel: 14 rooms. Facilities: shower, private bathroom.
Other points: credit cards accepted, bar, children's menu, à la carte menu, traditional decor, terrace, pets allowed.
🍴 Parc de la Courneuve; Paris sights.

CRESPIERES • Yvelines, 78121

🛏 AUBERGE DES ROUTIERS
(Mme Magdeleine Glatigny) Route Nationale 307 ☎ (1) 30.54.44.28
Menu: 58 Frs.
Restaurant: breakfast from 7.00. Lunch from 12.00 until 15.00. Dinner from 19.00 until 20.30.
Specialities: gibier (game), regional menu, home-cooking.
Other points: bar, children's menu, à la carte menu, traditional decor, terrace, pets allowed, car/lorry parking.
🍴 Versailles; Thoiry.

CRETEIL • Val-de-Marne, 94000

🍴 LE MIRABELLIER
(M. Marc Berthonnaud) A86, services at
Pompadour ☎ (1) 48.99.77.00
[Fax] 48.99.04.97
Directions: A86 Bobigny/Paris/Metz/Nancy.
Menu: 59 Frs (13th meal free).
Restaurant: breakfast from 6.00. Lunch from
10.30. Dinner served until 23.00.
Specialities: home-cooking.
Other points: credit cards accepted, children's
menu, lounge area, modern decor, pets allowed,
car/lorry parking.
◖€ *Paris sights.*

DEUIL-LA-BARRE • Val-d'Oise, 95170

🍴 AU COQ HARDI
(M. Gérard Lantinier) 62 bis avenue de la
Division Leclerc ☎ (1) 39.64.16.81
Directions: RN 328, towards Saint-Denis-Taverny.
Menu: 50 to 60 Frs (wine and coffee included).
Restaurant: breakfast from 9.00. Lunch from
11.30 until 15.00. Closed Sat, Sun.
Specialities: home-cooking.
Other points: bar.

For useful expressions *à l'hôtel*, *au restaurant*
or *en route*, turn to pages 8–13.

DOMONT • Val-d'Oise, 95330

🏨 LA VIEILLE AUBERGE
(M. Roger Badaire) 7 rue de l'Europe
☎ (1) 39.91.01.66
Languages spoken: Spanish.
Menu: 56 Frs.
Accommodation: 125 to 175 Frs.
Restaurant: breakfast from 6.30. Lunch from
11.30 until 14.30. Closed Sat, Sun and in Aug.
Specialities: home-cooking.
Hotel: 6 rooms. Facilities: shower.
Other points: bar, traditional decor, pets allowed,
car/lorry parking.

DROCOURT • Yvelines, 78440

🍴 AU RELAIS DU NORD
(M. Daniel Tirouard) 15 rue Nationale
☎ (1) 34.76.71.23
Directions: RN 183, between Mantes-la-Jolie and
Magny-en-Vexin.
Menu: 55 Frs.
Restaurant: breakfast from 7.00. Lunch from
12.00 until 14.00. Closed Sun.
Specialities: home-cooking.
Other points: credit cards accepted, bar,
children's menu, à la carte menu, traditional decor,
pets allowed, car/lorry parking.
◖€ *chateau at La Roche-Guyon (8km); Claude
Monet's house and garden at Giverny (20km);
Collégiale at Mantes-la-Jolie (9km).*

EPINAY-CHAMPLATREUX
Val-d'Oise, 95270

🍴 AUBERGE DU CHEVAL NOIR
(Mme Annick Muscat) Route Nationale 16
☎ (1) 34.71.01.70
Directions: RN 16, the Paris/Chantilly road.
Menu: 55 to 95 Frs.
Restaurant: breakfast from 7.00. Closed
2 weeks in June.
Specialities: regional menu, home-cooking.
Other points: credit cards accepted, bar,
children's menu, à la carte menu, traditional decor,
pets allowed, car/lorry parking.
◖€ *museum at Ecouen; musée du cheval (riding) at
Chantilly.*

EPONE • Yvelines, 78680

🏨 REST'AU VERT
(Mme Assunta Artier) Route de Gargenville
☎ (1) 30.95.60.20
Directions: RN 13, Paris/Caen autoroute, exit at
Epône towards Gargenville.
Languages spoken: Italian.
Menu: 60 Frs.
Accommodation: 120 Frs.
Restaurant: breakfast from 6.00. Lunch from
11.30 until 15.00. Dinner from 19.00 until 22.00.
Closed Sat, Sun.
Specialities: home-cooking.
Hotel: 14 rooms. Facilities: telephone.
Other points: credit cards accepted, bar,
children's menu, lounge area, terrace, pets
allowed, car/lorry parking.
◖€ *Collégiale at Mantes-la-Jolie; zoo at Thoiry;
château at Versailles; Paris sights.*

LES ESSARTS-LE-ROI
Yvelines, 78690

🍴 A LA GRACE DE DIEU
(M. Daniel Bigot) Route Nationale 10
☎ (1) 30.41.60.04
Directions: RN 10, Paris/Chartres road.
Menu: 50 to 55 Frs.
Restaurant: breakfast from 5.00. Lunch from
11.30 until 15.00. Dinner from 18.30 until 22.30.
Closed Sat, Sun, and in Aug.
Specialities: home-cooking.
Other points: credit cards accepted, bar, childen
welcome, pets allowed, car/lorry parking.
◖€ *chateaux at Rambouillet and Versailles; the
Chevreuse valley.*

🍴 LE RELAIS D'ARCOAT
(SARL Arcoat) 39 Route Nationale 10
☎ (1) 30.41.60.53
Directions: RN 10, between Rambouillet and Paris.
Languages spoken: English.
Menu: 55 Frs.
Restaurant: breakfast from 6.00. Lunch from
12.00 until 15.00. Dinner from 19.00 until 22.00.
Closed Sat after 3pm, Sun, public holidays and in
July.

Specialities: home-cooking.
Other points: credit cards accepted, bar, modern decor, car/lorry parking.

LA FERTE-GAUCHER
Seine-et-Marne, 77320

LE CONTRE-TEMPS
(M. Hervé Langle) 4 avenue de la Gare
☎ (1) 64.04.01.90
Directions: RN 34, Sézanne.
Languages spoken: English.
Menu: 60 to 120 Frs.
Restaurant: breakfast from 8.00. Lunch from 12.00 until 14.00. Dinner served from 19.30. Closed Sat evening, Sun.
Specialities: home-cooking.
Other points: credit cards accepted, bar, à la carte menu, traditional decor, terrace, pets allowed, car/lorry parking.

GUILLERVAL • Essonne, 91690

RELAIS DE MONDESIR
(M. Jean Picq) Hameau de Mondésir
☎ (1) 64.95.60.76 Fax 64.95.60.76
Directions: RN 20, Orléans.
Languages spoken: Spanish, Italian and Portuguese.
Menu: 50 Frs (wine included).
Restaurant: breakfast from 6.00. Closed Sat afternoon, Sun, and 1st 2 weeks in Aug.
Specialities: chili con carne, tripes maison, regional menu, home-cooking.
Other points: credit cards accepted, bar, children's menu, à la carte menu, lounge area, traditional decor, pets allowed, car/lorry parking.
⊄ chateau at Chaloux-sur-Mars; la Tour Blanche.

L'ISLE-ADAM • Val-d'Oise, 95290

AU RALLYE
(Mme Paulette Combes) 71 rue de Pontoise
☎ (1) 34.69.08.24
Directions: RN 322.
Restaurant: closed Sat evening, Sun evening, and in Aug.
Other points: bar.

LIMAY • Yvelines, 78520

LA MARMITE
(M. Michel Blanchard) 1 route de Meulan
☎ (1) 34.78.65.52 Fax 34.78.47.32
Directions: RN 190; A13, exit Mantes Est (East) / Limay.
Menu: 58 Frs (¼ bottle of wine included).
Restaurant: breakfast from 6.00. Lunch from 11.45 until 16.00. Dinner from 19.30 until 22.30. Closed Sat evening, Sun.
Specialities: cassoulet, choucroute, couscous, paella, home-cooking.
Other points: credit cards accepted, bar,

children's menu, modern decor, terrace, pets allowed, car/lorry parking.
⊄ chateau at Versailles; Mantes-la-Jolie (12thC Collégiale); Paris sights.

MAGNY-EN-VEXIN
Val-d'Oise, 95420

HOTEL DE LA GARE
(Mme Fabienne Degoul Alves) 65 rue de Beauvais ☎ (1) 34.67.20.70
Accommodation: 150 to 160 Frs.
Restaurant: dinner served until 22.00. Closed Sun, last week in Dec.
Specialities: couscous, home-cooking.
Hotel: 10 rooms. Facilities: shower.
Other points: credit cards accepted, bar, à la carte menu, pets allowed, car/lorry parking.

MANTES-LA-VILLE
Yvelines, 78200

LA DEMIE LUNE
(M. Stéphane Warniez) 51 boulevard Roger-Salengro ☎ (1) 34.77.03.66
Directions: Paris/Rouen autoroute, exit Mantes Sud towards Beauvais.
Languages spoken: English, Spanish and Italian.
Menu: 50 to 80 Frs.
Restaurant: breakfast from 7.00. Lunch from 11.30 until 15.00. Dinner from 19.00 until 21.00. Closed Sun.
Specialities: home-cooking.
Other points: credit cards accepted, bar, children's menu, à la carte menu, modern decor, pets allowed, car/lorry parking.
⊄ Collégiale at Mantes-la-Jolie; château d'Anet (20km); zoo at Thoiry (20km).

LE HOUDAN BAR
(M. Hocine Ouhab) 43 route de Houdan
☎ (1) 34.77.06.11
Directions: RN 13, Houdan.
Languages spoken: English.
Menu: 52 Frs.
Restaurant: breakfast from 8.30. Lunch from 12.00.
Specialities: couscous (at weekends), home-cooking.
Other points: credit cards accepted, bar, à la carte menu, traditional decor, terrace.
⊄ Collégiale at Mantes-la-Jolie (2km); chateau d'Anet (20km); zoo at Thoiry (30km).

MAROLLES-SUR-SEINE
Seine-et-Marne, 77130

AU RENDEZ-VOUS DES PECHEURS ET DES CHASSEURS
(Mme Rosette Bodic) 70 Grande Rue
☎ (1) 64.31.32.20
Menu: 60 to 110 Frs.
Accommodation: 110 Frs.
Restaurant: breakfast from 6.00. Meals until 20.00.

Specialities: home-cooking.
Hotel: 3 rooms. Facilities: shower, private bathroom.
Other points: bar, traditional decor, terrace, pets allowed.

MEAUX • Seine-et-Marne, 77100

🍽 RESTAURANT DE LA MARNE
(M. Alain Ramy) 3 avenue Foch
☎ (1) 64.34.06.31
Directions: RN 3, Paris/Châlons-sur-Marne road.
Languages spoken: English.
Menu: 39 to 138 Frs.
Restaurant: breakfast from 8.30. Closed Sun from 3pm.
Specialities: grillades (grills), home-cooking.
Other points: bar, children's menu, pets allowed, car parking.
◀ Meaux: cathedral, historical pageants (June–Sept); la Mer des Sables theme park at Ermenonville; EuroDisneyland (20km).

MONTEREAU-FAUT-YONNE
Seine-et-Marne, 77130

🍽 LES ROUTIERS
(Mme Marie-France Godayer) Route Nationale 105 ☎ (1) 64.70.24.40
Menu: 55 Frs (wine included).
Restaurant: breakfast from 7.00. Closed Sun.
Specialities: home-cooking.
Other points: children's menu, traditional decor, terrace, pets allowed, car/lorry parking.
◀ chateau at Fontainebleau.

MONTLHERY • Essonne, 91310

🏠 LE SOLOGNE
(M. Jacques Cheron) 65 route d'Orléans
☎ (1) 69.01.00.98
Directions: RN 20.
Menu: 52 Frs.
Accommodation: 120 to 180 Frs.
Restaurant: breakfast from 7.00. Lunch from 11.30 until 14.00. Dinner from 19.30 until 21.00. Closed Sun, and in Aug.
Specialities: home-cooking.
Hotel: ☆ 8 rooms. Facilities: shower, private bathroom, telephone.
Other points: credit cards accepted, bar, traditional decor, pets allowed, car/lorry parking.
◀ tower at Montlhéry; animal park at Saint-Vrain; Chevreuse valley; automobile competition circuit.

MONTREUIL
Seine-St-Denis, 93100

◗ LE RELAIS DES ROUTIERS
(Mmes Sol and Puech) 70 rue de Lagny
☎ (1) 48.51.54.41
Other points: bar.

LES MUREAUX • Yvelines, 78130

🏠 LE RELAIS ICI ON COUPE SOIF
(Mme Suzanne Compagnon) 102 avenue du Maréchal-Foch ☎ (1) 34.74.05.04
Directions: RD 14.
Restaurant: closed Sun and in Aug.
Hotel: 7 rooms.
Other points: bar.

PARIS • 75001–75020

🍽 AUX ROUTIERS
(M. Bernard Dubreuil) 50 bis rue Marx-Dormoy, 75018 ☎ (1) 46.07.93.80
Directions: Porte de la Chapelle; on main road north from Gare du Nord.
Menu: 65 to 90 Frs.
Restaurant: breakfast from 7.30. Lunch from 12.00 until 14.15. Dinner from 19.15 until 22.15. Closed Sun.
Specialities: couscous, paella, choucroute, home-cooking.
Other points: credit cards accepted, bar, traditional decor.
◀ Parc de la Villette; Paris sights.

🍽 CHEZ LEON
(Mme Grange) 5 rue de l'Isly, 75008
☎ (1) 43.87.42.77
Directions: between Gare St-Lazare and boulevard Haussmann.
Restaurant: dinner served until 21.00. Closed Sun, and in Aug.
Other points: bar.

PIERREFITTE-SUR-SEINE
Seine-St-Denis, 93380

🍽 LE BIARRITZ
(M. Mohamed Hammouti) 71 avenue Lénine
Directions: RN 1.
Languages spoken: English and Arabic.
Menu: 50 Frs.
Restaurant: breakfast from 6.00. Lunch 11.30 to 15.00. Dinner 19.00 to 23.00. Closed Sun.
Specialities: couscous, home-cooking.
Other points: bar, children's menu, modern decor, pets allowed, car/lorry parking.
◀ Musée de l'air at Le Bourget; Paris sights.

🍽 LE NORMANDIE
(Mme Marcelline Vidal) 105 avenue du Général-Gallièni ☎ (1) 48.26.55.62
Directions: RN 1, Porte de la Chapelle towards Beauvais.
Menu: 57 Frs 🕁

Restaurant: breakfast from 6.00. Lunch from 11.30 until 15.00. Dinner from 19.00 until 21.00. Closed Sun, and in Sept.
Specialities: confit de canard, paella, escalope Normande, home-cooking.
Other points: credit cards accepted, bar, children's menu, modern decor, pets allowed, car/lorry parking.
◁ *chateau at Ecouen (5km); Royaumont abbey; chateau at Chantilly (15km).*

LA PLAINE-SAINT-DENIS
Seine-St-Denis, 93210

⇌ LE CHRISTAL
(M. Claude Agnier) 101 avenue du Président-Wilson ☎ (1) 42.43.75.58
Directions: Porte de la Chapelle.
Languages spoken: English.
Menu: 50 to 86 Frs.
Restaurant: breakfast from 7.00. Lunch 12.00 to 16.00. Dinner 19.00 to 23.00. Closed Sun.
Other points: credit cards accepted, children's menu, à la carte menu, modern decor, pets allowed.
◁ *Saint-Denis basilica.*

PONTAULT-COMBAULT
Seine-et-Marne, 77340

🏨 LE RELAIS DU PAVE
(M. Albano Mota Dos Santos) 9 route de Paris ☎ (1) 60.28.00.21
Languages spoken: German, English and Portuguese.
Menu: 60 Frs (drink included).
Restaurant: lunch from 12.00 until 15.00. Dinner from 19.00 until 23.00. Closed Sun.
Specialities: regional menu, home-cooking.
Hotel: 44 rooms. Facilities: shower, private bathroom, television, telephone.
Other points: credit cards accepted, bar, children's menu, à la carte menu, lounge area, car/lorry parking.
◁ *EuroDisneyland; Paris sights.*

QUINCY-SOUS-SENART
Essonne, 91480

🏨 A LA BONNE TABLE
(M. Pierre Walter) 3 bis avenue Henri-Chasles ☎ (1) 69.00.93.81
Menu: 50 to 75 Frs.
Accommodation: 100 to 180 Frs.
Restaurant: breakfast from 5.30. Lunch from 11.30 until 14.30. Dinner from 19.45 until 21.30. Closed Sun, and in Feb.
Specialities: dishes from Normandy and Alsace, home-cooking.
Hotel: 5 rooms. Facilities: shower.
Other points: credit cards accepted, bar, children's menu, modern decor, terrace, pets allowed, car/lorry parking.
◁ *Paris sights; Corbeil; Melun; Fontainebleau; forêt de Senart.*

ROMAINVILLE
Seine-St-Denis, 93230

⇌ LE REFUGE – Chez Anna
(Mme Maria Vuko) 79 boulevard Henri-Barbusse ☎ (1) 48.91.04.85
Languages spoken: Spanish, Portuguese and Serbo-Croat.
Menu: 56 Frs.
Restaurant: lunch from 11.30 until 15.30. Closed Sun.

RUNGIS • Val-de-Marne, 94595

⇌ GRAND COMPTOIR DE RUNGIS
(M. Max Lemoine) place St-Hubert, Halles de Rungis ☎ (1) 46.86.29.30
[Fax] 46.87.82.30
Directions: RN 7.
Menu: 64 to 110 Frs.
Restaurant: breakfast from 5.30. Closed Sat, Sun, public holidays.
Specialities: home-cooking.
Other points: credit cards accepted, bar, à la carte menu, modern decor, terrace, pets allowed, car/lorry parking.
◁ *les Halles de Rungis (Paris fruit market).*

SAINT-DENIS
Seine-St-Denis, 93200

⇌ LA CHEMINEE
(M. Jacques Lebas) 56 rue Ambroise-Croizat ☎ (1) 48.20.98.58
Menu: 60 Frs.
Restaurant: breakfast from 7.00. Lunch from 11.30 until 14.30. Dinner from 19.00 until 22.00. Closed Sat, Sun, and in Aug.
Specialities: home-cooking.
Other points: credit cards accepted, bar, children's menu, lounge area, modern decor, pets allowed, car/lorry parking.

⇌ LE RELAIS DU FRET – Chez Daniel
(M. Daniel Dahan) 53 avenue du Président-Wilson, La Plaine Saint-Denis ☎ (1) 48.09.41.22 [Fax] 48.09.38.51
Directions: Porte de la Chapelle and Porte de Clignancourt.
Languages spoken: English.
Menu: 60 to 70 Frs.
Restaurant: breakfast from 6.30. Closed Sun.
Specialities: couscous, salade italienne, regional menu, home-cooking.
Other points: credit cards accepted, bar, children's menu, traditional decor, pets allowed.
◁ *Paris sights.*

⇌ RENDEZ-VOUS DES CHAUFFEURS
(Mme Micheline Sahut) 47 boulevard de la Libération ☎ (1) 48.20.13.81
Menu: from 49 Frs.
Restaurant: breakfast from 7.00. Lunch from 11.30 until 15.00. Closed Sat, Sun, and in Aug.

Specialities: home-cooking.
Other points: bar, pets allowed.

SAINT-GRATIEN
Val-d'Oise, 95210

⇒ LES ROUTIERS
(M. Amar Negaa) 57 boulevard Foch
☎ (1) 39.89.29.74
Other points: bar.

SAINT-MAUR-DES-FOSSES
Val-de-Marne, 94100

⇒ LA PASSERELLE
(M. Jean Dias) 45 boulevard du Général-
Férrié ☎ (1) 42.83.21.75
Languages spoken: Spanish, Italian and Portuguese.
Menu: 55 Frs.
Restaurant: breakfast from 6.30. Lunch from
11.30 until 15.30. Dinner from 19.00 until 22.00.
Closed Sun and public holidays.
Specialities: home-cooking.
Other points: credit cards accepted, bar, modern
decor, terrace, pets allowed.

SAINT-OUEN
Seine-St-Denis, 93400

🏠 AUX ROUTIERS SYMPAS
(M. Bernard Delouvrier) 93 boulevard Victor-
Hugo ☎ (1) 40.11.00.31
Directions: bridge of Saint-Ouen.
Menu: 49 Frs (wine included).
Accommodation: 90 Frs.
Restaurant: breakfast from 6.00. Lunch from
11.45 until 15.00. Dinner from 18.30 until 20.00.
Closed Sat evening, Sun, and in Aug.
Specialities: home-cooking.
Hotel: 9 rooms. Facilities: shower.
Other points: bar, traditional decor, pets allowed.
◅ *Paris sights.*

SANCY-LES-PROVINS
Seine-et-Marne, 77320

⇒ LE RELAIS DE SANCY
(M. Philippe Savage) Route Nationale 4
☎ (1) 64.01.92.07
Directions: RN 4.
Menu: 57 Frs.
Restaurant: breakfast from 4.00. Closed Sat, Sun,
and in Aug.
Specialities: home-cooking.
Other points: credit cards accepted, bar, modern
decor, car/lorry parking.

SURVILLIERS · Val-d'Oise, 95470

⇒ LE COQ CHANTANT
(Mme Edith Resslen) Route Nationale 17
☎ (1) 34.68.24.65

Directions: RN 17, Senlis.
Languages spoken: German and Portuguese.
Menu: 55 to 90 Frs.
Restaurant: breakfast from 6.00. Lunch from
11.45 until 14.30. Dinner served from 19.00 until
22.15. Closed Fri evening, Sat evening, Sun, and
the first two weeks in Aug.
Specialities: home-cooking.
Other points: credit cards accepted, bar, traditional decor, pets allowed, car/lorry parking.
◅ *abbey at Royaumont; chateau at Chantilly;
riding museum; Parc Astérix; EuroDisneyland at
Marne-la-Vallée; Ermenonville; Senlis.*

VARENNES-SUR-SEINE
Seine-et-Marne, 77130

🏠 SARL LE PETIT FOSSARD
(M. José Da Silva) Route Nationale 6
☎ (1) 64.32.17.47
Directions: RN 6, Paris/Sens road.
Languages spoken: Portuguese.
Menu: 57 to 80 Frs.
Accommodation: 100 to 120 Frs.
Restaurant: breakfast from 4.30. Lunch from
11.30 until 15.00. Dinner from 19.00 until 23.00.
Closed Sun.
Specialities: home-cooking.
Hotel: 6 rooms.
Other points: credit cards accepted, bar, à la carte
menu, traditional decor, pets allowed, car/lorry
parking.
◅ *Montereau cathedral; pottery museum;
chateau at Fontainebleau.*

LES ROUTIERS GUIDE TO
BRITAIN AND IRELAND

Whether on business or pleasure,
the *Les Routiers* guide to Britain and Ireland
lists an unrivalled choice of over 1,500
carefully selected hotels, restaurants, guesthouses
and inns, where you can dine and stay in comfort.
All have been inspected and personally
recommended and offer the ultimate in hospitality.

Available from all good bookshops, or direct
from the publishers, price **£10.99**.

VIRY-CHATILLON
Essonne, 91170

⇒ LES ROUTIERS
(M. Fernand Gadreau) 100 route de Fleury
☎ (1) 69.05.28.46
Directions: RN 7 and RD 91, exit Viry-Châtillon or
Grigny.
Restaurant: breakfast from 6.30. Lunch from 11.30
until 14.00. Dinner from 19.00 until 21.00. Closed
Sat, Sun, public holidays and in Aug.
Specialities: home-cooking.
Other points: bar.

VOULX · Seine-et-Marne, 77940

⊨ LA BRUYERE
(M. Alban Baldran) 72 Grande Rue
☎ (1) 64.31.92.41
Directions: RD 219, beyond Montereau towards Montargis.
Menu: 56–135 Frs 👒

Restaurant: lunch from 12.00 until 14.00. Dinner from 19.00 until 21.30. Closed last 2 weeks in Feb and last 2 weeks in Aug.
Specialities: huîtres, escargots, tête de veau, grillades (grills), home-cooking.
Other points: credit cards accepted, children's menu, à la carte menu, traditional decor, pets allowed.

NORTHERN FRANCE

The following *départements* are included in this chapter:

Aisne (02)
Nord (59)
Oise (60)

Pas-de-Calais (62)
Somme (80)

ABBEVILLE · Somme, 80100

⊨ AUBERGE FLEURIE
(M. Michel Rubin) 294 côte de la Justice
☎ 22.24.73.68
Directions: RN 1, Abbeville/Dunkerque/Rouen/Saint-Omer road.
Menu: 55 Frs.
Restaurant: breakfast from 5.00. Lunch from 11.30 until 15.00. Dinner from 19.00 until 23.00. Closed Sat, Sun.
Specialities: home-cooking.
Other points: credit cards accepted, bar, children's menu, traditional decor, pets allowed, car/lorry parking.
◁€ *museums and churches at Abbeville (15km).*

⊨ CHEZ GILBERT
(M. Marc Caron) 5 Route Nationale, Buigny-Saint-Maclou ☎ 22.24.20.47
Directions: RN 1, Boulogne-sur-Mer.
Menu: 50 to 80 Frs.
Restaurant: breakfast from 7.00. Lunch 12.00 to 14.00. Dinner 19.30 to 21.30. Closed Sat.
Specialities: home-cooking.
Other points: credit cards accepted, bar, terrace, pets allowed, car/lorry parking.
◁€ *Abbeville; chateaux; gardens at Valloires.*

ABSCON · Nord, 59215

🏠 LE MOULIN D'OR
(Mme Monique Bauduin) 17 place de-Gaulle
☎ 27.36.30.33
Directions: RN 45, between Douai and Denain.
Accommodation: 60 to 90 Frs.
Restaurant: closed in August.
Specialities: home-cooking.

Hotel: 16 rooms.
Other points: bar, traditional decor, car/lorry parking.
◁€ *musée de la mine (mining) (10km).*

AILLY-LE-HAUT-CLOCHER
Somme, 80690

⊨ LE RELAIS FLEURI
(M. Olivier Leblanc) 5 Route Nationale
☎ 22.28.01.07
Directions: between Amiens and Abbeville.
Languages spoken: English.
Menu: 39 to 89 Frs.
Restaurant: breakfast from 7.00. Lunch 12.00 to 15.00. Dinner 19.00 to 21.30. Closed Thurs.
Specialities: regional menu, home-cooking.
Other points: credit cards accepted, bar, à la carte menu, lounge area, modern decor, terrace, pets allowed, car/lorry parking.
◁€ *abbey at Saint-Riquier; Collégiale at Abbeville; museum.*

AMBLAINVILLE · Oise, 60110

⊨ CHEZ MARIE-ODILE
(Mme Marie-Odile Prunier) 40 rue Nationale
☎ 44.52.03.10
Directions: RN 327.
Restaurant: closed Sunday.
Other points: bar.

L'ARBRET · Pas-de-Calais, 62158

🏠 HOTEL DE LA GARE
(M. Rabah Bechadef) Route Nationale 44
☎ 21.48.24.33

Directions: RN 44, between Arras and Doullens.
Languages spoken: German.
Menu: 55 Frs.
Restaurant: breakfast from 5.00.
Specialities: couscous, home-cooking.
Hotel: 14 rooms.
Other points: credit cards accepted, bar,
children's menu, lounge area, traditional decor,
pets allowed, car/lorry parking.
∜ *chateau at Grand-Rullecourt.*

ARMENTIERES • Nord, 59280

➡ AUBERGE DE LA LYS
(Mme Jacqueline Leflon) 110 rue des
Résistants ☎ 20.77.21.83
Directions: RN 42, Dunkerque/Lille road.
Menu: 36 to 72 Frs.
Restaurant: breakfast from 7.00. Lunch from
12.00 until 14.00. Dinner from 19.00 until 22.00.
Closed Sun.
Specialities: regional menu, home-cooking.
Other points: credit cards accepted, bar,
children's menu, à la carte menu, traditional decor,
pets allowed, car/lorry parking.
∜ *base of Prés du Hem.*

➡ LA TERRASSE
(Mme Jocelyne Dubar) 112 rue des Résistants
☎ 20.35.44.80
Directions: RN 42, opposite the customs, near the
Prés du Hem.
Menu: 37 Frs.
Restaurant: lunch from 11.30 until 15.30. Dinner
from 18.00 until 23.00.
Specialities: home-cooking.
Other points: bar, terrace, pets allowed, car/lorry
parking.
∜ *base of Prés du Hem.*

AUCHEL • Pas-de-Calais, 62260

➡ LE RELAIS DU 5
(M. Yves Doyelle) 125 rue Laurent-Evrard
☎ 21.27.70.70
Menu: 55 Frs.
Restaurant: breakfast from 10.00. Lunch from
12.00 until 14.30. Dinner from 19.00 until 22.00.
Specialities: home-cooking.
Other points: credit cards accepted, bar,
children's menu, pets allowed, car/lorry parking.
∜ *base for Olhain area; chateau; hills of Artois.*

AUCHY-AU-BOIS
Pas-de-Calais, 62190

➡ LE VERT DRAGON
(Mme Patricia Godet) chaussée Brunehaut
☎ 21.26.64.29
Directions: between Bruay-la-Buissière and
Saint-Omer.
Languages spoken: German and English.
Menu: 55 Frs.

Restaurant: breakfast from 7.00.
Specialities: home-cooking.
Other points: credit cards accepted, bar,
children's menu, modern decor, pets allowed,
car/lorry parking.
∜ *base for Olhain; chateau; hills of Artois.*

AVELIN • Nord, 59710

➡ A L'EMBUSCADE
(Mme Geneviève Lemoine) 14 route de
Seclin ☎ 20.32.90.33
Directions: RD 949, exit at Seclin, towards
Valenciennes.
Menu: 35 to 70 Frs.
Restaurant: breakfast from 6.00. Lunch from
11.30 until 15.00. Dinner from 19.00 until 21.00.
Closed Sat afternoon, Sun.
Specialities: home-cooking.
Other points: credit cards accepted, bar,
children's menu, à la carte menu, traditional decor,
pets allowed, car/lorry parking.

AVESNES-SUR-HELPE • Nord, 59440

➡ CAFE MARGUERITTE – Au Routiers
(Mme Margueritte Sorriaux) 20 avenue
de la Gare ☎ 20.61.17.88
Directions: RN 2, Maubeuge/Paris road.
Menu: 48 to 55 Frs.
Accommodation: 60 Frs.
Restaurant: breakfast from 7.00. Lunch from
12.00 until 14.00. Closed 1st 2 weeks in Aug.
Specialities: home-cooking.
Hotel: 6 rooms.
Other points: bar, traditional decor, pets allowed,
car/lorry parking.

AWOINGT • Nord, 59400

➡ AUX CHANTS DES OISEAUX
(M. Jean-Pierre Plouquet) 3 route du Cateau
☎ 27.78.77.05
Directions: RN 43, between Cambrai and Le
Cateau.
Menu: 68 Frs.
Accommodation: 110 Frs.
Restaurant: breakfast from 7.00. Lunch from
11.00 until 15.00. Dinner from 18.00 until 22.00.
Closed Sat, and in Aug.
Specialities: tripes maison, moules, entrecôte à
l'échalote, regional menu.
Hotel: 11 rooms. Facilities: shower, private bathroom.
Other points: credit cards accepted, bar,
children's menu, modern decor, pets allowed,
car/lorry parking.

BAILLEUL • Nord, 59270

➡ AUBERGE DU SEAU
(M. Joël Dequidt) Chemin Départemental 933,
Le Seau ☎ 20.48.62.00

Directions: CD 933 from Dunkerque, exit 10, towards Nieppe-Argentières.
Accommodation: 130 to 200 Frs.
Restaurant: lunch from 12.00 until 14.30. Dinner from 19.00 until 22.00.
Specialities: steack de veau de la mer, côte à l'os, couscous de poissons, home-cooking.
Hotel: ✫ 11 rooms. Facilities: shower, private bathroom, television, telephone.
Other points: credit cards accepted, bar, children's menu, à la carte menu, traditional decor, terrace, pets allowed, car/lorry parking.
◀€ *Mont des Flandres; Mont Noir.*

☖ **CHEZ ANDRE**
(M. André Noorenberghe) Route Nationale 4671, Route de Lille ☎ 28.49.29.14
Directions: RD 933.
Restaurant: dinner until 21.00.
Other points: bar.

BAILLEUL-SUR-THERAIN
Oise, 60930

☖ **L'ALOUETTE**
(Mlle Valérie Duclos) 3 rue de Villers ☎ 44.07.55.62
Directions: between Beauvais and Mouy.
Menu: 56 Frs (wine and coffee included).
Restaurant: breakfast from 6.00. Closed Sat, Sun.
Specialities: home-cooking.
Other points: bar, children's menu.

BAILLEULVAL • Pas-de-Calais, 62123

☖ **RELAIS BAC DU SUD**
(M. Yves Sanson) Route Nationale 25 ☎ 21.58.79.12
Directions: RN 25, between Arras and Doullens.
Languages spoken: Dutch.
Menu: 60 Frs (wine and coffee included).
Accommodation: 120 to 170 Frs.
Restaurant: breakfast from 5.30. Lunch from 11.45 until 14.30. Dinner from 18.45 until 22.00. Closed Sun, 1st 2 weeks in Aug.
Specialities: home-cooking.
Hotel: 6 rooms.
Other points: credit cards accepted, bar, modern decor, terrace, pets allowed, car/lorry parking.
◀€ *caves at Naourc; Mont Saint-Eloi; Arras; Notre-Dame-de-Lorette at Vimy.*

BAPAUME • Pas-de-Calais, 62450

☖ **CHEZ BERNADETTE**
(Mme Bernadette Molle) 45 faubourg de Péronne ☎ 21.07.12.78
Directions: RN 17, Arras/Paris or Amiens/Cambrai road.
Menu: 55 Frs.
Accommodation: 110 to 200 Frs.
Restaurant: breakfast from 6.30. Lunch from 12.00 until 14.30. Dinner from 20.00 until 22.00. Closed Sat, Sun.

Specialities: home-cooking.
Hotel: ✫ 8 rooms. Facilities: telephone.
Other points: credit cards accepted, bar, traditional decor, pets allowed, car/lorry parking.
◀€ *Arras: belfry, squares and monuments.*

BAVAY • Nord, 59570

☞ **ETANG DU PRAY**
(M. Patrick Delbove) Route Nationale 49, Route de Valenciennes ☎ 27.39.83.93
Languages spoken: a little English.
Other points: bar, car/lorry parking.

BEAULENCOURT
Pas-de-Calais, 62450

☞ **LE RELAIS DE BEAULENCOURT**
(M. Maurice Pontonnier) 24 Route Nationale 17 ☎ 21.07.68.81
Directions: RN 17, between Péronne and Bapaume.
Menu: 58 Frs, plat du jour from 38 Frs.
Restaurant: breakfast from 7.30.
Specialities: home-cooking.
Other points: credit cards accepted, bar, children's menu, modern decor, terrace, pets allowed, car/lorry parking.
◀€ *1914–18 war museum.*

BEAUVAIS • Oise, 60000

☞ **LA TOUR EIFFEL**
(M. Michel Lorusso) 72 rue des Cheminots ☎ 44.02.47.40
Directions: RN 1, Zone Artisanale No. 1.
Menu: 60 Frs.
Restaurant: breakfast from 6.00. Closed Sat afternoon.
Specialities: couscous (on Thurs), home-cooking.
Other points: bar, children's menu, modern decor, terrace, pets allowed, car/lorry parking.
◀€ *Gerberoy (village in bloom); Beauvais cathedral; leisure park at Saint-Paul.*

BERCK-SUR-MER
Pas-de-Calais, 62600

☖ **RELAIS D'ARTOIS**
(M. Raoul Postel) 20 rue Alfred-Lambert ☎ 21.09.29.35
Specialities: home-cooking.
Hotel: 14 rooms.
Other points: bar, car/lorry parking.

BEUVRY-LA-FORET • Nord, 59310

☖ **A LA VIEILLE FRANCE**
(Mme Jacqueline Lasser) 2895 rue Albert-Ricquier ☎ 20.71.06.93
Directions: RN 49, between Lille and Valenciennes.

Menu: 70 Frs.
Accommodation: 120 to 200 Frs.
Restaurant: breakfast from 7.00. Lunch from 12.00 until 15.00. Dinner from 19.00 until 21.00.
Specialities: home-cooking.
Hotel: 11 rooms. Facilities: shower, private bathroom.
Other points: credit cards accepted, bar, children's menu, à la carte menu, terrace, pets allowed, car/lorry parking.
◀ *casino at Saint-Amand; forêt de Marchiennes (Belgium).*

BOULOGNE-SUR-MER
Pas-de-Calais, 62200

🍴 **LE MARIANY**
(Mme Paulette Witkowski) 54 avenue John-Kennedy ☎ 21.91.12.96
Directions: RN 1.
Languages spoken: Some English.
Menu: 63 Frs (drink included).
Accommodation: 95 to 180 Frs.
Restaurant: breakfast from 7.00. Lunch from 12.00 until 15.00. Dinner until 21.00. Closed Sun after lunch.
Specialities: home-cooking.
Hotel: 11 rooms.
Other points: credit cards accepted, bar, children's menu, à la carte menu, traditional decor, pets allowed.
◀ *old town and cathedral; Nausicaa (journey to the centre of the sea).*

BOURNEVILLE-MAROLLES
Oise, 60890

🍴 **LES ROUTIERS**
(Mme Huguette Picard-Mathias) 7 rue de Meaux ☎ 23.96.72.11
Directions: RD 936, between la Ferté-Milon and Meaux.
Menu: 60 to 75 Frs.
Restaurant: breakfast from 7.00.
Specialities: home-cooking.
Other points: bar, children's menu, à la carte menu, traditional decor, terrace, pets allowed, car/lorry parking.

BOVES • Somme, 80440

🍴 **LA GRENOUILLERE**
(M. Bouhou Ouannoune) Route Nationale 334 ☎ 22.09.31.26
Directions: RN 334, on the Amiens-Roye expressway.
Languages spoken: English.
Menu: 55 to 68 Frs.
Restaurant: breakfast from 6.00. Lunch from 11.00 until 15.00. Closed Sun (except for functions), and in Aug.
Specialities: couscous, home-cooking.

Other points: credit cards accepted, children's menu, traditional decor, terrace, pets allowed, car/lorry parking.
◀ *Amiens: cathedral, belfry.*

BRETEUIL • Oise, 60120

🍴 **AUBERGE DU MARAIS**
(Josiane and Jean-Paul Clément) 38 rue de Paris ☎ 44.80.12.21
Directions: RN 16, Clermont.
Menu: 57 Frs (wine included) to 85 Frs.
Restaurant: breakfast from 8.00. Lunch from 12.00 until 15.00. Dinner from 19.00 until 22.00. Closed Sun afternoon.
Specialities: ficelle picarde, home-cooking.
Other points: credit cards accepted, children's menu, traditional decor, terrace, pets allowed, car/lorry parking.
◀ *Gallo-Roman sites at Vendeuil-Caply (3km).*

BRUAY-LA-BUISSIERE
Pas-de-Calais, 62700

🍴 **LA LOUETTE**
(M. Philippe Chevalier – SARL Cali) 114 rue Raoul-Briquet ☎ 21.53.42.07
Directions: between Béthune and Saint-Pol-sur-Ternoise.
Languages spoken: German and English.
Menu: 60 Frs; plats du jour from 35 Frs.
Accommodation: 85 to 140 Frs.
Restaurant: breakfast from 5.00. Lunch from 11.30 until 14.30. Dinner from 19.00 until 21.00.
Specialities: home-cooking.
Hotel: ☆ 15 rooms. Facilities: shower, private bathroom.
Other points: credit cards accepted, bar, children's menu, traditional decor, pets allowed, car/lorry parking.
◀ *Olhain; chateaux; hills of Artois.*

BUIRONFOSSE • Aisne, 02620

🍴 **AUX AMIS DE LA ROUTE**
(Mme Danielle Douchez) Route Nationale 29 ☎ 23.97.24.05
Directions: RN 29, between Saint-Quentin and La Capelle.
Menu: 58 Frs (wine included).
Accommodation: 90 to 110 Frs.
Restaurant: breakfast from 7.00. Closed Sun.
Specialities: home-cooking.
Hotel: 5 rooms.
Other points: bar, children's menu, traditional decor, terrace, pets allowed, car/lorry parking.
◀ *La Capelle; Guise; clog museum.*

CAMBRAI • Nord, 59400

🍴 **LA GARGOTE**
(M. Jean Bedu) 136 boulevard Jean-Bart ☎ 27.81.07.18
Directions: A2 and A23, along the canal.

Menu: 60 Frs.
Restaurant: breakfast from 7.00. Lunch from 12.00 until 15.00. Dinner from 19.00 until 23.00. Closed Sun (except for groups and functions), and in Aug.
Specialities: andouillettes de Cambrai, clafoutis (cherry tart) maison, home-cooking.
Other points: bar, modern decor, terrace, pets allowed, car/lorry parking.
◀€ *Rue des Vignes; area of archeological interest; abbey at Vaucelle.*

CAPPELLE-EN-PEVELE • Nord, 59242

🍽 L'AS VEGAS
(Mme Eliane Duquesnoy) 13 rue de l'Obeau
☎ 20.61.83.10
Menu: 60 Frs (drink included).
Restaurant: breakfast from 8.30. Lunch from 12.00 until 14.30. Dinner from 19.00 until 20.30. Closed Sun.
Specialities: home-cooking.
Other points: credit cards accepted, bar, pets allowed, car/lorry parking.
◀€ *windmill at Vertain.*

CHAMBLY • Oise, 60230

🏨 LE RELAIS DE CHAMBLY
(Mme Françoise Violette) 660 avenue
Aristide-Briand ☎ 34.70.50.37
Directions: RN 1, Paris/Beauvais road via Beaumont-sur-Oise.
Menu: 65 Frs (wine and coffee included).
Accommodation: 130 Frs to 280 Frs.
Restaurant: breakfast from 7.00. Lunch from 12.00 until 15.30. Dinner from 19.00 until 20.30. Closed Sat, Sun, and from 20th Dec to 20th Jan.
Specialities: bourguignon, coq au vin, boeuf à la mode, home-cooking.
Hotel: 15 rooms. Facilities: shower, private bathroom, television.
Other points: bar, children's menu, lounge area, modern decor, terrace, pets allowed, car/lorry parking.
◀€ *Chantilly (20km); Senlis (28km); L'Ile Adam (10km); abbey at Royaumont (35km); abbey at Maubuisson; Beauvais; archeological museum at Guiry-en-Vexin; musée de l'outil (tools and implements).*

CHAULNES • Somme, 80320

🍽 A L'ESCALE DES ROUTIERS
(M. Jean-Claude Guerquin) Route Nationale
17, Fresnes ☎ 22.85.28.50
Directions: RN 17, exit Roye or Péronne.
Menu: 55 Frs.
Restaurant: breakfast from 5.30. Lunch from 11.30 until 14.30. Dinner from 19.00 until 22.00. Closed Sat, Sun, and in July.
Specialities: home-cooking.
Other points: credit cards accepted, bar,

children's menu, traditional decor, pets allowed, car/lorry parking.
◀€ *Péronne: town and chateau.*

CHAUNY • Aisne, 02300

🍽 LE CASAMANCE
(Mme Catherine Gauben) 92 rue de la
Chaussée ☎ 23.52.16.33
Directions: RN 83, between Noyon and Soissons.
Languages spoken: English.
Menu: 55 Frs (wine included).
Accommodation: 90 to 110 Frs.
Restaurant: breakfast from 7.00. Lunch from 11.30 until 14.30. Dinner from 18.30 until 21.30. Closed Sun.
Specialities: home-cooking
Hotel: 4 rooms.
Other points: bar, children's menu, à la carte menu, traditional decor, pets allowed, car/lorry parking.
◀€ *chateaux at Coucy and Blérancourt; forêt de Saint-Gobain; Laon.*

🍽 LE VAN GOGH
(Mme Christine Haudiquet) 37 rue
A.-Ternynck ☎ 23.39.40.32
Directions: between Noyon and Saint-Quentin.
Languages spoken: English.
Menu: 57 Frs.
Restaurant: breakfast from 9.00. Lunch from 12.00 until 14.00. Dinner from 19.00 until 20.30. Closed Sun.
Specialities: bourguignon, escalope à la crème, home-cooking.
Other points: bar, children's menu, traditional decor, pets allowed, car/lorry parking.
◀€ *Coucy-le-Château; Blérancourt Franco-American museum.*

CHEPY • Somme, 80210

🍽 RELAIS SANS BOIRE
(M. Jacky Sueur) 40 route de Oisemont, La
Croix-de-Pierre ☎ 22.26.26.67
Directions: RD 29, between Le Tréport and Oisemont.
Menu: 58 to 120 Frs.
Restaurant: breakfast from 6.30. Lunch from 11.30 until 14.30. Dinner from 19.00 until 22.00.
Specialities: ficelle picarde, ragoût, regional menu, home-cooking.
Other points: credit cards accepted, bar, children's menu, à la carte menu, traditional decor, terrace, pets allowed, car/lorry parking.
◀€ *chateau at Rambures; bay of the Somme; park at Marquantaire.*

COLEMBERT • Pas-de-Calais, 62142

🏨 CAFE HOTEL DU COMMERCE
(M. Jacques Delannoy) 38 Route Nationale
☎ 21.33.31.11

Directions: RN 42, between Boulogne-sur-Mer and Saint-Omer.
Menu: 58 Frs.
Accommodation: 140 to 180 Frs.
Restaurant: breakfast from 6.30 until 12.00. Dinner from 19.00 until 22.00.
Specialities: home-cooking.
Hotel: 8 rooms. Facilities: shower, private bathroom, television.
Other points: credit cards accepted, bar, children's menu, modern decor, pets allowed, car/lorry parking.
◁€ *maritime museum; 1939–45 war museum; leisure park at Bagatelle.*

COMPIEGNE • Oise, 60200

⊨ BAR DE LA MARINE
(M. Aimé Logghe) 17 rue de l'Estacade
☎ 44.40.26.37
Menu: 60 Frs.
Restaurant: breakfast from 6.00. Closed Sat, Sun and public holidays.
Specialities: home-cooking.
Other points: credit cards accepted, bar, modern decor, car/lorry parking.
◁€ *chateau; Napoleonic museum.*

COUCY-LE-CHATEAU • Aisne, 02380

🏨 LE LION ROUGE
(M. Patrick Clavet) 62 avenue Altenkessel
☎ 23.52.70.13
Directions: RN 1, between Soissons and Saint-Quentin.
Languages spoken: German and English.
Menu: 52 to 180 Frs.
Accommodation: 86 to 92 Frs.
Restaurant: breakfast from 7.00. Lunch from 11.30 until 14.30. Dinner from 18.30 until 21.30.
Specialities: flamiche picarde, magrets picards, foie gras, grillades, papillottes de poissons, cassoulet, regional menu.
Hotel: 13 rooms.
Other points: credit cards accepted, bar, children's menu, à la carte menu, lounge area, traditional decor, terrace, pets allowed, car/lorry parking.
◁€ *ruins and ramparts of the chateau at Coucy (tower and museum with model of the fortified town); forêt de Saint-Gobain; chateau and Franco-American museum at Blérancourt.*

CROIX • Nord, 59170

⊨ AUBERGE DU BON FRAISIER
(M. Jean-Louis de Meyer) 1 rue des Allumettes ☎ 20.70.98.14
Directions: on the expressway, exit at Croix-Wasquehal.
Menu: 49 Frs.
Restaurant: breakfast from 7.00. Closed Sat morning.
Specialities: home-cooking.

Other points: credit cards accepted, bar, children's menu, pets allowed, car/lorry parking.
◁€ *Parc Barbieux; orgues de Wasquehal.*

🏨 LE RELAIS CHEZ ALAIN
(Mme Georgette Caufriez) 53 avenue Georges-Hannart ☎ 20.72.59.08
Directions: RD 14, Lille/Tourcoing expressway, near station at Croix-Wasquehal.
Languages spoken: Spanish.
Menu: 35 to 60 Frs.
Accommodation: 100 to 150 Frs.
Restaurant: breakfast from 4.00. Lunch from 12.00 until 15.00. Dinner from 19.00 until 22.00. Closed Sun afternoon.
Specialities: home-cooking.
Hotel: 9 rooms. Facilities: shower, private bathroom, television, telephone.
Other points: credit cards accepted, bar, children's menu, à la carte menu, lounge area, traditional decor, car parking.
◁€ *Parc Barbieux; orgues de Wasquehal.*

CUCQ TREPIED
Pas-de-Calais, 62780

⊨ LES AMIS DE LA ROUTE
(M. Guy Dubois) 279 avenue d'Etaples
☎ 21.94.46.00
Directions: RD 940, between Berck and Etaples.
Menu: 55 to 120 Frs.
Restaurant: breakfast from 7.00.
Specialities: home-cooking.
Other points: credit cards accepted, bar, children's menu, traditional decor, pets allowed, car/lorry parking.
◁€ *Côte d'Opale beaches; leisure park at Bagatelle.*

CUVILLY • Oise, 60490

🏨 LA CAMPAGNARDE
(Daniel and Anne-Maryse Hillion Nicol) 5 route des Flandres ☎ 44.85.00.30
Directions: RN 17, Paris/Lille road.
Languages spoken: English.
Menu: 47 to 60 Frs.
Accommodation: 90 to 150 Frs.
Restaurant: breakfast from 5.00. Lunch from 11.00 until 15.00. Dinner from 19.00 until 22.30. Closed Sun.
Specialities: home-cooking.
Hotel: 9 rooms. Facilities: shower, private bathroom.
Other points: credit cards accepted, bar, children's menu, modern decor, pets allowed, car/lorry parking.
◁€ *Compiègne; valley of the Somme; Noyon.*

DESVRES • Pas-de-Calais, 62240

🏨 LE RELAIS DE LA BELLE CROIX
(M. Jean-Claude Grumelart) 1 rue du Bidet
☎ 21.91.65.81

Directions: RN 342, between Boulogne-sur-Mer and Longfossé.
Languages spoken: English.
Menu: 45 to 70 Frs.
Accommodation: 70 Frs (per person).
Restaurant: breakfast from 7.00. Closed Sun.
Specialities: regional menu.
Hotel: 5 rooms. Facilities: shower.
Other points: bar, children's menu, à la carte menu, modern decor, terrace, pets allowed, car/lorry parking.
◁€ *Nausicaa (journey to the centre of the sea); pottery and maritime museums.*

DIZY-LE-GROS • Aisne, 02340

LES ROUTIERS FRANCE EUROPE
(M. Jean-Claude Dubois) 78 Grande Rue
☎ 23.21.23.15
Directions: RD 366, to Reims/Vervins/Belgium.
Menu: 54 Frs.
Restaurant: breakfast from 6.00. Lunch from 11.00 until 14.00. Dinner from 19.00 until 21.00. Closed Sat afternoon, Sun, and last 2 weeks in August.
Other points: credit cards accepted, bar, traditional decor, pets allowed, car/lorry parking.

DOUAI • Nord, 59500

A L'EPI D'OR
(M. Michel Barjou) 38 faubourg d'Arras, Lambres ☎ 27.87.04.56
Directions: RN 17 and 34.
Restaurant: breakfast from 4.30. Dinner until 24.00. Closed Sat from 15.00, and Sun.
Hotel: 7 rooms.
Other points: bar.

DREUIL-LES-AMIENS
Somme, 80730

CHEZ JEAN-MARIE ET CHRISTIANE
(M. Jean-Marie Dumeige) 285 avenue Pasteur
☎ 22.54.10.72
Directions: RN 235, Picquigny.
Menu: 52 Frs.
Restaurant: breakfast from 6.30. Lunch from 11.45 until 14.00. Dinner from 19.30 until 21.00. Closed Sun, and in Aug.
Specialities: home-cooking.
Other points: traditional decor, pets allowed, car/lorry parking.
◁€ *Picard capital (1km).*

ECLAIBES • Nord, 59330

LE ROBINSON
(M. El Hadi Manseur) Route Nationale 2
☎ 27.57.81.26
Directions: RN 2.
Other points: bar.

ESTREES-DENIECOURT
Somme, 80200

AUBERGE DE LA MAIRIE
(Mme Claudette Demuynck Dehenry)
☎ 22.85.20.16
Directions: RN 336, exit A1 Péronne, on the right towards Amiens.
Menu: 55 to 65 Frs.
Accommodation: 100 to 225 Frs.
Restaurant: dinner from 19.00 until 23.00. Closed Sat, Sun, and in Aug.
Specialities: home-cooking.
Hotel: 7 rooms. Facilities: shower, private bathroom.
Other points: bar, à la carte menu, lounge area, terrace, pets allowed, car/lorry parking.

ESTREES-MONS • Somme, 80200

A LA POMME D'API
(M. Albert Gras) 28 Route Nationale
☎ 22.85.60.04
Directions: RN 29, exit Péronne, towards Saint-Quentin.
Menu: 58 Frs.
Restaurant: breakfast from 6.30. Lunch from 11.30 until 14.30. Dinner from 19.00 until 21.30. Closed Sun, and in Aug.
Specialities: home-cooking.
Other points: credit cards accepted, bar, children's menu, à la carte menu, lounge area, traditional decor, terrace, pets allowed, car/lorry parking.

ETROEUNGT • Nord, 59219

AU RELAIS DES COLOMBRES
(Mre Patrick Kucharski) Route Nationale 2
☎ 27.59.22.11 [Fax] 27.59.24.69
Directions: RN 2, between Avesnes-sur-Helpe and La Capelle.
Languages spoken: English, Italian and Polish.
Menu: 54 Frs.
Restaurant: breakfast from 6.00. Closed Sun.
Specialities: home-cooking.
Other points: credit cards accepted, bar, children's menu, modern decor, pets allowed, car/lorry parking.
◁€ *the Avesnois area.*

FLAVY-LE-MARTEL • Aisne, 02520

LE RELAIS DES ROUTIERS
(M. Jean-Paul Brière) 17 rue André-Brulé
☎ 23.52.51.31
Restaurant: dinner until 21.00. Closed Sat.
Specialities: home-cooking.
Other points: bar.

FLIXECOURT • Somme, 80420

LES FLONFLONS DU BAL
(M. Jean-Marc Rohaut) 16 rue
Georges-Clemenceau ☎ 22.51.36.34

Directions: RN 1, between Amiens and Abbeville.
Languages spoken: English.
Menu: 45 to 100 Frs.
Restaurant: breakfast from 6.00.
Specialities: canard aux navets, viandes grillées, couscous, regional menu, home-cooking.
Other points: credit cards accepted, bar, children's menu, à la carte menu, traditional decor, terrace, pets allowed, car/lorry parking.
◄€ *Samara Gallic settlement (5km); prehistoric caves at Naours (20km); Drugy farm (Jeanne d'Arc's prison: 15km); Amiens: 12thC Gothic cathedral (20km).*

FORMERIE • Oise, 60220

🍴 **CAFE DE LA PAIX**
(Mme Françoise Merlin) 8 rue Dornat
☎ 44.46.17.08
Directions: between Beauvais and Forges-les-Eaux.
Menu: 50 to 65 Frs.
Accommodation: 80 Frs.
Restaurant: breakfast from 4.30. Lunch from 11.30 until 15.00. Dinner from 19.30 until 21.30.
Specialities: couscous, paella, home-cooking.
Hotel: ☆ 5 rooms. Facilities: shower, private bathroom, television, telephone.
Other points: credit cards accepted, bar, children's menu, modern decor, terrace.
◄€ *Gerberoy; casino at Forges-les-Eaux.*

FROISSY • Oise, 60480

🍴 **LE BEAUVAIS BRETEUIL**
(M. Raymond Julen) 5 rue du Bois-Saint-Martin, Abbeville-Saint-Lucien ☎ 44.79.13.09
Directions: RN 1, between Beauvais and Amiens.
Menu: 52 to 95 Frs.
Accommodation: 100 to 150 Frs.
Restaurant: breakfast from 7.00. Lunch from 12.00 until 15.00. Dinner from 19.00 until 22.00. Closed Sat afternoon, Sun, 4 weeks in Aug and 2 weeks from Christmas Day.
Specialities: home-cooking.
Hotel: 5 rooms.
Other points: credit cards accepted, bar, children's menu, à la carte menu, traditional decor, pets allowed, car/lorry parking.
◄€ *cathedral at Beauvais; museum; place Jeanne-Hachette; parc Saint-Paul.*

GAMACHES • Somme, 80220

🍴 **LES ROUTIERS**
(Mme Evelyne Thery) 1 place du Général-Leclerc ☎ 22.30.17.30
Directions: between Eu and Aumale.
Menu: 55 to 110 Frs.
Restaurant: breakfast from 7.00. Lunch from 12.00 until 14.30.
Specialities: home-cooking.
Other points: credit cards accepted, bar, children's menu, pets allowed, car/lorry parking.
◄€ *Le Tréport; bay of the Somme; Côte d'Opale.*

GAVRELLE • Pas-de-Calais, 62580

🍴 **RELAIS DE LA CHAUMIERE**
(M. Franck Courcelle) 21 Route Nationale
☎ 21.58.16.99
Directions: RN 50, A1, exit Fresnes-les-Montaubant.
Languages spoken: English.
Menu: 45 Frs.
Restaurant: breakfast from 7.00.
Specialities: home-cooking.
Other points: credit cards accepted, bar, à la carte menu, traditional decor, pets allowed, car/lorry parking.
◄€ *war memorials.*

GHYVELDE • Nord, 59254

🍴 **LE SAINT-SEBASTIEN**
(Mme Edith Marie-Rubben) 161 rue
Nationale ☎ 28.26.61.95
Directions: Calais/Dunkerque/Belgium (Belgique) road, exit Ghyvelde.
Languages spoken: Dutch.
Menu: 45 to 180 Frs.
Restaurant: breakfast from 7.30. Lunch from 11.00 until 17.00. Closed Tues, and in Aug.
Specialities: Flemish dishes, fish, regional menu, home-cooking.
Other points: bar, children's menu, pets allowed, car/lorry parking.
◄€ *Bergues; Dunkerque; Flanders region; Belgium.*

HALLUIN • Nord, 59250

🍴 **AU ROUTIER**
(M. Richard Kozior) 196 rue de la Lys
☎ 20.23.88.20
Directions: RD 945, in Le Col Bras Industrial Zone (Z.I.).
Languages spoken: Dutch, Polish and Serbo-Croat.
Menu: 62 Frs.
Restaurant: breakfast from 6.30. Lunch from 11.30 until 14.00. Dinner from 19.00 until 21.00. Closed Sat afternoon, Sun, and in Aug.
Specialities: couscous (on Fri), home-cooking.
Other points: credit cards accepted, bar, traditional decor, pets allowed, car/lorry parking.

HIRSON • Aisne, 02500

🍴 **JUPITER**
(M. Guilio Corsini) 151 avenue Joffre
☎ 23.58.14.03
Directions: RN 43, at the Hirson exit for Paris or Lille.
Languages spoken: English and Italian.
Menu: 53 Frs.
Restaurant: breakfast from 6.00. Lunch from 11.30 until 17.00. Dinner from 17.00 until 22.00. Closed Sun, and in Aug.
Specialities: lasagne, pizza, spaghetti bolognaise, home-cooking.
Other points: credit cards accepted, bar, children's menu, à la carte menu, modern decor, pets allowed, car/lorry parking.
◄€ *abbey; forest; waterfalls; fountain.*

LA HOUSSOYE · Oise, 60390

☵ LE CHEVAL BLANC
(Mme Liliane Heythuyzen) 5 route de Gisors
☎ 44.81.40.40
Directions: RN 181.
Menu: 60 to 150 Frs.
Accommodation: 120 to 140 Frs.
Restaurant: breakfast from 7.00. Lunch from 11.30 until 14.30. Dinner from 19.30 until 21.30. Closed Sun.
Specialities: filet de daurade à la provençale, home-cooking.
Hotel: 4 rooms. Facilities: shower.
Other points: credit cards accepted, bar, children's menu, à la carte menu, traditional decor, terrace, pets allowed, car/lorry parking.
☵ *Saint-Germer-de-Fly abbey; Beauvais; Gisors.*

☵ LE RELAIS DE LA HOUSSOYE
(Mme Christine Sachot) 300 Route Nationale
☎ 22.40.57.29
Directions: RD 929, between Albert and Amiens.
Menu: 45 to 55 Frs.
Restaurant: breakfast from 7.00. Closed Sun.
Specialities: home-cooking.
Other points: credit cards accepted, bar, traditional decor, pets allowed, car/lorry parking.
☵ *Albert: Notre-Dame de Brebière, 1914–18 museum; Amiens; Villers-Bretonneux.*

HUMIERES · Pas-de-Calais, 62130

☵ LE BISON
(M. Michel Ponsot) 9 Route Nationale 39
☎ 21.04.58.39
Directions: RN 39, Arras/Le Touquet/Boulogne-sur-Mer.
Languages spoken: English and Italian.
Restaurant: breakfast from 5.00. Lunch from 11.00 until 15.00. Dinner from 19.00 until 22.00.
Specialities: fondue savoyarde, ficelle picarde, home-cooking.
Other points: credit cards accepted, bar, children's menu, à la carte menu, lounge area, modern decor, pets allowed, car/lorry parking.

☵ RELAIS ROUTIERS
(M. José Ternisien) 6 Route Nationale 39
☎ 21.41.85.77
Directions: RN 39, between Saint-Pol and Hesdin.
Menu: 48 Frs.
Restaurant: breakfast from 5.00. Lunch from 11.00 until 15.00. Dinner from 19.00 until 21.00. Closed Sun.
Specialities: home-cooking.
Other points: credit cards accepted, bar, modern decor, pets allowed, car/lorry parking.

HUPPY · Somme, 80140

☵ LE RELAIS DU BEL AIR
(Mme Nadine Martel) 42 Route Nationale
☎ 22.28.47.75

Directions: RN 28, between Rouen and Abbeville.
Menu: 55 to 85 Frs.
Restaurant: breakfast from 6.00. Closed Sun (out of season).
Specialities: home-cooking.
Other points: bar, children's menu, à la carte menu, terrace, pets allowed, car/lorry parking.
☵ *church and windmill*

LABOURSE · Pas-de-Calais, 62113

☵ RELAIS DU MOULIN
(Mme Fabienne Delfosse) 8 route de Lens
☎ 21.61.10.10
Directions: between Béthune and Lens.
Menu: 60 Frs (wine included).
Restaurant: breakfast from 6.00. Lunch from 12.00 until 15.30. Dinner from 19.30 until 24.00. Closed Sun.
Specialities: carbonnade flamande, potjewlech, home-cooking.
Other points: credit cards accepted, bar, children's menu, à la carte menu, traditional decor.
☵ *park at Aholain; Houlin de Beuvry.*

LABROYE · Pas-de-Calais, 62140

☵ CHEZ NATHALIE
(Mme Nathalie Joly) Route Nationale
☎ 21.86.83.10
Directions: RD 928, between Abbeville and Hesdin.
Menu: 50 to 85 Frs.
Restaurant: breakfast from 6.00. Lunch from 11.30 until 15.00. Dinner from 18.00 until 22.00.
Specialities: regional menu, home-cooking.
Other points: credit cards accepted, bar, children's menu, traditional decor, pets allowed, car/lorry parking.
☵ *river Authie valley.*

LAVERSINES · Oise, 60510

☵ LE RELAIS ROUTIER
(M. Marceau Forestier) 90 rue Saint-Germain
☎ 44.07.75.80
Directions: RN 31, between Reims and Rouen.
Menu: 58 Frs (wine included) to 70 Frs.
Restaurant: breakfast from 6.00. Lunch from 11.30 until 14.30. Dinner from 19.30 until 21.30. Closed Sat, Sun, last 2 weeks in Aug and 1 week at Christmas.
Specialities: paella (to order), home-cooking.
Other points: credit cards accepted, bar, traditional decor, pets allowed, car/lorry parking.
☵ *historic sites; Beauvais cathedral; angora factory tours.*

LEVIGNEN · Oise, 60800

☵ RELAIS DE LA II
(M. Jacques Carrier) Route Nationale 2
☎ 44.94.21.01

Directions: RN 2, Paris/Soissons road.
Menu: 53 to 70 Frs.
Restaurant: breakfast from 5.00. Lunch from
11.30 until 15.00. Dinner from 19.00 until 22.30.
Specialities: home-cooking.
Other points: credit cards accepted, bar, à la carte
menu, pets allowed, car/lorry parking.

LIEVIN • Pas-de-Calais, 62800

⊨ LE ZOLA
(Mme Pierrette Lemaire) 215 rue Emile-Zola
☎ 21.29.29.72
Menu: 50 to 60 Frs.
Restaurant: breakfast from 9.00. Closed Monday.
Specialities: home-cooking.
Other points: bar, lounge area, pets allowed,
car/lorry parking.

LONGUEAU • Somme, 80330

🏠 LE RELAIS DE L'HOTEL DE VILLE
(M. Konider Bellaredj) 105 avenue
Henri-Barbusse ☎ 22.46.16.14
Directions: RN 35.
Languages spoken: English and Arabic.
Restaurant: closed Sunday.
Hotel: 10 rooms.
Other points: bar.

LUMBRES • Pas-de-Calais, 62380

🏠 HOTEL MODERNE
(M. Pierre Fichaux) 18 rue François-Cousin
☎ 21.39.62.87
Directions: opposite the station.
Restaurant: dinner until 21.00. Closed Sun, Aug.
Hotel: 6 rooms.
Other points: bar.

MAIRIEUX • Nord, 59600

⊨ AUBERGE DU COCHER
(Mme Hélène Barrier) 27 rue de Mons
☎ 27.64.23.25
Directions: between Maubeuge and Mons.
Languages spoken: German and English.
Menu: 55 Frs.
Restaurant: breakfast from 5.00.
Specialities: home-cooking.
Other points: bar, modern decor, pets allowed,
car/lorry parking.
◁€ zoological gardens at Maubeuge; Mons; Baval:
Gallo-Roman remains; Belgium.

AUX MARAIS • Oise, 60000

⊨ AU GRAND R
(M. Marcel Boutoille) 12 route de Gisors
☎ 44.48.18.66
Directions: RN 981, between Mantes and Gisors.

Menu: 54 Frs.
Restaurant: breakfast from 5.30. Dinner served
until 21.30. Closed Sun.
Specialities: home-cooking.
Other points: credit cards accepted, bar, children's
menu, traditional decor, car/lorry parking.
◁€ Le Vexin; Beauvais.

MARCHELEPOT • Somme, 80200

🏠 RESTAURANT DU PARC
(M. Milorad Jovanovic) Route Nationale 17
☎ 22.83.90.85
Languages spoken: Serbo-Croat.
Menu: 58 Frs.
Accommodation: 100 Frs.
Restaurant: breakfast from 5.00. Lunch from
12.00 until 14.30. Dinner from 19.00 until 23.00.
Closed Sat, Sun, and in Aug.
Specialities: home-cooking.
Hotel: 2 rooms. Facilities: shower.
Other points: credit cards accepted, bar,
children's menu, traditional decor, pets allowed,
car/lorry parking.

MARQUISE • Pas-de-Calais, 62250

🏠 A LA DESCENTE DES VOYAGEURS
(Mme Nelly Brisbout) 17 rue du 8 mai
☎ 21.92.85.55
Directions: between Marquise and Guines.
Menu: 58 to 120 Frs.
Accommodation: 100 Frs (half board 160 Frs, full
board 190 Frs).
Restaurant: breakfast from 7.00. Lunch from
12.00 until 14.00. Dinner from 19.00 until 20.30.
Specialities: home-cooking.
Hotel: 4 rooms.
Other points: bar, modern decor.
◁€ fortress at Mimoueques; quarries; aviation
museum.

MAUBEUGE • Nord, 59600

⊨ LE BERLIOZ
(M. Philippe Cappeliez) 27 avenue de la Gare
☎ 27.64.68.79
Directions: RN 2.
Menu: 60 Frs (wine included).
Restaurant: breakfast from 8.00. Dinner served
until 23.30. Closed Sat evening, Sun, and the last
2 weeks in Aug.
Other points: bar, children's menu, à la carte
menu, car/lorry parking.

⊨ See also MAIRIEUX.

MAZINGARBE • Pas-de-Calais, 62670

⊨ AU RELAIS DES ROUTIERS
(Mme Geneviève Marcinkowski) 85 Route
Nationale 43 ☎ 21.72.00.09

Directions: RN 43, between Lens and Béthune
Languages spoken: German and Polish.
Menu: 55 Frs.
Restaurant: breakfast from 8.00. Lunch from
12.00 until 14.00. Closed Sun, and from 1st to
20th Aug.
Specialities: lapinaux aux pruneaux, canard,
regional menu, home-cooking.
Other points: bar, children's menu, modern
decor, car/lorry parking.
◁€ *Lorette; Vimy.*

MERLIMONT • Pas-de-Calais, 62155

≋ LE CURACAO
(M. Guy Arpin) 611 rue Auguste-Biblocq
☎ 21.09.45.45
Directions: RD 940, between Berck and Etaples.
Menu: 55 to 123 Frs, plat du jour from
42 Frs ⌣
Restaurant: breakfast from 7.00. Lunch from
11.30 until 15.30. Dinner from 19.00 until 23.00.
Specialities: fondue savoyarde, fruits de mer,
espadon (swordfish) à l'oseille, truite aux amandes,
émincé de canard aux groseilles, regional menu,
home-cooking.
Other points: credit cards accepted, bar,
children's menu, à la carte menu, terrace, pets
allowed, car/lorry parking.
◁€ *leisure park at Bagatelle; Côte d'Opale
beaches; le Touquet; Berck.*

MEZY-MOULINS • Aisne, 02650

≋ RESTAURANT DU CHEVAL NOIR
(Mme Martine Caron) 25 avenue de
Champagne ☎ 23.71.91.30
Directions: RN 3, between Dormans and
Château-Thierry.
Menu: 56 to 99 Frs.
Restaurant: breakfast from 8.00. Lunch from
12.00 until 15.00. Dinner from 19.00 until 22.30.
Closed Sun.
Specialities: pavé au roquefort, regional menu,
home-cooking.
Other points: bar, children's menu, à la carte
menu, lounge area, traditional decor, pets allowed,
car/lorry parking.

MONTDIDIER • Somme, 80500

🏠 LE RELAIS DU MOUTON D'OR
(M. Christian Parmentier) 10 boulevard
Debeney ☎ 22.78.03.43
Menu: 55 to 85 Frs.
Accommodation: 75 Frs.
Restaurant: breakfast from 7.00. Lunch from
12.00 until 14.00. Dinner from 19.00 until 21.00.
Closed Sun, and in Aug.
Specialities: regional menu, home-cooking.
Hotel: 5 rooms.
Other points: credit cards accepted, bar, modern
decor, pets allowed, car/lorry parking.

MOREUIL • Somme, 80110

≋ LA COLOMBE D'OR
(Mme Gismonde Tellier) 11 rue
Maurice-Garin ☎ 22.09.70.93
Directions: between Amiens and Compiègne.
Menu: 54 Frs.
Restaurant: breakfast from 7.00. Lunch from
11.30 until 19.00. Dinner served until 21.30.
Closed Sun.
Specialities: home-cooking.
Other points: credit cards accepted, bar,
children's menu, pets allowed, car/lorry parking.
◁€ *prehistoric caves at Naours (35km).*

OMIECOURT-PAR-CHAULNES
Somme, 80320

≋ AU BON ACCUEIL
(M. Allaoua Betroune) Route Nationale 17
☎ 22.85.42.49
Directions: RN 17, between Péronne and Roye.
Languages spoken: Arabic.
Menu: 56 to 85 Frs.
Restaurant: open 24 hours, closed Sun.
Specialities: couscous, paella, regional menu,
home-cooking.
Other points: credit cards accepted, bar, children's
menu, terrace, pets allowed, car/lorry parking.
◁€ *historial (wax museum) at Péronne.*

OVILLERS-LA-BOISSELLE
Somme, 80300

≋ LE POPPY
(M. Georges Vandenbulke) 4 route de
Bapaume ☎ 22.75.45.45 [Fax] 22.74.75.65
Directions: RD 329, between Bapaume and Albert.
Menu: 50 to 95 Frs.
Restaurant: breakfast from 6.30. Lunch from
12.00 until 15.00. Dinner from 19.00 until 22.30.
Closed Sat, Sun, and in Aug.
Specialities: home-cooking.
Other points: credit cards accepted, bar,
children's menu, traditional decor, terrace,
car/lorry parking.
◁€ *Battle of the Somme memorial; basilica at
Albert; other mementoes of the 1914–18 war.*

PERONNE • Somme, 80200

≋ LA CHAPELETTE – Chez Claud et Nicole
(Claude and Nicole Charpentier) 61 route de
Paris ☎ 22.84.10.82
Directions: RN 17, between Roye and Péronne.
Menu: 55 Frs.
Restaurant: breakfast from 7.00. Closed Sat
afternoon and Sun.
Specialities: home-cooking.
Other points: credit cards accepted, bar,
children's menu, à la carte menu, traditional decor,
pets allowed, car parking.
◁€ *bay of the Somme.*

PERONNE-ASSEVILLERS
Somme, 80200

⇌ L'ARCHE D'ASSEVILLERS EST
(M. Christian Soma) A1, services at Asseviller Est (accessible in Paris/Lille direction)
☎ 22.85.26.08 [Fax] 22.85.92.62
Restaurant: open until 24.00.
Other points: credit cards and foreign currency accepted.

⇌ L'ARCHE D'ASSEVILLERS OUEST
(M. Frédéric Magniez) A1, services at Asseviller Ouest (accessible in Lille/Paris direction) ☎ 22.85.20.35 [Fax] 22.85.24.11
Restaurant: open until 24.00.
Other points: credit cards accepted.

⇌ LES AS DU VOLANT
(Mme Magali Crappier) A1, services at Asseviller Ouest (accessible in Lille/Paris directions) ☎ 22.85.23.56 [Fax] 22.85.24.11
Other points: credit cards accepted.

PONT-REMY • Somme, 80580

⇌ LE CONTINENTAL
(Mme Ginette Thérasse) 9 rue Robert-Bordeux ☎ 22.27.12.89
Directions: main Paris/Boulogne-sur-Mer road.
Menu: 50 to 100 Frs.
Restaurant: breakfast from 8.30. Lunch from 12.00 until 14.30. Closed in Aug.
Specialities: regional menu, home-cooking.
Other points: bar, à la carte menu.

POULAINVILLE • Somme, 80260

⇌ LE RELAIS DE POULAINVILLE
(M. Jean-Pierre Hennebert) 2 Route Nationale ☎ 22.43.05.00
Directions: RN 25, between Amiens and Arras.
Menu: 58 Frs.
Restaurant: breakfast from 5.00. Lunch from 12.00 until 15.00. Dinner from 19.00 until 22.00. Closed Sat, Sun, and the last 2 weeks in Aug.
Specialities: home-cooking.
Other points: credit cards accepted, bar, children's menu, pets allowed, car/lorry parking.
◖ cathedral at Amiens; les Hortillons.

QUAEDYPRE • Nord, 59380

⇌ L'GITANT
(M. José Lermytte) Chemin Départemental 916 ☎ 28.68.69.87
Directions: CD 916, exit 16, towards Wormhout.
Menu: 35 to 160 Frs.
Restaurant: breakfast from 7.00. Lunch from 12.00 until 15.00. Dinner from 19.00 until 22.00. Closed Sat, and the 1st 2 weeks in Aug.
Specialities: carbonnade flamande, Potche Uleech, regional menu.

Other points: credit cards accepted, bar, children's menu, à la carte menu, traditional decor, pets allowed, car/lorry parking.
◖ ramparts at Bergues; circuit of villages in bloom; port of Dunkerque.

RENESCURE • Nord, 59173

⇌ LA CLE DES CHAMPS
(Mme Marlène Deman-Lamiaux) 'La Clé des Champs', 89 Route de Saint-Omer
☎ 28.49.81.12
Directions: RN 42, between Saint-Omer and Hazebrouck.
Menu: 40 Frs.
Restaurant: lunch from 11.30 until 14.00. Closed Sat afternoon, Sun.
Specialities: home-cooking.
Other points: credit cards accepted, traditional decor, pets allowed, car/lorry parking.
◖ Cassel (10km); Andouarois (9km).

RESSONS-SUR-MATZ • Oise, 60490

⇌ L'ARCHE DE RESSONS OUEST
(M. Lionel Violette) A1, services at Ressons Ouest, (accessible Lille/Paris direction)
☎ 44.42.57.17 [Fax] 44.42.52.33
Restaurant: open until 24.00.
Other points: credit cards and foreign currency accepted.

ROLLOT • Somme, 80500

⇌ LE RELAIS DE LA MADELEINE
(Mme Caroline Priou) 88 rue de la Madeleine
☎ 22.78.02.81
Directions: RD 935, between Compiègne and Amiens.
Menu: 48 to 70 Frs.
Restaurant: breakfast from 8.00. Closed Mon, and in Aug.
Specialities: home-cooking.
Other points: bar, children's menu, à la carte menu, traditional decor, terrace, pets allowed, car/lorry parking.
◖ Compiègne; valley of the Somme.

ROUBAIX • Nord, 59100

⇌ LE CALAIS
(Mme Josette Vaze) 2 quai de Calais
☎ 20.26.00.35
Languages spoken: German, English and Dutch.
Menu: 50 Frs (wine included).
Restaurant: breakfast from 6.00. Lunch from 12.00 until 14.30. Dinner from 19.30 until 22.30. Closed Sat afternoon, Sun, in Aug and end Dec.
Specialities: home-cooking.
Other points: credit cards accepted, bar, modern decor, pets allowed, car/lorry parking.

SAINT-INGLEVERT
Pas-de-Calais, 62250

≈ LA MURAILLE
(Mme Jocelyne Salmon) Route Nationale 1
☎ 21.33.75.44
Directions: between Calais and Boulogne-sur-Mer.
Languages spoken: some English.
Menu: 65 to 95 Frs.
Restaurant: breakfast from 6.00. Lunch from
11.00 until 15.00. Closed Sat, Sun, and 3 weeks in
Aug.
Specialities: petit salé (pickled pork), home-
cooking.
Other points: credit cards accepted, bar, à la carte
menu, modern decor, pets allowed, car/lorry
parking.

SAINT-OMER • Pas-de-Calais, 62500

🛏 LA RENAISSANCE
(Vanyper SARL) 10 place du 11 Novembre
☎ 21.38.26.55
Directions: RN 43.
Languages spoken: English and German.
Menu: 53 Frs.
Accommodation: 120 to 140 Frs.
Restaurant: breakfast from 6.30. Lunch from
12.00 until 14.00. Dinner from 20.00 until 21.00.
Closed Sat evening (except bookings), Sun, and
3 weeks in Aug.
Specialities: regional menu, home-cooking.
Hotel: 18 rooms.
Other points: credit cards accepted, bar, à la carte
menu, traditional decor, pets allowed, car/lorry
parking.
❊ Marais Audomarois; cathedral; museums.

SAINT-PAUL • Oise, 60650

≈ LE RELAIS SAINT-PAUL
(Mme Jeanne-Lise Faure) Route Nationale 31
☎ 44.82.20.19
Directions: RN 31, Beauvais/Rouen/Le Havre.
Menu: 55 Frs.
Restaurant: breakfast from 5.00.
Specialities: home-cooking.
Other points: bar, children's menu, traditional
decor, terrace, pets allowed, car/lorry parking.
❊ leisure park at Saint-Paul; abbey at Saint-
Germer-de-Fly; Beauvais; Gerberoy (village in
bloom).

SAINT-QUENTIN-LAMOTTE
Somme, 80880

≈ A GROS JACQUES
(Mme Jeanine Decayeux) Route
Départementale 925 ☎ 22.60.41.14
Directions: RD 925, between Eu, towards
Abbeville.
Menu: 58 to 68 Frs.
Restaurant: breakfast from 7.00. Lunch from

12.00 until 14.30. Closed Sat, Sun, and the last
2 weeks in Aug.
Specialities: home-cooking.
Other points: credit cards accepted, bar, modern
decor, pets allowed, car/lorry parking.
❊ Eu; le Tréport; coast of Picardy.

SAINT-RIQUIER • Somme, 80135

≈ LE CENTULOIS
(Mme Lili Colinet) 70 rue du Général-de-
Gaulle ☎ 22.28.88.15
Restaurant: closed Wednesday.
Other points: bar.

SALOUEL • Somme, 80480

≈ AUBERGE DU TROU NORMAND
(M. Jean-Michel Picard) 75 route de Rouen
☎ 22.95.53.90
Directions: RN 29, Rouen.
Restaurant: breakfast from 5.00. Lunch from
11.30 until 15.00. Dinner from 19.00 until 21.00.
Closed Sat, Sun (except bookings).
Specialities: home-cooking.
Other points: bar, children's menu, traditional
decor.

SERIFONTAINE • Oise, 60590

🛏 LE RELAIS FLEURI
(Mme Annick Fontaine) 22 rue Hacque
☎ 44.84.89.17
Directions: between Gournay-sur-Bray and Gisors.
Menu: 62 to 90 Frs.
Accommodation: 90 to 160 Frs.
Restaurant: lunch from 12.00 until 14.00. Dinner
from 19.00 until 21.00. Closed Sat, Sun.
Specialities: home-cooking.
Hotel: 9 rooms. Facilities: shower, private
bathroom.
Other points: bar, modern decor, car parking.
❊ cathedral and tapestry museum at Beauvais
(40km); abbey at Saint-Germer-de-Fly (10km).

STEENVOORDE • Nord, 59114

**≈ CAFETERIA DE STEENVOORD
SAINT-ELOI**
(M. Alain Bara) A25, services at Saint-Eloi
(accessible in Dunkerque/Lille direction)
☎ 28.49.74.92 [Fax] 28.49.70.22
Other points: credit cards and foreign currency
accepted.

**≈ CAFETERIA DE STEENVOORD
SAINT-LAURENT**
(M. Alain Bara) A25, services at Saint-Laurent
(accessible in Dunkerque/Lille direction)
☎ 28.49.71.33 [Fax] 28.49.70.22
Other points: credit cards and foreign currency
accepted.

TATINGHEM • Pas-de-Calais, 62500

⇌ LE TRUCK WASH
(Jacques and Christine Leroy) Zone Artisanale
☎ 21.98.45.45
Directions: RN 42, between Boulogne-sur-Mer and Saint-Omer.
Languages spoken: English.
Menu: 55 Frs (coffee included).
Restaurant: breakfast from 7.00. Lunch from 12.00 until 14.30. Dinner from 19.30 until 21.00. Closed Sat afternoon, Sun, in Aug and in Dec.
Specialities: home-cooking.
Other points: credit cards accepted, bar, children's menu, modern decor, terrace, pets allowed, car/lorry parking.
◑€ *cathedral at Saint-Omer.*

TOURCOING • Nord, 59200

🏠 AU SIGNAL D'ARRET
(M. Michel Guilbert) 28 rue des Francs
☎ 20.26.56.74
Directions: exit 15: Les Francs, turn right at the lights.
Menu: 62 Frs.
Accommodation: 95 to 145 Frs.
Restaurant: breakfast from 6.30. Lunch from 11.30 until 15.00. Dinner from 19.30 until 21.30. Closed Sat, Sun, and the middle 2 weeks in Aug.
Specialities: home-cooking.
Hotel: 5 rooms. Facilities: television.
Other points: credit cards accepted, bar, children's menu, traditional decor, pets allowed, car/lorry parking.

TROSLY-BREUIL • Oise, 60350

⇌ LA TERRASSE
(M. Enso Dal Sacco) 47 route de Reims
☎ 44.85.70.39
Directions: RN 31, between Compiègne and Soissons.
Languages spoken: German and Italian.
Menu: 55 Frs (drink included).
Restaurant: breakfast from 4.00. Dinner served until 22.00. Closed Fri evening, Sat, Sun, and 2 weeks in July.
Specialities: goulash, regional menu, home-cooking.
Other points: credit cards accepted, bar, modern decor, terrace, pets allowed, car/lorry parking.
◑€ *chateau and forest at Compiègne (10km); chateau at Pierrefonds (8km); Armistice railway-carriage.*

URVILLERS • Aisne, 02690

⇌ L'ARCHE DE SAINT-QUENTIN-URVILLERS
(Mme Isabelle Inigo) A26, services at Urvillers-Saint-Quentin (accessible in both directions) ☎ 23.08.87.08 Fax 23.08.96.49
Restaurant: open until 24.00.
Other points: credit cards and foreign currency accepted.

VALENCIENNES • Nord, 59300

🏠 AUBERGE DE LA POTERNE – Café des Routiers
(M. Jean Demolle) 9 boulevard Eisen
☎ 27.46.44.98
Directions: RN 29, exit Valenciennes Sud (South).
Menu: 58 Frs.
Accommodation: 90 to 160 Frs.
Restaurant: breakfast from 7.00. Lunch from 12.00 until 14.00. Dinner served from 19.30 until 21.30. Closed Sat afternoon, Sun, and public holidays.
Specialities: home-cooking.
Hotel: 12 rooms. Facilities: shower.
Other points: bar, modern decor, pets allowed, car/lorry parking.
◑€ *museum; fortifications; basilica.*

VENDIN-LEZ-BETHUNE
Pas-de-Calais, 62232

⇌ LA MOTTE DOREE
(Mme Marie-France de Greef) 18 route de Saint-Venant ☎ 21.57.25.24
Directions: RD 937, between Béthune and Dunkerque.
Menu: 30 to 50 Frs.
Restaurant: breakfast from 7.00. Lunch from 11.00 until 15.00. Dinner served from 18.00 until 1.00. Closed Sun.
Specialities: flamiche flamande, couscous, home-cooking.
Other points: bar, children's menu, lounge area, traditional decor, pets allowed, car/lorry parking.
◑€ *belfry at Béthune.*

VILLERS-BRETONNEUX
Somme, 80380

🏠 LE MELBOURNE
(M. Sébastien Mansion) 2 rue de la Gare
☎ 22.48.00.14
Directions: RN 29, Amiens/Saint-Quentin road.
Languages spoken: English.
Menu: 55 Frs (coffee included).
Accommodation: 70 to 100 Frs.
Restaurant: breakfast from 7.00. Lunch from 12.00 until 14.30. Dinner served from 19.00 until 22.00. Closed Sun, and in Aug.
Specialities: home-cooking.
Hotel: 8 rooms.
Other points: bar, children's menu, pets allowed, car/lorry parking.
◑€ *Amiens, the capital of Picardy; Australian 1939–45 museum and memorial.*

VILLERS-COTTERETS • Aisne, 02600

🏠 AU BOUT DU MONDE
(Mme Michèle Dorge) route de la Ferté-Milon
☎ 23.96.07.12
Directions: RD 936, Meaux.
Menu: 55 to 95 Frs.
Accommodation: 95 to 130 Frs.

Restaurant: breakfast from 6.30. Lunch from 11.30 until 15.00. Dinner served from 19.00 until 22.00. Closed Sun, public holidays, Christmas Day for 2 weeks, and 2 weeks in Aug.
Specialities: confit, pierre gourmande confit, escargots 'Alexandre Dumas', regional menu, home-cooking.
Hotel: 5 rooms.
Other points: credit cards accepted, bar, children's menu, à la carte menu, terrace, pets allowed, car/lorry parking.
Alexandre Dumas museum; chateau of François 1er; musée du bois (woodcraft).

WORMHOUT · Nord, 59470

CAFE DE LA FORGE
(Mme Claudine Macker) 84 Grand'Place
☎ 28.65.62.33
Directions: RD 916.
Menu: 30 to 50 Frs.
Restaurant: breakfast from 6.00. Lunch from 11.30 until 14.30. Closed last 2 weeks in Aug to end 1st week in Sept.
Other points: children's menu, traditional decor.
museum; windmill.

NORTH-EAST FRANCE

The following *départements* are included in this chapter:

Ardennes (08)	Marne (51)
Aube (10)	Meurthe-et-Moselle (54)
Bas-Rhin (67)	Meuse (55)
Côte-d'Or (21)	Moselle (57)
Doubs (25)	Nièvre (58)
Haut-Rhin (68)	Saône-et-Loire (71)
Haute-Marne (52)	Territoire-de-Belfort (90)
Haute-Saône (70)	Vosges (88)
Jura (39)	Yonne (89)

ANCERVILLE · Meuse, 55170

LE RELAIS
(Mme Renée Lange) 59 route de Saint-Dizier
☎ 29.75.30.13
Directions: RN 4, the Paris/Strasbourg road.
Languages spoken: Italian and Polish.
Menu: 55 to 75 Frs.
Accommodation: 110 to 150 Frs.
Restaurant: breakfast from 7.00. Lunch from 12.00 until 14.00. Dinner from 19.00 until 21.00. Closed Sat and Sun afternoon, and in Sept.
Specialities: tête de veau, andouillettes, choucroute, regional menu, home-cooking.
Hotel: ☆ 12 rooms. Facilities: shower, private bathroom.
Other points: credit cards accepted, bar, children's menu, à la carte menu, lounge area, traditional decor, terrace, car parking.
Lac du Der-Chantecoq; Vaucouleurs; Domrémy; Colombey-les-Deux-Eglises; Bar-le-Duc; Saint-Dizier.

LES ROUTIERS
Your assurance of Quality and Value

ANLEZY · Nièvre, 58480

HOTEL DU COMMERCE
(M. Max Larrive) place du Bourg
☎ 86.60.23.98
Directions: between Château-Chinon and Decize.
Languages spoken: Dutch.
Menu: 55 Frs (wine included).
Restaurant: breakfast from 7.00. Lunch from 11.30 until 15.00. Dinner from 19.00 until 21.00. Closed Mon.
Specialities: home-cooking.
Other points: bar, children's menu, traditional decor, terrace, pets allowed, car/lorry parking.
Musée de la mine (mining); parc régional du Morvan.

ARC-LES-GRAY · Haute-Saône, 70100

LES ROUTIERS
(Mme Henriette Demoulin) 4 place Aristide-Briand, La Croisée ☎ 84.65.37.23
Restaurant: closed Sun.
Other points: bar.

ARCES • Yonne, 89320

🍽 RELAIS DE LA FORET D'OTHE
(Mme Yolande Misura) 15 place de l'Eglise
☎ 86.88.10.44
Directions: RD 905.
Menu: 55 to 150 Frs.
Accommodation: 90 to 150 Frs.
Restaurant: breakfast from 6.30. Lunch from
12.00 until 14.00. Closed Wed.
Specialities: jambon au Chablis, caneton au cidre,
regional menu.
Hotel: ☆ 7 rooms. Facilities: shower.
Other points: bar, children's menu, traditional
decor, car/lorry parking.
🌤 *cider route; Saint-Florentin; Sens.*

ARCHES • Vosges, 88380

🍽 LA TRUITE RENOMMEE
(Mme Josseline Hagenauer) 1 rue d'Epinal
☎ 29.32.79.13 [Fax] 29.32.61.00
Directions: Epinal-Remiremont.
Languages spoken: English, German and Italian.
Menu: 52 to 110 Frs.
Accommodation: 200 to 240 Frs.
Restaurant: breakfast from 6.00. Lunch from
12.00 until 14.30. Dinner from 19.00 until 23.00
Specialities: truite 'Fumée-Vosgien' (smoked),
regional menu, home-cooking.
Hotel: ☆ ☆ 8 rooms. Facilities: shower, private
bathroom, television, telephone.
Other points: credit cards accepted, bar,
children's menu, à la carte menu, lounge area,
traditional decor, pets allowed, car/lorry parking.
🌤 *Musée de l'imagerie (printing) at Epinal;
Gerardmer; Thann.*

ARNAY-LE-DUC • Côte-d'Or, 21230

🍽 RELAIS ROUTIERS LE SAINT-PRIX
(M. Robert Tonelli) Sivry ☎ 80.84.81.74
Directions: RN 6, towards Chalon-sur-Saône.
Languages spoken: English and Italian.
Menu: 54 to 70 Frs.
Accommodation: 120 to 140 Frs.
Restaurant: breakfast from 6.00. Lunch from
11.45 until 14.00. Dinner from 19.30 until 22.00.
Closed Sun.
Specialities: boeuf bourguignon, home-cooking.
Hotel: 6 rooms. Facilities: shower.
Other points: credit cards accepted, bar,
traditional decor, terrace, car/lorry parking.
🌤 *chateaux at Neufchâteau and Rochepot;
hospice de Beaune.*

ATHIS • Marne, 51150

🍽 AU BON ACCUEIL
(M. Daniel Bourscheidt) 12 route
Départementale ☎ 26.57.62.61
Directions: between Epernay and Châlons-sur-
Marne.
Menu: 50 Frs.

Accommodation: 120 to 150 Frs.
Restaurant: breakfast from 6.30. Lunch from
11.30 until 14.30. Dinner from 19.30 until 21.00.
Closed Sun, and in Aug.
Specialities: home-cooking.
Hotel: 5 rooms. Facilities: shower, private bathroom.
Other points: credit cards accepted, bar,
traditional decor, pets allowed, car/lorry parking.
🌤 *tours of the wine-cellars and hills of the
Champagne region (Reims, Epernay 13km); Marne
valley.*

ATTIGNY • Ardennes, 08130

🍽 CHEZ NICOLE
(Mme Nicole Pienne) 16 place Charlemagne
☎ 24.71.20.69
Menu: 40 to 70 Frs.
Restaurant: breakfast from 5.00. Lunch from
11.00 until 15.00. Dinner from 19.30 until 23.30
Specialities: home-cooking.
Hotel: 3 rooms. Facilities: shower, private bathroom.
Other points: bar, children's menu, pets allowed,
car/lorry parking.

AUBETERRE • Aube, 10150

🍽 LES TILLEULS
(M. Raymond Mielle) ☎ 25.37.51.11
Directions: RN 77.
Menu: 48 to 55 Frs.
Restaurant: dinner until 22.00
Specialities: home-cooking.
Other points: credit cards accepted, bar, à la carte
menu, car/lorry parking.
🌤 *lake and forêt d'Orient; Troyes: cathedral.*

AUMETZ • Moselle, 57710

🍽 CAFE DE LA POSTE
(Mme Linda Cossa) 15 rue Foch
☎ 82.91.91.71
Directions: RN 52, the Hayange/Longwy road.
Languages spoken: Italian.
Menu: 47 Frs.
Accommodation: 120 to 150 Frs.
Restaurant: breakfast from 6.00. Lunch from
12.00 until 15.00. Dinner from 19.00 until 21.00.
Closed Tues afternoon.
Specialities: Italian dishes, regional menu,
home-cooking.
Hotel: 6 rooms. Facilities: shower.
Other points: credit cards accepted, bar,
children's menu, à la carte menu, modern decor,
pets allowed, car/lorry parking.
🌤 *Musée de la mine (mining); metallic church.*

AUTECHAUX • Doubs, 25110

🍽 RELAIS DE L'AUTOROUTE – Chez
Simone
(Mme Simone Courtial) ☎ 81.84.01.14
Directions: Baume-les-Dames exit, towards
Lure/Vesoul.

Languages spoken: a little English and Spanish.
Menu: 58 to 62 Frs (drink and coffee included).
Restaurant: breakfast from 9.00. Lunch from
11.00 until 15.00. Dinner from 19.00 until 24.00.
Closed Sun, public holidays, and 2 weeks in Aug.
Specialities: croûtes aux champignons, 3-cheese
fondue, canard à l'ananas, choucroute garnie,
home-cooking.
Other points: bar, children's menu, lounge area,
traditional decor, terrace, pets allowed, car/lorry
parking.
◀ caves at La Glacière; gouffre (abyss) de
Poudrey; saut (falls) du Doubs (Villers-le-Lac); lac de
Bonnal; chateaux at Belvoir and Joux.

AUTUN • Saône-et-Loire, 71400

≈ LE CLUB
(Mme Eva Rizzo) 13 route de Beaune
☎ 85.52.27.72
Languages spoken: German, English, Italian,
Spanish.
Menu: 59 to 79 Frs.
Restaurant: breakfast from 6.30. Lunch from
11.30 until 14.00. Dinner from 19.00 until 21.30.
Closed Sun, and in Aug.
Specialities: Italian and Calabrian dishes, regional
menu, home-cooking.
Other points: credit cards accepted, bar, à la carte
menu, terrace, car/lorry parking.
◀ Gallo-Roman town: Roman theatre, temples;
Gothic cathedral; son et lumière at the Roman
theatre (in summer).

AUVILLERS-LES-FORGES
Ardennes, 08260

≈ L'ARRET DES ROUTIERS
(Mme Nicole Bonnaire) ☎ 24.54.32.77
Directions: Charleville-Mézières/Hirson.
Menu: 50 Frs.
Accommodation: 75 to 110 Frs.
Restaurant: breakfast from 6.00. Lunch from
12.00 until 15.00. Dinner from 19.00 until 21.00.
Closed Sat afternoon.
Specialities: home-cooking.
Hotel: 5 rooms. Facilities: shower.
Other points: credit cards accepted, bar, lounge
area, modern decor, terrace, pets allowed, car
parking.
◀ Meuse and Semoy valleys.

AUXERRE • Yonne, 89000

≈ LE SAINTE NITASSE
(Mme Corinne Courault) Route de Chablis
☎ 86.46.95.07
Directions: RN 65, Auxerre South.
Languages spoken: English.
Menu: 55 to 85 Frs ⌣
Accommodation: 100 to 130 Frs.
Restaurant: breakfast from 7.00. Lunch from
12.00 until 14.30. Dinner from 19.30 until

22.30. Closed Sat and Sun.
Specialities: home-cooking.
Hotel: ✰ 31 rooms. Facilities: shower, private
bathroom.
Other points: credit cards accepted, bar, à la carte
menu, traditional decor, pets allowed, car/lorry
parking.
◀ medieval monuments in Auxerre; Avallon;
Vézelay; Joigny.

BEAUMONT-SUR-VESLE
Marne, 51360

≈ LA MAISON DU CHAMPAGNE
(M. Marc Boulard) 2 rue du Port
☎ 26.03.92.45 [Fax] 26.03.97.59
Directions: RN 44, between Reims and Châlons-
sur-Marne.
Languages spoken: German, English.
Menu: 54 to 220 Frs ⌣
Accommodation: 110 to 300 Frs.
Restaurant: breakfast from 7.00. Lunch from
12.00 until 14.15. Dinner from 19.00 until 21.00.
Closed Sun, Mon evening, 2 weeks in Feb and
2 weeks in Nov.
Specialities: terrine du chef, rognons de veau au
ratafia, canard aux griottes (duck with cherries),
soufflé au Marc, regional menu, home-cooking.
Hotel: ✰ ✰ 13 rooms. Facilities: shower, private
bathroom, television, telephone.
Other points: credit cards accepted, bar,
children's menu, à la carte menu, traditional decor,
terrace, pets allowed, car/lorry parking.
◀ champagne cellars; vineyards; remains of
1914–18 war; Fort de la Pompelle; Faux de Verzy;
cathedral at Reims; Le Thau palace.

BEAUNE • Côte-d'Or, 21200

≈ AUBERGE DE LA GARE
(SARL Auberge de la Gare) 11 avenue des
Lyonnais ☎ 80.22.11.13
Directions: RN 74.
Restaurant: dinner until 20.00. Closed Sun, public
holidays, and in Aug.
Hotel: 6 rooms.
Other points: bar.

BEAUREPAIRE-EN-BRESSE
Saône-et-Loire, 71580

≈ LE RELAIS DES PLATANES
(Mme Thérèse Cornet) ☎ 85.74.11.01
Directions: RN 78, between Lons-le-Saunier and
Louhans.
Languages spoken: English.
Menu: 55 Frs.
Accommodation: 90 to 100 Frs.
Restaurant: breakfast from 7.00. Lunch from
11.00 until 14.00. Dinner from 19.00 until 21.00.
Specialities: poulet aux écrevisses, saumon à
l'oseille, grenouilles fraiches, regional menu,
home-cooking.

Hotel: 6 rooms. Facilities: shower, private bathroom.
Other points: bar, children's menu, terrace, car/lorry parking.

BELLEVILLE-SUR-MEUSE
Meuse, 55430

🍽 **CHEZ DEDE**
(M. André Buffelo) 164 avenue du Général-de-Gaulle ☎ 29.84.57.85
Directions: Charleville.
Languages spoken: English and Italian.
Menu: 50 Frs.
Restaurant: breakfast from 5.00. Lunch from 11.30 until 15.00. Closed Sun afternoon, public holidays and 1 week in Sept.
Specialities: home-cooking.
Other points: bar, traditional decor, pets allowed, car/lorry parking.
🍃 Douaumont and Verdun battlefields; Verdun: citadel.

BINING • Moselle, 57410

🍽 **AUBERGE AU TILLEUL**
(M. Gilles Ehré) 2 rue du Tilleul
☎ 87.09.74.86
Languages spoken: German and English.
Menu: 50 to 120 Frs.
Restaurant: breakfast from 9.00. Lunch from 12.00 until 14.00. Closed Wed afternoon, Thurs, last 2 weeks in Sept.
Specialities: backeoffe, couscous, paella, choucroute, regional menu, home-cooking.
Other points: credit cards accepted, bar, children's menu, à la carte menu, traditional decor, car/lorry parking.
🍃 the Maginot line; musée du cristal (crystal) at Saint-Louis (30km); citadel at Bitche (20km).

BLACY • Marne, 51300

🍽 **LE RELAIS DE MAISON BLANCHE**
(Mme Claudine Simioni) 8 route de Paris
☎ 26.74.44.98
Directions: Paris, exit at Vitry-le-François.
Menu: 55 Frs.
Restaurant: lunch from 11.00 until 15.00. Dinner from 19.00 until 24.00. Closed from Sat 15.00 to Sun 24.00.
Specialities: home-cooking.
Other points: credit cards accepted, bar, children's menu, traditional decor, pets allowed, car/lorry parking.
🍃 Champagne route, towards Epernay; lac du Der (20km); Reims.

BLAGNY • Ardennes, 08110

🍽 **BAR LES ROUTIERS**
(SNC Biagio-Cailleux) 37 Route Nationale
☎ 24.22.00.23

Directions: RN 43, between Sedan and Charleville-Mézières.
Menu: 35 to 47 Frs.
Restaurant: breakfast from 6.30. Lunch from 12.00 until 14.00. Dinner from 19.00 until 21.00. Closed Sat, and in Aug.
Specialities: home-cooking.
Other points: bar, children's menu.

BLANZY • Saône-et-Loire, 71450

🍽 **RELAIS DE LA GARE**
(M. Bernard Borowski) 16 rue de la Gare
☎ 85.68.03.05
Directions: La Fiolle Michelin factory exit.
Languages spoken: English.
Restaurant: dinner until 22.00.
Specialities: boeuf bourguignon, côtes de porc vigneronnes, regional menu, home-cooking.
Other points: credit cards accepted, bar, traditional decor, terrace, pets allowed, car/lorry parking.
🍃 Musée de la mine (mining); various wine-cellars (20km); the pyramid.

BLENOD-LES-PONT-A-MOUSSON
Meurthe-et-Moselle, 54700

🍽 **SARL CHEZ FERNANDE**
(Mme Louisette Pereira) 88 avenue Victor-Claude ☎ 83.81.03.54
Directions: RN 57, between Nancy and Metz.
Languages spoken: German and Portuguese.
Menu: 50 Frs.
Accommodation: 80 Frs (1 person) to 100 Frs (2 person).
Restaurant: breakfast from 6.00. Lunch from 11.00 until 14.00. Dinner from 19.00 until 23.00. Closed Sat afternoon, Sun, and in Aug.
Specialities: couscous, paella, choucroute, potée lorraine, home-cooking.
Hotel: 2 rooms. Facilities: shower, private bathroom.
Other points: credit cards accepted, bar, children's menu, à la carte menu, traditional decor, terrace, pets allowed.
🍃 abbey at Pont-à-Mousson; Metz: portes (gates) des allemands; Nancy: portes d'or.

BOUILLY • Aube, 10320

🏠 **AU RELAIS MONTAIGU**
(M. René Braux) 300 rue au Fébvres, Souligny
☎ 25.40.20.20
Directions: RN 77, Auxerre.
Menu: 55 to 80 Frs.
Accommodation: 85 to 150 Frs.
Restaurant: breakfast from 6.30. Lunch from 12.00 until 14.00.
Specialities: regional menu, home-cooking.
Hotel: ☆ 13 rooms. Facilities: shower, telephone.
Other points: credit cards accepted, bar,

children's menu, lounge area, traditional decor, terrace, car/lorry parking.
🐾 *Troyes: museums; lake and forêt d'Orient; churches.*

🍴 BOUXWILLER • Bas-Rhin, 67330

🍴 AU SOLEIL
(M. Charles Jaeger) 71 Grand'Rue
☎ 88.70.70.06
Directions: RD 6 and 7.
Languages spoken: German and English.
Menu: 35 to 150 Frs 🍷
Accommodation: 130 to 250 Frs.
Restaurant: breakfast from 8.00. Lunch from 11.30 until 14.15. Dinner from 19.30 until 21.15. Closed Wed, Sun evening, early July, school and public holidays.
Specialities: choucroute, coq au Riesling, sandre (a freshwater fish) à l'oseille, regional menu.
Hotel: ☆ ☆ 16 rooms. Facilities: shower, private bathroom, television, telephone.
Other points: credit cards accepted, bar, à la carte menu, pets allowed, car/lorry parking.
🐾 *Bouxwiller: museum; Lichtenberg.*

🍴 BRETHENAY • Haute-Marne, 52000

🍴 🍴 See CHAUMONT.

🍴 BRIENNE • Saône-et-Loire, 71290

🍴 AUX AMIS DE LA ROUTE
(Mme Elsa Busca) Les Bas de Brienne, Cuisery
☎ 85.40.04.18
Directions: RD 975, Bourg-en-Bresse.
Menu: 65 to 100 Frs.
Restaurant: closed Sun, and in Aug.
Specialities: Italian dishes, home-cooking.
Other points: credit cards accepted, bar, à la carte menu, lounge area, traditional decor, terrace, pets allowed, car/lorry parking.

🍴 BRIENON-SUR-ARMANCON
Yonne, 89210

🍴 LES ROUTIERS DE BOURGOGNE
(M. Christian Dussart) 21 Route de Joigny
☎ 86.43.00.63
Directions: the Joigny/Saint-Florentin road.
Languages spoken: English, Polish and Russian.
Menu: 50 Frs.
Accommodation: 80 to 100 Frs.
Restaurant: breakfast from 5.00. Closed Sat afternoon and Sun.
Specialities: home-cooking.
Hotel: 9 rooms. Facilities: shower.
Other points: credit cards accepted, bar, traditional decor, terrace, pets allowed, car/lorry parking.
🐾 *Joigny (22km); Auxerre (20km); Chablis (20km).*

🍴 BRUAILLES • Saône-et-Loire, 71500

🍴 RELAIS DES QUATRE CHEMINS
(M. Thierry Rousse) Les Quatre Chemins, Louhans ☎ 85.75.15.81
Directions: RD 972.
Menu: 50 to 120 Frs.
Restaurant: closed Wed afternoon.
Specialities: home-cooking.
Hotel: 5 rooms.
Other points: bar, à la carte menu.

🍴 BUCEY-LES-GY • Haute-Saône, 70700

🍴 CAFE DE LA GARE – Les Routiers
(M. Gérard Bole-Besançon) rue de la Gare
☎ 84.32.92.02
Directions: RD 474, between Dijon and Vesoul.
Menu: 60 Frs (drinks included).
Restaurant: breakfast from 5.00. Lunch from 11.30 until 14.00. Closed Sat and Sun.
Specialities: home-cooking.
Other points: credit cards accepted, bar, children's menu, traditional decor, terrace, pets allowed, car/lorry parking.

🍴 LA CELLE-SUR-LOIRE
Nièvre, 58440

🍴 LA BELLE ETOILE
(Mme Brigitte Foucher) Route Nationale 7
☎ 86.26.05.10 [Fax] 86.26.04.34
Directions: RN 7, the Paris/Nevers road.
Languages spoken: English and Spanish.
Menu: 54 Frs (wine included) to 85 Frs.
Restaurant: breakfast from 6.00. Closed 1 week at Christmas.
Specialities: home-cooking.
Other points: credit cards accepted, bar, children's menu, à la carte menu, terrace, pets allowed, car/lorry parking.
🐾 *Sancerre; Saint-Fargeau; potteries at Saint-Amand.*

🍴 CHAGNY • Saône-et-Loire, 71150

🍴 HOTEL TERMINUS
(M. Serge Savoye) avenue de la Gare
☎ 85.87.18.13
Directions: RN 6, Beaune/Chalon-sur-Saône.
Languages spoken: English.
Menu: 60 Frs (wine and coffee included) to 120 Frs.
Accommodation: 90 to 160 Frs.
Restaurant: breakfast from 6.30. Lunch from 12.00 until 14.30. Dinner from 19.00 until 22.00. Closed Sat evening and Sun evening.
Specialities: regional menu, home-cooking.
Hotel: 13 rooms.
Other points: credit cards accepted, bar, children's menu, à la carte menu, traditional decor, pets allowed, car/lorry parking.
🐾 *Beaune (14km); Chalon (17km); Chagny.*

CHALLUY • Nièvre, 58000

RELAIS DU PONT CARREAU
(Mme Fernande Taillemitte) ☎ 86.21.00.02
Directions: RN 7.
Hotel: 4 rooms
Other points: bar.

CHALONS-SUR-MARNE
Marne, 51000

LE BOEUF MODE DU MONT-SAINT-MICHEL
(M. Robert Legrand) ☎ 26.68.05.08
[Fax] 26.65.59.71
Directions: on the Troyes road.
Menu: 48 to 118 Frs.
Restaurant: breakfast from 5.00. Lunch from 11.45 until 14.00. Dinner from 19.00 until 22.00. Closed Sat until 10th Sept.
Specialities: poulet aux écrevisses, boeuf mode, escargots, cuisses de grenouilles, regional menu, home-cooking.
Other points: credit cards accepted, bar, children's menu, à la carte menu, lounge area, modern decor, terrace, pets allowed, car/lorry parking.
◁€ *champagne cellars; Reims: cathedral; Notre-Dame Lépine.*

**LES ROUTIERS
ACCOMMODATION DIRECTORY**

This handy directory lists an extensive choice of *Les Routiers*-recommended places offering comfortable accommodation in relaxed surroundings throughout the British Isles.

Available from selected *Les Routiers* establishments or direct from the publishers, price **£2**.

CHAMPAGNOLE • Jura, 39300

LES ROUTIERS
(M. Guy Chagre) La Billaude, Commune du Vaudioux ☎ 84.51.60.33
Directions: RN 5, the Paris/Geneva road.
Menu: 60 to 120 Frs.
Restaurant: breakfast from 7.00. Lunch from 12.00 until 14.00. Closed Sun, and 2 weeks in Aug.
Specialities: home-cooking.
Other points: bar, children's menu, modern decor, car/lorry parking.
◁€ *waterfalls at La Billaude; Le Hérisson; lakes; Frasnois; Ilay; Bonlieu; Chalain.*

CHAMPLOST • Yonne, 89210

AU BON ACCUEIL
(SNC Duteriez – Le Leuch) 23 Route Nationale 5 ☎ 86.43.14.71
Directions: RN 5, between Sens and Dijon.
Menu: 55 to 70 Frs.

Restaurant: breakfast from 6.00. Lunch from 11.00 until 14.00. Dinner from 19.00 until 21.00. Closed Sun.
Specialities: home-cooking.
Other points: bar, car/lorry parking.
◁€ *Mont-Avrollot (archeological site).*

CHAMPS-SUR-YONNE
Yonne, 89290

L'ARCHE DE VENOY-EST
(M. Jean-Philippe Bleriot) A6, services at Venoy Soleil-Levant (accessible Lyon/Paris direction) ☎ 86.40.22.44 [Fax] 86.40.23.73
Restaurant: open 24 hours.
Other points: credit cards and foreign currency accepted.

L'ARCHE DE VENOY-OUEST
(M. Sanjay Batsou) A6, services at Venoy Grosse-Pierre (accessible in Paris/Lyon direction) ☎ 86.40.35.52 [Fax] 86.40.23.73
Restaurant: open 24 hours.
Other points: credit cards and foreign currency accepted, lorry parking.

CHATELET-SUR-RETOURNE
Ardennes, 08300

LE RELAIS PONT ROYAL
(M. Yves Detruiseaux) Châtelet-sur-Retourne ☎ 24.38.93.27
Menu: 52 to 150 Frs.
Restaurant: breakfast from 6.00. Dinner until 24.00. Closed Tues.
Specialities: regional menu, home-cooking.
Other points: credit cards accepted, bar.
◁€ *Champagne region.*

CHATENOIS • Vosges, 88170

L'ARCHE DE VITTEL-SANDAUCOURT
(M. Aimé Henry) A31, services at Sandaucourt (accessible in both directions) ☎ 29.94.66.40 [Fax] 29.94.54.51
Restaurant: open until 24.00.
Other points: credit cards and foreign currency accepted.

CHAUDENEY
Meurthe-et-Moselle, 54200

LE MIRABELLIER
(M. Jean-Louis Cutxan) A31, services at Toul-Dommartin (accessible in both directions) ☎ 83.64.64.01 [Fax] 83.64.51.37
Directions: A31, the Luxembourg/Metz/Nancy/Dijon road.
Languages spoken: German and English.
Menu: 59 Frs.
Restaurant: breakfast from 6.00. Meals from 11.00 until 23.00.
Other points: credit cards accepted, bar,

children's menu, lounge area, modern decor, terrace, car/lorry parking.
⋲ Nancy: place Stanislas; Toul region wine route.

CHAUMONT • Haute-Marne, 52000

🏠 BELLEVUE – Les Routiers
(Mme Micheline Bourgoin) Route Nationale, Brethenay ☎ 25.32.51.02
Directions: RN 67, Chaumont exit, towards Saint-Dizier.
Menu: 55 Frs.
Accommodation: 100 to 200 Frs.
Restaurant: breakfast from 7.30. Lunch from 12.00 until 14.00. Dinner from 19.00 until 21.00. Closed Sun, and end Aug/beginning Sept.
Specialities: tripes maison, poisson au beurre blanc, home-cooking.
Hotel: 8 rooms. Facilities: shower.
Other points: credit cards accepted, bar, children's menu, à la carte menu, lounge area, traditional decor, terrace, pets allowed, car/lorry parking.
⋲ Chaumont; basilica Saint-Jean, chateau; Colombey-les-Deux-Eglises (25km).

🍴 LA HALTE DU VIADUC
(M. Serge Richoux) Route de Paris
☎ 25.03.55.59
Directions: RN 65.
Languages spoken: English.
Menu: 58 Frs (wine included).
Restaurant: breakfast from 6.00. Lunch 11.30 to 15.00. Dinner 18.30 to 23.00. Closed Sat and Sun.
Specialities: tête de veau, regional menu, home-cooking.
Other points: credit cards accepted, bar, modern decor, pets allowed, car/lorry parking.
⋲ viaduct; Colombey-les-Deux-Eglises.

CHELSEY • Côte-d'Or, 21430

🏠 LES ROUTIERS – Chez Ursula et Bernard
(M. Bernard Sentein) Route Nationale 6
☎ 80.84.40.42
Directions: RN 6, midway between Saulieu and Arnay-le-Duc.
Languages spoken: German and English.
Menu: 61 Frs.
Accommodation: 90 to 210 Frs.
Restaurant: breakfast from 5.00. Lunch from 12.00 until 15.00. Dinner from 19.00 until 24.00. Closed Sat, Sun, and 3 weeks in Aug.
Specialities: pintade rotie, home-cooking.
Hotel: 5 rooms. Facilities: shower.
Other points: bar, traditional decor, pets allowed, car/lorry parking.
⋲ Musée de l'Art de la Table (culinary arts) at Arnay-le-Duc; Saulieu.

CHEMAUDIN • Doubs, 25320

🍴 LA COCOTTE
(M. Christian Grosperrin) La Cocotte
☎ 81.58.64.70

Directions: RN 73, between Dole and Besançon.
Menu: 45 to 55 Frs.
Restaurant: breakfast from 6.00. Lunch from 11.00 until 15.00. Dinner from 19.00 until 23.00. Closed Sun.
Specialities: choucroute, regional menu.
Other points: credit cards accepted, bar, children's menu, modern decor, pets allowed, car/lorry parking.
⋲ caves at Osselle (5km); gouffre (abyss) du Poudrey; citadel at Besançon (7km).

CHENEVIERES
Meurthe-et-Moselle, 54122

🍴 RELAIS DES ROUTIERS
(Mme Agnès Remy) 10 Route Nationale
☎ 83.72.62.75
Directions: RN 59, Saint-Dié.
Menu: 50 Frs.
Restaurant: breakfast from 6.00. Lunch from 11.00 until 15.00. Dinner from 18.00 until 20.30. Closed Sun.
Specialities: home-cooking.
Other points: credit cards accepted, bar, children's menu, à la carte menu, modern decor, terrace, pets allowed, car/lorry parking.
⋲ chateau at Lunéville; Baccarat crystal-works.

LE CHESNE • Ardennes, 08390

🏠 LA CHARRUE D'OR
(Mme Suzanne Fischbach) 2 Grande Rue
☎ 24.30.10.41
Directions: between Châlons-sur-Marne and Liège.
Languages spoken: German, English, Italian, Spanish.
Menu: 59 Frs (wine included) to 134 Frs.
Accommodation: 140 to 160 Frs.
Restaurant: breakfast from 7.00. Lunch from 12.00 until 14.00. Dinner from 19.00 until 21.00.
Specialities: regional menu, home-cooking.
Hotel: 7 rooms.
Other points: credit cards accepted, bar, children's menu, à la carte menu, lounge area, traditional decor, terrace, pets allowed, car/lorry parking.
⋲ Charleville-Mézières.

CLAIRVAUX-LES-LACS • Jura, 39130

🍴 LES ROUTIERS
(M. Denis Perrin) 4 route de Lons
☎ 84.25.85.57
Directions: Genève.
Languages spoken: English and Italian.
Menu: 58 Frs.
Restaurant: breakfast from 7.00. Lunch from 11.30 until 14.30. Dinner from 19.00 until 22.00. Closed Sun (out of season).
Specialities: home-cooking.
Other points: credit cards accepted, children's menu, à la carte menu, traditional decor, terrace, pets allowed, car/lorry parking.

CLEREY-SUD • Aube, 10390

🍽 FRANCO-BELGE
(Mme Marthe Bencherif) 1 avenue de
Bourgogne, Route Nationale 71
☎ 21.46.01.50
Directions: RN 71, the Troyes/Dijon road.
Languages spoken: English.
Menu: 60 Frs (wine included).
Restaurant: breakfast from 5.30. Lunch from
12.00 until 14.30. Dinner from 19.00 until 22.00.
Closed Sun.
Specialities: paella, couscous, tagine (North
African speciality), regional menu, home-cooking.
Other points: credit cards accepted, bar,
children's menu, à la carte menu, traditional decor,
terrace, pets allowed, car/lorry parking.
🔎 lake and forêt d'Orient.

CLUNY • Saône-et-Loire, 71250

🍽 AUBERGE DU CHEVAL BLANC
(Elvire Bouillin) 1 rue Porte de Mâcon
☎ 85.59.01.13 [Fax] 85.59.13.32
Directions: RN 980, between Mâcon and
Chalon-sur-Saône.
Menu: 77 to 185 Frs 🖐
Restaurant: lunch from 11.45 until 14.00. Dinner
from 18.45 until 21.00. Closed Fri evening, Sat,
and from Dec to Feb.
Specialities: pavé charolais sauce morilles
(mushrooms), cuisses de grenouilles à la crème, noix
de veau au crémont de Bourgogne, regional menu.
Other points: credit cards accepted, children's
menu, traditional decor, pets allowed, car/lorry
parking.
🔎 Cluny: abbey, musée Hochier, stud-farm
(haras), Norman buildings; chateau at Cormatin;
Roche de Solutré.

COLIGNY • Marne, 51130

🍽 LE VAL DES MARAIS
(M. Michel Lagnié) 61 rue Saint-Gond
☎ 26.52.23.15
Directions: Vertus/Coligny.
Menu: 56 Frs.
Restaurant: breakfast from 6.30. Lunch from
12.00 until 13.30. Dinner from 19.00 until 20.30.
Specialities: home-cooking.
Other points: credit cards accepted, bar,
traditional decor, pets allowed.
🔎 wine-cellars at Epernay (30km).

COLLONGES-LES-PREMIERES
Côte-d'Or, 21110

🍽 A LA BONNE AUBERGE
(M. Michel Garnier) 8 rue de la Gare
☎ 80.31.32.01
Directions: RN 5, between Genlis and Auxonne.
Menu: 55 Frs.
Restaurant: breakfast from 6.00. Lunch from
11.00 until 15.00. Dinner from 19.00 until 21.00.

Closed Sun, and in Aug.
Specialities: home-cooking.
Other points: bar, children's menu, traditional
decor, pets allowed, car/lorry parking.
🔎 Musée de Bonaparte at Auxonne; Mont-Roland.

COLOMBEY-LES-BELLES
Meurthe-et-Moselle, 54170

🍽 AUBERGE LORRAINE
(M. Claude Arnould) 71 rue Carnot
☎ 83.52.00.23 [Fax] 83.52.85.66
Directions: RN 74, Neufchâteau.
Menu: 51 to 105 Frs.
Restaurant: breakfast from 7.00. Lunch from
11.30 until 14.30. Dinner from 19.00 until 22.00.
Closed 1 week at Christmas.
Specialities: home-cooking.
Other points: credit cards accepted, bar, children's
menu, à la carte menu, pets allowed, car/lorry parking.
🔎 Domrémy; Nancy; Toul; Baccarat crystal-
works; Vannes-le-Châtel.

COMBLANCHIEN • Côte-d'Or, 21700

🏨 AUBERGE DU GUIDON
(M. André Vauchez) Route Nationale 74
☎ 80.62.94.39
Directions: RN 74, between Beaune and Dijon.
Menu: 58 Frs.
Accommodation: 70 to 120 Frs.
Restaurant: breakfast from 6.00. Lunch from
12.00 until 14.30. Dinner from 19.00 until 22.00.
Closed Sat, Sun, and mid-Aug.
Specialities: home-cooking.
Hotel: 8 rooms.
Other points: bar, traditional decor, pets allowed,
car/lorry parking.
🔎 Nuits-Saint-Georges; Beaune.

CONNANTRE • Marne, 51230

🏨 LA GRAPPE D'OR
(M. Pascal Dufour) rue de la Gare
☎ 26.81.04.62
Directions: RN 4.
Menu: 52 Frs (drink included).
Accommodation: 80 to 120 Frs.
Restaurant: breakfast from 6.45. Lunch from
12.00 until 14.00. Dinner from 19.00 until 21.00.
Closed Sat afternoon, Sun, 2 weeks in Aug and
2 weeks from Christmas Day.
Specialities: home-cooking.
Hotel: 8 rooms. Facilities: shower, private
bathroom.
Other points: credit cards accepted, bar, car/lorry
parking.

CONSENVOYE • Meuse, 55110

🏨 AUBERGE LORRAINE
(Mme Denise Poussant) 16 Grande Rue
☎ 29.85.80.19

Directions: RD 964, Verdun/Sedan/Charleville.
Languages spoken: English.
Menu: 49 to 85 Frs.
Accommodation: 90 to 110 Frs.
Restaurant: breakfast from 7.30. Lunch from
11.30 until 14.00. Dinner from 18.30 until 21.00.
Closed Sat, and the 1st 2 weeks in Sept.
Specialities: potée lorraine, couscous, choucroute,
tarte à l'oignon, quiche lorraine, regional menu,
home-cooking.
Hotel: 6 rooms. Facilities: shower.
Other points: credit cards accepted, bar,
children's menu, à la carte menu, traditional decor,
terrace, pets allowed, car/lorry parking.
∉ *Verdun: battlefield memorial, remains of
military cemetery, relics of the 1914–18 war.*

COOLE • Marne, 51320

LES ROUTIERS
(M. Jean-Marie Brisson) Route Nationale 4
☎ 26.74.34.79
Menu: 53 Frs.
Restaurant: breakfast from 8.00. Closed Sat
afternoon, Sun, and 2 weeks in July.
Other points: bar.

CORBIGNY • Nièvre, 58800

LES AMIS DES ROUTIERS
(Mme Colette Perini) 8 rue de Clamecy
☎ 86.20.19.77
Directions: RD 985.
Menu: 55 Frs.
Restaurant: lunch from 12.00 until 15.30. Dinner
from 19.30 until 21.30. Closed Sat afternoon, Sun,
public holidays and 15th Aug to 8th Sept.
Specialities: home-cooking.
Other points: credit cards accepted, bar,
traditional decor, pets allowed, car/lorry parking.
∉ *Parc régional du Morvan (14km); musée du
septennat (President Mitterrand's term of office) at
Château-Chinon (30km).*

COSNE-SUR-LOIRE • Nièvre, 58200

LA TASSEE
(M. Maurice Chet) Route Nationale 7
☎ 86.26.11.76
Directions: RN 7, Nevers southern (Sud) exit.
Languages spoken: English.
Restaurant: breakfast from 6.00. Lunch from
12.00 until 13.30. Dinner from 20.00 until 21.30.
Closed Sun and public holidays, and in Aug.
Specialities: home-cooking.
Other points: credit cards accepted, bar,
children's menu, à la carte menu, modern decor,
pets allowed, car/lorry parking.
∉ *Sancerre; Pouilly-sur-Loire.*

LES 3 COULEURS
(M. Jean & Pierre Morfaux) 21 rue
Saint-Agnan ☎ 86.28.23.50

Directions: RN 7, Nevers.
Menu: 52 to 130 Frs 🥄
Accommodation: 100 to 180 Frs.
Restaurant: breakfast from 6.30. Lunch from
12.00 until 15.00. Dinner from 19.00 until 20.30.
Closed 2nd week of Dec to 1st week of Jan.
Specialities: coq au vin, cuisses de grenouilles à la
provençale, regional menu, home-cooking.
Hotel: ☆ 13 rooms. Facilities: shower.
Other points: credit cards accepted, bar, lounge
area, modern decor, pets allowed.
∉ *Sancerre; Pouilly-sur-Loire; banks of the Loire;
musée de la Loire.*

COURCELLES-CHAUSSY • Moselle, 57530

AUBERGE DE LA GARE
(M. Pierre Papalia) avenue de la Libération
☎ 87.64.00.22
Directions: RN 3.
Languages spoken: German, English and Italian.
Menu: 58 (coffee included) to 89 Frs.
Accommodation: 80 to 140 Frs.
Restaurant: breakfast from 6.00. Lunch from
12.00 until 14.00. Dinner from 19.00 until 22.00.
Specialities: Italian dishes, regional menu, home-
cooking.
Hotel: 12 rooms.
Other points: credit cards accepted, bar,
traditional decor, terrace, pets allowed, car/lorry
parking.
∉ *Lorraine region; Metz (15km); parc Wallibie
Schtroumph (15km).*

COURSON-LES-CARRIERES • Yonne, 89560

LE RELAIS DE COURSON
(M. José Carvalho) Route Nationale 151
☎ 86.41.52.58
Directions: RN 151, between Auxerre and
Clamecy.
Languages spoken: English, Spanish and
Portuguese.
Menu: 57 to 87 Frs.
Restaurant: breakfast from 6.30. Lunch from
11.00 until 15.00. Dinner from 18.30 until 24.00.
Specialities: home-cooking.
Other points: credit cards accepted, bar, à la carte
menu, lounge area, modern decor, terrace, pets
allowed.
∉ *abbey at Vézelay (30m); caves at Aray (25km);
Avallon (35km).*

CRENEY • Aube, 10150

RESTAURANT DU CENTRE
(M. Jacques Jeandon) 29 route de Brienne
☎ 25.81.39.79
Directions: RD 960, Troyes/Brienne/Saint-Dizier.
Menu: 58 Frs.
Restaurant: breakfast from 6.00. Lunch from

11.00 until 14.30. Dinner from 19.00 until 22.00.
Specialities: home-cooking.
Other points: credit cards accepted, bar,
traditional decor, pets allowed, car/lorry parking.
◁€ *lake and forêt d'Orient; Brevonne; Dienville.*

CRESANCEY • Haute-Saône, 70100

⇌ AUBERGE DE LA PETITE FRINGALE
(M. Jean-Paul Loisel) Route Départementale 7
☎ 84.31.56.08
Languages spoken: English.
Restaurant: dinner until 21.00. Closed Mon and
Thurs mornings, Wed afternoon.
Other points: bar, car/lorry parking.

LE CREUSOT • Saône-et-Loire, 71200

🏠 LE RELAIS
(M. Guy Beauclair) 26 rue de l'Yser
☎ 85.55.03.34
Directions: RN 80.
Menu: 50 Frs.
Accommodation: 100 to 170 Frs.
Restaurant: lunch from 12.00 until 13.45. Dinner
from 19.00 until 20.45. Closed Sat.
Specialities: home-cooking.
Hotel: 12 rooms.
Other points: credit cards accepted, bar, à la carte
menu, modern decor, pets allowed, car/lorry parking.

CUSSY-LES-FORGES • Yonne, 89420

⇌ LE RELAIS 6
(M. Hamid Adjaoud) Route Nationale 6
☎ 86.33.10.14
Directions: RN 6, Avallon exit, towards Lyon.
Languages spoken: Arabic.
Menu: 54 to 70 Frs.
Restaurant: breakfast from 5.00. Closed Sun.
Specialities: couscous maison, paella, home-cooking.
Other points: credit cards accepted, bar, à la carte
menu, terrace, pets allowed, car/lorry parking.
◁€ *Marvan region; Vézelay, Bourgogne wine-
cellars; caves at Arcy (15km); Vallée du Cousin;
Avallon: ramparts.*

DANJOUTIN
Territoire-de-Belfort, 90400

⇌ LE CHALET FLEURI
(Mme Janine Toesca) 2 rue du Bosmont
☎ 84.28.56.12
Directions: the Lyon/Germany/Switzerland road.
Menu: 48 to 56 Frs (wine included).
Restaurant: breakfast from 6.30. Lunch 11.00 to
15.00. Dinner 19.00 to 23.00. Closed Sun.
Specialities: home-cooking.
Other points: credit cards accepted, bar, à la carte
menu, lounge area, traditional decor, terrace, pets
allowed, car/lorry parking.
◁€ *Belfort.*

DANNEMOINE • Yonne, 89700

🏠 A LA BONNE AUBERGE
(Mme Nicole Verdin) Route Départementale
905 ☎ 86.55.54.22
Directions: RD 905, the Paris/Geneva road.
Menu: 55 to 60 Frs.
Accommodation: 60 to 100 Frs.
Restaurant: breakfast from 7.00. Lunch from
12.00 until 13.30. Dinner from 19.30 until 21.00.
Specialities: home-cooking.
Hotel: 13 rooms. Facilities: shower.
Other points: credit cards accepted, bar,
traditional decor, car/lorry parking.
◁€ *la Fosse Dionne at Tonnerre; château de Tanlay
at Ancy-le-Franc.*

DECIZE • Nièvre, 58300

⇌ LE BEL AIR
(M. Dominique Rocq) 164 avenue de Verdun
☎ 86.25.01.86
Directions: RN 81, the Nevers/Mâcon road.
Menu: 55 Frs (wine included).
Restaurant: breakfast from 5.45. Meals from
11.00 until 21.30. Closed Sun evening.
Specialities: regional menu, home-cooking.
Other points: bar, traditional decor, terrace, pets
allowed, car/lorry parking.

DEVAY • Nièvre, 58300

⇌ L'ETRIER
(M. Jean-Marc Boutet) Route Nationale
☎ 86.50.37.77
Languages spoken: German.
Restaurant: dinner until 22.00.
Other points: bar.

DORLISHEIM • Bas-Rhin, 67120

🏠 HOTEL RESTAURANT DE LA GARE
(M. René Jost) 4 avenue de la Gare
☎ 88.38.14.28
Languages spoken: German.
Accommodation: 70 to 90 Frs.
Restaurant: breakfast from 6.15. Lunch from
12.00 until 13.30. Dinner from 19.00 until 20.30.
Closed Sat afternoon, Sun afternoon, end Aug/
beginning Sept.
Specialities: home-cooking.
Hotel: 7 rooms. Facilities: shower.
Other points: traditional decor, pets allowed,
car/lorry parking.

ECROUVES
Meurthe-et-Moselle, 54200

🏠 LE RELAIS MATHY – Les Routiers
(M. Paul Mathy) 825 avenue du 15ème Génie,
Toul ☎ 83.43.04.27
Directions: RD 400, Toul Centre/Saint-Mihiel/
Ecrouves.

Menu: 59 to 76 Frs.
Accommodation: 98 to 156 Frs.
Restaurant: breakfast from 6.00. Lunch from 12.00 until 14.00. Dinner from 19.00 until 21.30. Closed from Fri 15.00 to Sun 10.00, and 1 week at Christmas.
Specialities: tête de veau, coq au vin, cervelle (brains), ris de veau (sweetbreads), gibier (game) (in season), home-cooking.
Hotel: 16 rooms.
Other points: credit cards accepted, bar, children's menu, à la carte menu, traditional decor, terrace, pets allowed, car/lorry parking.
◁€ *cathedral and ramparts at Toul; church at Ecrouves; fort at Villey-le-Sec; Saint-Gengoult cloister.*

EPERNAY • Marne, 51200

🍽 **LES ROUTIERS – Chez Madame Préjent**
(Mme Marie-Louise Préjent) 13 rue Jean-Jacques Rousseau ☎ 26.55.23.29
Directions: RN 3.
Menu: 65 to 95 Frs.
Accommodation: 100 to 165 Frs.
Restaurant: breakfast from 6.00. Closed Sat evening, Sun, and in Jan.
Specialities: regional menu home-cooking.
Hotel: 15 rooms. Facilities: shower, private bathroom.
Other points: bar, children's menu, modern decor, pets allowed, car/lorry parking.
◁€ *champagne cellars; musée du vignoble (vineyards).*

EPINAL • Vosges, 88000

🍽 **LE RELAIS DE L'ABATTOIR**
(M. Gérard Didier) 63 rue de Nancy ☎ 29.82.32.13
Directions: RN 57.
Restaurant: breakfast from 5.00. Dinner from 19.00 until 24.00. Closed Sun, and from mid-July to mid-Aug.
Specialities: home-cooking.
Other points: credit cards accepted, bar.
◁€ *Musée de l'imagerie (printing) at Epinal.*

EPINEAU-LES-VOVES • Yonne, 89400

🍽 **RELAIS DES SIX BOULES**
(M. Ahmed Betroune) 2 route de Chambéry ☎ 86.91.20.45
Directions: RN 6.
Languages spoken: Arabic and German.
Other points: bar.

ETANG-SUR-ARROUX
Saône-et-Loire, 71190

🍽 **HOTEL DE LA GARE**
(M. Pierre Bouteloup) rue d'Autun ☎ 85.82.23.76

Directions: RD 994.
Menu: 55 Frs.
Accommodation: 95 to 130 Frs.
Restaurant: lunch from 11.30 until 13.30. Dinner from 19.00 until 20.00. Closed Sun.
Specialities: home-cooking.
Hotel: 7 rooms. Facilities: shower, private bathroom.
Other points: bar, modern decor, terrace, pets allowed, car/lorry parking.
◁€ *Parc régional du Morvan; La Boulaye: temple Kagouling; Autun; Huchon; Mont-Beuvray.*

ETOGES • Marne, 51270

🍽 **LE CAVEAU DE L'ANCIENNE FORGE**
(SARL La Forge) Grande Rue
☎ 26.59.32.79
Restaurant: dinner until 20.00. Closed Wed.
Other points: bar.

EVANS • Jura, 39700

🍽 **RELAIS 73**
(Mme Yvette Arbey) Route Nationale 73
☎ 84.81.37.29 [Fax] 84.81.38.57
Directions: RN 73.
Menu: 55 Frs (wine and coffee included).
Restaurant: breakfast from 5.00.
Specialities: home-cooking.
Other points: bar, car/lorry parking.

FONTAINES • Saône-et-Loire, 71150

🍽 **LE RELAIS FLEURI**
(M. Claude Ecaille) Route Nationale 6, Le Gauchard ☎ 85.43.11.69
Directions: RN 6.
Menu: 55 Frs (wine and coffee included).
Restaurant: breakfast from 6.00. Lunch from 11.30 until 14.30. Dinner from 19.00 until 21.30. Closed Sat, Sun, and 1 week from Christmas Day.
Specialities: home-cooking.
Other points: bar, pets allowed, car/lorry parking.

FONTVANNES • Aube, 10190

🍽 **AUBERGE DE LA VANNE**
(M. Michel Dubrulle) 1 rue Léandre-Denis
☎ 25.70.37.60
Directions: RN 60, the Troyes/Sens road.
Languages spoken: English.
Menu: 55 Frs.
Accommodation: 80 Frs.
Restaurant: breakfast from 6.00. Lunch from 11.30 until 13.30. Closed Sun.
Specialities: home-cooking.
Hotel: 8 rooms. Facilities: shower, private bathroom.
Other points: bar, à la carte menu, lounge area, pets allowed, car/lorry parking.
◁€ *lakes and forêt d'Orient; Troyes (15km).*

FRAIZE • Vosges, 88230

🛏 AUBERGE VOSGIENNE
(M. Michel Gense) 14 rue du Général-Ingold
☎ 29.50.30.46
Directions: RN 415, Colmar via the Col-du-Bonhomme.
Menu: 55 Frs (wine included) to 120 Frs.
Accommodation: 100 to 160 Frs.
Restaurant: breakfast from 8.00. Lunch from 12.00 until 14.00. Dinner from 19.00 until 21.00. Closed Wed, and last 2 weeks in Sept.
Specialities: home-cooking.
Hotel: 7 rooms. Facilities: shower.
Other points: credit cards accepted, bar, children's menu, à la carte menu, traditional decor, terrace, car/lorry parking.
◁ Col-du-Bonhomme.

FRASNE • Doubs, 25560

🍴 L'ARC-EN-CIEL
(M. Claude Guyon) 98 Grand'Rue
☎ 81.49.83.68
Directions: between Champagnole and Pontarlier.
Menu: 55 Frs.
Restaurant: breakfast from 8.00. Lunch from 12.00 until 14.00. Closed Tues afternoon.
Specialities: regional menu, home-cooking.
Other points: bar, children's menu, modern decor, pets allowed, car/lorry parking.
◁ chateau at Joux (17km); gouffre (abyss) de Poudrey; lake at Saint-Point; Salins-les-Bains.

FROUARD
Meurthe-et-Moselle, 54390

🍴 CHEZ VIVIANE – COTE ROUTE
(Mme Viviane Poirot) 1 rue de la Salle
☎ 83.49.03.52
Languages spoken: German.
Menu: 45 Frs and 65 Frs (at weekends).
Restaurant: breakfast from 9.30. Lunch from 12.00 until 14.00. Dinner from 19.30 until 21.30. Closed Mon afternoon.
Specialities: couscous, choucroute, paella, home-cooking.
Other points: bar, children's menu, modern decor, pets allowed, car/lorry parking.

🍴 LA GRANDE CHOPE
(Mme Christiane Pallagi) 4 rue de la Gare
☎ 93.49.05.64
Directions: RN 57, Metz.
Languages spoken: Hungarian.
Menu: 43 Frs.
Restaurant: breakfast from 7.00. Lunch from 11.30 until 14.00. Closed Sat, Sun, and in Aug.
Specialities: home-cooking.
Other points: bar, modern decor, pets allowed, car parking.
◁ Moselle valley; Nancy: place Stanislas.

🍴 LA PRAIRIE
(M. Bernard Van Der Weckene) 6 rue de l'Ambanie ☎ 83.49.31.02
Directions: the Nancy/Metz road (via the Nancy/Frouard bridge).
Menu: 55 Frs (wine included).
Restaurant: breakfast from 7.00. Lunch from 12.00 until 14.30. Dinner from 18.30 until 22.00. Closed Sat, and in Aug.
Specialities: home-cooking.
Other points: bar, traditional decor, terrace, pets allowed, car/lorry parking.
◁ Nancy; Liverdun.

FUMAY • Ardennes, 08170

🛏 HOTEL LION
(Mme Edith Potier) 41 rue de la Céramique
☎ 24.41.10.27
Directions: RN 51, opposite the station.
Menu: 60 Frs (coffee included).
Restaurant: breakfast from 7.00. Lunch from 12.00 until 14.00. Dinner from 18.00 until 21.00. Closed Sun afternoon, and in Aug or Sept.
Specialities: couscous and cassoulet, home-cooking.
Hotel: ☆ 7 rooms. Facilities: shower, private bathroom.
Other points: bar, children's menu, traditional decor, pets allowed, lorry parking.
◁ Musée de l'ardoise (slate).

GENELARD • Saône-et-Loire, 71420

🍴 LE PROVENCAL
(Mme Pascale Rizard) place du Champ-de-Foire ☎ 85.79.28.90
Directions: RN 70, between Montceau-les-Mines and Digoin.
Languages spoken: English.
Menu: 55 Frs.
Restaurant: breakfast from 8.00. Lunch from 11.30 until 14.00. Dinner from 19.00 until 21.00.
Specialities: home-cooking.
Other points: bar, children's menu, à la carte menu, traditional decor, terrace, pets allowed, car/lorry parking.
◁ foie gras production at La Noie; marché aux puces (flea market); ferronnerie d'art (craft blacksmith).

GERMIGNY • Yonne, 89600

🛏 RELAIS DES ROUTIERS
(Mme Maria Lecoutre) 24 route de Saint-Florentin ☎ 86.35.06.39
Languages spoken: Italian.
Menu: 55 Frs.
Restaurant: breakfast from 5.30. Lunch from 11.30 until 14.00. Dinner from 19.00 until 20.30.
Specialities: regional menu.
Hotel: 5 rooms. Facilities: shower, private bathroom.
Other points: credit cards accepted, bar, children's menu, traditional decor, pets allowed, car/lorry parking.

GOLBEY • Vosges, 88190

≈ RELAIS DU PETIT CERF
(M. Christian Kuntz) 63 rue du Général-Leclerc ☎ 29.34.23.25
Directions: RD 166 and RD 460
Menu: 62 Frs (wine and coffee included).
Restaurant: breakfast from 7.00. Lunch from 11.30 until 15.00. Dinner from 18.00 until 20.00. Closed Sun, public holidays and in Aug.
Specialities: home-cooking.
Other points: credit cards accepted, bar, modern decor, pets allowed, car/lorry parking.
❧ Musée de l'imagerie (printing) at Epinal.

GUEMAR • Haut-Rhin, 68970

🛏 A L'ANGE
(M. Michel Schwariz) 16 route de Selestat ☎ 89.71.83.03
Languages spoken: German.
Menu: 56 to 90 Frs.
Accommodation: 150 Frs.
Restaurant: breakfast from 7.00. Lunch from 11.00 until 14.30. Dinner from 19.00 until 21.00. Closed Sat.
Specialities: Alsace dishes, regional menu.
Hotel: 10 rooms. Facilities: shower, private bathroom.
Other points: credit cards accepted, bar, children's menu, à la carte menu, traditional decor, pets allowed, car/lorry parking.
❧ wine route; Colmar.

GUERIGNY
Nièvre, 58130

🛏 HOTEL DU COMMERCE
(M. Gérard Page) 2 Grande Rue ☎ 86.37.32.77
Directions: RD 977, the Nevers/Auxerre road.
Languages spoken: German.
Menu: 60 to 85 Frs.
Accommodation: 155 to 215 Frs.
Restaurant: breakfast from 6.30. Lunch from 11.30 until 13.30. Dinner from 19.00 until 20.30. Closed Sat afternoon and Sun (out of season), and from 20th Dec to 5th Jan.
Specialities: regional menu.
Hotel: 8 rooms. Facilities: shower.
Other points: credit cards accepted, bar, children's menu, traditional decor, terrace, pets allowed, car/lorry parking.
❧ museum of old Guérigny; duke's palace at Nevers; musée du septennat (President Mitterrand's term of office) at Château-Chinon (60km).

GUMBRECHTSHOFFEN
Bas-Rhin, 67110

≈ AU SOLEIL
(Mme Liliane Peifer) 30 rue Principale ☎ 88.72.90.77
Directions: RN 62 and RD 242, between Niederbronn and Haguenau.

Languages spoken: German.
Menu: 32 to 100 Frs.
Accommodation: 130 Frs.
Restaurant: breakfast from 6.00. Dinner from 19.00 until 22.00. Closed Sun afternoon, and in Aug.
Specialities: gibier, choucroute alsacienne, couscous, pigeonneau, regional menu, home-cooking.
Hotel: 3 rooms. Facilities: shower, telephone.
Other points: bar, à la carte menu, lounge area, traditional decor, pets allowed, car/lorry parking.
❧ parc régional des Vosges du Nord; chateaux; museums; distilleries; potteries.

GUMERY • Aube, 10400

🛏 AU RELAIS
(Mme Evelyne Visse) 3 route de Sens ☎ 25.39.16.01
Directions: RD 439, between Sens and Nogent-sur-Seine.
Languages spoken: English.
Menu: 57 Frs.
Accommodation: 100 to 140 Frs.
Restaurant: breakfast from 6.00. Lunch from 11.30 until 14.00. Dinner from 19.00 until 21.00. Closed Sat, and 2 weeks in Aug.
Specialities: home-cooking.
Hotel: 5 rooms. Facilities: shower.
Other points: credit cards accepted, bar, children's menu, lounge area, traditional decor, terrace, pets allowed, car/lorry parking.
❧ chateau at La Motte-Tilly; museum at Nogent-sur-Seine; Provins: ramparts.

GUNDERSHOFFEN
Bas-Rhin, 67110

≈ RESTAURANT COUCOU
(M. René Adolff) Route de Bitche ☎ 88.72.92.02 Fax 88.72.88.82
Directions: between Haguenau and Sarreguemines.
Languages spoken: German.
Menu: 60 Frs (wine included).
Restaurant: breakfast from 6.00.
Specialities: regional menu, home-cooking.
Other points: credit cards accepted, bar, children's menu, à la carte menu, modern decor, terrace, pets allowed, car/lorry parking.
❧ chateau at Lischtenberg; Niederbronn; Strasbourg.

HABSHEIM • Haut-Rhin, 68440

≈ A LA VILLE DE MULHOUSE
(Mme Gabrielle Danjean-Rusch) 76 rue du Général-de-Gaulle ☎ 89.44.31.33
Directions: RN 66.
Languages spoken: German and English.
Other points: bar.

HAGONDANGE • Moselle, 57300

🚪 LES ROUTIERS
(Mme Martine Bognolo) 36 rue de Metz
☎ 87.71.46.63
Directions: RN 53, Metz.
Menu: 54 Frs (¼ of wine included).
Accommodation: 115 to 165 Frs.
Restaurant: breakfast from 8.00. Lunch from
12.00 until 14.00. Closed Sat afternoon, Sun
afternoon, and in Aug.
Specialities: home-cooking.
Hotel: 9 rooms. Facilities: shower, private
bathroom.
Other points: credit cards accepted, bar,
traditional decor.
🖉 Annéville-les-Thermes; parc Bing-Bang
Strouchps.

HUTTENHEIM • Bas-Rhin, 67230

🍽 AU JARDIN DES ROSES
(M. Maurice Schneider) Route Nationale 83
☎ 88.74.41.44
Directions: RN 83.
Languages spoken: German.
Menu: 38 to 70 Frs.
Restaurant: breakfast from 5.00. Lunch from
11.00 until 14.00. Closed Sat.
Specialities: home-cooking.
Other points: credit cards accepted, à la carte
menu, modern decor, terrace, pets allowed, car/
lorry parking.

HYEVRE-PAROISSE • Doubs, 25110

🚪 RELAIS LA CREMAILLERE
(M. Alfred Ziss) Baume-les-Dames
☎ 81.84.07.88
Directions: RN 83, exit A36 Baume-les-Dames
(10km)/Isle-sur-le-Doubs/Clerval (15km).
Languages spoken: German and English.
Menu: 60 to 180 Frs 🍷
Accommodation: 230 to 260 Frs.
Restaurant: closed Sat, and in Oct.
Specialities: coq au vin, canard à l'orange, fritures
(whitebait), carpes, regional menu, home-cooking.
Hotel: ☆ ☆ ☆ 21 rooms. Facilities: shower,
private bathroom, television, telephone.
Other points: credit cards accepted, bar,
children's menu, à la carte menu, traditional decor,
terrace, pets allowed, car/lorry parking.
🖉 Jura mountains; grotte (cave) de La Glacière;
saut (falls) du Doubs; Besançon: citadel.

IMLING-SARREBOURG
Moselle, 57400

🍽 LE RELAIS DE LA FERME
(M. Jean-Luc Steiner) Route de Sarrebourg
☎ 87.23.68.72
Directions: RN 4, the Paris/Strasbourg road.
Languages spoken: German.

Menu: 30 to 160 Frs.
Restaurant: breakfast from 4.30. Lunch from
11.30 until 14.30. Dinner from 18.30 until 22.30.
Closed Fri from 15.00 and 2 weeks in Aug.
Specialities: fondue, tripes, tête de veau, regional
menu.
Other points: credit cards accepted, bar,
children's menu, à la carte menu, traditional decor,
pets allowed, car/lorry parking.
🖉 Rocher du Dabo; museum at Sarrebourg;
Chagall's stained-glass windows; little train at
Abreschwiller.

IS-SUR-TILLE
Côte-d'Or, 21120

🍽 CAFE DU MIDI – Les Routiers
(M. Philippe Chalopet) 2 place Villeneuve-
Motet ☎ 80.95.07.51
Menu: 57 Frs.
Restaurant: breakfast from 6.00. Lunch from
11.30 until 14.30.
Specialities: home-cooking.
Other points: bar, pets allowed, car/lorry parking.

L'ISLE-SUR-LE-DOUBS
Doubs, 25250

🚪 LE CHAPAGOYE
(Mme Françoise Hausermann) 14 rue de-
Lattre-de-Tassigny ☎ 81.96.32.60
Directions: RN 83, between Besançon and Belfort.
Languages spoken: German and English.
Menu: 50 Frs (wine included) to 120 Frs.
Accommodation: 80 to 240 Frs.
Restaurant: breakfast from 7.00. Lunch from
11.30 until 14.00. Dinner from 18.30 until 21.30.
Closed Wed afternoon, and from 15th Dec to
15th Jan.
Specialities: regional menu, home-cooking.
Hotel: 5 rooms. Facilities: shower.
Other points: credit cards accepted, bar,
children's menu, à la carte menu, traditional decor,
terrace, car/lorry parking.
🖉 caves; chateau; springs; glass-works.

JOUDES-CUISEAUX
Saône-et-Loire, 71480

🍽 LE FRANC-COMTOIS
(M. Gilles Borges) Route Nationale 83
☎ 85.72.57.09
Directions: Besançon Bourg.
Menu: 55 Frs (wine included).
Restaurant: breakfast from 6.15. Lunch from
11.30 until 14.30. Dinner from 19.00 until 22.00.
Closed Sun afternoon.
Specialities: home-cooking.
Other points: credit cards accepted, bar,
children's menu, modern decor, terrace, pets
allowed, car/lorry parking.
🖉 Jura wine route; church at Brou; Ecomusée at
Cuiseaux.

JUZANVIGNY • Aube, 10500

⇌ CHEZ JACKY ET ROSE
(M. Jacques Deflin) Brienne-le-Château
☎ 25.92.80.57
Directions: RD 400.
Restaurant: dinner until 24.00. Closed Sat, Sun, Aug.
Other points: bar.

KOGENHEIM • Bas-Rhin, 67230

🏨 A L'ETOILE
(M. Robert Rapp) 36 route de Strasbourg
☎ 88.74.70.02
Directions: RN 83, between Selestat and Benfeld.
Languages spoken: German.
Menu: 35 to 90 Frs.
Accommodation: 100 to 150 Frs.
Restaurant: breakfast from 7.15. Lunch from
12.00 until 15.00. Dinner from 19.00 until 24.00.
Closed Mon evening, and 3 weeks in Jan.
Specialities: couscous, cheval braisé, home-cooking.
Hotel: ☆ 9 rooms. Facilities: shower, private
bathroom.
Other points: credit cards accepted, bar, à la carte
menu, traditional decor, pets allowed, car/lorry
parking.
◁€ leisure park at Rust; la montagne des singes
(monkey mountain); Germany (15km).

LANGRES • Haute-Marne, 52200

🏨 LA BONNE AUBERGE
(SNC Baumann/Olivier) faubourg de la
Collinière ☎ 25.87.09.18
Directions: RN 74, the Chaumont/Dijon road.
Menu: 60 to 85 Frs.
Restaurant: breakfast from 6.00. Lunch from
12.00 until 14.00. Dinner from 19.00 until 21.30.
Closed Sun, and 2 weeks from Christmas Day.
Specialities: home-cooking.
Hotel: 6 rooms.
Other points: bar, à la carte menu.

🏨 LE RELAIS DE LA COLLINIERE
(Mme Annick Gallier) faubourg de la
Collinière ☎ 25.87.03.27
Directions: RN 19, the Chaumont/Dijon road.
Menu: 58 Frs (wine included).
Accommodation: 75 to 175 Frs.
Restaurant: breakfast from 6.00. Lunch from
12.00 until 15.00. Dinner from 19.00 until 22.30.
Closed Sun afternoon.
Specialities: couscous, home-cooking.
Hotel: 7 rooms.
Other points: bar, traditional decor, pets allowed,
car/lorry parking.
◁€ Langres (Roman town).

LESMENILS
Meurthe-et-Moselle, 54700

⇌ LE ZENIUM
(M. Bernard Stabile – SACLOM) Tête de
Saint-Euchamps ☎ 83.82.81.38

Directions: the Metz/Nancy road, exit 28.
Languages spoken: German, English and Italian.
Menu: 45 to 175 Frs.
Restaurant: breakfast from 5.30. Lunch from
11.30 until 15.00. Dinner from 18.30 until 23.30.
Closed Sat lunch.
Other points: credit cards accepted, bar,
children's menu, à la carte menu, lounge area,
modern decor, terrace, car/lorry parking.
◁€ Nancy; Metz; Pont-à-Mousson.

LOISY-PONT-A-MOUSSON
Meurthe-et-Moselle, 54700

⇌ RESTAURANT DU RELAIS DE L'OBRION
(Mme Jacqueline Frères) A31, services at
l'Obrion ☎ 83.81.18.89 [Fax] 83.84.01.85
Directions: A31, Luxembourg/Nancy/Dijon.
Languages spoken: German and English.
Menu: 59 Frs.
Restaurant: breakfast from 6.00. Meals from
11.00 until 23.00
Other points: credit cards accepted, bar,
children's menu, modern decor, terrace, car/lorry
parking.
◁€ Prémontrées abbey; Pont-à-Mousson; Nancy:
place Stanislas.

LONGEAU • Haute-Marne, 52250

🏨 AUBERGE ROUTIERE – Chez Patricia
(Mme Patricia Godart) Route Nationale 74
☎ 25.88.42.16
Directions: RN 74; off A31, between Langres and
Dijon, exit Langres South (Sud).
Menu: 52 to 110 Frs.
Accommodation: 75 to 130 Frs.
Restaurant: breakfast from 5.30. Closed Sat
(except school holidays).
Specialities: home-cooking.
Hotel: 9 rooms.
Other points: credit cards accepted, bar,
children's menu, à la carte menu, traditional decor,
pets allowed.
◁€ Langres (10km); Gallo-Roman excavations at
Andilly (30km); numerous lakes (étangs).

🏨 CAFE DES ROUTIERS
(Mme Edwige Denis) Route Nationale
☎ 25.88.40.51
Directions: RN 74, between Langres and Dijon,
exit Langres South (Sud).
Menu: 35 to 100 Frs.
Accommodation: 75 to 100 Frs.
Restaurant: breakfast from 6.30. Lunch from
12.00 until 14.00. Dinner from 19.00 until 22.00.
Closed Fri afternoon.
Specialities: terrine maison, steack à l'ail, home-
cooking.
Hotel: 7 rooms.
Other points: credit cards accepted, bar,
children's menu, à la carte menu, traditional decor,
pets allowed, car parking.

❧ *Langres: fortifications; Villegusien lake; Gallo-Roman excavations at Andilly; caves at Sabinus; source of the Marne; forêt and lac de Liez.*

LOUHANS • Saône-et-Loire, 71500

⇶ LES ROUTIERS
(M. Michel Alexandre) 19 rue Lucien-Guillemaut ☎ 85.75.11.75
Directions: RN 78.
Menu: 45 to 100 Frs.
Restaurant: breakfast from 6.30. Lunch from 11.30 until 14.00. Closed Sun, and in Aug.
Specialities: poulet de Bresse, tête de veau, home-cooking.
Other points: bar, children's menu.

LUDELANGE • Moselle, 57710

⇶ L'ESCALE
(M. Jean-Claude Nedellec) Route Nationale 51 ☎ 82.91.87.97
Directions: RN 52 and 521, between Metz and Longwy.
Languages spoken: German, English, Spanish, Italian.
Menu: 60 Frs (wine included).
Restaurant: breakfast from 6.00.
Specialities: home-cooking.
Other points: bar, lounge area, modern decor, terrace, pets allowed, car/lorry parking.
❧ *Musée des mines (mining) at Aumetz; Longwy; Luxembourg.*

LUGNY • Saône-et-Loire, 71260

⇶ L'ARCHE DE MACON-PORT DE BOURGOGNE
(M. Blaise Sorlet) A6, services at Saint-Albain-La-Salle (accessible in both directions) ☎ 85.33.19.80 [Fax] 85.33.12.98
Restaurant: open 24 hours.
Other points: credit cards accepted.

LUSIGNY-SUR-BARSE
Aube, 10270

🏠 AUBERGE DES PRAIRIES
(Mme Monique Mireux) Route Nationale 19 ☎ 25.41.20.32
Directions: RN 19.
Menu: 55 Frs.
Accommodation: 80 Frs.
Restaurant: dinner until 22.00.
Specialities: home-cooking.
Hotel: 4 rooms. Facilities: shower, private bathroom.
Other points: credit cards accepted, bar, à la carte menu, pets allowed, car/lorry parking.
❧ *lake and forêt d'Orient; tour of Troyes with its nine churches.*

MAILLY-LE-CAMP • Aube, 10230

🏠 RESTAURANT DU CENTRE
(SNC Barvidat-Mantz) 64 rue du Général-de-Gaulle ☎ 25.37.30.08
Directions: RN 77, Mailly centre.
Menu: 62 to 125 Frs.
Accommodation: 80 to 200 Frs.
Restaurant: breakfast from 6.30. Lunch from 11.30 until 14.30. Dinner from 17.00 until 23.00. Closed Fri afternoon and Sat afternoon.
Specialities: andouillettes de Troyes, home-cooking.
Hotel: 14 rooms. Facilities: shower.
Other points: credit cards accepted, bar, à la carte menu, traditional decor, terrace, pets allowed, car/lorry parking.

For useful expressions *à l'hôtel, au restaurant* or *en route*, turn to pages 8–13.

MAISONNEUVE-RIOZ
Haute-Saône, 70190

🏠 LES ROUTIERS
(Mme Chantal Cartier) Quenoche ☎ 84.91.80.54
Directions: RN 57, between Vesoul and Besançon.
Languages spoken: English.
Menu: 55 Frs.
Accommodation: 80 to 200 Frs.
Restaurant: breakfast from 6.00. Lunch from 11.30 until 15.00. Dinner from 19.00 until 22.00. Closed Sat, Sun, 2 weeks in Aug and 1 week at Christmas.
Specialities: home-cooking.
Hotel: 8 rooms.
Other points: credit cards accepted, bar, children's menu, lounge area, traditional decor, terrace, pets allowed, car/lorry parking.
❧ *Rioz: lake; medieval village of Fondermand.*

MAIZIERES-LA-GRANDE-PAROISSE
Aube, 10510

⇶ LE RELAIS DE POUSSEY
(Mme Sylvaine Gaillard) La Glacière Industrial Zone (Z.I.) ☎ 25.24.27.96
Directions: RN 19.
Languages spoken: English.
Restaurant: closed Sun.
Other points: bar.

MARCHAUX • Doubs, 25640

⇶ L'ARCHE DE BESANCON-MARCHAUX
(M. Pascal Legal) A36, services at Besançon-Marchaux (accessible in both directions) ☎ 81.57.90.78 [Fax] 81.57.90.33
Restaurant: open until 23.00.
Other points: credit cards and foreign currency accepted.

MENIL-SUR-BELVITTE
Vosges, 88700

≈ LES ROUTIERS
(Mme Nelly Nicolas-Jacquot) ☎ 29.65.15.02
Directions: RN 435, between Sarrebourg and Epinal.
Menu: 58 Frs.
Restaurant: breakfast from 7.00.
Specialities: tête de veau, home-cooking.
Other points: bar, children's menu, traditional decor.
◀ *Baccarat crystal-works; medieval buildings at Rambervillers.*

MERCUREY • Saône-et-Loire, 71640

🛏 LE MERCUREY
(Mme Roseline Goy) Grande Rue
☎ 85.45.13.56
Directions: RD 978, on the Autun road.
Languages spoken: English.
Menu: 54 to 150 Frs.
Accommodation: 110 to 150 Frs.
Restaurant: breakfast from 6.30. Lunch from 11.00 until 15.00. Dinner from 18.00 until 22.00.
Specialities: coq au vin, poissons, cuisses de lapin, bourguignon, home-cooking.
Hotel: ☆ 8 rooms. Facilities: shower.
Other points: credit cards accepted, bar, children's menu, à la carte menu, traditional decor, pets allowed, car parking.
◀ *Touches and environs.*

MESGRIGNY • Aube, 10170

≈ LA BELLE ETOILE
(Mme Sylvie Schmutz) La Belle Etoile, Route Nationale 19 ☎ 25.21.15.70
Directions: RN 19, Paris.
Menu: 59 Frs.
Restaurant: breakfast from 4.30. Lunch from 11.30 until 16.00. Dinner from 18.30 until 22.00. Closed Sat evening and Sun.
Specialities: home-cooking.
Other points: credit cards accepted, bar, children's menu, traditional decor, terrace, pets allowed, car/lorry parking.
◀ *Troyes; Champagne region.*

MESSIA-SUR-SORNE • Jura, 39570

≈ LA CHARMILLE
(M. Patrick Vaucher) 570 Route de Lyon
☎ 84.24.65.92
Directions: RN 83, Lons-le-Saunier exit, towards Lyon.
Languages spoken: English.
Menu: 50 Frs.
Restaurant: lunch 12.00 to 14.00. Closed Sun.
Specialities: home-cooking.
Other points: bar, traditional decor, terrace, pets allowed, car parking.
◀ *Baume wine-cellars; waterfalls at Le Hérisson; le pont (bridge) de la Pyle.*

MONETEAU • Yonne, 89470

🛏 AU RENDEZ-VOUS DES PECHEURS
(M. Michel Rabuat) 14 route d'Auxerre
☎ 86.40.63.32
Menu: 56 Frs.
Accommodation: 140 Frs.
Restaurant: breakfast from 7.00. Lunch from 12.00. Dinner from 19.30 until 22.00. Closed Sun.
Specialities: poissons, grillades (grills).
Hotel: 6 rooms.
Other points: bar, car/lorry parking.

MORVILLARS
Territoire-de-Belfort, 90120

≈ LA CARPE D'OR
(Mme Colette Jenn) 1 rue de-Lattre-de-Tassigny ☎ 84.27.80.71
Languages spoken: English.
Menu: 49 to 85 Frs.
Restaurant: breakfast from 6.00. Lunch from 12.00 until 15.00. Dinner from 19.00 until 23.00.
Specialities: regional menu, home-cooking.
Other points: credit cards accepted, bar, children's menu, à la carte menu, lounge area, traditional decor, terrace, pets allowed, car/lorry parking.
◀ *le Lion de Belfort (statue); Switzerland.*

MOUCHARD • Jura, 39330

🛏 LA TONNELLE – Relais Routiers
(M. Bernard Miller) Pagnoz
☎ 84.37.81.17
Directions: RN 83.
Menu: 60 to 110 Frs.
Accommodation: 100 to 200 Frs.
Restaurant: breakfast from 6.30. Lunch from 12.00 until 13.30. Dinner from 19.30 until 22.30. Closed Sat evening, Sun, and in Aug.
Specialities: regional menu, home-cooking.
Hotel: 12 rooms. Facilities: shower.
Other points: credit cards accepted, bar, children's menu, à la carte menu, lounge area, traditional decor, terrace, pets allowed, car/lorry parking.

MOULIN-DES-MALADES
Jura, 39700

≈ AU RENDEZ-VOUS DE LA MARINE
(Mlle Josette Bullet) 73 Route Nationale
☎ 84.71.32.10
Directions: RN 73.
Menu: 49 to 67 Frs.
Restaurant: open 24 hours.
Specialities: croûte forestière, coq au vin, regional menu.
Other points: bar, children's menu, à la carte menu.

MULHOUSE • Haut-Rhin, 68100

AUBERGE LEFEBVRE
(Mme Monique Guerquin) 82 rue Lefebvre
☎ 89.46.25.25
Menu: 55 Frs.
Restaurant: breakfast from 7.00. Lunch from
11.00 until 15.00. Dinner from 19.00 until 23.00.
Closed Sun.
Specialities: home-cooking.
Other points: credit cards accepted, bar,
traditional decor.
◁€ *Mulhouse: museums; Alsace: Ecomusée.*

MYENNES • Nièvre, 58440

LE RANCH
(M. Roger Dufour) 68 rue de Paris
☎ 86.28.00.98
Menu: 50 Frs.
Restaurant: breakfast from 6.00
Other points: bar, car/lorry parking.

NANCY
Meurthe-et-Moselle, 54000

RESTAURANT DU PORT
(M. Claude Dopp) 5 rue Henri-Bazin
☎ 83.35.49.85
Directions: RN 4.
Languages spoken: English and German.
Menu: 50 Frs
Restaurant: breakfast from 6.30. Closed Fri
evening, Sat, Sun, public holidays and in Aug.
Specialities: coq au vin, gibier (game), regional
menu, home-cooking.
Other points: bar, traditional decor, pets allowed,
car/lorry parking.
◁€ *place Stanislas; botanical garden; aquarium;
museum.*

NAVILLY • Saône-et-Loire, 71270

AU BOIS DE BOULOGNE
(M. André Grapinet) ☎ 85.49.10.40
Directions: RN 83 bis.
Restaurant: closed Wed, and 21st Dec to 21st Jan.
Other points: bar.

NEUVY-SAUTOUR • Yonne, 89570

AU BON COIN – Chez Gérard
(M. Gérard Charpignon) 29 route de Troyes
☎ 86.56.35.52
Directions: RN 77, between Troyes and Auxerre.
Menu: 47 Frs.
Restaurant: breakfast from 4.00. Lunch from
12.00 until 14.00. Dinner from 19.00 until 21.00.
Closed Sat afternoon, Sun, and in Aug.
Specialities: home-cooking.
Other points: bar, pets allowed, car/lorry parking.
◁€ *listed church.*

LA NOCLE-MAULAIX
Nièvre, 58250

HOTEL DE LA POSTE
(M. Marcel Senotier) ☎ 86.30.80.32
Directions: Autun.
Menu: 38 to 115 Frs.
Restaurant: breakfast from 7.00. Lunch from
12.00 until 13.30. Closed Mon, and in Sept.
Specialities: home-cooking.
Other points: bar, à la carte menu, traditional
decor.

NOUZONVILLE • Ardennes, 08700

RESTAURANT DE LA PLACE
(Mme Annie Boquillon) 15 place Gambetta
☎ 24.53.80.43
Menu: 47 Frs.
Accommodation: 60 to 90 Frs.
Restaurant: breakfast from 7.00. Lunch from
12.00 until 13.30. Dinner from 19.30 until 20.30.
Closed Sat afternoon and Sun afternoon.
Specialities: home-cooking.
Hotel: 6 rooms. Facilities: shower, private bathroom.
Other points: credit cards accepted, bar,
traditional decor, pets allowed, car/lorry parking.
◁€ *Meuse and Semoy valleys; Belgium (10km).*

NOVION-PORCIEN
Ardennes, 08270

LE FRANCO-BELGE
(Mlle Simone Boniface) place de la Gare
☎ 24.53.80.43
Directions: RN 985, Rocroi.
Menu: 42 Frs.
Restaurant: breakfast from 7.00. Lunch from
12.00 until 14.30. Dinner from 19.00 until 21.30.
Closed Sun morning.
Specialities: home-cooking.
Other points: bar, traditional decor, pets allowed,
car/lorry parking.

OGEVILLER
Meurthe-et-Moselle, 54450

LE RELAIS DE LA VERDURETTE
(Michel and Lydie Martin) 22 route de
Strasbourg ☎ 24.38.70.06
Directions: RN 4, the Paris/Strasbourg road.
Languages spoken: German.
Menu: 54 Frs (wine included).
Restaurant: breakfast from 8.00. Closed Sat, Sun,
and in Aug.
Specialities: home-cooking.
Other points: bar, car/lorry parking.

ORNANS • Doubs, 25290

LE PROGRES
(M. Louis Perriot-Comte) 11 rue Jacques-
Gervais ☎ 83.72.24.65

Directions: RD 67, between Besançon and Lausanne.
Languages spoken: German and English.
Menu: 50 to 140 Frs 🍴
Accommodation: 195 to 310 Frs.
Restaurant: breakfast from 7.00. Lunch from 11.30. Dinner from 19.00. Closed Sun (in Jan and Feb).
Specialities: truite, terrine maison, escargots maison, filet de poissons, home-cooking.
Hotel: ☆ 19 rooms. Facilities: shower, private bathroom, telephone.
Other points: credit cards accepted, bar, children's menu, à la carte menu, lounge area, traditional decor, pets allowed, car/lorry parking.
◀€ Loue valley; lakes; national fishing centre at Ornans; Trépot; musée de la fromagerie (cheese-making); musée de la vigne et du vin (wine-making and viticulture); musée Courbet; musée de l'eau et de la pêche (fishing).

OSTHEIM • Haut-Rhin, 68150

🍴 **HOTEL-RESTAURANT BALTZINGER**
(M. Claude Meinrad) 16 route de Colmar
☎ 81.62.16.79 [Fax] 81.62.19.10
Directions: RN 83, the Strasbourg/Colmar road, Ostheim-Riquewihr exit.
Languages spoken: German, English and Italian.
Menu: 68 to 140 Frs.
Accommodation: 200 to 290 Frs.
Restaurant: breakfast from 7.00. Lunch from 12.00 until 14.00. Dinner from 19.00 until 21.00. Closed Tues (out of season), and in Jan.
Specialities: choucrouote, jambonneau, truites, regional menu.
Hotel: ☆ ☆ 36 rooms. Facilities: shower, private bathroom, television, telephone.
Other points: credit cards accepted, bar, children's menu, à la carte menu, lounge area, traditional decor, terrace, pets allowed, car/lorry parking.
◀€ Alsace wine route; Ribeauvillé; Riquewihr; Haut-Koenigsbourg: chateau; parc des cigognes (storks) at Hunawihr; Colmar.

PERTHES • Haute-Marne, 52100

🍴 **CHEZ JEAN**
(Mme Laurence Kaczmarek) Route Nationale 4
☎ 87.47.95.51 [Fax] 89.49.02.45
Menu: 51,70 to 66 Frs.
Accommodation: 62 to 94 Frs.
Restaurant: closed Sat afternoon, Sun, and in Aug.
Hotel: 26 rooms.
Other points: bar, children's menu, à la carte menu, pets allowed, car/lorry parking.
◀€ lac du Der.

PETIT-REDERCHING
Moselle, 57410

🍴 **AUBERGE DE LA FROHMUHL**
(M. Antoine Bach) 33 route de Strasbourg
☎ 25.56.40.27

Directions: Bitche.
Languages spoken: German and English.
Menu: 60 to 130 Frs.
Restaurant: breakfast from 7.00. Lunch from 11.30 until 14.00. Dinner from 18.00 until 22.00.
Specialities: pierrade, pizzas, tartes flambées, home-cooking.
Other points: credit cards accepted, bar, children's menu, à la carte menu, traditional decor, terrace, pets allowed, car/lorry parking.
◀€ the Maginot line; citadel at Bitche (10km); Fort Casso at Rohrbach; musée du verre et du sabot (glass/clogs).

🍴 **RESTAURANT DE LA GARE**
(M. Bernard Vogel) 6 rue de Strasbourg
☎ 87.96.43.52
Directions: RN 62, near the station.
Languages spoken: German.
Menu: 55 to 85 Frs.
Restaurant: breakfast from 6.00. Lunch from 12.00 until 14.00. Dinner from 19.00 until 20.30. Closed Sat, and from 14th July to 15th Aug.
Specialities: estomac de porc farci, tête de veau, backeoffe, choucroute, fresh fish, regional menu, home-cooking.
Other points: credit cards accepted, bar, à la carte menu, modern decor, terrace, pets allowed, car/lorry parking.
◀€ citadel at Bitche; Maginot line; Roman remains at Bliesbruck; faïencerie (pottery) at Sarreguemines; museum and crystal factory at Meisenthal.

PLOMBIERES-LES-BAINS
Vosges, 88370

🍴 **TOURING STRASBOURGEOIS**
(M. Alain Robert) 3 place Beaumarchais
☎ 87.09.81.09
Directions: RN 57.
Menu: 72 to 130 Frs.
Accommodation: 100 to 195 Frs.
Restaurant: breakfast from 7.00. Lunch from 12.00 until 13.30. Dinner from 19.00 until 20.30. Closed Sat evening and Sun (from 1st Oct to 30th Apr), and in Nov.
Specialities: terrine maison, truite à la crème, vacherin (meringue dessert) glacé, regional menu, home-cooking.
Hotel: ☆ 13 rooms. Facilities: shower, private bathroom, television, telephone.
Other points: credit cards accepted, bar, children's menu, à la carte menu, lounge area, modern decor, terrace, pets allowed, car/lorry parking.
◀€ thermal resort; private pond (fishing for guests).

POIX-TERRON • Ardennes, 08430

🍴 **LE GODILLOT**
(M. José Michel) 26 place de la Gare
☎ 29.66.00.70 [Fax] 29.66.01.06
Directions: opposite the chemist.
Menu: 55 Frs (drink included).

Accommodation: 90 Frs per person.
Restaurant: breakfast from 6.30. Lunch from
11.30 until 14.00. Dinner from 19.30 until 21.00.
Closed Fri afternoon, Sat, Sun, between Christmas
Day and New Year's Day.
Specialities: couscous, lasagne maison, home-
cooking.
Hotel: 6 rooms. Facilities: private bathroom.
Other points: credit cards accepted, bar, car/lorry
parking.
◄€ *Meuse valley (30km); lac de Bairen (15km).*

PONT-A-BINSON • Marne, 51700

☞ RESTAURANT DE LA GARE
(Mme Viviane Gosset) 22 rue du Général-
Leclerc ☎ 24.35.61.46
Directions: RN 3, Epernay.
Languages spoken: German and English.
Menu: 55 Frs (coffee included).
Accommodation: 140 (half board) to 185 Frs (full
board).
Restaurant: breakfast from 6.30. Lunch from
12.00 until 14.00. Dinner from 19.00 until 21.00.
Specialities: home-cooking.
Hotel: 4 rooms. Facilities: shower.
Other points: bar, traditional decor, pets allowed,
car/lorry parking.
◄€ *Moët-et-Chandon cellars; Champagne route.*

PONTIGNY • Yonne, 89230

🏠 RELAIS DE PONTIGNY
(Mme Carole Leducq) 9 rue Paul-Desjardin
☎ 26.58.30.41
Directions: RN 77, the Auxerre/Troyes road.
Languages spoken: German, English and Italian.
Menu: 52 to 95 Frs.
Restaurant: breakfast from 6.00. Lunch from
12.00 until 14.15. Dinner from 19.00 until 22.00.
Closed Sun, and from mid-Dec to mid-Jan.
Specialities: regional menu, home-cooking.
Hotel: 8 rooms.
Other points: bar, children's menu, à la carte
menu.

PREMERY • Nièvre, 58700

☞ LE ROUTIER
(M. Jean-Jacques Lemarié) 8 route de Lurcy
☎ 86.47.54.48
Directions: RD 977, between Clamecy and Nevers.
Languages spoken: German and English.
Menu: 55 Frs.
Restaurant: breakfast from 6.00. Lunch from
12.00 until 14.30. Dinner from 19.30 until 21.00.
Specialities: home-cooking.
Hotel: 2 rooms. Facilities: shower, private
bathroom, television.
Other points: credit cards accepted, bar,
children's menu, traditional decor, terrace, pets
allowed, car/lorry parking.
◄€ *Le Morvan: museums, chateau.*

PREZ-SOUS-LAFAUCHE
Haute-Marne, 52700

☞ LES 3 VALLEES
(Mme Eliane Trommenschlager)
☎ 86.37.97.59
Directions: the Chaumont/Nancy road.
Menu: 60 to 150 Frs.
Restaurant: lunch from 11.00 until 14.00. Dinner
from 19.00 until 23.00. Closed Sat evening, Sun
evening, and in Aug.
Specialities: home-cooking.
Other points: credit cards accepted, bar,
children's menu, à la carte menu, traditional decor,
car/lorry parking.

PROSNES • Marne, 51400

☞ RELAIS CONSTANTINE
(M. René Roselet) 'Constantine', Route
Nationale ☎ 25.31.57.84
Directions: RD 31, A4 Reims exit, towards Sainte-
Menehould.
Menu: 50 to 100 Frs.
Accommodation: 90 to 240 Frs.
Restaurant: breakfast from 6.30. Lunch from
12.00 until 13.30. Dinner from 19.00 until 21.00.
Closed Sat, Sun, and last 2 weeks in Aug.
Specialities: tête de veau, home-cooking.
Hotel: 3 rooms. Facilities: shower, private
bathroom.
Other points: credit cards accepted, bar, à la carte
menu, modern decor, car/lorry parking.
◄€ *wine-cellars and champagne vineyards;
museum; 1914–18 cemeteries; cathedral at Reims;
windmill at Valmy; Faux-de-Verzy.*

RACHECOURT-SUR-MARNE
Haute-Marne, 52170

☞ L'AURORE
(M. Marius Narat) avenue de Belgique
☎ 26.61.70.70
Directions: RN 67, Chaumont.
Menu: 55 to 70 Frs.
Accommodation: 107 to 200 Frs.
Restaurant: breakfast from 8.30. Lunch from
12.00 until 14.00.
Specialities: cabillaud (cod) sauce hollandaise,
andouillette, home-cooking.
Hotel: 4 rooms. Facilities: shower, private
bathroom.
Other points: credit cards accepted, bar,
children's menu, à la carte menu, traditional decor,
terrace, car parking.
◄€ *chateau at Joinville; lac du Der.*

REGUISHEIM • Haut-Rhin, 68890

☞ RESTAURANT A L'ANGE
(M. Raymond Bertrand) 90 Grand'Rue
☎ 25.04.41.58
Directions: RD 201, Meyenheim.

Languages spoken: German.
Menu: 40 to 60 Frs.
Restaurant: breakfast from 6.00. Lunch from 12.00 until 13.30. Dinner from 19.00 until 21.30. Closed Sat, Sun, and in Aug.
Specialities: home-cooking 5 rooms.
Other points: credit cards accepted, bar, à la carte menu, traditional decor, pets allowed, car/lorry parking.

REIMS • Marne, 51000

LA BELLE EPOQUE

(Mme Chantal Persem) 7–9 boulevard Gustave-Eiffel ☎ 89.81.12.66
Directions: between Charleville-Mézières and Reims.
Menu: 57 Frs.
Restaurant: breakfast from 7.00. Lunch from 11.30 until 15.00. Closed Sun.
Specialities: home-cooking.
Other points: credit cards accepted, bar, pets allowed, car/lorry parking.
❮❮ Reims.

REVIN • Ardennes, 08500

CHEZ ALEX

(Mme Josepha Mahut) 6 rue Voltaire
☎ 26.02.37.16 Fax 26.07.10.87
Directions: RN 388.
Restaurant: dinner until 21.00.
Other points: bar.

LA RIVIERE-DE-CORPS
Aube, 10300

LA QUEUE DE LA POELE

(M. Gaby Barbier) rue Lafontaine
☎ 24.40.12.91
Directions: RN 60, Sens.
Menu: 58 to 120 Frs.
Restaurant: breakfast from 6.30. Lunch from 11.30 until 14.00. Dinner from 19.00 until 22.00. Closed Sun evening, and 3 weeks in Aug.
Specialities: andouillette de Troyes, regional menu, home-cooking.
Other points: credit cards accepted, bar, children's menu, traditional decor, terrace, pets allowed, car/lorry parking.
❮❮ Troyes: cathedral, maison de l'outil (tools), old quarters; forêt d'Orient and de Dienville; Nigloland leisure park.

LA ROCHE-VINEUSE
Saône-et-Loire, 71960

RELAIS ROUTIERS – Chez France

(Mme France Brouillon) place du Chaucher
☎ 25.74.47.94 Fax 25.49.84.01
Directions: RN 79, between Mâcon and Charolles, via the tourist route.
Restaurant: breakfast from 5.30. Dinner until 23.00. Closed Sat afternoon, Sun, and in Aug.

Specialities: home-cooking.
Other points: credit cards accepted, bar, children's menu, pets allowed, car/lorry parking.
❮❮ Roche de Solutré; prehistoric sites; chateau; Cluny: abbey and stud-farm (haras).

RONCHAMP • Haute-Saône, 70250

A LA POMME D'OR

(Mme Lucette Cenci) rue Le Corbusier
☎ 85.37.71.51
Directions: RN 19, between Belfort and Vesoul.
Languages spoken: German and English.
Menu: 55 to 210 Frs.
Accommodation: 120 to 210 Frs.
Restaurant: breakfast from 6.00. Lunch from 12.00 until 14.30. Dinner from 19.00 until 22.30.
Specialities: regional menu, home-cooking.
Hotel: ☆ ☆ 40 rooms. Facilities: shower, private bathroom, television, telephone.
Other points: credit cards accepted, bar, children's menu, à la carte menu, pets allowed, car/lorry parking.
❮❮ Le Corbusier chapel; musée de la mine (mining); pools (étangs).

ROSOY • Yonne, 89100

LA MAISON BLANCHE

(Mme Martine Boire) 31 route Nationale 6
☎ 84.20.62.12 Fax 84.63.59.45
Directions: RN 6.
Menu: 55 to 98 Frs.
Restaurant: breakfast from 6.00. Lunch from 11.45 until 14.00. Dinner from 19.00 until 22.00. Closed Sun evening.
Specialities: moules à la chablisienne, couscous, rognons de boeuf maison, home-cooking.
Hotel: 5 rooms. Facilities: shower.
Other points: credit cards accepted, bar, children's menu, à la carte menu, modern decor, pets allowed, car/lorry parking.
❮❮ Sens: cathedral; museum; windmill/garden at Tan.

ROUVRAY • Côte-d'Or, 21530

LE RELAIS DE LA CROISEE

(M. Richard Farnaud) La Croisée
☎ 86.97.14.52
Directions: RN 6.
Menu: 29 to 78 Frs.
Restaurant: breakfast from 6.00.
Specialities: home-cooking.
Other points: bar, à la carte menu, lounge area, traditional decor, terrace, pets allowed, car/lorry parking.

ROYE • Haute-Saône, 70200

LE RELAIS DES ROUTIERS

(Mme Huguette Kuhn) 50 rue de la Verrerie
☎ 80.64.79.61 Fax 80.64.71.52

Directions: RN 19, the Paris/Belfort road.
Menu: 40 to 50 Frs.
Restaurant: breakfast from 7.30. Lunch from 12.00 until 13.30. Dinner from 19.00 until 20.00. Closed Sun, and in Aug.
Specialities: home-cooking.
Other points: bar, children's menu, modern decor, pets allowed, car/lorry parking.
◄€ *Ronchamp: Le Corbusier chapel; the Saône-Vosges.*

RUPT-SUR-MOSELLE
Vosges, 88360

L'ETAPE
(Mme Catherine Lemonnier) 'Les Meix', Route Nationale 66 ☎ 84.30.06.48
Directions: RN 66, Mulhouse.
Languages spoken: German.
Menu: 45 Frs.
Restaurant: breakfast from 6.00. Lunch from 11.00 until 13.45. Dinner from 18.00 until 20.45. Closed Sun afternoon.
Specialities: home-cooking.
Other points: credit cards accepted, bar, pets allowed, car/lorry parking.

RYE • Jura, 39230

CHEZ LUCETTE
(Mme Lucette Cambazard)
☎ 29.24.35.17
Directions: RD 468, between Dijon and Lons-le-Saunier.
Menu: 58 to 75 Frs.
Restaurant: breakfast from 6.30. Lunch from 11.30 until 14.00. Closed Thurs afternoon, first 2 weeks in Aug and last 2 weeks in Dec.
Specialities: regional menu, home-cooking.
Other points: bar, traditional decor, car/lorry parking.
◄€ *vineyards; Jura countryside; chateau.*

SAINT-AUBIN-SUR-LOIRE
Saône-et-Loire, 71140

RESTAURANT DE L'AMITIE
(SNC Maison-Gaumard) Le Bourg
☎ 84.48.61.60
Directions: RD 979, between Mâcon and Nevers.
Languages spoken: German, English and Spanish.
Menu: 50 to 120 Frs.
Accommodation: 85 Frs.
Restaurant: breakfast from 7.00. Lunch from 11.30 until 13.45. Dinner from 19.00 until 21.00. Closed Mon afternoon, and 1 week at Christmas.
Specialities: tripes, coq au vin, home-cooking.
Hotel: 4 rooms. Facilities: shower, private bathroom.
Other points: bar, children's menu, à la carte menu, traditional decor, terrace, pets allowed, car/lorry parking.
◄€ *'le Vieux Bourbon', wine-cellars.*

SAINT-DENIS-LES-SENS
Yonne, 89100

LES CERISIERS
(M. Michel Ferrière) 1 rue de Paris
☎ 85.53.91.09
Directions: RN 360: A6, Sens exit.
Languages spoken: English.
Menu: 57 Frs.
Restaurant: breakfast from 7.00. Lunch from 11.00 until 14.00. Dinner from 19.00 until 21.00. Closed weekends (except bookings: minimum of 30 people), and in Aug.
Specialities: home-cooking.
Other points: bar, children's menu, modern decor, terrace, pets allowed, car/lorry parking.
◄€ *Sens: cathedral, museums and gardens.*

SAINT-DIE • Vosges, 88100

LA CROISETTE
(M. Bernard Roumier) 41 avenue de Verdun
☎ 86.65.28.52
Directions: RN 59.
Menu: 58 Frs.
Restaurant: breakfast from 8.00. Dinner until 22.00. Closed at New Year.
Specialities: couscous (Sat), Vosges regional meal (Sun), home-cooking.
Other points: credit cards accepted, bar.

SAINT-DIZIER • Haute-Marne, 52100

LE MOLIERE
(M. Gérard Delaporte) 10 rue Molière
☎ 29.56.14.37
Directions: 400 metres from the RN 4.
Languages spoken: German and English.
Menu: 53 to 90 Frs.
Restaurant: breakfast from 7.30. Lunch from 11.30 until 14.30. Dinner from 19.30 until 23.30. Closed Sat evening and Sun.
Specialities: moules/frites, couscous, paella, choucroute, regional menu, home-cooking.
Other points: credit cards accepted, bar, children's menu, à la carte menu, pets allowed, car/lorry parking.
◄€ *lac du Der.*

SAINT-EUSEBE
Saône-et-Loire, 71120

LE PONT DES MORANDS
(Mme Joëlle Martin) Pont des Morands
☎ 25.56.63.05
Directions: Le Creusot/Paray-le-Monial expressway.
Menu: 60 Frs.
Accommodation: 85 Frs.
Restaurant: breakfast from 5.30. Lunch from 11.45 until 14.30. Dinner from 19.30 until 22.00. Closed Sat.
Specialities: home-cooking.
Hotel: 9 rooms.

Other points: credit cards accepted, bar, children's menu, lounge area, modern decor, terrace, pets allowed, car/lorry parking.
◀ *Musée de la mine (mining) at Blanzy; étang (pond) Berthaud.*

SAINT-HIPPOLYTE • Doubs, 25190

🍴 LE GRAND CLOS
(Mme Martine Lepême) ☎ 85.78.46.45
Directions: RN 437, Belfort/Pontarlier/Besançon.
Languages spoken: German.
Menu: 55 to 90 Frs.
Accommodation: 115 to 150 Frs.
Restaurant: breakfast from 6.00. Lunch from 11.00 until 14.00. Dinner from 18.00 until 22.00. Closed Sat (out of season).
Specialities: jambon de montagne, regional menu, home-cooking.
Hotel: 6 rooms. Facilities: shower, private bathroom.
Other points: credit cards accepted, bar, à la carte menu, traditional decor, terrace, pets allowed, car/lorry parking.
◀ *chateau; saut (falls) du Doubs; caves.*

SAINT-LOUP-DE-VARENNES
Saône-et-Loire, 71240

🍴 LA PETITE AUBERGE
(Mme Sonia Gaudillat) Route Nationale 6
☎ 81.96.51.12
Directions: RN 6, the Chalon/Mâcon road.
Menu: 45 to 62 Frs.
Restaurant: breakfast from 6.30. Dinner until 23.00. Closed Sun, and in Dec.
Specialities: home-cooking.
Other points: credit cards accepted, bar, children's menu, à la carte menu, traditional decor, pets allowed, car/lorry parking.
◀ *lakes at Loives; musée de la photographie.*

SAINT-LOUP-SUR-SEMOUSE
Haute-Saône, 70800

🍴 HOTEL DE LA TERRASSE
(M. Jean Ballot) rue de la Gare
☎ 85.44.21.87
Directions: RN 64.
Restaurant: closed Sun, and 1st 2 weeks in Aug.
Hotel: 4 rooms.
Other points: bar.

SAINT-MIHIEL • Meuse, 55300

🍴 LE RELAIS DES ROUTIERS
(M. Claude Dervin) 19 rue de Verdun
☎ 84.49.02.20
Directions: RD 964, Verdun.
Menu: 52 Frs.
Accommodation: 110 Frs.
Restaurant: breakfast from 7.00. Lunch from

12.00 until 15.00. Dinner from 20.00 until 23.00. Closed Sun, and in Aug.
Specialities: couscous, regional menu, home-cooking.
Hotel: 8 rooms. Facilities: shower, private bathroom.
Other points: credit cards accepted, bar, children's menu, traditional decor, terrace, pets allowed, car parking.
◀ *lac de Madine; Meuse region; Verdun.*

SAINT-PHAL • Aube, 10130

🍴 RESTAURANT DU COMMERCE
(M. Daniel Godefroy) ☎ 29.89.00.44
Directions: RN 77, the Auxerre/Troyes road.
Languages spoken: German.
Menu: 55 to 145 Frs.
Restaurant: breakfast from 8.00. Lunch from 11.00 until 13.30. Dinner from 19.00 until 20.45. Closed Mon afternoon, and in Aug.
Specialities: ris de veau, terrines maison, regional menu.
Other points: credit cards accepted, bar, children's menu, traditional decor, pets allowed, car/lorry parking.
◀ *forêt d'Othe; lake and forêt d'Orient; forêt de Troyes.*

SAINT-PIERRE-LE-MOUTIER
Nièvre, 58240

🍴 RELAIS SAINT-IMBERT
(Mlle Pia Fressle) Route Nationale 7,
Saint-Imbert ☎ 25.42.16.39
[Fax] 25.42.14.65
Directions: RN 7, between Nevers and Moulins.
Languages spoken: German.
Menu: 35 to 72 Frs.
Restaurant: breakfast from 5.00. Lunch from 12.00 until 14.30. Dinner from 19.00 until 22.30. Closed Sat and Sun.
Specialities: choucroute, potée, boeuf stroganoff, poissons, roti de porc à la bière, regional menu, home-cooking.
Other points: credit cards accepted, bar, children's menu, traditional decor, terrace, pets allowed, car/lorry parking.
◀ *Boleine arboretum; chateaux.*

SAINT-PIERREMONT
Vosges, 88700

🍴 LE RELAIS VOSGIEN
(Mme Christiane Thénot-Prévost)
☎ 86.38.61.65
Directions: RD 414, between Luneville and Rambervillers.
Languages spoken: German.
Menu: 63 to 220 Frs.
Accommodation: 210 to 330 Frs.
Restaurant: breakfast from 7.00. Lunch from 12.00 until 13.30. Dinner from 18.30 until 20.30.

Closed Sat morning, and last 2 weeks in Dec.
Specialities: home-cooking.
Hotel: ☆ ☆ 17 rooms. Facilities: shower, private bathroom, television, telephone.
Other points: credit cards accepted, bar, children's menu, à la carte menu, lounge area, traditional decor, terrace, pets allowed, car/lorry parking.
◀€ *Lunéville ('le petit Versailles'); Baccarat crystal-works; springs and ponds.*

SAINT-SAUVEUR
Haute-Saône, 70300

🍴 **CHEZ MAXIM**
(M. Joël Lack) 10 avenue Georges-Clemenceau ☎ 29.65.02.46
Fax 29.65.02.83
Directions: RN 57, between Nancy and Besançon.
Languages spoken: German and English.
Menu: 50 to 95 Frs.
Accommodation: 90 to 130 Frs.
Restaurant: breakfast from 6.30. Lunch from 11.30 until 15.00. Dinner from 19.00 until 22.30. Closed Sun evening, and in Feb.
Specialities: jambon de Luxeuil, kirsch de Fougerolles, cancoillotte (goat's cheese), regional menu, home-cooking.
Hotel: 5 rooms. Facilities: shower, private bathroom.
Other points: credit cards accepted, bar, children's menu, traditional decor, pets allowed, car/lorry parking.
◀€ *Luxeuil: basilica, maison du cardinal, tour des Echevins, tour du Bailly; kirsch distilleries at Fougerolles; glass-works (verrerie) at La Rochère; hermitage de Saint-Valbert.*

SAINT-YAN • Saône-et-Loire, 71600

🍴 **HOTEL DE LA GARE**
(M. Pascal Germain) 12 rue de la Gare
☎ 84.40.02.91 Fax 84.93.65.45
Directions: RN 70, between Digoin and Roanne.
Menu: 52 to 130 Frs.
Accommodation: 80 to 140 Frs.
Restaurant: breakfast from 7.30. Lunch from 12.00 until 14.00. Dinner from 19.00 until 21.00. Closed Sun, and from mid-Aug to mid-Sept.
Specialities: escargots, grenouilles, coq au vin, canard à l'orange, home-cooking.
Hotel: 6 rooms.
Other points: credit cards accepted, bar, children's menu, à la carte menu, traditional decor, terrace, car/lorry parking.
◀€ *basilica at Paray-le-Monial; Autin.*

SAINTE-MARGUERITE
Vosges, 88100

🍴 **LE RELAIS DES AMIS**
(Mme Josiane Bonhomme) 486 rue d'Alsace
☎ 85.84.97.20

Directions: RN 59, the road to the Sainte-Marie-Mines tunnel.
Accommodation: 100 to 160 Frs.
Restaurant: breakfast from 7.00. Lunch from 12.00 until 14.00. Dinner from 19.00 until 21.00. Closed Sat, Sun.
Specialities: backeoffe and other regional dishes, home-cooking.
Hotel: ☆ 16 rooms. Facilities: shower.
Other points: bar, traditional decor, terrace, pets allowed, car/lorry parking.
◀€ *Alsace region 20 minutes away.*

SALINS-LES-BAINS • Jura, 39110

🍴 **BAR RESTAURANT DES SPORTS**
(Mme Liliane Vacelet) 107 avenue de la République ☎ 29.56.17.23
Menu: 32 to 65 Frs.
Restaurant: breakfast from 6.00. Lunch from 11.00 until 14.00. Dinner from 18.00 until 21.00. Closed Sun.
Specialities: fondue savoyarde, truite aux amandes, regional menu, home-cooking.
Other points: bar, children's menu, à la carte menu, traditional decor.
◀€ *casino; museum; church.*

SARREGUEMINES • Moselle, 57200

🍴 **HOTEL RESTAURANT DE L'ABATTOIR**
(M. Camille Fasel) 19 rue du Bac
☎ 87.98.15.39
Directions: Bitche or Forbach-St-Avold.
Languages spoken: German.
Menu: 38 to 60 Frs.
Accommodation: 80 to 120 Frs.
Restaurant: breakfast from 5.00. Lunch from 12.00 until 14.00. Dinner from 19.00 until 21.00. Closed Sat afternoon, Sun, and 1 week in Aug.
Specialities: choucroute garnie, home-cooking.
Hotel: 11 rooms. Facilities: shower, private bathroom.
Other points: bar, modern decor, pets allowed, car/lorry parking.
◀€ *pottery (faïencerie); Bliesbruck: archeological site; citadelle at Bitche; parc régional des Vosges du Nord.*

SAULIEU • Côte-d'Or, 21210

🍴 **AUX POIDS LOURDS**
(Mme Michèle Godet) 12 rue Courtépée
☎ 81.64.19.83 Fax 80.64.19.83
Directions: RN 6, Lyon.
Menu: 55 Frs.
Accommodation: 65 to 95 Frs.
Restaurant: breakfast from 7.30. Lunch from 12.00 until 14.00. Closed Sat, Sun, and in Aug.
Specialities: home-cooking.
Hotel: 4 rooms. Facilities: shower.
Other points: credit cards accepted, bar, traditional decor, car/lorry parking.
◀€ *museum; basilica; lakes.*

SEDAN • Ardennes, 08200

⇛ CHEZ LOULOUTE
(Mme Thérèse Varloteaux) 56 avenue de la
Marne ☎ 24.27.16.62
Directions: RN 43, Charleville-Mézières.
Menu: 53 Frs (wine included).
Restaurant: breakfast from 5.30.
Specialities: home-cooking.
Other points: credit cards accepted, bar,
children's menu, traditional decor, pets allowed,
car/lorry parking.
◁≣ chateau-fort (fortified castle); musée de
l'aviation; musée du feutre (felt); Maginot line.

SELTZ • Bas-Rhin, 67470

🛏 L'HOMME SAUVAGE
(M. Philippe Hoerd) 40 rue Principale
☎ 88.86.50.60
Directions: the Strasbourg/Frankfurt road.
Languages spoken: German.
Menu: 55 Frs (wine included).
Accommodation: 100 to 150 Frs.
Restaurant: breakfast from 6.00. Lunch from
11.30. Dinner until 23.00.
Specialities: regional menu, home-cooking.
Hotel: 7 rooms.
Other points: bar, children's menu, à la carte
menu, traditional decor, terrace, pets allowed,
car/lorry parking.
◁≣ Maginot line; Germany.

SENAN • Yonne, 89710

⇛ HOTEL DE LA CROIX BLANCHE
(M. Jean-Claude Lecourt) 16 rue d'Aillant
☎ 86.63.41.31
Directions: RD 955.
Restaurant: closed Sun afternoon.
Other points: bar.

SENNECEY-LE-GRAND
Saône-et-Loire, 71240

⇛ L'ARCHE DE CHALON-LA-FERTE
(M. Antoine Rivasseau) A6, services at
Chalon-la-Ferté (accessible in Paris/Lyon
direction) ☎ 85.44.21.79 [Fax] 85.44.13.78
Restaurant: open 24 hours.
Other points: credit cards and foreign currency
accepted.

⇛ L'ARCHE DE CHALON-SAINT-AMBREUIL
(M. Bruno Brenez) A6, services at Saint-
Ambreuil (accessible in Lyon/Paris direction)
☎ 85.44.20.64 [Fax] 85.44.13.12
Restaurant: open 24 hours.
Other points: credit cards and foreign currency
accepted.

SOMMESSOUS • Marne, 51320

⇛ LE MIRABELLIER
(SARL SG2R) A26, Châlons/Troyes road,
services at Sommessous ☎ 26.70.17.04
[Fax] 26.70.42.10
Menu: 59 Frs.
Restaurant: breakfast from 6.00. Meals until 23.00.
Specialities: home-cooking.
Other points: credit cards accepted, children's
menu, lounge area, modern decor, car/lorry
parking.

SOULAINES DHUYS • Aube, 10200

⇛ LE RELAIS DES ROUTIERS
(Mme Yvette Demongeot) Route
Départementale 960 ☎ 25.92.76.10
Directions: RD 960, between Troyes and Nancy.
Menu: 48 to 75 Frs.
Restaurant: breakfast from 8.00. Lunch from
12.00 until 14.30. Dinner from 19.00 until 22.00.
Closed Sun.
Specialities: regional menu.
Other points: credit cards accepted, bar, modern
decor, pets allowed, car/lorry parking.
◁≣ lac du Der (15km); Dienville (sailing port)
(20km).

SPINCOURT • Meuse, 55230

⇛ HOTEL RESTAURANT DE LA GARE
(M. Bruno Campolmi) ☎ 29.85.96.93
Languages spoken: German, English, Spanish and
Italian.
Menu: 60 Frs.
Accommodation: 170 Frs.
Restaurant: breakfast from 10.00. Closed Tues.
Specialities: Italian dishes, home-cooking.
Hotel: 4 rooms. Facilities: shower.
Other points: bar, traditional decor, pets allowed,
car/lorry parking.
◁≣ Verdun (25km).

STENAY • Meuse, 55700

⇛ BAR DES SANGLIERS – La Mangeoire
(M. Daniel Demacon) 1 rue Carnot
☎ 29.80.60.06
Directions: RD 947, Reims road.
Languages spoken: German.
Menu: 60 to 150 Frs.
Accommodation: 120 to 150 Frs.
Restaurant: breakfast from 6.30. Lunch from
11.30 until 14.00. Dinner from 19.30 until 21.00.
Closed Sat, and in Aug.
Specialities: home-cooking.
Hotel: 4 rooms. Facilities: shower, private
bathroom.
Other points: credit cards accepted, bar, à la carte
menu, modern decor, pets allowed, car/lorry
parking.
◁≣ Musée de la bière (beer).

STRASBOURG-MEINAU
Bas-Rhin, 67100

⇌ BRASSERIE DES BATELIERS
(M. and Mme Jean-Claude Piccinelli) 33 rue de la Plaine de Bouchers, Meinau Industrial Zone (Z.I.) ☎ 88.39.19.50
Directions: RN 4.
Languages spoken: German and Spanish.
Menu: 40 to 75 Frs.
Restaurant: breakfast from 6.45. Lunch from 11.30 until 14.30. Dinner from 19.00 until 22.00. Closed Sat (from 15.00), Sun, and 3 weeks between July and Oct.
Specialities: regional menu, home-cooking.
Other points: credit cards accepted, à la carte menu, traditional decor, terrace, pets allowed, car/lorry parking.
◀ pont couvert (covered bridge); 'la Petite France'; cathedral.

SUBLIGNY • Yonne, 89100

⇌ RELAIS DE SUBLIGNY
(M. Jean-Pierre Closier) 17 route de Courtenay ☎ 86.88.83.22
Directions: RN 60, between Troyes and Orléans.
Menu: 60 Frs (wine included).
Restaurant: breakfast from 7.00. Lunch from 11.30 until 14.30. Dinner from 19.00 until 22.00. Closed Sun evening and Mon.
Specialities: Burgundian dishes, regional menu, home-cooking.
Other points: credit cards accepted, bar, children's menu, traditional decor, terrace, pets allowed, car/lorry parking.

SUIPPES • Marne, 51600

⇌ AU BON COIN
(SDF Tiloca) 25 rue de la Libération ☎ 26.70.05.84
Directions: RN 77 and 31, between Sedan and Charleville.
Languages spoken: Italian.
Menu: 59 to 90 Frs.
Restaurant: breakfast from 8.00. Dinner from 19.00 until 21.00.
Specialities: Italian dishes, home-cooking.
Other points: credit cards accepted, bar, traditional decor, terrace, pets allowed, car parking.

THAON-LES-VOSGES
Vosges, 88150

⇌ RELAIS ROUTIERS 60 10
(M. Robert Gehin) 200 rue de Lorraine ☎ 29.39.21.67
Directions: RN 57, Epinal.
Menu: 50 to 70 Frs.
Accommodation: 110 Frs.
Restaurant: breakfast from 5.00. Lunch from 11.45 until 13.30. Dinner from 19.00 until 20.30. Closed Sat lunch and Sun.

Specialities: tête de veau, home-cooking.
Hotel: 4 rooms. Facilities: television.
Other points: credit cards accepted, bar, children's menu, modern decor, pets allowed, car/lorry parking.
◀ musée de l'imagerie (printing) at Epinal (9km).

TIL-CHATEL • Côte-d'Or, 21120

⇌ LE RELAIS DES PEUPLIERS
(Mme Judith Ezzedine) Route Nationale 74 ☎ 80.95.20.14 [Fax] 80.95.13.54
Directions: RN 74, the Dijon/Langres road.
Menu: 60 Frs (wine and coffee included).
Restaurant: breakfast from 7.00. Lunch from 11.30 until 14.30. Dinner from 18.30 until 22.00. Closed Sun.
Specialities: home-cooking.
Other points: credit cards accepted, children's menu, lounge area, modern decor, terrace, pets allowed, car/lorry parking.
◀ Til-Chatel; caves at Bèze.

TORCY • Saône-et-Loire, 71210

⇌ LA SPIAGGIA
(M. Salvatore Lotito) Route Expresse, Montchanin ☎ 85.55.35.45
Directions: RN 80
Languages spoken: English and Italian.
Restaurant: breakfast from 7.00. Lunch from 12.00 until 14.00. Dinner from 19.00 until 23.00.
Specialities: Italian dishes.
Other points: credit cards accepted, bar, à la carte menu, modern decor, terrace, pets allowed, car/lorry parking.

LA TOUR-DU-MEIX • Jura, 39270

⇌ AUBERGE DU PONT DE LA PYLE
(M. Jacques Berger) Route Nationale 470 ☎ 84.25.41.92 [Fax] 84.25.42.16
Directions: RN 470, between Lons-le-Saunier and Saint-Claude, via Orgelet.
Languages spoken: English and German.
Menu: 60 to 180 Frs 🛏
Restaurant: breakfast from 8.00. Lunch from 12.00 until 15.00. Dinner from 19.00 until 22.00. Closed in Oct.
Specialities: filets de perches au beurre, cuisses de grenouilles, home-cooking.
Other points: credit cards accepted, bar, children's menu, à la carte menu, traditional decor, terrace, pets allowed, car/lorry parking.
◀ lake at Vouglans; waterfalls at Le Hérisson; caves at Osselles and Moidon; dam at Vouglans; musée du jouet (toys).

TREMBLOIS-LES-ROCROI
Ardennes, 08150

⇌ RELAIS ROUTIERS DU PIQUET
(M. Gérard Clérice) Le Piquet ☎ 24.35.13.86

Directions: RN 43, Charleville-Mézières/Lille road.
Languages spoken: Spanish and Portuguese.
Menu: 54 Frs.
Restaurant: breakfast from 6.15. Lunch from 11.30 until 14.30. Dinner from 19.00 until 21.00. Closed Sat, Sun, and 3 weeks in Aug.
Specialities: home-cooking.
Other points: credit cards accepted, bar, terrace, car/lorry parking.
◀€ *Meuse valley; Vieilles-Forges lake; Rocroi.*

TRESNAY • Nièvre, 58240

〓€ LA SCIERIE
(M. Martial Pettinger) Route Nationale 7
☎ 86.38.62.14
Directions: RN 7, between Saint-Pierre-le-Moutier and Moulins.
Languages spoken: English.
Menu: 55 Frs
Restaurant: open 24 hour. Lunch from 12.00 until 14.30. Dinner from 19.30 until 23.30. Closed Sat, Sun, and in Aug.
Specialities: home-cooking.
Other points: credit cards accepted, bar, à la carte menu, lounge area, modern decor, car/lorry parking.

TRONSANGES • Nièvre, 58400

〓€ L'AUBERGE DU SOLEIL LEVANT
(Mme Renée Reichhard) Route Nationale 7, Barbeloup ☎ 86.37.84.02
Directions: RN 7.
Menu: 48 to 65 Frs.
Restaurant: breakfast from 6.00. Lunch from 12.00 until 14.00. Closed Sun, and mid-Sept.
Specialities: home-cooking.
Other points: bar, children's menu, traditional decor, pets allowed.

🏠 SARL DE LA CROIX DU PAPE – Chez l'Auvergnat
(Mme Agnès Dumaine) Barbeloup
☎ 86.37.84.03
Directions: RN 7, Nevers.
Menu: 57 to 100 Frs.
Accommodation: 120 to 136 Frs.
Restaurant: breakfast from 5.00
Hotel: 6 rooms. Facilities: shower, private bathroom.
Other points: credit cards accepted, bar, children's menu, à la carte menu, lounge area, modern decor, terrace, pets allowed, car/lorry parking.
◀€ *La Charité-sur-Loire; Vaux; the Loire.*

TROYES • Aube, 10000

🏠 LE SPLENDID
(M. Dominique Gilles) 44 boulevard Carnot
☎ 25.73.08.52
Languages spoken: English.
Accommodation: 125 to 250 Frs.
Hotel: ☆ ☆ 16 rooms. Facilities: shower, private bathroom, television, telephone.

Other points: restaurant, credit cards accepted, traditional decor, pets allowed, car parking.
◀€ *Troyes (historic capital of the Champagne region): numerous museums, old quarters; Aube lakes; Champagne vineyards.*

UCKANGE • Moselle, 57270

〓€ LE PRESSOIR
(M. Silvio Piccin) 22 rue Jeanne d'Arc
☎ 82.58.20.38
Directions: RD 952.
Restaurant: breakfast from 4.30. Closed Sat, Sun, in Aug and 2 weeks from Christmas Day.
Other points: bar.

UNIENVILLE • Aube, 10140

〓€ CHEZ CHRISTIANE ET MARCEL
(Mme Christiane Saget) ☎ 25.92.70.80
Menu: 50 Frs (drink and coffee included).
Restaurant: breakfast from 7.30. Lunch from 11.30 until 13.30. Dinner from 19.00 until 20.00.
Specialities: home-cooking.
Other points: bar, pets allowed, car/lorry parking.

VARENNES-LE-GRAND
Saône-et-Loire, 71240

🏠 HOTEL RESTAURANT DU COMMERCE
(M. Bertrand Chavanis – SARL Fidem) Route Nationale 6 ☎ 85.44.22.34
Directions: RN 6, between Chalon-sur-Saône and Lyon.
Languages spoken: English.
Menu: 60 Frs (wine and coffee included) to 80 Frs.
Accommodation: 110 to 240 Frs.
Restaurant: breakfast from 5.00. Closed Sat evening and Sun lunch.
Specialities: regional menu, home-cooking.
Hotel: 14 rooms. Facilities: shower, private bathroom, television, telephone.
Other points: credit cards accepted, bar, children's menu, à la carte menu, lounge area, terrace, pets allowed, car/lorry parking.
◀€ *Chalon; Tournus; Cluny.*

VARENNES-LES-MACON
Saône-et-Loire, 71000

🏠 LA HALTE DES ROUTIERS
(M. René Massonneau) Route Nationale 6
☎ 85.34.70.44 [Fax] 85.29.29.03
Directions: RN 6, exit at Mâcon Sud (south).
Accommodation: 85 to 140 Frs.
Restaurant: breakfast from 5.30. Closed Sat from 10.00, Sun, and last 2 weeks in Aug.
Hotel: 24 rooms.
Other points: credit cards accepted, bar, children's menu, traditional decor, pets allowed, car/lorry parking.
◀€ *Roche-de-Solutré.*

VELAINE-EN-HAYE
Meurthe-et-Moselle, 54840

⇌ LE MOUTON D'OR
(Mme Martine Contal) Route Nationale 4
☎ 83.23.28.71
Menu: 59 to 180 Frs.
Restaurant: breakfast from 7.00. Lunch from 11.45 until 14.00. Dinner from 19.30 until 22.00. Closed Sun evening.
Specialities: viandes rouges, abats (offal), regional menu, home-cooking.
Other points: credit cards accepted, bar, children's menu, à la carte menu, traditional decor, pets allowed, car/lorry parking.
◁€ *Nancy: museums, place Stanislas; Toul; the Moselle.*

⇌ RESTAURANT DU PARC
(M. Patrick Hebacker) 6 allée des Erables
☎ 83.23.28.48 Fax 83.23.26.70
Directions: the Toul/Paris road.
Restaurant: breakfast from 9.00. Lunch from 11.30 until 14.00. Closed Sat and Sun (except bookings).
Specialities: regional menu, home-cooking.
Other points: credit cards accepted, bar, children's menu, à la carte menu, modern decor, pets allowed, car/lorry parking.
◁€ *Toul: cathedral; Nancy: place Stanislas.*

VENDENHEIM • Bas-Rhin, 67550

⇌ LE RELAIS DE LA MAISON ROUGE
(Mme Germaine Michielin-Chast) 2 route de Brumath ☎ 88.69.51.79
Directions: RN 63.
Languages spoken: German.
Menu: 55 to 125 Frs 🍽
Restaurant: breakfast from 10.00. Lunch from 12.00 until 14.00. Dinner from 19.00 until 22.00. Closed Tues evening and Wed.
Specialities: rognons de veau, choucroute, regional menu, home-cooking.
Other points: credit cards accepted, bar, children's menu, à la carte menu, traditional decor, pets allowed, car/lorry parking.
◁€ *Alsatian house; Strasbourg cathedral; parc régional des Vosges du Nord.*

VERDUN • Meuse, 55100

🛏 A LA BONNE AUBERGE
(Mme Yolande Gaïotti-Morano) 11 avenue Garibaldi ☎ 29.86.05.16
Directions: RN 3, near railway station (SNCF).
Languages spoken: German and English.
Menu: 50 to 75 Frs.
Accommodation: 65 to 91 Frs.
Restaurant: breakfast from 5.30. Dinner until 24.00.
Specialities: home-cooking.
Hotel: 7 rooms.
Other points: bar, à la carte menu, traditional decor, pets allowed.
◁€ *battlefields.*

🛏 BAR DU COMMERCE
(Mme Marie-Odile Vincent) Route Nationale 3, Eix-Abaucourt ☎ 29.88.31.94
Directions: RN 3, Luxembourg/Metz/Longuy.
Languages spoken: English.
Menu: 35 to 120 Frs.
Accommodation: 120 Frs.
Restaurant: breakfast from 5.00.
Specialities: escalope à la crème, home-cooking.
Hotel: 9 rooms. Facilities: shower, private bathroom.
Other points: credit cards accepted, bar, children's menu, à la carte menu, lounge area, traditional decor, terrace, pets allowed, car/lorry parking.
◁€ *battlefield at Verdun; cemetery at Douaumont; Fort de Vaux; 1914–18 war sites; Maginot line.*

⇌ L'ARCHE DE VERDUN-SAINT-NICOLAS
(M. Jean-Claude Moulotu) A4, services at Saint-Nicolas (accessible in both directions)
☎ 29.86.41.18 Fax 29.86.64.65
Restaurant: open 24 hours.
Other points: credit cards accepted.

VERMENTON • Yonne, 89270

🛏 LE NOUVEAU RELAIS
(M. Pierre Jean) 74 Route Nationale 6
☎ 86.81.51.51
Directions: RN 6, the Paris/Lyon road.
Accommodation: 90 Frs.
Restaurant: breakfast from 6.30. Closed Sun, and mid-Dec to mid-Jan.
Specialities: boeuf bourguignon, coq au vin, escalope milannaise, regional menu, home-cooking.
Hotel: 12 rooms.
Other points: bar, à la carte menu, traditional decor, pets allowed, car/lorry parking.
◁€ *Avallon; Auxerre.*

VILLENEUVE-AU-CHEMIN
Aube, 10130

⇌ LE PETIT SAINT-JEAN
(M. Nafaa Nait Mohand) Route Nationale 77
☎ 25.42.10.51
Directions: RN 77, between Troyes and Auxerre.
Languages spoken: Arabic.
Menu: 54 to 65 Frs.
Restaurant: breakfast from 8.00. Lunch from 10.00 until 14.00. Dinner until 23.00.
Specialities: couscous, home-cooking.
Other points: credit cards accepted, bar, children's menu, à la carte menu, traditional decor, terrace, pets allowed, car parking.

VILLENEUVE-L'ARCHEVEQUE
Yonne, 89190

🛏 L'ESCALE 60
(M. Dominique Boire) 10 route de Sens
☎ 86.86.74.42
Directions: RN 60, between Sens and Troyes.
Languages spoken: English.
Menu: 53 Frs.

Accommodation: 110 to 170 Frs.
Restaurant: breakfast from 7.00. Lunch 11.30 to 13.30. Dinner 19.00 to 21.00. Closed Sat and Sun.
Specialities: escalope normande, coq au vin, rognon de génisse (heifer) maison, home-cooking.
Hotel: 10 rooms. Facilities: shower.
Other points: credit cards accepted, bar, à la carte menu, modern decor, terrace, pets allowed, car/lorry parking.
◀€ Sens: cathedral (25km).

VILLEVALLIER • Yonne, 89330

🏨 **RELAIS 89**
(Mme Yvette Petit) 9 rue de la République
☎ 86.91.11.17
Directions: RN 89, between Joigny and Sens.
Menu: 58 Frs.
Accommodation: 85 to 140 Frs.
Restaurant: breakfast from 6.00. Closed Sat, Sun.
Specialities: home-cooking.
Hotel: 6 rooms. Facilities: shower, private bathroom.
Other points: credit cards accepted, bar, children's menu, à la carte menu, modern decor, terrace, pets allowed, car/lorry parking.
◀€ Yonne valley.

VITRY-EN-CHAROLLAIS
Saône-et-Loire, 71600

🍴 **TOM BAR**
(M. André Borrego) Route Nationale 79
☎ 85.81.02.85
Directions: between Paray-le-Monial and Digoin.
Languages spoken: Spanish.
Restaurant: dinner until 22.30.
Specialities: Italian dishes, regional menu.
Other points: credit cards accepted, bar, children's menu, à la carte menu, traditional decor, terrace, pets allowed, car/lorry parking.
◀€ basilica at Paray-le-Monial (4km); aqueduct at Digoin (4km).

VITTEAUX • Côte-d'Or, 21350

🍴 **RELAIS DE LA ROUTE BLANCHE**
(M. Roger Le Gall) rue de Verdun ☎ 80.49.60.13
Directions: RN 5, Dijon.
Menu: 60 Frs (drink included).
Restaurant: breakfast from 7.00. Lunch from 12.00 until 14.30. Dinner from 19.00 until 21.00. Closed Sun, and from mid-Aug to mid-September.
Specialities: boeuf bourguignon, jambon persillé, home-cooking.
Other points: credit cards accepted, bar, traditional decor, pets allowed, car/lorry parking.
◀€ Dijon; Semur-en-Auxois; Alésia.

VITTONVILLE
Meurthe-et-Moselle, 54700

🍴 **L'AIGLE D'OR**
(Eliane and Eric Lanzi) Route Nationale 57, Pont-à-Mousson ☎ 83.81.04.08

Directions: RN 57, between Metz and Nancy.
Languages spoken: Dutch and Italian.
Menu: 50 to 75 Frs.
Restaurant: breakfast from 5.00. Dinner until 22.30. Closed Sat after 10.00 and Sun.
Specialities: home-cooking.
Other points: bar, children's menu, à la carte menu, lounge area, modern decor, pets allowed, car/lorry parking.
◀€ Buttes-de-Mousson: historic chateau; lac de Madine.

WASSELONNE • Bas-Rhin, 67310

🏨 **AU ROCHER**
(M. André Hecker) 18 route de Strasbourg
☎ 88.87.06.72
Directions: RN 4, between Saverne and Strasbourg.
Languages spoken: German and English.
Menu: 60 to 100 Frs.
Accommodation: 100 to 250 Frs.
Restaurant: breakfast from 6.30. Lunch from 11.30 until 14.30. Dinner from 19.00 until 21.00. Closed Sun.
Specialities: choucroute paysanne, cuisses de grenouilles à la provençale, boeuf bourguignon, home-cooking.
Hotel: 8 rooms. Facilities: shower, private bathroom.
Other points: credit cards accepted, bar, children's menu, à la carte menu, traditional decor, pets allowed, car/lorry parking.
◀€ Haut-Koenigsbourg: chateau; Strasbourg: cathedral; Mont-Saint-Odile; Saverne.

WITTELSHEIM • Haut-Rhin, 68310

🏨 **HOTEL DES VOSGES**
(M. Doris Riedle) 137 rue de Reiningue
☎ 89.55.10.20
Directions: RN 83, between Mulhouse and Thann.
Languages spoken: German and Italian.
Menu: 50 to 120 Frs.
Accommodation: 130 to 160 Frs.
Restaurant: breakfast from 5.00. Lunch from 12.00 until 14.00. Dinner from 19.00 until 21.00. Closed Sun.
Specialities: choucroute, carpes, regional menu, home-cooking.
Hotel: 13 rooms.
Other points: credit cards accepted, bar, children's menu, à la carte menu, traditional decor, car/lorry parking.
◀€ miner's house; musée de l'automobile et du chemin de fer (cars and railways).

WOIPPY • Moselle, 57140

🍴 **CHARDON LORRAIN**
(Mme Françoise De Cecco) 58 rue de Metz
☎ 87.30.46.61
Languages spoken: German.
Menu: 55 Frs.
Accommodation: 100 Frs.
Restaurant: breakfast from 5.00. Lunch from 11.30 until 14.30. Dinner from 19.00 until 20.00.

Closed Wed afternoon, and 20th Dec to 5th Jan.
Specialities: choucroute, home-cooking.
Hotel: 3 rooms. Facilities: shower.
Other points: credit cards accepted, bar, lounge area, modern decor, terrace, pets allowed, car/lorry parking.
⋖ *Metz; Saint-Quentin; pool (étang).*

XONRUPT-LONGEMER
Vosges, 88400

🛏 **LA PIERRE CHARLEMAGNE – Chez Dédé**
(M. André Caël) Le Saut-des-Cuves
☎ 29.63.03.86
Languages spoken: German and English.
Menu: 55 to 80 Frs.
Accommodation: 130 to 180 Frs.
Restaurant: breakfast from 9.00. Lunch from 12.00 until 14.30. Dinner from 19.00 until 22.00. Closed Mon, last 2 weeks in June and Oct.
Specialities: choucroute, quiche, truite meunière,

regional menu, home-cooking.
Hotel: 8 rooms. Facilities: shower, private bathroom, telephone.
Other points: credit cards accepted, bar, children's menu, à la carte menu, traditional decor, pets allowed, car/lorry parking.

YUTZ • Moselle, 57110

🍴 **PIZZERIA DU RELAIS**
(M. Noël Rubeillon) 140 Route Nationale
☎ 82.56.00.28
Directions: RN 153, Trêve.
Menu: 35 to 65 Frs.
Restaurant: breakfast from 6.30. Lunch from 12.00 until 14.00. Dinner from 19.00 until 22.00. Closed Sun, and 2 weeks in July.
Specialities: filet de sole aux lardons, regional menu, home-cooking.
Other points: credit cards accepted, bar, children's menu, à la carte menu, modern decor, pets allowed, car/lorry parking.

NORTH-WEST FRANCE

The following *départements* are included in this chapter:

<table>
<tr><td>Calvados (14)</td><td>Manche (50)</td></tr>
<tr><td>Côtes-d'Armor (22)</td><td>Mayenne (53)</td></tr>
<tr><td>Eure (27)</td><td>Morbihan (56)</td></tr>
<tr><td>Finistère (29)</td><td>Orne (61)</td></tr>
<tr><td>Ille-et-Vilaine (35)</td><td>Sarthe (72)</td></tr>
<tr><td>Loire-Atlantique (44)</td><td>Seine-Maritime (76)</td></tr>
<tr><td>Maine-et-Loire (49)</td><td>Vendée (85)</td></tr>
</table>

L'AIGUILLON-SUR-VIE
Vendée, 85220

🍴 **RELAIS LA GREVE**
(M. Jean-Pierre Alfonsi) 5 rue des Sables
☎ 51.22.86.23
Directions: between Challans and Les Sables d'Olonne.
Languages spoken: English.
Menu: 50 Frs (wine included) to 65 Frs.
Restaurant: breakfast from 6.30. Lunch from 11.30 until 15.00. Dinner from 19.00 until 22.00. Closed Sun.
Specialities: home-cooking.
Other points: credit cards accepted, bar, children's menu, lounge area, traditional decor, terrace, pets allowed, car/lorry parking.
⋖ *Les Sables d'Olonne (20km); Challans (22km).*

AIZENAY • Vendée, 85190

🛏 **LE SAINT-BENOIST**
(Mme Marie-Danielle Baalouch) 35 rue du Maréchal-Leclerc ☎ 51.94.60.17
Fax 51.48.30.91
Directions: RD 948, between La Rochelle and Saint-Nazaire.
Languages spoken: German, English and Spanish.
Menu: 45 Frs (wine included) to 130 Frs.
Accommodation: 90 to 140 Frs.
Restaurant: breakfast from 6.30. Lunch from 11.30 until 14.00. Dinner from 19.00 until 21.30.
Specialities: home-cooking.
Hotel: ☆ 17 rooms. Facilities: shower, private bathroom, television, telephone.
Other points: credit cards accepted, bar, children's

menu, à la carte menu, lounge area, modern decor, terrace, pets allowed, car/lorry parking.
◀ *La Roche-sur-Yon; Les Sables d'Olonne.*

ALVIMARE • Seine-Maritime, 76640

⬛ AUX AMIS DE LA ROUTE – Chez Yanik et Martine
(M. Yanik Bellenger) Route Nationale 15
☎ 35.96.01.50
Directions: RN 15, main Le Havre/Rouen road.
Menu: 57 Frs.
Restaurant: breakfast from 4.00. Closed Sun.
Specialities: fruits de mer (on Fridays), home-cooking.
Other points: credit cards accepted, bar, children's menu, lounge area, traditional decor, pets allowed, car/lorry parking.
◀ *Le Havre; le chêne (oak) d'Allouville.*

AMBENAY • Eure, 27250

⬛ HOTEL DE LA RISLE
(M. Jean-Louis Marcilly) 9 rue Guy-Lacombe
☎ 32.24.63.45
Directions: RD 830, Rugles.
Menu: 50 Frs.
Accommodation: 100 to 150 Frs.
Restaurant: breakfast from 6.00. Lunch from 12.00 until 14.00. Dinner from 19.30 until 21.30. Closed Sun.
Specialities: home-cooking.
Hotel: 6 rooms. Facilities: shower.
Other points: credit cards accepted, bar, lounge area, traditional decor, car/lorry parking.

AMBREUMESNIL
Seine-Maritime, 76550

⬛ LE TORTILLARD
(Mme Gilberte Dolbec) Hameau Ribeuf
☎ 35.83.17.00
Directions: RD 152.
Menu: 50 Frs.
Specialities: cassoulet, couscous, home-cooking.
Other points: bar, children's menu, à la carte menu, modern decor, pets allowed, car/lorry parking.
◀ *le manoir d'Ango.*

ANETZ • Loire-Atlantique, 44150

⬛ LE RELAIS DE LA BARBINIERE
(Mme Sylvie Dronet) La Barbinière, Route Nationale 23 ☎ 40.83.11.25
Directions: RN 23, the Nantes/Angers road.
Languages spoken: English.
Menu: 48 Frs.
Accommodation: 175 Frs (overnight stop).
Restaurant: breakfast from 6.00. Lunch from 11.30 until 14.00. Dinner from 19.30 until 21.30. Closed Sat, Sun, 1 week in Aug, 1 week at Christmas.
Specialities: home-cooking.
Hotel: 4 rooms. Facilities: shower, private bathroom, television, telephone.

Other points: credit cards accepted, bar, children's menu, traditional decor, pets allowed, car/lorry parking.
◀ *Saint-Florent-le-Vieil: church, observatory.*

ANGERS • Maine-et-Loire, 49100

⬛ LA HAUTE CHAINE
(M. Jean-Claude Derouet) 7 boulevard Ayrault, place Saint-Serge ☎ 41.43.88.99
Directions: the Paris/Nantes road, Saint-Serge exit.
Menu: 56 Frs (wine included) to 68 Frs.
Accommodation: 120 Frs.
Restaurant: breakfast from 5.00. Lunch from 11.30 until 14.30. Dinner from 19.00 until 23.00. Closed Sat and Sun.
Specialities: tripes à la mode de Caen, poulet basquaise, home-cooking.
Hotel: 10 rooms. Facilities: television.
Other points: credit cards accepted, bar, children's menu, à la carte menu, lounge area, modern decor, terrace, pets allowed, car/lorry parking.
◀ *Angers: chateau, jardin des plantes, palais des congrès.*

⬛ LE RELAIS DE L'ARCEAU
(M. Bruno Hérant) 47 rue Guillaume-Lekeu
☎ 41.43.86.25
Languages spoken: English.
Menu: 54 to 64 Frs.
Restaurant: breakfast from 6.00. Lunch from 11.30 until 15.00. Closed Sun.
Specialities: couscous, home-cooking.
Other points: credit cards accepted, bar, children's menu, modern decor, terrace, pets allowed, car/lorry parking.
◀ *Château du Roi René; Cointreau factory.*

AUBE • Orne, 61270

⬛ LE PETIT QUEBEC
(M. Jean-Claude Rialland) 47 route de Paris
☎ 33.24.55.34
Directions: RN 26, between L'Aigle and Argentan.
Languages spoken: English and Spanish.
Menu: 50 Frs.
Restaurant: breakfast from 5.00. Lunch from 11.00 until 14.00. Dinner from 19.00 until 21.00. Closed Sat, Sun and the 1st 2 weeks in Aug.
Specialities: home-cooking.
Other points: credit cards accepted, bar, children's menu, à la carte menu, traditional decor, terrace, pets allowed, car/lorry parking.
◀ *the old forge, with the 'plus gros marteau du monde' (biggest hammer in the world); Comtesse de Ségur's museum (children's author).*

AUMALE • Seine-Maritime, 76390

⬛ HOTEL DE LA GARE
(M. Claude Donront) 9 place de la Gare
☎ 35.94.61.00 [Fax] 35.94.41.67
Directions: RN 29, between Rouen and Amiens.
Menu: 59 Frs.

Restaurant: breakfast from 7.00. Closed Sun.
Specialities: home-cooking.
Other points: credit cards accepted, bar,
children's menu, pets allowed, car/lorry parking.
◀€ chateau at Rambures.

AUTHEUIL-AUTHOUILLET
Eure, 27490

〒 **CHEZ PIERROT**
(M. Pierre Denoitte) 17 rue de Pacy
☎ 32.34.67.67
Directions: RD 316 and 836, exit at Gaillon
towards Evreux.
Restaurant: breakfast from 6.30. Lunch from
12.00 until 14.00. Dinner until 21.00. Closed Sun
afternoon, and mid-Aug.
Specialities: home-cooking.
Other points: bar, traditional decor, terrace, car/
lorry parking.
◀€ Eure valley.

AUVERSE • Maine-et-Loire, 49490

〒 **CHEZ NANOU**
(Mlle Véronique Chasseau) Route de Noyant,
Le Bourg ☎ 41.82.20.13
Directions: RD 766, the Angers/Tours road.
Languages spoken: English.
Menu: 53 to 63 Frs.
Restaurant: breakfast from 6.30. Lunch from
12.00 until 14.00. Dinner from 19.00 until 21.00.
Closed Sun (out of season), and mid-Sept to
mid-Oct.
Specialities: home-cooking.
Other points: bar, traditional decor, pets allowed,
car/lorry parking.
◀€ Loire chateaux.

AVRANCHES • Manche, 50300

〒 **LES ROUTIERS**
(M. Georges Hippolyte) 70 rue de la
Constitution ☎ 33.58.01.13
Directions: RN 176.
Menu: 47 Frs.
Restaurant: breakfast from 9.00. Closed Sun (out
of season), and in Sept.
Specialities: home-cooking.
Other points: bar.

BAGNEUX • Maine-et-Loire, 49400

〒 **RELAIS DE BOURNAN**
(Mme Jeanine Sanzay) 288 rue du Pont-
Fouchard ☎ 41.50.18.02
Directions: RN 160, between Cholet and Niort.
Menu: 55 Frs.
Restaurant: breakfast from 6.30. Lunch from
11.30 until 14.00. Closed Sat afternoon and Sun
(out of season).
Specialities: home-cooking.
Other points: bar, children's menu, traditional

decor, pets allowed, car/lorry parking.
◀€ caves à champignons (mushroom cellars);
chateau.

BALLEROY • Calvados, 14490

🛏 **LE RELAIS DE LA FORET**
(M. Christian Desobeaux) ☎ 31.21.39.78
[Fax] 31.21.44.19
Directions: RD 572, between Bayeux and
Saint-Lô.
Menu: 52 to 158 Frs ⬠
Accommodation: 180 to 190 Frs.
Restaurant: breakfast from 5.00. Lunch from
11.30 until 15.00. Dinner from 19.00 until 24.00.
Specialities: home-cooking.
Hotel: ☆ 10 rooms. Facilities: shower, private
bathroom, television, telephone.
Other points: credit cards accepted, bar,
children's menu, à la carte menu, traditional decor,
terrace, pets allowed, car/lorry parking.
◀€ chateau at Balleroy; musée de la mine (mining);
Bayeux tapestry.

LA BARRE-EN-OUCHE • Eure, 27330

〒 **CHEZ JACKY ET CORINNE**
(M. Jacky Scipion) Grande Rue
☎ 32.44.35.28
Directions: RN 833, the Paris/Evreux road.
Menu: 52 Frs.
Restaurant: breakfast from 7.30. Lunch from 11.30
until 15.00. Dinner from 19.00 until 21.00. Closed
Sun afternoon, 2 weeks in Aug and 2 weeks in Dec.
Specialities: escalope normande, home-cooking.
Other points: bar, children's menu, traditional
decor, pets allowed, car/lorry parking.
◀€ chateau at Beaumesnil (8km).

BAYEUX • Calvados, 14400

〒 **LA COLOMBE**
(M. Gérard Hardy) 13 route de Caen
☎ 31.92.13.65 [Fax] 31.21.12.26
Directions: RN 13, Cherbourg.
Menu: 48 to 130 Frs ⬠
Restaurant: breakfast from 7.00. Lunch from
12.00 until 15.00. Dinner from 18.00 until 21.00.
Closed Sat evening and Sun (out of season).
Specialities: fruits de mer, regional menu, home-
cooking.
Other points: credit cards accepted, bar, children's
menu, à la carte menu, lounge area, modern decor,
terrace, pets allowed, car/lorry parking.
◀€ landing beaches; cathedral; museums.

BEAUCE • Ille-et-Vilaine, 35133

〒 **AUX BECS FINS**
(M. Pierrick Roux) 19 route de Paris
☎ 99.99.08.00
Directions: RN 12, the Paris/Brest road, 3km
before Fougères.

Menu: 50 Frs.
Restaurant: breakfast from 6.30. Lunch from
12.00 until 14.00. Dinner from 19.30 until 21.30.
Closed Sun, public holidays, and in Aug.
Specialities: home-cooking.
Other points: credit cards accepted, bar,
children's menu, à la carte menu, traditional decor,
pets allowed, car/lorry parking.
chateau at Fougères.

BEAUVOIR-EN-LYONS
Seine-Maritime, 76220

**RELAIS NORMAND – Chez
Françoise et Julien**
(M. Julien Jue) Les Carreaux, Route Nationale 31
☎ 35.90.17.20
Directions: RN 31, the Rouen/Reims road.
Menu: 59,80 Frs (coffee included).
Restaurant: breakfast from 5.00. Lunch from
11.00 until 14.00. Dinner from 19.00 until 21.00.
Closed Sat, Sun, public holidays, 1 week in May,
2 weeks in Aug and 1 week in Dec.
Specialities: home-cooking.
Other points: credit cards accepted, bar,
traditional decor, car/lorry parking.
*Les Andelys; Lyons-la-Forêt; chateaux de
Vascoeuil and de Martainville.*

BEAUVOIR-SUR-MER
Vendée, 85230

AU RELAIS DU GOIS
(M. Gilles Grondin) Route Nationale 148
☎ 51.68.70.31
Directions: RN 148, between Noirmoutier and
Le Gois.
Menu: 55 to 160 Frs.
Restaurant: lunch from 12.00 until 14.00. Closed
in Dec.
Specialities: fruits de mer, poissons, regional menu.
Other points: credit cards accepted, bar,
children's menu, à la carte menu, traditional decor,
terrace, pets allowed, car/lorry parking.
*passage du Gois (a low-tide causeway, unique
in Europe, across to l'Ile de Noirmoutier).*

BEDEE • Ille-et-Vilaine, 35137

HOTEL DU COMMERCE
(M. Jean-Louis Rigoreau) 14 place de l'Eglise
☎ 99.07.00.37
Directions: RN 12, between Rennes and Saint-
Brieuc.
Languages spoken: English.
Menu: 58 to 105 Frs
Accommodation: 103 to 139 Frs.
Restaurant: breakfast from 6.30. Lunch from
12.00 until 14.00. Dinner from 19.30 until 21.00.
Closed Sat evening, Sun, and 3 weeks in Aug.
Specialities: coquilles Saint-Jacques à la Bretonne,
gibelotte (hare or rabbit) au cidre, poissons, home-
cooking.

Hotel: ☆ 22 rooms. Facilities: shower, private
bathroom, television, telephone.
Other points: credit cards accepted, bar,
children's menu, à la carte menu, modern decor,
pets allowed, car/lorry parking.
étang (pool) de Blavon; Neo-Gothic church.

BEIGNON • Morbihan, 56380

LES ROUTIERS
(Mme Berthe-Simone Labbé) place de l'Eglise
☎ 97.75.74.37
Directions: RN 24, between Rennes and Lorient.
Restaurant: breakfast from 6.30. Lunch from
12.00 until 14.00. Dinner from 19.00 until 21.30.
Closed Sat (from 13.00).
Specialities: fruits de mer, terrine du chef, home-
cooking.
Hotel: 6 rooms.
Other points: credit cards accepted, bar,
children's menu, à la carte menu, traditional decor,
car/lorry parking.
*Forêt de Brocéliande; Gulf of Morbihan;
Vannes: city of pirates; military academy at
Coëtquidan.*

BELLENGREVILLE • Calvados, 14370

LES ROUTIERS
(M. Désiré Desmeulles) 16 rue de Paris
☎ 31.23.61.50
Directions: RN 13.
Menu: 50 Frs.
Restaurant: breakfast from 7.00. Closed Sun.
Other points: à la carte menu.

BELLEVUE-COETQUIDAN
Morbihan, 56380

L'UNION
(M. Olivier Guérin) 3 avenue Brocéliande
☎ 97.75.71.46
Menu: 47 to 52 Frs.
Accommodation: 90 to 130 Frs.
Restaurant: breakfast from 7.00. Lunch from
12.00 until 14.00. Dinner from 19.00 until 21.00.
Closed Sun, and in Aug.
Specialities: home-cooking.
Hotel: 5 rooms. Facilities: shower.
Other points: credit cards accepted, bar,
children's menu, modern decor, pets allowed, car
parking.
*Coëtquidan: military academy museum (1km),
10km from Paimpont.*

BERNAY • Eure, 27300

L'ESCARBILLE
(Mme Raymonde Perrier) 29 boulevard
Dubus ☎ 32.43.60.43
Directions: between Alençon and Rouen.
Menu: 52 Frs (plat du jour from 35 Frs).

Restaurant: breakfast from 5.00. Lunch from 12.00 until 14.00. Dinner from 19.00 until 21.30. Closed Sun.
Specialities: regional menu, home-cooking.
Other points: credit cards accepted, bar, children's menu, à la carte menu, terrace, pets allowed, car/lorry parking.
Le Bec-Hellouin; musée de l'automobile; Lisieux basilica.

BERNAY-CARSIX • Eure, 27300

🏨 **L'ESCALE**
(M. Michel Silliau) carrefour de Malbrouck
☎ 32.44.79.99
Directions: RN 13, Lisieux.
Menu: 55 to 58 Frs.
Accommodation: 110 to 120 Frs.
Restaurant: breakfast from 4.30. Lunch from 11.00 until 15.00. Dinner from 19.00 until 21.00. Closed Sat afternoon, Sun, 1st 2 weeks in Aug.
Specialities: home-cooking.
Hotel: 6 rooms. Facilities: shower, private bathroom.
Other points: credit cards accepted, bar, children's menu, traditional decor, car/lorry parking.
Abbaye du Bec-Hellouin; Château-Gaillard; Giverny; Vernon.

BESSE-SUR-BRAYE
Sarthe, 72310

🏨 **LES ROUTIERS**
(Mme Nadine Lenoir) 19 avenue de la Gare
☎ 43.35.30.22
Menu: 49 to 53 Frs.
Accommodation: 130 to 165 Frs.
Restaurant: breakfast from 8.00. Lunch from 12.00 until 14.00. Dinner from 19.30 until 21.30. Closed Sun, end Aug/beginning of Sept.
Specialities: home-cooking.
Hotel: ☆ 13 rooms. Facilities: shower, private bathroom, television, telephone.
Other points: credit cards accepted, bar, children's menu, traditional decor, pets allowed, car/lorry parking.
chateau at Courtanvaux (2km).

BEUZEVILLE • Eure, 27210

🍽 **CAFE DE L'ESPERANCE**
(Mme Denise Deguine) 4 rue Pasteur
☎ 32.57.70.60
Directions: Honfleur or Caen.
Languages spoken: English.
Menu: 48 Frs.
Restaurant: closed Sat afternoon, Sun afternoon, and 2 weeks in Aug.
Specialities: couscous, choucroute, escalope viennoise, lapin chasseur, home-cooking.
Other points: bar, traditional decor, pets allowed.
Honfleur; Deauville; Trouville.

BEZU-SAINT-ELOI • Eure, 27660

🍽 **AUBERGE DE LA LEVRIERE**
(M. Yves Roquain) 42 route de Gisors
☎ 32.55.07.12
Directions: between Gisors and Rouen.
Menu: 50 Frs.
Restaurant: breakfast from 6.30. Lunch from 12.00 until 15.00. Dinner from 19.00 until 21.30. Closed Sat lunch, and in Aug/Sept.
Specialities: moules normandes, poissons, regional menu, home-cooking.
Other points: bar, children's menu, à la carte menu, traditional decor, pets allowed, car/lorry parking.
Gisors.

BIVILLE-LA-BAIGNADE
Seine-Maritime, 76890

🍽 **LA CUILLERE EN BOIS**
(Mme Yvette Guerillon) ☎ 35.32.88.81
Directions: RN 27.
Restaurant: closed Wed.
Other points: bar.

BLAIN • Loire-Atlantique, 44130

🍽 **LE RELAIS DU CHATEAU**
(Mlle Francesca Bonhomme) Le Gravier
☎ 40.79.97.11
Directions: RN 171, between Saint-Nazaire (40km) and Rennes (80km).
Menu: 45 Frs.
Restaurant: breakfast from 6.00. Lunch from 11.30 until 15.00. Dinner from 19.00 until 21.30. Closed Sat and Sun.
Specialities: home-cooking.
Other points: credit cards accepted, bar, traditional decor, pets allowed, car/lorry parking.
chateau at La Groulais; forêt du Gavres.

BOISNEY • Eure, 27800

🍽 **CHEZ BILL**
(M. Jean-Jacques Billy) Route Nationale 13
☎ 32.46.23.43
Directions: RN 13, the Evreux/Lisieux road.
Menu: 50 Frs.
Restaurant: breakfast from 5.00. Closed Sat, Sun.
Specialities: home-cooking.
Other points: credit cards accepted, bar, children's menu, traditional decor, pets allowed, car/lorry parking.
Le Bec-Hellouin; zoo at Cerza.

BOLBEC • Seine-Maritime, 76210

🏨 **AUBERGE NORMANDE**
(M. Gérard Baudribos) Route Nationale 15, Trouville-Alliquerville ☎ 35.31.15.21
Menu: 57 Frs.
Accommodation: 90 Frs.
Restaurant: breakfast from 5.45. Lunch from

11.30 until 14.30. Dinner from 19.00 until 21.30.
Closed Sat, Sun, and 2 weeks in Aug.
Specialities: home-cooking.
Hotel: 5 rooms. Facilities: private bathroom.
Other points: credit cards accepted, bar, modern
decor, terrace, pets allowed, car/lorry parking.

LA BONNEVILLE-SUR-ITON
Eure, 27190

▣ LE CAFE DES SPORTS
(M. Roland Fontaine) 45 rue Jean-Maréchal
☎ 32.37.10.16
Directions: RN 830, Conches via Vallée de l'Iton.
Menu: 50 Frs.
Restaurant: breakfast from 6.30. Closed last week
in Dec.
Specialities: home-cooking.
Hotel: 6 rooms. Facilities: shower, private bathroom,
television.
Other points: bar, children's menu, pets allowed,
car/lorry parking.
◀€ étang de la Noé.

BOSGUERARD-DE-MARCOUVILLE
Eure, 27520

▣ LA TETE D'OR
(M. Serge Vannier) Route Nationale 138
☎ 35.87.60.24
Directions: RN 138, between Bernay and Rouen.
Accommodation: 110 to 250 Frs.
Restaurant: breakfast from 6.30. Lunch from
12.00 until 14.30. Dinner from 19.00 until 21.30.
Closed Fri, and 2 weeks in Dec.
Specialities: boeuf bourguignon, regional menu,
home-cooking.
Hotel: ☆ 10 rooms. Facilities: television, telephone.
Other points: credit cards accepted, bar,
children's menu, à la carte menu, lounge area,
terrace, pets allowed, car/lorry parking.
◀€ Le Bec-Hellouin.

BOUGUENAIS
Loire-Atlantique, 44340

➤ A LA FERME
(M. Yvon Burlot) 65 rue de la Pierre
☎ 40.65.23.58
Directions: RN 751, in the Cheviré industrial zone
(Z.I.).
Menu: 50 to 55 Frs.
Restaurant: breakfast from 7.00. Closed Sat, Sun.
Specialities: home-cooking.
Other points: traditional decor, pets allowed, car/
lorry parking.
◀€ Loire valley; Nantes.

BOURG-BEAUDOUIN • Eure, 27380

➤ AU PECHE MIGNON
(M. Pascal Lenoir) 19 route de Paris
☎ 32.49.05.20

Directions: RN 14, 20km from Rouen, towards
Pontoise.
Menu: 53 to 60 Frs.
Restaurant: breakfast from 7.00. Lunch from
11.00 until 16.00. Dinner from 19.00 until 23.00.
Closed Sun.
Specialities: home-cooking.
Other points: credit cards accepted, bar,
children's menu, lounge area, car/lorry parking.
◀€ chateaux de Martinville and de Vascoeuil;
abbaye de Mortemer; Rouen: cathedral; Ry: musée
des automates (automata).

BOURGNEUF-EN-MAUGES
Maine-et-Loire, 49290

▣ RELAIS DE LA BOULE D'OR
(Anne-Marie and Thierry Véron) 6 rue Notre-
Dame ☎ 41.78.03.61
Directions: RD 762.
Menu: 50 to 160 Frs.
Accommodation: 100 to 150 Frs.
Restaurant: breakfast from 6.30. Lunch from
12.00 until 14.00. Dinner from 19.00 until 20.00.
Closed Wed afternoon (hotel closed weekends).
Specialities: home-cooking.
Hotel: 5 rooms. Facilities: shower, private
bathroom.
Other points: bar, traditional decor, car/lorry
parking.

BOURNEZEAU • Vendée, 85480

➤ LE RELAIS DU CHEVAL BLANC
(Mme Sylvia Demesy) 29 rue Jean-Grolleau
☎ 51.40.71.54
Directions: RD 949 and 948, La Roche-sur-Yon/
Fontenay-le-Comte road.
Languages spoken: Spanish.
Menu: 47 Frs.
Restaurant: dinner until 22.00.
Specialities: home-cooking.
Other points: credit cards accepted, bar,
children's menu, à la carte menu, traditional decor,
terrace, pets allowed, car/lorry parking.
◀€ La Roche-sur-Yon (20km); le Puy du Fou
(35km); beaches (20km).

BREAL-SOUS-MONTFORT
Ille-et-Vilaine, 35310

➤ LE RELAIS RENNES-LORIENT
(M. André Tardif) RN24/RD62 interchange,
Bellevue ☎ 99.60.04.20
Menu: 50 to 115 Frs.
Restaurant: breakfast from 7.00. Lunch from
11.30 until 15.30. Dinner from 18.00 until 23.30.
Brasserie-grill open from 7.00 to 00.30.
Specialities: choucroute, jambon du pays grillé,
poisson, bavette, regional menu, home-cooking.
Other points: credit cards accepted, bar,
children's menu, à la carte menu, modern decor,
terrace, pets allowed, car/lorry parking.
◀€ Forêt de Paimpont/Brocéliande; pays de
Monfort; Ecomusée; Saint-Cyr-Coëtquidan; moulin

de la Roche; chateaux of Artois, Chesnais and Haute Forêt; Mordelles.

BRECE • Mayenne, 53120

⊨ LE DOMINO
(Mme Janine Carlin) 1 rue du Lavoir
☎ 43.08.62.72
Directions: Mayenne.
Menu: 50 Frs.
Restaurant: breakfast from 8.00. Lunch from 12.00 until 14.00. Dinner from 19.00 until 21.00.
Specialities: home-cooking.
Other points: credit cards accepted, bar, traditional decor, pets allowed, car/lorry parking.

BRECOURT-DOUAINS • Eure, 27120

⊨ LE PACY-VERNON
(M. Alain Cote) Route Nationale 181
☎ 32.52.44.67
Directions: RN 181, between Pacy-sur-Eure and Vernon.
Menu: 55 Frs.
Restaurant: breakfast from 5.30. Closed Sat, Sun, and 1 week from 14th July.
Specialities: home-cooking.
Other points: bar, traditional decor, pets allowed, car/lorry parking.
⋘ *Claude Monet museum at Giverny; bird park at Bernay; chateau de Bizy.*

BRETEUIL-SUR-ITON • Eure, 27160

⊨ LE RELAIS DES MARES
(M. Danick Guiot) Le Chesne
☎ 32.29.85.09
Directions: RD 840, Rouen.
Menu: 52 Frs.
Restaurant: breakfast from 5.00. Lunch from 11.00 until 15.00. Dinner from 19.30 until 22.00. Closed Sat and Sun.
Specialities: regional menu.
Other points: bar, traditional decor, pets allowed, car/lorry parking.
⋘ *Center Parc.*

BRETTEVILLE-SUR-DIVES
Calvados, 14170

⊨ LE BRETTEVILLAIS
(Mme Patricia Dufailly) ☎ 31.20.13.31
Directions: RD 16, Crèvecoeur-en-Auge/Saint-Pierre-sur-Dives road.
Menu: 53 Frs.
Restaurant: breakfast from 6.30. Closed Sun.
Specialities: home-cooking.
Other points: bar, children's menu, terrace, pets allowed, car/lorry parking.
⋘ *basilica at Lisieux; chateau at Crèvecoeur-en-Auge; abbatiale (abbey-church) at Saint-Pierre-sur-Dives.*

BRIX • Manche, 50700

⊨ LE CLOS NORMAND
(Mme Josiane Germain) ☎ 33.41.94.35
Directions: RN 13.
Other points: bar.

BROGLIE • Eure, 27270

🍴 LES TOURISTES ET LES ROUTIERS
(M. Jean-Louis Bunel) 47 rue Augustin-Fresnel
☎ 32.44.60.38
Directions: RN 138, the Rouen/Alençon road.
Menu: 55 to 83 Frs.
Accommodation: 100 to 140 Frs.
Restaurant: breakfast from 11.00. Lunch from 12.00 until 14.00. Dinner from 19.30 until 22.00. Closed Wed, and end Sept/beginning of Oct.
Specialities: côte de veau normande, rognons au Porto, home-cooking.
Hotel: 5 rooms. Facilities: shower, private bathroom.
Other points: credit cards accepted, bar, children's menu, à la carte menu, modern decor, pets allowed, car/lorry parking.
⋘ *Charenton valley; jardin aquatique de Broglie; basilica at Lisieux.*

LE BUEIL • Eure, 27730

🍴 LA TRUITE
(M. Jean Curtelin) 3 Grande Rue – Route d'Anet ☎ 32.26.22.35
Directions: between Pacy-sur-Eure and Ivry-la-Bataille.
Menu: 58 to 130 Frs.
Accommodation: 120 to 150 Frs.
Restaurant: breakfast from 6.00. Lunch from 12.00 until 15.00. Dinner from 19.00 until 22.00. Closed in Aug.
Specialities: filet de canard aux morilles, home-cooking.
Hotel: 9 rooms. Facilities: private bathroom.
Other points: credit cards accepted, bar, children's menu, à la carte menu, lounge area, terrace, pets allowed, car/lorry parking.
⋘ *Eure valley; chateau d'Anet; Giverny; chateau de Bizy at Vernon.*

CABOURG • Calvados, 14490

🍴 L'AUBERGE DES VIVIERS
(M. Jean-Louis Delatte) avenue Charles-de-Gaulle ☎ 31.91.05.10 [Fax] 31.24.77.72
Directions: RD 514.
Languages spoken: English, Spanish and Italian.
Menu: 56 to 135 Frs 🍽
Accommodation: 150 to 350 Frs.
Restaurant: breakfast from 8.00. Closed 10th Jan to 10th Feb.
Specialities: crevettes grises sautées à la Trouvillaise, planche de poissons grillés, langoustines et gambas grillées, magret de canard aux deux pommes, regional menu, home-cooking.

Hotel: ✩ ✩ 7 rooms. Facilities: shower, private bathroom, television, telephone.
Other points: credit cards accepted, bar, children's menu, à la carte menu, lounge area, traditional decor, terrace, pets allowed, car parking.
◁ *Honfleur; pays d'Auge; landing beaches.*

⇶ LE COLOMBIER
(M. Gérard Baudel) Petiville ☎ 31.78.00.67
Directions: RD 513, between Caen and Cabourg.
Menu: 57 Frs.
Restaurant: breakfast from 6.30. Lunch from 12.00 until 14.30. Closed Sun, and from 20th Dec to 4th Jan.
Specialities: home-cooking.
Other points: credit cards accepted, bar, children's menu, modern decor.

CAEN-VENOIX • Calvados, 14350

🍽 LE VELODROME
(M. Daniel Levigoureux) 9 avenue Henry-Cheron ☎ 31.74.40.71
Directions: RN 175, on the road to Vire, towards Mont-Saint-Michel.
Menu: 55 Frs (coffee included).
Accommodation: 120 to 145 Frs (60 Frs for extra bed).
Restaurant: breakfast from 7.00. Lunch from 11.30 until 14.00. Dinner from 19.00 until 20.30. Closed Sat evening, Sun, and in Aug.
Specialities: home-cooking.
Hotel: 9 rooms. Facilities: shower.
Other points: bar, modern decor, pets allowed.
◁ *landing beaches; Caen.*

CAGNY • Calvados, 14630

🍽 HOTEL DE LA POSTE
(Mme Annick Robenard) 32 route de Paris
☎ 31.23.41.26
Directions: RN 13, between Caen and Lisieux.
Menu: 48 Frs.
Accommodation: 120 to 150 Frs.
Restaurant: breakfast from 6.00. Dinner from 19.00 until 20.30. Closed Sat afternoon and Sun.
Specialities: regional menu, home-cooking.
Hotel: 5 rooms. Facilities: shower.
Other points: credit cards accepted, bar, modern decor, pets allowed, car/lorry parking.

CALIGNY • Orne, 61100

⇶ RELAIS DU PONT DE VERE
(M. Henri Vivier) Le Pont de Vère
☎ 33.65.65.60
Directions: RD 962, Caen.
Menu: 54 and 57 Frs (coffee included).
Restaurant: breakfast from 7.00. Lunch from 11.30 until 14.30. Dinner from 19.00 until 21.30. Closed Sat evening, Sun, and 3 weeks in Aug.
Specialities: tripes, home-cooking.
Other points: credit cards accepted, bar,

children's menu, modern decor, car/lorry parking.
◁ *la Suisse normande; Bagnoles-de-l'Orne; le Mont de Cerisy-Belle-Etoile.*

CALLAC-DE-BRETAGNE
Côtes-d'Armor, 22160

⇶ LE KERGUIVIOU
(Mme Muriel Aubry) Zone Artisanale
☎ 96.45.92.08
Directions: RD 787, between Guingamp and Carhaix.
Menu: 49 to 120 Frs.
Restaurant: breakfast from 6.30.
Specialities: fruits de mer, regional menu, home-cooking.
Other points: credit cards accepted, bar, children's menu, à la carte menu, lounge area, modern decor, terrace, pets allowed, car/lorry parking.
◁ *Gorges du Corong.*

CARCAGNY • Calvados, 14740

⇶ AUX JOYEUX ROUTIERS
(M. Michel Pacary) Le Hameau Saint-Léger
☎ 31.80.22.01
Directions: D 82, between Caen and Bayeux.
Languages spoken: English and Italian.
Menu: 52 Frs.
Restaurant: breakfast from 7.30. Lunch from 11.45 until 14.00. Dinner from 19.00 until 21.00. Closed Fri evening, Sat and Sun.
Specialities: boudin noir, tripes, petit salé, pâtisseries maison, regional menu, home-cooking.
Other points: bar, children's menu, traditional decor, pets allowed, car/lorry parking.
◁ *Bayeux: tapestry (8km); Caen: peace memorial (20km); landing beaches (15km).*

CARENTAN • Manche, 50500

⇶ LE DERBY
(Mme Elisabeth Lepelletier) 12 rue de la 101ᵉᵐᵉ Airborne ☎ 33.42.04.77
Directions: RN 13, between Cherbourg and Caen.
Languages spoken: English.
Menu: 50 Frs (¼ bottle of wine included).
Restaurant: breakfast from 6.00. Lunch from 12.00 until 15.00. Closed Sat afternoon and Sun.
Specialities: tripes maison, home-cooking.
Other points: bar, children's menu, pets allowed, car parking.
◁ *landing beaches; listed church and town hall (mairie); marina.*

CARHAIX-PLOUGUER
Finistère, 29270

🍽 AU CHEVAL BRETON
(M. Louis Le Mignon) 2 boulevard de la République ☎ 98.93.01.38
Directions: RN 164.
Restaurant: closed Sat, Sun, and in Aug.

Specialities: home-cooking.
Hotel: 10 rooms.
Other points: bar, pets allowed, lorry parking.

CAST • Finistère, 29150

🛏 LE RELAIS SAINT-GILDAS
(Mme Marie Philippe) 11–13 rue du Kreisker
☎ 98.73.54.76
Directions: between Châteaulin and Douarnenez.
Languages spoken: English.
Menu: 48 to 195 Frs 🍷
Accommodation: 130 to 190 Frs.
Restaurant: breakfast from 7.00. Lunch from 12.00 until 14.30. Dinner from 19.00 until 21.30. Closed Sat, and in Nov.
Specialities: fruits de mer, couscous maison, regional menu, home-cooking.
Hotel: 12 rooms. Facilities: shower.
Other points: credit cards accepted, bar, children's menu, à la carte menu, lounge area, traditional decor, terrace, pets allowed, car/lorry parking.
◂ *chapels and calvaires (crosses); Locronan (ancient town, 7km); Douarnenez fishing port (18km); Pointe du Raz (40km); Châteaulin: fishing, canal (7km); beaches.*

CAUDAN • Morbihan, 56850

🍴 LE BOUTON D'OR
(M. Aimé Le Bail) Zone Artisanale Kergoussel
☎ 97.81.16.01
Directions: RD 81, exit at Lanester – parc des expositions.
Languages spoken: English.
Menu: 45 Frs.
Restaurant: breakfast from 7.00. Lunch from 11.30 until 14.30. Closed Sat, Sun, and 3 weeks in Aug.
Specialities: couscous de poisson, regional menu, home-cooking.
Other points: bar, lounge area, traditional decor, terrace, car/lorry parking.
◂ *marina; Lorient.*

CAUDEBEC-LES-ELBEUF
Seine-Maritime, 76320

🍴 LE TIVOLI BAR
(Mme Claudette Touchard) 43 rue Félix-Faure
☎ 35.77.19.54
Directions: Elbeuf, on the road to Pont-de-l'Arche.
Menu: 50 Frs (wine included).
Restaurant: breakfast from 6.00. Lunch 11.30 to 14.30. Dinner 18.30 to 20.00. Closed Sun.
Specialities: home-cooking.
Other points: bar, modern decor.

CAULNES • Côtes-d'Armor, 22350

🍴 LES ROUTIERS
(Mme Marie-Thérèse Gaudrel) 40 rue de la Gare ☎ 96.83.94.14

Restaurant: dinner until 22.00.
Other points: bar.

CAUVERVILLE-EN-ROUMOIS
Eure, 27350

🍴 LE MEDINE
(M. Jean-Pierre Ferrette) Route Nationale 175
☎ 32.57.01.55
Directions: RN 175, Médine/Pont-Audemer crossroads.
Menu: 49 to 52 Frs (wine included).
Restaurant: breakfast from 6.00. Lunch from 11.00 until 17.00. Closed Sat, Sun, and in Aug.
Specialities: choucroute, pizzas, couscous, home-cooking.
Other points: bar, children's menu, traditional decor, pets allowed, car/lorry parking.
◂ *Château Robert-le-Diable; maquis Barneville; pont de Tancarville.*

CEAUCE • Orne, 61330

🍴 LE RELAIS DE L'ETAPE
(Mme Michèle Gérault) 21 rue de Domfront
☎ 33.30.84.04
Directions: RD 962, the Laval/Caen road.
Menu: 50 Frs.
Restaurant: breakfast from 7.45. Lunch from 12.00 until 14.00. Closed Sun.
Specialities: fruits de mer (to order), home-cooking.
Other points: credit cards accepted, bar, children's menu, traditional decor, terrace, pets allowed, car/lorry parking.
◂ *Bagnoles-de-l'Orne; Saint-Fraimbault (village in bloom).*

CHAIGNES • Eure, 27120

🍴 AUBERGE MA NORMANDIE
(M. Yves Holliger) Route Nationale 13
☎ 32.36.95.52 Fax 32.36.82.13
Directions: RN 13, the Paris/Lisieux road.
Languages spoken: English.
Menu: 60 to 75 Frs.
Restaurant: breakfast from 4.30. Lunch from 11.00 until 14.00. Dinner until 23.00. Closed Sat evening and Sun (except bookings).
Specialities: regional menu, home-cooking.
Other points: credit cards accepted, bar, à la carte menu, lounge area, traditional decor, pets allowed, car/lorry parking.
◂ *Giverny; chateaux d'Anet and de Bizy at Vernon.*

CHAILLE-LES-MARAIS
Vendée, 85450

🍴 AU CHTI-MI
(M. Jean-Pierre Tison) 13 rue Principale, Le Sableau ☎ 51.56.70.87
Directions: RN 137, the Nantes/La Rochelle road.
Languages spoken: English.

Menu: 52 to 62 Frs.
Restaurant: breakfast from 5.00. Lunch from
11.30 until 14.30. Dinner from 19.00 until 21.00.
Closed Sat afternoon and Sun (out of season).
Specialities: home-cooking.
Other points: credit cards accepted, bar,
children's menu, traditional decor, pets allowed,
car/lorry parking.
◁ La Venise Verte ('Green Venice') marshlands.

CHALLANS · Vendée, 85300

◁ RELAIS DE LA NOUE
(Mme Monique Menez) place Victor-
Charbonnel ☎ 51.93.20.20
Directions: RN 148.
Menu: 44 to 51 Frs.
Restaurant: breakfast from 7.00. Lunch from
11.30 until 14.30. Dinner from 19.30 until 21.00.
Closed Sat, Sun, and 3 weeks in Aug.
Specialities: home-cooking.
Other points: bar, children's menu, traditional
decor, pets allowed, car/lorry parking.

CHAMBRETAUD · Vendée, 85500

◁ AUBERGE BEL'AIR
(Mme Jacqueline Martin) Route du Puy
du Fou ☎ 51.67.51.61
Directions: RN 160, between Les Herbiers (7km)
and Cholet (18km).
Menu: 55 to 180 Frs.
Restaurant: breakfast from 7.00. Lunch from
12.00 until 15.00. Dinner from 19.00 until 22.00.
Specialities: Provençal dishes, regional menu,
home-cooking.
Other points: credit cards accepted, bar,
children's menu, à la carte menu, traditional decor,
terrace, pets allowed, car/lorry parking.
◁ le Puy du Fou; le Mont des Allouettes.

CHAMPAGNE · Sarthe, 72470

◁ LE RELAIS DES FOUGERES
(M. Antoine Michelic) Route de Saint-Calais
☎ 43.89.50.96
Directions: RN 157, between Le Mans and Saint-
Calais.
Menu: 49 to 85 Frs.
Restaurant: breakfast from 6.00. Lunch from
11.30 until 14.00. Dinner from 18.30 until 20.00.
Closed Sat afternoon and Sun.
Specialities: home-cooking.
Other points: credit cards accepted, bar, à la carte
menu, traditional decor, terrace, pets allowed,
car/lorry parking.

CHAMPTOCE-SUR-LOIRE
Maine-et-Loire, 49170

◁ HOTEL LES RIVETTES
(Mme Agnès Chêne) Route de Montjean
☎ 41.39.91.75

Directions: the Angers/Nantes road.
Languages spoken: English and Spanish.
Menu: 44 Frs.
Accommodation: 100 to 145 Frs.
Restaurant: breakfast from 7.30. Lunch from
11.45 until 15.00. Dinner from 19.00 until 20.30.
Closed Sat and Sun.
Specialities: tripes à l'Angevine, canard sauce
muscade, pot au feu, boeuf bourguignon, home-
cooking.
Hotel: 4 rooms. Facilities: shower.
Other points: bar, children's menu, traditional
decor, terrace, pets allowed, car/lorry parking.
◁ Loire valley and chateaux; chateau of Gilles de
Rais.

CHANGE · Mayenne, 53810

◁ LE RELAIS DE NIAFLES
(Mme Marie-Françoise Carret) 25 rue
des Tisserants ☎ 43.53.76.15
Directions: A81, exit 3, towards Laval.
Menu: 50 Frs.
Restaurant: breakfast from 5.00. Closed Sat, Sun,
and in Aug.
Specialities: home-cooking.
Other points: credit cards accepted, bar,
children's menu, pets allowed, car/lorry parking.
◁ chateau at Laval; abbaye de Clermont; river
Mayenne.

CHANGE-LES-LAVAL
Mayenne, 53810

◁ CHEZ CHRISTIANE
(Mme Christiane Pouteau) Les Chênes Secs
☎ 43.56.16.06
Directions: RN 30; A81, 2km from exit 4 in the
direction of Fougères.
Menu: 50 Frs.
Accommodation: 100 to 150 Frs.
Restaurant: breakfast from 6.00. Lunch from
12.00 until 14.30. Dinner from 19.00 until 22.30.
Closed Sun evening and evenings of public
holidays.
Specialities: fruits de mer, home-cooking.
Hotel: 7 rooms. Facilities: shower, private
bathroom, telephone.
Other points: credit cards accepted, bar,
children's menu, traditional decor, terrace, pets
allowed, car/lorry parking.
◁ abbaye de Clermont; musée des Chouans
(militant Breton royalists of 1793).

LA CHAPELLE-CARO
Morbihan, 56460

◁ HOTEL DE LA GARE
(Mme Marie-Claire Boulvais) La Gare
☎ 97.74.93.47
Directions: RN 166, Vannes.
Restaurant: breakfast from 7.00. Lunch from
11.00 until 15.00. Dinner from 19.00 until 22.00.

Closed last week in Dec.
Specialities: home-cooking.
Other points: bar, children's menu.

LA CHAPELLE-CRAONNAISE
Mayenne, 53230

⌹ CAFE DES SPORTS
(M. Jean-François Littée) Le Bourg
☎ 43.98.81.80
Directions: RN 171, the Châteaubriant/Laval/
Nantes road.
Menu: 45 Frs.
Restaurant: breakfast from 7.30
Other points: bar, children's menu, modern
decor, terrace, pets allowed, car parking.
◁€ musée de Tatin; chateau at Craon.

LA CHAPELLE-DU-BOIS
Sarthe, 72400

⌹ LE RELAIS
(M. Jean-Claude Lhérault) 3 rue de la Poste
☎ 43.93.18.69 [Fax] 43.71.29.30
Directions: RD 59, between La Ferté-Bernard and
Mamers.
Menu: 50 to 150 Frs.
Accommodation: 120 to 150 Frs.
Restaurant: breakfast from 7.30. Lunch from
11.30 until 15.00. Dinner from 19.00 until 20.00.
Closed Sun afternoon.
Specialities: home-cooking
Hotel: 3 rooms. Facilities: shower, private
bathroom.
Other points: credit cards accepted, bar,
children's menu, à la carte menu, lounge area,
modern decor, pets allowed, car/lorry parking.
◁€ belvedere in the Forêt de Perseigne; pool.

LA CHAPELLE-SAINT-AUBERT
Ille-et-Vilaine, 35140

⌹ LE RELAIS PARIS-BREST
(M. Denis Potrel) La Salorgue
☎ 99.98.82.04
Directions: RN 12, between Fougères and Rennes.
Menu: 46 to 75 Frs.
Restaurant: breakfast from 7.00. Closed Sun (in
winter).
Specialities: paella, couscous, home-cooking.
Other points: credit cards accepted, bar,
children's menu, pets allowed, car/lorry parking.
◁€ chateau at Fougères.

CHASSILLE • Sarthe, 72540

⌹ LE PETIT ROBINSON
(M. Olivier Fournigault) Le Petit Robinson
☎ 43.88.92.01
Directions: RN 157, Le Mans/Laval road.
Menu: 52 Frs.
Accommodation: 90 to 110 Frs.

Restaurant: breakfast from 5.00. Lunch from
11.00 until 14.00. Dinner from 18.30 until 23.00.
Closed Sat, Sun, and in Aug.
Specialities: tête de veau sauce ravigote, tarte
tatin, home-cooking.
Hotel: 5 rooms. Facilities: shower, private
bathroom.
Other points: credit cards accepted, bar,
traditional decor, car/lorry parking.
◁€ grottes (caves) de Saulges (20km).

CHATEAU-GONTIER
Mayenne, 53200

⌹ L'ETOILE
(M. Norbert Corvé) 43 rue Garnier
☎ 43.07.20.80
Directions: RN 162, the Angers/Laval road.
Menu: 48 Frs (wine included).
Restaurant: breakfast from 8.00. Lunch from
11.45 until 14.30. Dinner from 19.00 until 21.00.
Closed Sun, public holidays, and in Aug.
Specialities: home-cooking.
Other points: credit cards accepted, bar,
children's menu, modern decor, pets allowed, car/
lorry parking.
◁€ chateaux; Mayenne river trips.

CHATEAU-L'HERMITAGE
Sarthe, 72510

⌹ LA BELLE CROIX
(M. Bruno David) La Belle Croix
☎ 43.46.35.73
Directions: RD 307, Le Lude.
Menu: 49 Frs.
Restaurant: breakfast from 7.00.
Specialities: home-cooking.
Other points: bar, children's menu, traditional
decor, pets allowed, car/lorry parking.
◁€ Le Lude; Le Mans.

CHATEAUBRIANT
Loire-Atlantique, 44110

⌹ SARL LE TUGNY
(M. Jean-Louis Boisgard) rue du Général-
Eisenhower, Zone Industrielle (Z.I.) Centre
Leclerc ☎ 40.28.29.58
Directions: RN 171, the Châteaubriant/Saint-
Nazaire road.
Restaurant: breakfast from 8.00. Closed Sun
evening.
Specialities: home-cooking.
Other points: credit cards accepted, bar,
children's menu, lounge area, modern decor,
terrace, pets allowed, car/lorry parking.
◁€ chateau; carrière des fusillés.

⌸ SARL PARIS-OCEAN
(Mme Maryse Gelée) 25 rue d'Ancenis
☎ 40.81.21.79
Directions: Route de Laval, behind the station.

Languages spoken: English and Spanish.
Menu: 35 to 125 Frs.
Accommodation: 85 to 100 Frs.
Restaurant: breakfast from 6.30. Lunch from 12.00 until 15.00. Dinner from 19.30 until 23.00. Closed Sun.
Specialities: rognons de veau flambés, truite 'Paris-Océan', regional menu.
Hotel: ☆ 7 rooms.
Other points: credit cards accepted, bar, children's menu, à la carte menu, modern decor, terrace, pets allowed, car/lorry parking.
◀ chateau.

CHATEAULIN • Finistère, 29150

🏨 **HOTEL DE LA GARE**
(M. Philippe Delicourt) 39 rue de la Gare ☎ 98.86.01.26
Directions: Brest/Quimper autoroute, Crozon/Douarnenez exit.
Menu: 45 to 180 Frs.
Accommodation: 100 to 190 Frs.
Restaurant: breakfast from 6.30. Lunch from 11.30 until 15.30. Dinner from 19.00 until 22.00. Closed Sat afternoon (in winter).
Specialities: poissons and fruits de mer (to order), regional menu, home-cooking.
Hotel: 12 rooms. Facilities: shower, private bathroom, television.
Other points: credit cards accepted, bar, children's menu, lounge area, modern decor, terrace, pets allowed, car/lorry parking.

CHATEAUTHEBAUD
Loire-Atlantique, 44690

🏨 **LA SAUCISSE VOLANTE**
(Mme Janine Roy) Le Butay ☎ 40.06.63.55
Directions: RN 137, the Nantes/La Rochelle road.
Menu: 55 to 70 Frs.
Accommodation: 100 Frs.
Restaurant: breakfast from 5.00. Lunch from 11.30 until 14.30. Dinner from 19.00 until 22.30. Closed Sat evening and Sun.
Specialities: home-cooking.
Hotel: 5 rooms.
Other points: credit cards accepted, bar, children's menu, traditional decor, terrace, pets allowed, car/lorry parking.
◀ Nantes; African safari (35km).

CHEMILLE • Maine-et-Loire, 49120

🍽 **SARL L'ESCALE**
(M. Bernard Routhiau) rue du Foirial ☎ 41.30.63.79
Directions: RN 160, the Cholet/Angers road.
Menu: 52 to 65 Frs.
Restaurant: breakfast from 6.00. Lunch from 11.45 until 14.30. Dinner from 19.30 until 22.30. Closed Sat and Sun.
Specialities: home-cooking.

Other points: credit cards accepted, bar, children's menu, lounge area, modern decor, pets allowed, car/lorry parking.
◀ zoo at Doué-la-Fontaine; Loire valley.

CHERBOURG • Manche, 50100

🏨 **LES ROUTIERS**
(Mme Viviane Couvrie) 8–10 rue de l'Onglet ☎ 33.53.08.15
Languages spoken: English and Spanish.
Menu: 55 to 85 Frs.
Accommodation: 80 to 190 Frs.
Restaurant: breakfast from 5.30. Lunch from 12.00 until 13.45. Dinner from 19.00 until 22.00.
Specialities: fruits de mer, poissons, regional menu, home-cooking.
Hotel: 20 rooms. Facilities: shower.
Other points: credit cards accepted, bar, children's menu, pets allowed.
◀ Le Cotentin.

🍽 **See also LA GLACERIE**

CHOLET • Maine-et-Loire, 49300

🏨 **HOTEL-RESTAURANT LES ROUTIERS**
(M. Michel Dubillot) 13 place de la République ☎ 41.62.11.09
Menu: 49 Frs.
Accommodation: 80 to 100 Frs.
Restaurant: breakfast from 6.45. Lunch from 12.00 until 14.00. Dinner from 19.30 until 21.00. Closed Sun, and from 13th July to 16th Aug.
Specialities: home-cooking.
Hotel: 19 rooms.
Other points: bar, modern decor, car parking.

🍽 **LE RELAIS DES PRAIRIES**
(M. Claude Albert) 3 boulevard du Pont-de-Pierre, Parc des Prairies ☎ 41.58.09.39
Directions: RN 160, opposite the aerodrome.
Languages spoken: German and English.
Menu: 45 to 155 Frs.
Restaurant: breakfast from 6.30. Lunch from 12.00 until 14.00. Dinner from 19.30 until 21.00. Closed Sat (except bookings), and from 25th Dec to 2nd Jan.
Specialities: onglet (beef) à l'échalotte, côte de boeuf, tête de veau, home-cooking.
Other points: credit cards accepted, bar, children's menu, à la carte menu, terrace, pets allowed, car/lorry parking.
◀ lac de Ribou (7km); lac du Verdon (7km); le Puy du Fou (25km).

CLERMONT-CREANS • Sarthe, 72200

🍽 **LE CREANS**
(Mme Marie-France Rouault) 19 rue Nationale ☎ 43.45.20.13
Directions: RN 23, Le Mans/Angers/Saumur road.
Menu: 52 Frs.

Restaurant: breakfast from 5.00. Closed Sun.
Specialities: home-cooking.
Other points: credit cards accepted, bar, children's menu, modern decor, terrace, pets allowed, car/lorry parking.
⫷ zoo at La Flèche (3km); Mareil village; chateaux at Créans and Le Lude.

COEMONT-VOUVRAY
Sarthe, 72500

🍴 **LE BON COIN**
(Mme Jouanneau) ☎ 43.44.04.17
Directions: RN 158.
Restaurant: breakfast from 7.00. Lunch from 11.30 until 15.00. Closed Sun, and in Aug.
Specialities: home-cooking.
Other points: bar, children's menu, traditional decor, terrace, pets allowed, car/lorry parking.
⫷ Loir valley.

COLOMBELLES • Calvados, 14460

🏠 **LES VIKINGS**
(M. Jean-Claude Musson) 3 route de Cabourg
☎ 31.72.18.83
Directions: RD 513.
Menu: 51 to 90 Frs.
Accommodation: 95 to 130 Frs.
Restaurant: breakfast from 6.30. Dinner from 19.00 until 21.30. Closed Sun, and in Aug.
Specialities: home-cooking.
Hotel: 32 rooms. Facilities: shower, private bathroom.
Other points: credit cards accepted, bar.

COLPO • Morbihan, 56390

🏠 **AUX DELICES DE L'OCEAN**
(M. Jean-Claude Le Guillan) 1 avenue de la Princesse ☎ 97.66.82.21
Directions: the Vannes/Saint-Brieuc road.
Languages spoken: English and Spanish.
Menu: 44 to 150 Frs.
Accommodation: 90 to 250 Frs.
Restaurant: breakfast from 8.00. Lunch from 12.00 until 14.30. Dinner from 19.30 until 21.00. Closed Sun evening, and in July.
Specialities: fruits de mer, home-cooking.
Hotel: 10 rooms. Facilities: shower, private bathroom.
Other points: credit cards accepted, bar, children's menu, à la carte menu, traditional decor, pets allowed, car/lorry parking.
⫷ Forêt de Lanvaux; Gulf of Morbihan.

CONCOURSON-SUR-LAYON
Maine-et-Loire, 49700

🍴 **AUBERGE DU HAUT LAYON**
(M. Bernard Battais) 7 Route Nationale
☎ 41.59.27.60

Directions: RD 160, the Tours/Nantes road.
Languages spoken: English.
Menu: 54 to 75 Frs.
Restaurant: breakfast from 6.30. Lunch from 12.00 until 14.30. Dinner from 19.00 until 21.00. Closed Sun evening.
Specialities: home-cooking.
Other points: credit cards accepted, bar, children's menu, à la carte menu, traditional decor, pets allowed, car/lorry parking.
⫷ zoo (3km); troglodyte village (10km); rose garden.

CONDE-SUR-HUISNE • Orne, 61110

🍴 **L'EUROPEENNE**
(SARL L'Européenne) La Fourche
☎ 37.52.53.18
Directions: RN 23, between Chartres and Le Mans.
Languages spoken: English, Spanish and Italian.
Menu: 50 Frs.
Restaurant: breakfast from 12.00. Lunch from 12.00 until 14.00. Dinner from 18.00 until 22.00. Closed Sun (out of season), and from 20th Dec to 6th Jan.
Specialities: Spanish dishes, home-cooking.
Other points: credit cards accepted, traditional decor, terrace, pets allowed, car/lorry parking.

CONDE-SUR-NOIREAU
Calvados, 14110

🏠 **HOTEL LES PROMENADES**
(M. Michel Jomat) 2 rue Motte-de-Lutre, corner of rue Saint-Martin ☎ 31.69.03.36
Directions: RD 562, the Caen/Flers/Laval road.
Menu: 47 to 115 Frs.
Accommodation: 120 to 150 Frs.
Restaurant: breakfast from 6.30. Lunch from 12.00 until 13.30. Dinner from 19.00 until 20.30. Closed Sun, public holidays, and in Aug.
Specialities: rognons de veau au calvados, home-cooking.
Hotel: 6 rooms. Facilities: shower.
Other points: credit cards accepted, bar, children's menu, à la carte menu, terrace, pets allowed, car/lorry parking.
⫷ château de Pontecoulant; la Suisse normande.

CONNERRE • Sarthe, 72160

🏠 **LA BICHE DOREE**
(M. Dominique Hérault) Route Nationale 23, La Belle Inutile ☎ 43.76.70.45
Directions: RN 23, Le Mans/Paris road.
Languages spoken: some English.
Menu: 52 Frs.
Accommodation: 90 to 120 Frs.
Restaurant: breakfast from 5.00. Lunch from 12.00 until 15.00. Dinner from 19.00 until 22.00. Closed Sat, Sun and public holidays.
Specialities: couscous (Thurs), home-cooking.
Hotel: 10 rooms. Facilities: shower.

Other points: credit cards accepted, bar, children's menu, traditional decor, pets allowed, car/lorry parking.
◀ *automobile museum; Le Mans 24-hour-race circuit; animal reserve at Pescheray (7km); étang (pool) de Tuffé.*

CORBON • Calvados, 14340

⊨ LE RELAIS SAINT-JEAN
(M. Jean-Hugues Neveu) Route Nationale 13, Carrefour Saint-Jean ☎ 31.63.05.33
Directions: RN 13, between Lisieux and Caen.
Menu: 50 Frs.
Restaurant: breakfast from 6.00.
Specialities: home-cooking.
Other points: bar, children's menu, traditional decor, pets allowed, car/lorry parking.
◀ *basilica at Lisieux (20km).*

CORNE • Maine-et-Loire, 49250

⊨ LE RELAIS DE LA CROIX BLANCHE
(M. Jean-Noël Pignard) Route Nationale 147
☎ 41.45.01.82 [Fax] 41.54.87.19
Directions: RN 147, the Tours/Nantes road, via Saumur.
Menu: 53 Frs.
Restaurant: breakfast from 6.30. Lunch from 12.00 until 13.30. Dinner from 19.30 until 21.00. Closed Sat evening, Sun, 1 week in Aug, 1 week at Christmas.
Specialities: home-cooking.
Other points: credit cards accepted, bar, traditional decor, terrace, pets allowed, car/lorry parking.
◀ *chateau de Montgeoffroy at Maze; chateau at Pignerolle; musée de la communication at Saint-Barth.*

CORNEVILLE-SUR-RISLE
Eure, 27500

⊨ RELAIS DU BOULANGARD
(M. Francis Egret) ☎ 32.57.01.27
Directions: RN 180, between Pont-Audemer and Rouen or Brionne.
Menu: 49 to 55 Frs.
Restaurant: breakfast from 7.30. Closed Sat and Sun.
Specialities: home-cooking.
Other points: bar, children's menu, pets allowed, car/lorry parking.
◀ *les cloches (clocks) de Corneville; pont de Tancarville.*

CORPS-NUDS • Ille-et-Vilaine, 35150

⊨ LES ROUTIERS
(Mme Solange Piel) 7 place de l'Eglise
☎ 99.44.00.25
Directions: the Rennes/Châteaubriant road.

Menu: 46 Frs.
Restaurant: breakfast from 7.00. Lunch from 12.00 until 13.30. Closed Sat, Sun, and in Aug.
Specialities: home-cooking.
Other points: credit cards accepted, bar, car/lorry parking.

COUDEVILLE • Manche, 50290

⊨ LA POMME D'ARGENT
(M. Abdel Ben Mustapha) La Plesse
☎ 33.90.03.33
Directions: between Coutances and Granville.
Languages spoken: English.
Menu: 55 to 95 Frs – plat du jour from 40 Frs.
Restaurant: breakfast from 8.00. Lunch from 12.00 until 14.30. Dinner from 19.00 until 21.30.
Specialities: couscous, tagine, home-cooking.
Other points: credit cards accepted, bar, children's menu, à la carte menu, traditional decor, terrace, pets allowed, car/lorry parking.
◀ *Granville: haute ville, port, Aquarium du Roc; Coutances: cathedral; Abbaye de la Lucerne; Mont-Saint-Michel; zoo at Champrepus.*

COUTANCES • Manche, 50202

🛏 LE RELAIS DU VIADUC
(M. Jean-Marc Harau) 25 avenue de Verdun
☎ 33.45.02.68
Directions: RN 171, between Granville and Saint-Lô.
Languages spoken: English.
Menu: 54 to 160 Frs ☜
Accommodation: 150 to 200 Frs.
Restaurant: breakfast from 8.00. Lunch from 12.00 until 14.00. Dinner from 19.00 until 21.00. Closed Sat (in winter), and 3 weeks in March.
Specialities: langouste gratinée, tripes maison, gigot d'agneau, calmars à l'américaine, filet de merlu sauce moutarde, confit de manchons de canard, émincé de dinde normande, regional menu.
Hotel: 7 rooms. Facilities: shower, private bathroom, television, telephone.
Other points: credit cards accepted, bar, children's menu, à la carte menu, traditional decor, pets allowed, car/lorry parking.
◀ *cathedral at Coutances; château du Grato.*

🛏 SARL CLOSERIE DES LILAS
(M. Gilles Letourneur) 1 rue des Abattoirs
☎ 33.45.53.23
Menu: 50 Frs.
Accommodation: 118 to 130 Frs.
Restaurant: breakfast from 6.30. Closed Sat afternoon and Sun.
Specialities: regional menu, home-cooking.
Hotel: 16 rooms.
Other points: credit cards accepted, bar, children's menu, traditional decor, terrace, pets allowed, car/lorry parking.
◀ *Mont-Saint-Michel (45km); musée de la 2ème guerre mondiale (2nd World War).*

COUVILLE • Manche, 50690

🛏️ LE BOURG NEUF
(M. Yves Anquetil) Le Bourg Neuf
☎ 33.52.01.76 [Fax] 33.52.01.76
Directions: between Cherbourg and Valognes.
Menu: 48 to 55 Frs.
Restaurant: breakfast from 6.00. Lunch from 12.00 until 16.00. Dinner from 19.00 until 22.00. Closed Tues afternoon, and in Aug.
Specialities: home-cooking.
Other points: credit cards accepted, bar, children's menu, à la carte menu, traditional decor.

CROISILLES • Calvados, 14220

🛏️ RELAIS DE LA FORGE
(Mme Monique Gibon) Le Bourg à Cambro
☎ 31.79.71.80
Directions: RD 962, the Caen/Flers road.
Menu: 50 Frs.
Restaurant: breakfast from 6.00. Lunch from 11.00 until 15.00. Closed Sun (out of season).
Specialities: riz cauchois, home-cooking.
Other points: credit cards accepted, bar, children's menu, modern decor, car/lorry parking.
◀ pont du Hom; aquatic centre at Thury-Harcourt.

CROISY-SUR-ANDELLE
Seine-Maritime, 76780

🛏️ LE RELAIS DU COMMERCE
(Mme Colette Belière) Route Nationale 31
☎ 35.23.61.82
Directions: RN 31, the Rouen/Beauvais road.
Menu: 55 to 80 Frs.
Restaurant: breakfast from 5.00. Lunch from 11.00 until 15.00. Dinner from 19.00 until 22.30. Closed Sun (out of season), and Christmas holidays.
Specialities: entrecôte, tête de veau, potée à l'ancienne, tarte aux pommes, home-cooking.
Other points: credit cards accepted, bar, children's menu, modern decor, terrace, pets allowed, car/lorry parking.
◀ chateau at Vascoeuil; Forêt de Lyons.

LA CROIX-BEAUCHENE
Maine-et-Loire, 49490

🛏️ RELAIS DE LA CROIX-BEAUCHENE
(M. Jean-Louis Metzger) Route Départementale 767 ☎ 41.82.14.63
Directions: RD 767, between Le Lude and Noyant.
Menu: 48 Frs.
Restaurant: breakfast from 6.00.
Specialities: home-cooking.
Other points: bar, children's menu, traditional decor, terrace, pets allowed, car/lorry parking.
◀ chateaux at Saumur and Le Lude; Loire wine-cellars.

CROIX-MARE • Seine-Maritime, 76190

🛏️ LE BON ACCUEIL
(M. Christian Lemaitre) Route Nationale 15
☎ 35.91.25.86
Directions: RN 15, between Rouen and Yvetot.
Menu: 55 Frs.
Restaurant: breakfast from 4.00. Closed Sat, Sun, 2 weeks in May and 2 weeks in winter.
Specialities: home-cooking.
Other points: credit cards accepted, bar, children's menu, traditional decor, terrace, pets allowed, car/lorry parking.
◀ Bénédictine liqueur production at Fécamp (35km); parc régional de Brotonne; Rouen: cathedral.

CUON • Maine-et-Loire, 49150

🛏️ LA POMM'DE PIN
(Mme Yvette Pécot) Route Nationale 938, Le Bourg ☎ 41.82.75.74
Directions: RN 938.
Menu: 48 to 118 Frs.
Restaurant: lunch from 11.30 until 14.30. Dinner from 19.30 until 22.00. Closed Mon afternoon, and last 3 weeks in Aug.
Specialities: home-cooking.
Hotel: 4 rooms. Facilities: shower, private bathroom.
Other points: credit cards accepted, bar, children's menu, à la carte menu, lounge area, traditional decor, terrace, pets allowed, car/lorry parking.

DENEE • Maine-et-Loire, 49190

🛏️ LE PENALTY
(M. Alain Saulgrain) place Muller
☎ 41.78.72.03
Languages spoken: German.
Restaurant: dinner until 22.00. Closed Sun afternoon, and 1 week at Christmas.
Other points: bar.

DERVAL • Loire-Atlantique, 44590

🛏️ LE RELAIS DE DERVAL
(M. Jean-Joseph Bonnet) Carrefour Industriel des Estuaires ☎ 40.07.77.77
[Fax] 40.07.77.78
Directions: RN 171, the Nantes/Rennes road.
Menu: 49 to 138 Frs.
Restaurant: breakfast from 5.00. Lunch from 11.30 until 14.00. Dinner from 19.00 until 22.30.
Specialities: beurre blanc, home-cooking.
Other points: credit cards accepted, bar, children's menu, à la carte menu, lounge area, modern decor, terrace, pets allowed, car/lorry parking.

DIEPPE • Seine-Maritime, 76200

🛏️ CAFE DE L'AVENIR
(M. Benoît Pan) 10 cours de Dakar, Port de Commerce ☎ 35.84.18.10

Directions: RN 15.
Menu: 51 Frs.
Restaurant: breakfast from 4.30. Lunch from 11.00 until 14.00. Closed Sun, and in Aug.
Specialities: home-cooking.
Other points: bar, traditional decor, pets allowed, car/lorry parking.
Dieppe.

DINAN • Côtes-d'Armor, 22100

LA MARMITE
(M. Gérard Bouillet) 91 rue de Brest
☎ 96.39.04.42
Directions: RN 176, Saint-Brieuc.
Languages spoken: English.
Menu: 48 to 80 Frs
Accommodation: 120 to 190 Frs.
Restaurant: breakfast from 7.00. Lunch from 12.00 until 14.00. Dinner from 19.30 until 21.00. Closed Sat evening, Sun (out of season), and 3 weeks in July.
Specialities: blancs de seiches à l'armoricaine, regional menu, home-cooking.
Hotel: 5 rooms.
Other points: credit cards accepted, bar, children's menu, modern decor, terrace, pets allowed, car parking.
Mont-Saint-Michel; Cap-Fréhel; Dinan (medieval city); Saint-Malo.

For the very best in food and drink
while travelling in Britain,
why not become a member of
Club Bon Viveur,
Les Routiers' Ultimate Dining Scheme?
See back of book for further details.

DINARD • Ille-et-Vilaine, 35800

L'EPICURIEN
(M. Marc Arnoult) 28 rue de la Corbinais
☎ 99.46.10.84
Menu: 45 to 80 Frs
Accommodation: 120 to 170 Frs.
Restaurant: breakfast from 10.00. Lunch from 12.00 until 14.30. Dinner from 19.30 until 22.00. Closed Sat and Sun evening (out of season).
Specialities: home-cooking.
Hotel: 9 rooms. Facilities: shower.
Other points: credit cards accepted, bar, children's menu, traditional decor, pets allowed, car/lorry parking.
Dinard; Saint-Malo; Dinan.

DISSAY-SOUS-COURCILLON
Sarthe, 72500

RELAIS MAINE TOURAINE
(Mme Colette Petit) Route Nationale 138
☎ 43.44.09.08
Directions: RN 138.

Restaurant: dinner until 22.00.
Specialities: fruits de mer, terrines and pâtisserie maison, regional menu.
Other points: bar, traditional decor.
Loire chateaux.

DOL-DE-BRETAGNE
Ille-et-Vilaine, 35120

LE RELAIS DE BELLE LANDE
(M. Jean-Yves Beubry) 23 bis rue de Rennes
☎ 99.48.06.14
Directions: RN 12, between Combourg and Rennes.
Languages spoken: English.
Menu: 50 to 95 Frs
Restaurant: breakfast from 6.30. Lunch from 11.45 until 14.00. Dinner from 16.00 until 21.00. Closed Sun evening.
Specialities: mussel dishes: moules marinières, bouchots de la baie, moules de bouchots; paella, couscous, home-cooking.
Other points: bar, children's menu, à la carte menu, traditional decor, terrace.
Mont-Saint-Michel; Saint-Malo; Dinan; Combourg.

DOLO • Côtes-d'Armor, 22270

LES VALLEES
(Mme Ginette Petureau) Les Vallées
☎ 96.31.64.62
Directions: RN 12, between Rennes and Saint-Brieuc.
Menu: 50 Frs.
Restaurant: breakfast from 6.00. Lunch from 11.30 until 14.30. Dinner from 19.00 until 24.00. Closed Sat afternoon and Sun.
Specialities: home-cooking.
Other points: bar, traditional decor, pets allowed, car/lorry parking.
Abbaye de Boquen; lakes at Jugon; chateau at La Hunaudaye.

DOMFRONT • Orne, 61700

LA CROIX DES LANDES
(M. Claude Leveau) Route de la Ferté-Macé
☎ 33.38.51.35
Directions: RD 908, La Ferté-Macé.
Languages spoken: English and Spanish.
Menu: 53 Frs.
Accommodation: 90 to 165 Frs.
Restaurant: breakfast from 5.30. Lunch from 11.00 until 14.30. Dinner from 19.00 until 22.00. Closed Sat evening and Sun.
Specialities: home-cooking.
Hotel: 8 rooms. Facilities: shower, telephone.
Other points: credit cards accepted, bar, children's menu, traditional decor, pets allowed, car/lorry parking.
la Suisse normande (60km); Mont-Saint-Michel (80km); Saint-Fraimbault (20km); forêt d'Andaine (5km); leisure centre at La Ferté-Macé (20km).

DOUE-LA-FONTAINE
Maine-et-Loire, 49700

🏠 **CHEZ PAUL**
(SARL Type-Bassant) Zone Industrielle
(Z.I.), Route de Montreuil ☎ 41.59.03.33
[Fax] 41.59.00.34
Directions: Angers/Poitiers or Cholet/Saumur road.
Languages spoken: English.
Menu: 57 Frs.
Accommodation: 160 to 220 Frs.
Restaurant: breakfast from 4.30. Lunch from
11.00 until 15.00. Dinner from 18.30 until 22.00.
Closed Sun (out of season), and 1st 3 weeks in Aug.
Specialities: home-cooking.
Hotel: ✪ ✪ 20 rooms. Facilities: shower, private
bathroom, television, telephone.
Other points: credit cards accepted, bar,
children's menu, à la carte menu, lounge area,
modern decor, terrace, car/lorry parking.
◀ *troglodyte dwellings; 16thC sculpted cavern;
rose gardens; musée des vieux métiers (ancient
crafts); Anjou vineyards; zoo; Saumur; Cadre Noir,
musée des blindés (armoured tanks).*

DOZULE • Calvados, 14430

🍽 **CHEZ MICHEL**
(M. Michel Martin) Route de Rouen,
Putot-en-Auge ☎ 31.79.20.29
Menu: 60 Frs.
Restaurant: breakfast from 5.00. Lunch from
11.30 until 15.00. Dinner from 19.00 until 22.00.
Closed Sat, Sun, and in Aug.
Specialities: regional menu, home-cooking.
Other points: credit cards accepted, bar, children's
menu, modern decor, terrace, car/lorry parking.
◀ *basilica at Lisieux; Croix Delande.*

DUCEY • Manche, 50220

🏠 **LE MONTGOMERY**
(Mme Marie-Thérèse Brosset) 44 rue du
Genie ☎ 33.48.51.36
Directions: RN 176, between Saint-Hilaire-du-
Harcouët and Avranches.
Menu: 55 Frs.
Accommodation: 90 to 190 Frs.
Restaurant: breakfast from 7.00. Lunch from
12.00 until 15.00. Dinner from 19.00 until 21.00.
Closed Sun afternoon (from Jan to end March).
Specialities: home-cooking.
Hotel: 7 rooms.
Other points: bar, children's menu, à la carte
menu, terrace, pets allowed, car parking.
◀ *Mont-Saint-Michel; dam at Vezins; Avranches
museum; zoo at Champrepus; Saint-Symphorien;
falls at Mortain.*

DURANVILLE • Eure, 27230

🍽 **LES ARCADES**
(Mme Geneviève Boga) Route Nationale 13
☎ 32.46.83.01

Directions: RN 13, between Evreux and Lisieux.
Menu: 50 to 60 Frs.
Restaurant: breakfast from 5.30. Lunch from
11.30 until 15.30. Dinner from 19.00 until 24.00.
Closed from Sat 15.00 to Sun 22.00.
Specialities: home-cooking.
Other points: credit cards accepted, bar, children's
menu, modern decor, pets allowed, car/lorry parking.
◀ *Lisieux.*

ECARDENVILLE-LA-CAMPAGNE
Eure, 27170

🏠 **AUBERGE DU RELAIS**
(M. Jean-Claude Lothon) Route Nationale 13
☎ 32.35.05.32
Directions: RN 13, the Paris/Lisieux/Caen road.
Menu: 55 to 95 Frs.
Accommodation: 90 to 110 Frs.
Restaurant: breakfast from 5.00. Lunch from
11.00 until 14.00. Dinner from 18.30 until 22.00.
Closed Sat evening and Sun (out of season), Sat
evening (in season) and Christmas Day.
Specialities: coquilles Saint-Jacques, home-cooking.
Hotel: 10 rooms. Facilities: shower.
Other points: credit cards accepted, bar,
traditional decor, pets allowed, car/lorry parking.
◀ *chateau du champs de bataille; chateau
d'Harcourt; abbaye du Bec-Hellouin.*

ECORPAIN • Sarthe, 72120

🍽 **LE RELAIS DE LA JAGOTIERE**
(Mme Mireille Gaborit) La Jagotière
☎ 43.35.12.00
Directions: RN 157, between Bouloire and Saint-
Calais.
Menu: 50 Frs.
Restaurant: breakfast from 6.00. Lunch from
12.00 until 14.00. Dinner from 19.00 until 21.00.
Specialities: home-cooking.
Other points: bar, traditional decor, terrace, pets
allowed, car/lorry parking.

ELVEN • Morbihan, 56250

🏠 **LE RELAIS DE L'ARGOUET**
(M. André Le Douarin) 36 avenue de l'Argoët
☎ 97.53.32.98
Directions: RN 166.
Languages spoken: English.
Menu: 52 to 150 Frs 🍽
Accommodation: 125 to 220 Frs.
Restaurant: breakfast from 6.30. Lunch from
12.00 until 14.00. Dinner from 19.30 until 22.00.
Closed Sat (out of season), and 2 weeks in Nov.
Specialities: fruits de mer, poissons, regional
menu.
Hotel: ✪ 12 rooms. Facilities: shower, private
bathroom, telephone.
Other points: credit cards accepted, bar,
children's menu, à la carte menu, modern decor,
terrace, pets allowed, car/lorry parking.
◀ *tours de l'Argoët (highest dungeon in France);
grottes (caves) de Callac; Gulf of Morbihan.*

EMONDEVILLE • Manche, 50310

➡ LE COUP DE FREIN
(M. Albert Jean) Route Nationale 13
☎ 33.41.22.74
Directions: RN 13, Cherbourg.
Menu: 54 Frs (coffee included).
Restaurant: breakfast from 6.30. Lunch from
11.30 until 14.30. Dinner from 19.30 until 22.30.
Closed Sat, Sun, and 3 weeks in Aug.
Specialities: home-cooking.
Other points: credit cards accepted, bar, modern
decor, car/lorry parking.
◁ *Sainte-Mère l'Eglise; landing beaches; Cherbourg;
Saint-Vaast-le-Hague; Sarre valley; Ile de Tatihou.*

EPERRAIS • Orne, 61400

➡ LA PETITE VALLEE
(Mme Monique Germond) La Petite Vallée
☎ 33.83.91.34
Directions: RD 938, between Mortagne and
Bellême.
Languages spoken: English.
Menu: 48 Frs.
Restaurant: breakfast from 8.00. Closed Sun
(except July and Aug), last 2 weeks in June, mid-
Dec to mid-Jan.
Specialities: couscous (Saturdays, to order),
regional menu, home-cooking.
Other points: credit cards accepted, children's
menu, à la carte menu, traditional decor, terrace,
pets allowed, car/lorry parking.
◁ *Forêt de Bellême: Gallo-Roman fountain; filet
(lace) de La Perrière; chateaux.*

EQUEURDREVILLE • Manche, 50120

🍴 RESTAURANT DE LA HAGUE
(M. Claude Lamy) 120 rue de la Paix
☎ 33.93.88.46
Directions: RD 901.
Languages spoken: English.
Menu: 42 Frs.
Accommodation: 100 to 200 Frs.
Restaurant: breakfast from 6.30. Lunch from
12.00 until 14.30. Dinner from 19.30 until 20.45.
Closed Sat, Sun, and last 2 weeks in Aug.
Specialities: boeuf bourguignon, home-cooking.
Hotel: 20 rooms. Facilities: shower.
Other points: credit cards accepted, bar, pets
allowed, car parking.

ERBRAY • Loire-Atlantique, 44110

🍴 LE SAINT-HUBERT
(M. Bernard Bellanger) 1 place du Calvaire,
La Touche ☎ 40.55.08.37
Directions: RD 163, between Châteaubriant and
Angers.
Menu: 48 Frs (wine included) to 120 Frs.
Accommodation: 150 to 250 Frs.
Restaurant: breakfast from 6.00. Lunch from

11.00 until 14.30. Dinner from 19.00 until 22.30.
Closed Fri evening.
Specialities: fruits de mer and poisson au beurre
blanc (to order), regional menu, home-cooking.
Hotel: ☆ ☆ 8 rooms. Facilities: shower, private
bathroom, telephone.
Other points: credit cards accepted, bar, children's
menu, à la carte menu, lounge area, modern decor,
terrace, pets allowed, car/lorry parking.
◁ *chateau at La Motte-Glain and La Chapelle-Glain;
chateau at Châteaubriant; carrière des fusillés.*

LES ESSARTS • Vendée, 85140

➡ LE RELAIS DU PINIER
(Mme Jacqueline Dupont) Route Nationale
160 ☎ 51.62.81.69
Directions: RN 160, La Roche-sur-Yon.
Menu: 48 to 60 Frs.
Restaurant: breakfast from 7.00. Lunch from
12.00 until 14.30. Dinner until 21.00. Closed Sat
and Sun (out of season).
Specialities: home-cooking.
Other points: bar, children's menu, à la carte menu.

EXMES • Orne, 61310

➡ HOTEL DU COMMERCE
(Mme Fernande Simon) Grande Rue
☎ 33.39.93.04
Directions: CD 14, the Rouen/Granville road.
Menu: 53 to 100 Frs.
Restaurant: breakfast from 7.00. Lunch from
11.00 until 14.00.
Specialities: Norman dishes, home-cooking.
Hotel: 4 rooms. Facilities: shower.
Other points: bar, children's menu, traditional
decor.
◁ *Haras du Pin (deer-breeding).*

EZY-SUR-EURE • Eure, 27530

🍴 HOTEL TERMINUS – Chez Annie
(Mme Annie Veisen) 16 boulevard Ulysse-
Lavertue ☎ 37.64.73.24
Menu: 54 to 100 Frs (drink included).
Accommodation: 120 to 200 Frs.
Restaurant: breakfast from 6.30. Lunch from
12.00 until 14.00. Dinner from 19.00 until 20.30.
Closed Sat, and in Aug.
Specialities: boeuf bourguignon, cassoulet, home-
cooking.
Hotel: 11 rooms. Facilities: shower.
Other points: bar, traditional decor, pets allowed,
car/lorry parking.
◁ *chateau d'Anet; musée du Peigne.*

FALAISE • Calvados, 14700

➡ L'ESCALE
(M. Claude Russeau) 16 rue du Pavillon
☎ 31.90.12.67

Directions: between Argentan and Caen.
Menu: 50 to 70 Frs.
Restaurant: breakfast from 6.00. Closed Sun, and in Aug.
Specialities: regional menu, home-cooking.
Other points: bar, children's menu, à la carte menu, modern decor, car/lorry parking.
◀€ *chateau at Falaise; la Suisse normande.*

🍴 LE RELAIS DES ROUTIERS
(M. Christian Durand) 33 avenue d'Hastings
☎ 31.90.04.67
Directions: RN 158, Caen exit, towards Le Mans.
Menu: 48 Frs.
Accommodation: 100 to 140 Frs.
Restaurant: breakfast from 6.30. Lunch from 12.00 until 13.30. Dinner from 17.30 until 20.30. Closed Sun, public holidays, and in July.
Specialities: home-cooking.
Hotel: 5 rooms.
Other points: credit cards accepted, bar, children's menu, traditional decor, pets allowed, car/lorry parking.
◀€ *Falaise; chateaux (including that of William the Conqueror); churches.*

FALLERON • Vendée, 85670

🍴 CHEZ MARLENE
(Mme Marlène Poterlot) 54 rue Nationale
☎ 51.35.50.22
Menu: 47 Frs.
Restaurant: lunch from 11.00 until 14.00. Dinner until 20.00. Closed Sun (out of season).
Specialities: home-cooking.
Other points: credit cards accepted, bar, traditional decor, pets allowed, car/lorry parking.
◀€ *Ile de Noirmoutier and Ile d'Yeu (35km).*

LE FAOUET • Morbihan, 56320

🍴 LE RELAIS DES HALLES
(M. Armel Le Puil) 19 rue du Soleil
☎ 97.23.07.66
Directions: RN 782, between Lorient and Roscoff.
Languages spoken: English and Breton.
Menu: 48 Frs.
Accommodation: 80 to 130 Frs.
Restaurant: breakfast from 7.00. Lunch from 12.00 until 14.00. Dinner from 19.30 until 21.00. Closed Sun, and in Sept.
Specialities: home-cooking.
Hotel: 8 rooms. Facilities: shower, private bathroom, telephone.
Other points: bar, children's menu, pets allowed, car/lorry parking.
◀€ *15thC market and chapels.*

🍴 LE TY GRAVIC
(M. Alain Halter) Route de Gourin
☎ 97.23.07.04
Directions: RD 769, the Lorient/Roscoff road.
Languages spoken: English, Italian, Finnish, Swedish.

Menu: 46 Frs.
Restaurant: breakfast from 7.00. Closed Sun.
Specialities: home-cooking.
Other points: credit cards accepted, bar, children's menu, traditional decor, pets allowed, car/lorry parking.
◀€ *15thC markets; chapels of Sainte-Barbe and Saint-Fiacre.*

FERRIERES-EN-BRAY
Seine-Maritime, 76220

🍴 HOTEL DU CHEMIN DE FER
(M. Jean-Serge Feret) 26 avenue de la Gare
☎ 35.90.01.61
Directions: RN 31, Rouen or Beauvais.
Menu: 47 Frs.
Accommodation: 100 to 150 Frs.
Restaurant: breakfast from 7.00. Lunch from 12.00 until 15.00. Dinner from 19.30 until 22.30. Closed Sat, Sun, public holidays, and 3 weeks in May.
Specialities: home-cooking.
Hotel: 10 rooms. Facilities: shower.
Other points: bar, modern decor, pets allowed, car/lorry parking.
◀€ *Saint-Germer-de-Fly; Gerberoy.*

LA FERTE-BERNARD • Sarthe, 72400

🍴 L'ARCHE DE LA FERTE-BERNARD
(M. Gaston Bisson) A11, services at La Ferté-Bernard (accessible in both directions)
☎ 43.93.41.02 [Fax] 43.93.42.58
Restaurant: open 24 hours.
Other points: credit cards and foreign currency accepted.

FLERS • Orne, 61100

🍴 HOTEL DES TOURISTES
(M. Maurice Dupont) 80 rue de Paris
☎ 33.65.25.57
Menu: 45 to 65 Frs.
Accommodation: 80 to 120 Frs.
Restaurant: breakfast from 7.00. Lunch from 12.00 until 16.00. Dinner from 19.00 until 22.00. Closed Sun, and in Aug.
Specialities: tripes, home-cooking.
Hotel: 12 rooms.
Other points: credit cards accepted, bar, children's menu, à la carte menu, traditional decor.
◀€ *chateau at Flers; Bagnoles-de-l'Orne; la Suisse normande.*

FLEURY-SUR-ORNE
Calvados, 14123

🍴 LA POMME D'OR
(Mme Emilienne François) 20 route d'Harcourt ☎ 31.82.36.87
Directions: RD 562, Caen-Flers, towards Laval.
Menu: 48 to 50 Frs.

Restaurant: breakfast from 7.00. Lunch from 12.00 until 15.00. Closed Sun, public holidays, and in Aug.
Specialities: home-cooking.
Other points: credit cards accepted, bar, modern decor, pets allowed, car/lorry parking.

LA FONTAINE-SAINT-MARTIN
Sarthe, 72330

≡€ **LE CHENE VERT**
(Mme Marie-Louise Flameygh) Le Chêne Vert
☎ 43.87.80.84
Directions: RN 23, Nantes.
Menu: 55 to 65 Frs.
Restaurant: breakfast from 7.00. Lunch from 11.00 until 15.00. Dinner from 19.00 until 22.00. Closed Sat, Sun, and in Aug.
Specialities: andouillette grillée, regional menu, home-cooking.
Other points: credit cards accepted, bar, children's menu, à la carte menu, traditional decor, pets allowed, lorry parking.
◀€ chateau at Le Lude; zoo at La Flèche; museum and Le Mans 24-hour-race circuit.

FOUCARMONT
Seine-Maritime, 76340

≡€ **CAFE DU MARCHE – Chez Régine**
(Mme Régine Recoquillon) 35 rue Douce
☎ 35.94.83.14
Directions: RN 28, the Rouen/Abbeville road.
Menu: 47 Frs.
Restaurant: breakfast from 7.00. Lunch from 12.00 until 15.00. Dinner from 19.00 until 20.30. Closed Sat, Sun, and 3 weeks in Aug.
Specialities: home-cooking.
Other points: bar, children's menu, modern decor, pets allowed, car/lorry parking.
◀€ Côte d'Opale; bay of the Somme (35km).

FOUGERES • Ille-et-Vilaine, 35300

🏨 **AUX AMIS DE LA ROUTE**
(M. Michel Bastien) 6 boulevard Saint-Germain ☎ 99.99.07.62
Directions: RN 12, the Rennes/Saint-Malo road.
Languages spoken: English and German.
Menu: 60 Frs (drink included).
Accommodation: 140 to 150 Frs.
Restaurant: breakfast from 7.00. Lunch from 12.00 until 14.00. Dinner from 19.30 until 21.00. Closed Sun, and 1 week at Christmas.
Specialities: couscous, choucroute, coq au vin, regional menu, home-cooking.
Hotel: ☆ 12 rooms. Facilities: shower, private bathroom.
Other points: credit cards accepted, bar, children's menu, lounge area, terrace, car/lorry parking.
◀€ Saint-Malo; Mont-Saint-Michel; Fougères: park, forest and chateau.

GAEL • Ille-et-Vilaine, 35290

🏨 **LES ROUTIERS**
(Mme Annick Rebillard) place des Tilleuls
☎ 99.07.72.39
Directions: the Dinan/Lorient road.
Menu: 46 Frs.
Accommodation: 83 to 126 Frs.
Restaurant: breakfast from 7.00. Lunch from 11.30 until 14.30. Dinner from 19.00 until 21.00. Closed Fri after 15.00.
Specialities: tête de veau à l'ancienne (Wed), couscous and choucroute (Thurs), regional menu, home-cooking.
Hotel: 5 rooms. Facilities: shower, private bathroom, telephone.
Other points: credit cards accepted, bar, children's menu, lounge area, traditional decor, pets allowed, car/lorry parking.
◀€ forêt de Paimpont.

GIBERVILLE • Calvados, 14730

≡€ **LE STOP**
(Mme Irène Barthélémy) 47 rue de la Liberté
☎ 31.84.52.63
Directions: RN 175, Cabourg.
Languages spoken: English.
Menu: 48 Frs.
Restaurant: breakfast from 8.00. Closed Sun.
Specialities: tripes à la mode de Caen, couscous, choucroute, home-cooking.
Other points: credit cards accepted, bar, children's menu, traditional decor, pets allowed, car/lorry parking.
◀€ landing beaches.

GISORS • Eure, 27140

≡€ **BAR DE L'AVENUE**
(M. Roussel) Route de Dieppe
☎ 32.27.19.45
Directions: RN 15, between Dieppe and Gournay.
Languages spoken: English.
Menu: 60 Frs.
Accommodation: 120 to 160 Frs.
Restaurant: breakfast from 7.00. Closed Sun, and in Aug.
Specialities: home-cooking.
Other points: credit cards accepted, bar, children's menu, terrace, car/lorry parking.
◀€ Gisors: early medieval chateau; les Andelys; Claude Monet's house at Giverny.

LA GLACERIE • Manche, 50470

≡€ **LE RELAIS DE LA GLACERIE**
(M. Paul Roupsard) Route Nationale 13
☎ 33.44.13.54
Directions: RN 13, Cherbourg.
Menu: 50 Frs.
Restaurant: breakfast from 6.00. Lunch from 12.00 until 14.00. Dinner from 19.30 until 21.00. Closed Sat, Sun, and from 20th July to 8th Aug.

Specialities: home-cooking.
Other points: credit cards accepted, bar, children's menu, à la carte menu, lounge area, modern decor, terrace, pets allowed, car/lorry parking.
◁€ *landing beaches; Cherbourg; cap La Hague.*

GODERVILLE
Seine-Maritime, 76110

≠ **RELAIS DE SAINT-SAUVEUR**
(M. Philippe Guérin) Saint-Sauveur-d'Emalleville ☎ 35.27.21.56
Directions: CD 925, between Le Havre and Fécamp.
Menu: 50 to 65 Frs.
Restaurant: breakfast from 6.30. Lunch from 11.30 until 13.30. Dinner from 19.00 until 20.30. Closed Sat, and in Aug.
Specialities: home-cooking.
Other points: bar, pets allowed, car/lorry parking.
◁€ *Etretat cliffs; Fécamp.*

LA GOUESNIERE
Ille-et-Vilaine, 35350

🛏 **LE RELAIS ROUTIERS**
(Mme Marie-Thé Bourgalais) 2 rue d'Halet ☎ 99.58.80.57
Directions: Dol-de-Bretagne/Dinard/Saint-Malo.
Menu: 48 to 50 Frs.
Accommodation: 140 to 190 Frs.
Restaurant: breakfast from 7.00. Lunch from 11.30 until 14.00. Dinner from 19.00 until 21.30. Closed Sun.
Specialities: home-cooking.
Hotel: 13 rooms. Facilities: shower.
Other points: bar, traditional decor, car/lorry parking.
◁€ *Saint-Malo; Cancale; Mont-Saint-Michel; Dinan; Dinard.*

LE GOULET • Eure, 27950

🛏 **LE TERMINUS**
(M. Claude Hard) 30 route de Rouen ☎ 32.52.50.07
Directions: RN 15, the Vernon/Rouen road.
Menu: 55 Frs.
Accommodation: 120 to 150 Frs.
Restaurant: breakfast from 6.00. Lunch from 11.30 until 15.00. Dinner from 19.30 until 20.30. Closed Sat, Sun, 3 weeks in Aug and 1 week from Christmas Day.
Specialities: home-cooking.
Hotel: 18 rooms. Facilities: shower, private bathroom.
Other points: credit cards accepted, bar, children's menu, traditional decor, pets allowed, car/lorry parking.
◁€ *Claude Monet's house and garden at Giverny; Château-Gaillard; les Andelys.*

GOUSTRANVILLE • Calvados, 14430

≠ **AU BON ACCUEIL**
(M. Roger Chornet) ☎ 31.79.21.90
Directions: RN 175, Dozulé exit, towards Caen.
Languages spoken: English and Spanish.
Menu: 50 to 98 Frs.
Restaurant: breakfast from 6.30. Closed Sat afternoon, Sun (out of season), and 1 week at Christmas.
Specialities: home-cooking.
Other points: credit cards accepted, bar, traditional decor, terrace, pets allowed, car/lorry parking.
◁€ *landing beaches; Beuvron-en-Auge; Croix Glorieuses at Dozulé; Norman village at Dives-sur-Mer.*

GRAINVILLE • Eure, 27380

≠ **LE RELAIS DE GRAINVILLE**
(Mme Edwige Legatt) 40 route Nationale ☎ 32.48.06.28
Directions: RN 14, the Paris/Rouen/Le Havre road.
Menu: 50 Frs.
Restaurant: breakfast from 5.00. Lunch from 11.30 until 14.30. Closed Sat afternoon, Sun, and 1 week at Christmas.
Specialities: home-cooking.
Other points: credit cards accepted, bar, traditional decor, pets allowed, car/lorry parking.
◁€ *Château-Gaillard (15km); Rouen (25km); les Andelys.*

GRAVIGNY • Eure, 27930

🛏 **HOTEL DES SPORTS**
(M. Tarik Senouci) 109 avenue Aristide-Briand ☎ 32.33.16.19
Languages spoken: English, Spanish and Arabic.
Menu: 49 Frs.
Accommodation: 80 Frs.
Restaurant: breakfast from 7.00. Lunch from 12.00 until 14.30. Dinner from 19.30 until 21.30. Closed Sun.
Specialities: Oriental dishes, couscous.
Hotel: 7 rooms. Facilities: shower, private bathroom.
Other points: bar, children's menu, modern decor, terrace, pets allowed, car/lorry parking.

GREMONVILLE
Seine-Maritime, 76970

≠ **LA CHAUMIERE**
(M. Christian Le Masurier) place de l'Eglise ☎ 35.56.45.65
Directions: RN 15, between Rouen and Saint-Valery-en-Caux.
Languages spoken: English.
Menu: 50 to 120 Frs.
Restaurant: breakfast from 8.00. Lunch from 11.00. Dinner until 21.00. Closed Tues afternoon and Wed afternoon.

Specialities: lapin au cidre, langue à la sauce piquante, rognons en sauce, home-cooking.
Other points: bar, children's menu, traditional decor, terrace, pets allowed, car/lorry parking.
◀ *Yvetot: round church (5km); Saint-Valery: beach (25km); le chêne (oak-tree) d'Allouville-Bellefosse.*

LE GUE-DE-LA-CHAINE
Orne, 61130

≡ LE GUE ROUTIER
(Mme Marylène Disztl) 3 route de Mamers
☎ 33.73.02.66
Directions: between Mamers and Bellême.
Menu: 55 to 58 Frs.
Restaurant: breakfast from 6.30.
Specialities: home-cooking.
Other points: bar, children's menu, modern decor, pets allowed, car/lorry parking.
◀ *Forêt de Bellême: golf course.*

GUENIN • Morbihan, 56150

≡ LE RELAIS DE BON VALLON
(M. Joël Le Hazif) Zone Industrielle (Z.I.) de Bon Vallon ☎ 97.39.10.40
Directions: between Lorient and Rennes.
Languages spoken: English.
Menu: 54 to 195 Frs.
Restaurant: breakfast from 5.00. Lunch from 11.30 until 14.30. Dinner from 19.00 until 23.00.
Specialities: regional menu.
Other points: credit cards accepted, bar, children's menu, modern decor, terrace, pets allowed, car/lorry parking.

LA GUERCHE-DE-BRETAGNE
Ille-et-Vilaine, 35130

🛏 LE RELAIS DU PONT D'ANJOU
(M. André Moussu) 11 faubourg d'Anjou
☎ 99.96.23.10
Directions: RN 176, the Rennes/Angers road.
Menu: 44 to 125 Frs 〜
Restaurant: breakfast from 6.45. Lunch from 11.00 until 15.00. Dinner from 19.00 until 22.00. Closed Sun evening.
Specialities: fruits de mer, couscous, paella, regional menu, home-cooking.
Hotel: ☆ 12 rooms.
Other points: bar, children's menu, à la carte menu.

GUILBERVILLE • Manche, 50160

≡ RESTAURANT LE POTEAU
(M. Frédy Menant) Le Poteau
☎ 33.56.73.10
Directions: RN 175.
Languages spoken: German and English.
Restaurant: dinner until 24.00. Closed Sat and Sun, and Christmas holidays.
Other points: bar, car/lorry parking.

GURUNHUEL • Côtes-d'Armor, 22390

≡ CHEZ GILBERTE
(M. Yves Georgelin) Kérambellec
☎ 96.21.81.00
Directions: RN 787.
Restaurant: breakfast from 7.30. Lunch from 12.00 until 14.00. Closed Sat lunch, Sun lunch, and in July.
Specialities: home-cooking.
Other points: credit cards accepted, bar, modern decor.

LE HAVRE • Seine-Maritime, 76600

≡ AU TELEPHONE
(M. Jean-Claude Bouillon) 173 boulevard Amiral-Mouchez ☎ 35.53.24.76
Directions: in the l'Eure district.
Languages spoken: English.
Menu: 54 Frs (wine included).
Restaurant: breakfast from 7.00. Closed Sat, Sun, and in July.
Specialities: home-cooking.
Other points: credit cards accepted, bar, traditional decor, pets allowed, car/lorry parking.

≡ LE P'TIT COMPTOIR
(M. Bernard Rondel) 31 rue du Général-Faidherbe ☎ 35.42.78.72
Directions: in the Saint-François district.
Menu: 60 to 84 Frs.
Restaurant: breakfast from 8.00. Lunch from 12.00 until 14.15. Dinner from 19.15 until 21.30. Closed Sun, public holidays, and from 20th Dec to 15th Jan.
Specialities: choucroute aux 3 poissons, home-cooking.
Other points: bar, children's menu, à la carte menu.

≡ LE RELAIS
(M. Didier Eudes) 128 boulevard de Graville
☎ 34.74.06.32
Directions: take autoroute towards Le Havre, left at 1st lights.
Languages spoken: English.
Menu: 55 to 120 Frs.
Restaurant: breakfast from 6.30. Lunch from 11.45 until 14.30. Dinner from 18.45 until 22.30. Closed Sun.
Specialities: saumon, canard gras, regional menu.
Other points: credit cards accepted, bar, children's menu, à la carte menu, lounge area, traditional decor, pets allowed, car/lorry parking.
◀ *Le Havre port.*

≡ LE RELAIS DES ROUTIERS
(Mme Marie-Pierre Priser) 57 rue Marceau
☎ 35.24.54.48
Directions: RN 15.
Menu: 50 Frs.
Restaurant: breakfast from 7.00. Lunch from 11.30 until 16.00. Dinner from 19.00 until 23.00. Closed Fri evening, and from 23rd Dec to 7th Jan.
Specialities: fruits de mer, home-cooking.

Other points: bar, children's menu, traditional decor, car/lorry parking.
◀ *Le Havre port; seaside.*

🏛 LE WELCOME
(Mme Marie-Pierre Priser) 55–57 quai de Southampton ☎ 35.43.17.84
Directions: RN 13 bis.
Accommodation: 90 to 180 Frs.
Restaurant: lunch from 12.00 until 15.00. Dinner from 19.00.
Specialities: huîtres, fruits de mer, regional menu.
Hotel: 8 rooms. Facilities: shower, private bathroom, telephone.
Other points: credit cards accepted, bar, à la carte menu, modern decor, car/lorry parking.
◀ *Le Havre port; seaside.*

LA HAYE-DU-PUITS • Manche, 50250

🍽 RESTAURANT DU CHATEAU
(M. André Maleuvre) 16 rue du Château ☎ 33.46.03.42
Directions: between Coutances and Cherbourg.
Menu: 50 Frs.
Restaurant: breakfast from 7.00. Lunch from 11.30 until 14.30. Dinner from 19.00 until 22.00. Closed Sat evening, Sun and 2 weeks in Aug.
Specialities: home-cooking.
Other points: credit cards accepted, bar, children's menu, modern decor, terrace, pets allowed, car/lorry parking.

LA HAYE-PESNEL • Manche, 50320

🍽 CHEZ ARMELLE
(Mme Armelle Jacquette) rue de la Libération ☎ 33.61.50.83
Languages spoken: English.
Menu: 54 to 90 Frs 🖐
Restaurant: breakfast from 8.00. Dinner until 22.00. Closed Sat, Sun, and in Dec.
Specialities: coquilles Saint-Jacques, escalope de veau à la crème, regional menu, home-cooking.
Other points: credit cards accepted, bar, children's menu, à la carte menu, traditional decor, terrace, pets allowed, car/lorry parking.
◀ *Abbaye de la Lucerne; zoo at Champrepus.*

L'HERBERGEMENT • Vendée, 85260

🍽 LES ROUTIERS
(M. Michel Bretin) 17 rue Georges-Clemenceau ☎ 51.42.80.71
Directions: RD 763, between Nantes and La Roche-sur-Yon.
Menu: 49 Frs.
Restaurant: breakfast from 7.30. Lunch from 11.45 until 14.30. Closed Sun, and in Aug.
Specialities: home-cooking.
Other points: credit cards accepted, bar, children's menu, lorry parking.
◀ *château de La Chabotterie; memorial of 1793 Vendée uprising.*

LES HERBIERS • Vendée, 85500

🏛 L'OREE DES BOIS VERTS
(M. René Joulin) Route des Sables ☎ 51.91.00.18 [Fax] 51.64.97.70
Directions: RN 160, between Angers and La Roche-sur-Yon.
Menu: 46 Frs.
Accommodation: 115 to 220 Frs.
Restaurant: breakfast from 7.00. Lunch from 12.00 until 14.00. Dinner from 19.30 until 21.30. Closed Sun, All Saints' Day (1st Nov) and first 2 weeks in May.
Specialities: home-cooking.
Hotel: ☆ 11 rooms. Facilities: shower, private bathroom, television, telephone.
Other points: credit cards accepted, bar, lounge area, traditional decor, terrace, pets allowed, car/lorry parking.
◀ *le Puy du Fou; l'étang de la Tricherie; Abbaye de la Grainetière.*

HERIC • Loire-Atlantique, 44810

🍽 LE BIEF
(M. Didier Créteau) Bout de Bois, Route Nationale 137 ☎ 40.57.60.54
Directions: RN 137, the Nantes/Rennes road.
Languages spoken: English and Italian.
Menu: 56 Frs (drink and coffee included).
Restaurant: breakfast from 6.00. Lunch from 12.00 until 14.00. Dinner from 19.00 until 21.30. Closed Sun, and last 2 weeks in Aug.
Specialities: home-cooking.
Other points: credit cards accepted, bar, children's menu, lounge area, traditional decor, pets allowed, car/lorry parking.
◀ *Nantes; Brest; pool.*

L'HERMITAGE • Ille-et-Vilaine, 35590

🍽 LE VILLAGE
(M. Christian Laillé) 21 rue de Rennes ☎ 99.64.03.31
Directions: RD 125, between Montfort and Rennes.
Menu: 52 Frs.
Restaurant: breakfast from 7.00. Lunch from 11.45 until 14.00. Closed Sun, and in Aug.
Specialities: couscous, tripes, regional menu, home-cooking.
Other points: credit cards accepted, bar, children's menu, traditional decor, car/lorry parking.

LE HINGLE-LES-GRANITS
Côtes-d'Armor, 22100

🍽 LES ROUTIERS
(M. Rémy Pessel) rue de la Gare ☎ 96.83.58.45
Directions: RN 166.
Languages spoken: English.
Menu: 44 Frs.

Restaurant: breakfast from 6.30. Lunch from 11.30 until 14.00. Closed Sun.
Specialities: home-cooking.
Other points: bar, traditional decor.
◆€ *Dinan; the northern coast.*

L'HOPITAL-CAMFROUT
Finistère, 29460

≈€ **LES ROUTIERS**
   (M. Bernard Hamery) 68 rue Emile-Salaun
   ☎ 98.20.01.21
Directions: RN 170, Brest/Quimper autoroute, Daoulas exit.
Menu: 47 to 150 Frs.
Restaurant: breakfast from 8.00. Lunch from 12.00 until 14.00. Closed Mon afternoon.
Specialities: fruits de mer, regional menu, home-cooking.
Other points: credit cards accepted, bar, à la carte menu, traditional decor, pets allowed, car/lorry parking.
◆€ *abbey at Daoulas (2km); parc régional d'Armorique (10km); beaches and presqu'île de Crozon (peninsula) (30km).*

HOTTOT-LES-BAGUES
Calvados, 14250

≈€ **LE RELAIS DE LA MANCHE**
   (M. Roland Jeanne) Route de Caumont
   ☎ 31.80.81.72
Menu: 50 Frs.
Restaurant: breakfast from 6.00. Lunch from 11.30 until 14.00. Closed Sat, in June and Sept.
Specialities: home-cooking.
Other points: credit cards accepted, bar, traditional decor, terrace.

HYENVILLE • Manche, 50660

≈€ **LE RELAIS DE LA SIENNE**
   (M. Guy Defontaine) Le Pont ☎ 33.45.82.22
Directions: RD 73, between Coutances and Granville.
Menu: 55 Frs.
Restaurant: breakfast from 5.00. Closed Sun (out of season).
Specialities: home-cooking.
Other points: credit cards accepted, bar, children's menu, à la carte menu, terrace, pets allowed, car/lorry parking.
◆€ *bell foundry at Villedieu-les-Poêles; Granville; zoo at Champrepus.*

JALLAIS • Maine-et-Loire, 49510

🏠 **LE VERT GALANT – La Croix Verte**
   (M. Pierre Gaillard) place de la Mairie
   ☎ 41.64.20.22 [Fax] 41.64.15.17
Directions: 15km from Cholet.
Languages spoken: English.
Menu: 55 Frs (wine included) to 200 Frs 🥄

Accommodation: 180 to 250 Frs.
Restaurant: breakfast from 7.00. Lunch from 12.00 until 14.00. Dinner from 17.00 until 22.00.
Specialities: salade rillauds d'Anjou chauds, pavé boeuf au Chinon, brochet au beurre blanc, civet de porcelet ivre de vin, regional menu.
Hotel: ☆ ☆ 20 rooms. Facilities: shower.
Other points: credit cards accepted, bar, children's menu, à la carte menu, lounge area, traditional decor, terrace, pets allowed, car/lorry parking.
◆€ *le Puy du Fou; Muscadet and Anjou wine regions; handkerchief museum at Cholet; musée de la guerre (war) de Vendée; the banks of the Loire; zoo at Doué-la-Fontaine and amphitheatre.*

JANZE • Ille-et-Vilaine, 35150

🏠 **HOTEL RESTAURANT BAR METAYER**
   (M. Michel Métayer) 5 rue Jean-Marie-Lacire
   ☎ 99.47.05.10
Accommodation: 140 to 160 Frs.
Restaurant: breakfast from 7.00. Lunch from 12.00 until 14.00. Dinner from 19.00 until 20.30.
Specialities: home-cooking.
Hotel: 7 rooms. Facilities: shower, private bathroom, television, telephone.
Other points: bar, modern decor, car/lorry parking.

JARZE • Maine-et-Loire, 49140

≈€ **LE MOULINET**
   (M. Daniel Domas) Route Nationale 766
   ☎ 41.95.47.52
Directions: RN 766, Angers/Tours via Seiches/Loir-Baugé.
Menu: 50 Frs.
Restaurant: lunch from 11.30 until 14.30. Dinner from 18.30 until 21.30. Closed Sun evening.
Specialities: fruits de mer.
Other points: bar, pets allowed, car/lorry parking.

JOSSELIN • Morbihan, 56120

≈€ **LA ROCHETTE – Les Routiers**
   (Mme Annie Le Corre) 128 rue Glatinier
   ☎ 97.22.27.29
Languages spoken: English.
Menu: 43 to 70 Frs.
Restaurant: breakfast from 8.00. Lunch from 12.00 until 14.00. Dinner from 19.00 until 21.30. Closed Sat and Sun (out of season).
Specialities: home-cooking.
Other points: credit cards accepted, bar, children's menu, traditional decor, terrace, pets allowed, lorry parking.
◆€ *chateau at Josselin; musée des poupées (dolls).*

JOUE-DU-BOIS • Orne, 61320

≈€ **LE RELAIS DU MANOIR**
   (Mme Violaine Vulovic) Le Bourg
   ☎ 33.37.48.54
Directions: RN 12, Alençon.

Languages spoken: English and Serbo-Croat.
Menu: 50 to 80 Frs.
Restaurant: breakfast from 7.00. Lunch from
11.30 until 14.30. Dinner from 19.00 until 21.30.
Closed Sun.
Specialities: regional menu.
Other points: credit cards accepted, bar, children's
menu, traditional decor, terrace, pets allowed, car/
lorry parking.
◁€ manoir (manor) of Joué-du-Bois; Forges;
chateau at Carrouges; casino at Bagnoles-de-l'Orne.

LA JUMELLIERE
Maine-et-Loire, 49120

🍴 **LA BOULE D'OR**
(Mme Janine Sécher) 2 rue du Val-de-Loire
☎ 41.64.33.23
Directions: RD 961, the Cholet/Angers road – exit
at Chemillé, then 5km on the left.
Menu: 52 to 170 Frs.
Accommodation: 100 to 170 Frs.
Restaurant: breakfast from 7.15. Lunch from
11.45 until 14.00. Dinner from 19.00 until 20.15.
Closed Sun.
Specialities: saumon au beurre blanc, home-
cooking.
Hotel: 6 rooms. Facilities: shower, private bathroom,
television.
Other points: credit cards accepted, bar, children's
menu, traditional decor, pets allowed, car/lorry
parking.
◁€ musée des vieux métiers (ancient crafts) (9km);
musée de la vigne (vineyards) (8km); jardin des
plantes médicinales (6km); Angevin coastline (13km);
chateau at Serrant (17km).

JURQUES • Calvados, 14260

🍴 **AU BON ACCUEIL**
(M. Christian Lesage) Route de Vire
☎ 31.77.81.17
Directions: RD 577 – exit at bypass (déviation) if
coming from Caen, at Vire interchange.
Menu: 50 Frs (wine included).
Restaurant: lunch from 11.45 until 14.00. Dinner
from 19.00 until 21.30. Closed Sun (from 15.00).
Specialities: regional menu, home-cooking.
Other points: credit cards accepted, bar, children's
menu, à la carte menu, car/lorry parking.
◁€ zoo at Jurques (3km); Bungy (10km); gorges of
the Vire.

KERFAVEN • Finistère, 29230

🍴 **RESTAURANT DE KERFAVEN**
(M. Vincent Pronost) ☎ 98.20.41.26
Directions: RD 712, between Landivisiau and
Landernau.
Languages spoken: English.
Menu: 50 Frs (coffee included).
Restaurant: breakfast from 6.00. Closed Sat, Sun,
2 weeks in July and 1 week in Aug.

Specialities: kigar, farz, home-cooking.
Other points: credit cards accepted, bar, children's
menu, lounge area, terrace, pets allowed, car/lorry
parking.
◁€ Brest (35km); Roscoff (25km); Breton calvaires
(crosses).

KERGONAN-LANGUIDIC
Morbihan, 56440

🍴 **LE RELAIS KERGONAN**
(M. André Le Garrec) 9 rue du Commerce
☎ 97.85.90.69
Directions: RN 24, the Rennes/Lorient road.
Menu: 45 Frs.
Restaurant: breakfast from 8.00. Lunch from 11.30
until 14.00. Closed Sat, and last 2 weeks in Dec.
Specialities: home-cooking.
Other points: credit cards accepted, bar,
children's menu, modern decor, terrace, pets
allowed, car/lorry parking.
◁€ Ecomusée at 16thC Breton village of Poul-
Fetan; Blavet valley.

KERHOSTIN • Morbihan, 56510

🍴 **LA CHALOUPE**
(Mlle Christiane Bouvrande) 10 rue Hoche
☎ 97.30.91.54
Directions: Quiberon.
Menu: 50 to 75 Frs.
Accommodation: 150 Frs.
Restaurant: breakfast from 8.00. Lunch from
12.00 until 14.00. Closed Mon afternoon and Sun.
Specialities: regional menu, home-cooking.
Hotel: 6 rooms. Facilities: shower.
Other points: credit cards accepted, bar, lounge
area, traditional decor, terrace, pets allowed, car
parking.

LAMBALLE
Côtes-d'Armor, 22400

🍴 **LA TOUR D'ARGENT**
(M. Claude Mounier) 2 rue du Docteur-
Lavergne ☎ 96.31.01.37 [Fax] 96.31.37.59
Directions: RD 12, between Rennes and Saint-Brieuc.
Languages spoken: English.
Menu: 78 to 180 Frs 🍵
Accommodation: 180 to 350 Frs.
Restaurant: breakfast from 7.00. Lunch from
12.00 until 15.00. Dinner from 19.00 until 22.00.
Closed Sat (out of season).
Specialities: crevettes grillées, canard à l'orange,
blancs de seiches, fruits de mer, regional menu,
home-cooking.
Hotel: ☆ ☆ 31 rooms. Facilities: shower, private
bathroom, television, telephone.
Other points: credit cards accepted, bar, children's
menu, lounge area, terrace, pets allowed, car parking.
◁€ Saint-Malo; Mont-Saint-Michel; Dinan; Cap
Fréhel; the coast; haras (stud-farm) national; Ile de
Bréhat.

LANDEBIA • Côtes-d'Armor, 22130

🍴 AU RENDEZ-VOUS DES AMIS
(Mme Michèle Abbé) 17 rue de la Gare
☎ 96.84.48.22
Directions: RD 768, between Lamballe and Plancoët.
Languages spoken: English and Spanish.
Menu: 45 to 150 Frs.
Accommodation: 90 to 130 Frs.
Restaurant: breakfast from 7.00. Lunch from 11.00 until 15.00. Dinner from 19.00 until 22.00.
Specialities: poissons, paella, couscous, regional menu, home-cooking.
Hotel: 12 rooms. Facilities: shower.
Other points: credit cards accepted, bar, children's menu, lounge area, modern decor, terrace, pets allowed, car/lorry parking.
◄ Mont-Saint-Michel; Saint-Malo; Côte d'Emeraude (Emerald coast); forêt la Hunaudaye and medieval chateau.

LANDERONDE • Vendée, 85150

🍴 L'HORTENSE
(M. Michel Migran) Route Nationale 160, Les Loges ☎ 51.34.22.81
Directions: RN 160, Les Sables d'Olonne.
Menu: 50 Frs (wine included) to 160 Frs 🥄
Restaurant: breakfast from 7.00. Lunch from 12.00. Dinner from 19.00 until 21.00. Closed Sun.
Specialities: coquilles Saint-Jacques, terrine de filet de sole, fruits de mer (to order), home-cooking.
Other points: credit cards accepted, bar, à la carte menu, traditional decor, terrace, pets allowed, car/lorry parking.
◄ La Roche-sur-Yon (10km); Les Sables d'Olonne (25km).

LANDEVANT • Morbihan, 56690

🍴 LE RELAIS DU PELICAN
(M. Bourn) 14 Route Nationale
☎ 97.56.93.12
Directions: RN 165.
Restaurant: closed Mon evening, Tues, Oct 🥄
Other points: bar.

LANDIVISIAU • Finistère, 29400

🍴 LE TERMINUS
(M. Raymond Floch) 94 avenue Foch
☎ 98.68.02.00
Directions: RN 12, Brest, exit Ouest (west).
Languages spoken: English.
Menu: 65 to 110 Frs 🥄
Accommodation: 95 to 130 Frs.
Restaurant: breakfast from 6.00. Lunch from 11.00 until 15.00. Dinner from 19.30 until 22.00. Closed Sat, Sun evening, and 3 weeks in Aug.
Specialities: fruits de mer, poissons, home-cooking.
Hotel: ☆ 25 rooms. Facilities: shower.
Other points: credit cards accepted, bar, children's

menu, à la carte menu, lounge area, modern decor, car/lorry parking.
◄ Brest; Breton calvaires (crosses); the coastline; les 'enclos'; Roscoff.

LANESTER • Morbihan, 56600

🍴 LA ROTONDE
(Mme Cécile Mercier) 120 rue Jean-Jaurès
☎ 97.76.06.37
Directions: RN 24, Lorient.
Menu: 40 to 60 Frs.
Accommodation: 90 to 140 Frs.
Restaurant: breakfast from 7.00. Lunch from 12.00 until 14.00. Dinner from 19.00 until 21.00. Closed Sat afternoon, Sun, last 2 weeks in Aug and 2 weeks at Christmas.
Specialities: home-cooking.
Hotel: ☆ 14 rooms. Facilities: shower, private bathroom.
Other points: credit cards accepted, bar, à la carte menu, traditional decor, pets allowed, car/lorry parking.
◄ beaches.

LANISCAT • Côtes-d'Armor, 22570

🍴 AUBERGE DU DAOULAS
(Mme Marie-Claude Quemener) rue de Bon-Repos ☎ 96.24.81.78
Directions: RN 164, between Rostrenen and Mur-de-Bretagne.
Menu: 52 Frs.
Accommodation: 130 to 185 Frs.
Restaurant: breakfast from 6.30. Lunch from 11.30 until 14.30. Dinner from 19.00 until 21.00.
Specialities: home-cooking.
Hotel: 7 rooms.
Other points: credit cards accepted, bar, children's menu, lounge area, traditional decor, terrace, pets allowed, car/lorry parking.
◄ Lac de Guerlédan; abbaye de Bon-Repos; Les Forges-des-Salles; Daoulas valley.

LANNION • Côtes-d'Armor, 22300

🍴 LA CROIX ROUGE
(M. Claude Brozec) La Croix Rouge, Ploumilliau ☎ 96.35.45.08
Directions: Lannion, towards Morlaix.
Menu: 49 to 150 Frs.
Restaurant: lunch from 11.30 until 14.30. Dinner from 19.00 until 21.30. Closed last 2 weeks in Aug.
Specialities: fruits de mer (Sunday), home-cooking.
Hotel: 16 rooms.
Other points: credit cards accepted, bar, pets allowed, car/lorry parking.

LAVAL • Mayenne, 53000

🍴 BAR DE LA GARE
(Mme Claudia Helbert) 107 avenue Robert-Buron ☎ 43.53.94.88

Directions: RN 162 and RD 53.
Restaurant: breakfast from 7.00. Closed Mon.
Other points: bar, traditional decor, terrace, pets allowed.
◀€ old Laval.

LA LEUE • Vendée, 85210

🏠 **LES ROUTIERS**
(SARL Charbonneau-Daviet)
Route Nationale 137 ☎ 51.94.41.46
Directions: RN 137.
Menu: 60 Frs.
Accommodation: 60 to 120 Frs.
Restaurant: breakfast from 6.00. Lunch from 12.00 until 14.30. Dinner from 19.30 until 22.00. Closed Sat, Sun, and in July.
Specialities: home-cooking.
Hotel: 8 rooms.
Other points: credit cards accepted, bar, traditional decor, car/lorry parking.
◀€ dam at l'Angle-Guignard; maison de-Lattre-de-Tassigny; le Puy du Fou; château de Clemenceau; seaside.

LES ROUTIERS GUIDE TO BRITAIN AND IRELAND

Whether on business or pleasure, the Les Routiers guide to Britain and Ireland lists an unrivalled choice of over 1,500 carefully selected hotels, restaurants, guesthouses and inns, where you can dine and stay in comfort. All have been inspected and personally recommended and offer the ultimate in hospitality.

Available from all good bookshops, or direct from the publishers, price £10.99.

LIGNOL • Morbihan, 56160

🏠 **RELAIS DES VOYAGEURS**
(M. Bernard Le Solliec) 4 rue de la Mairie
☎ 97.27.03.48
Directions: RD 782, the Pontivy/Quimper road via Le Faouet.
Menu: 50 Frs.
Accommodation: 90 to 120 Frs.
Restaurant: breakfast from 7.00. Lunch from 12.00 until 14.00. Dinner from 19.00 until 21.00. Closed Mon afternoon.
Specialities: home-cooking.
Hotel: 7 rooms.
Other points: credit cards accepted, bar, children's menu, lounge area, traditional decor, pets allowed, car/lorry parking.
◀€ Kernascleden: church (5km); étang (pool) at Priziac; zoo at Le Harlay (20km).

LISIEUX • Calvados, 14100

🏠 **LE PARIS-CHERBOURG**
(M. Joël Louis) 113 avenue du 6 juin
☎ 31.62.63.38

Directions: RN 13, the Caen/Lisieux road.
Menu: 50 Frs.
Accommodation: 120 Frs (extra bed 30 Frs).
Restaurant: breakfast from 6.30.
Specialities: home-cooking.
Hotel: 6 rooms. Facilities: shower.
Other points: credit cards accepted, bar, children's menu, à la carte menu, modern decor, terrace, pets allowed, car parking.
◀€ basilica at Lisieux; zoo at Cerza.

LOCMARIA-GRAND-CHAMPS
Morbihan, 56390

🍴 **LA MARMITE**
(M. Jean-Pierre Joulaud) Collec
☎ 97.66.66.80
Directions: RD 767, 10km from Vannes, towards Pontivy.
Menu: 45 to 200 Frs.
Restaurant: breakfast from 5.30. Lunch from 11.30 until 15.00. Dinner from 18.30 until 22.00.
Specialities: regional menu.
Other points: credit cards accepted, bar, children's menu, à la carte menu, modern decor, pets allowed, car/lorry parking.
◀€ Gulf of Morbihan.

LOIRE • Maine-et-Loire, 49440

🍴 **AU RENDEZ-VOUS DES ROUTIERS**
(M. Philippe Audouin) 24 rue de la Libération
☎ 41.94.10.83
Directions: RD 923, the Nantes/Laval road.
Menu: 51 Frs (wine included).
Restaurant: breakfast from 6.30. Lunch from 11.30. Dinner from 19.00 until 20.00. Closed first 2 weeks in July.
Specialities: canard au muscadet, beurre blanc, pintade (guinea-fowl) aux raisins, home-cooking.
Other points: credit cards accepted, bar, children's menu, traditional decor, pets allowed, car/lorry parking.
◀€ la Mine Bleue.

LONGUE • Maine-et-Loire, 49160

🍴 **LE RELAIS DES SOUVENETS – Chez Réjane**
(Mme Réjane Taugourdeau) Les Souvenets
☎ 41.52.13.86
Directions: RN 147.
Restaurant: breakfast from 7.30. Closed Sat, Sun, and in Aug.
Specialities: home-cooking.
Other points: credit cards accepted, bar, pets allowed, car/lorry parking.
◀€ Saumur: chateau.

🍴 **SARL LE RELAX**
(M. Chevré) Route Nationale 147
☎ 41.52.68.81
Directions: RN 147, between Saumur (15km) and Angers (40km).
Menu: 55 (wine included) to 135 Frs.

Restaurant: breakfast from 6.00. Closed Sun.
Specialities: regional menu, home-cooking.
Other points: credit cards accepted, bar, children's menu, à la carte menu, terrace, pets allowed, car/lorry parking.
⊲€ *Saumur: vineyards; Loire chateaux.*

LORIENT • Morbihan, 56100

⊐€ L'ALBATROS
(Mme Marie Legouic) 56 avenue de
la Perrière ☎ 97.37.55.76
Menu: 45 Frs (wine included).
Restaurant: breakfast from 9.00. Lunch from
11.00 until 15.30. Dinner from 19.00 until 22.00.
Open 24 hours in June, July and Aug. Closed Sat
and Sun (in winter).
Specialities: home-cooking.
Other points: credit cards accepted, bar, children's
menu, traditional decor, pets allowed.
⊲€ *marina and fishing port.*

LOUARGAT • Côtes-d'Armor, 22540

⊐€ LE CONCORDE
(Mme Paulette Entzmann) 34 rue Prunus
☎ 96.43.13.75
Directions: RN 12, between Guingamp and Morlaix.
Menu: 50 to 90 Frs.
Restaurant: breakfast from 8.00. Lunch from
12.00 until 14.00. Dinner from 19.00 until 21.00.
Closed Mon afternoon.
Specialities: home-cooking.
Other points: credit cards accepted, bar, children's
menu, à la carte menu, lounge area, terrace, pets
allowed, car/lorry parking.

LOUDEAC • Côtes-d'Armor, 22600

⊐€ LE STOP
(M. Yves Gicquel) Le Haut-Breuil
☎ 96.28.01.76
Directions: RN 164, Rennes.
Languages spoken: English.
Menu: 45 to 75 Frs.
Restaurant: breakfast from 6.00. Closed Sun.
Other points: credit cards accepted, bar,
traditional decor.

🛏 LES ROUTIERS
(M. Dominique Le Cozannet) 7 rue Lavergne
☎ 96.28.01.44
Directions: RN 164.
Languages spoken: English.
Menu: 45 to 55 Frs.
Accommodation: 75 to 130 Frs.
Restaurant: breakfast from 7.00. Lunch from
12.00 until 14.00. Dinner from 19.00 until 21.00.
Closed Sun.
Specialities: fruits de mer, regional menu, home-
cooking.
Hotel: ✰ 44 rooms. Facilities: shower, private
bathroom, television, telephone.

Other points: credit cards accepted, bar, pets
allowed, car parking.
⊲€ *lac de Guerlédan (15km).*

LOUVIERS • Eure, 27400

⊐€ L'ARCHE DE VIRONVAY
(M. Patrick Lafuente) A13, services at
Vironvay (accessible in both directions)
☎ 32.40.21.51 [Fax] 32.25.20.04
Other points: credit cards and foreign currency
accepted.

⊐€ LE BAR DES FLEURS
(M. Michel Desrolles) 57 rue Saint-Jean
☎ 32.40.10.64
Menu: 50 Frs.
Accommodation: 100 Frs.
Restaurant: breakfast from 6.00. Lunch from
11.45. Closed Sun.
Specialities: home-cooking.
Other points: credit cards accepted, bar, children's
menu, modern decor, pets allowed, car/lorry parking.
⊲€ *Château-Gaillard: costumes museum, cathedral.*

LUCEAU • Sarthe, 72500

⊐€ LA CROIX DE PAILLE
(M. Jacques-Yves Moreau) Route du Mans,
Château-du-Loir ☎ 43.44.05.50
Directions: RN 138, between Le Mans and Tours.
Restaurant: breakfast from 6.00. Closed Sat
evening and Sun, and in Aug.
Specialities: home-cooking.
Other points: credit cards accepted, bar, children's
menu, pets allowed, car/lorry parking.

LE LUDE • Sarthe, 72800

⊐€ CHEZ FERNANDE
(M. Gilbert Moire) 14 boulevard de l'Hospice
☎ 83.81.03.54
Languages spoken: German and Portuguese.
Menu: 52 Frs.
Restaurant: breakfast from 6.00. Lunch from
11.30 until 14.00. Dinner from 19.00 until 21.30.
Closed Sat evening and Sun.
Specialities: couscous, paella, choucroute, potée
lorraine, home-cooking.
Other points: credit cards accepted, bar,
children's menu, traditional decor, terrace, pets
allowed, car parking.
⊲€ *Pont-à-Mousson; portes d'or Stanislas; lac de la
Madine.*

MACHECOUL
Loire-Atlantique, 44270

🛏 LA BICYCLETTE D'ARGENT
(Mme Marie-Joseph Baudry) 6 place du Pont
☎ 40.78.50.48
Languages spoken: English.

Menu: 45 to 120 Frs.
Accommodation: 90 to 180 Frs.
Restaurant: breakfast from 6.00. Lunch from
11.45 until 14.00. Dinner from 19.00 until 21.00.
Closed Sat (out of season), 1st week in May and
1st week in Nov.
Specialities: beurre blanc, anguilles (eels), cuisses
de grenouilles, regional menu, home-cooking.
Hotel: 9 rooms. Facilities: shower.
Other points: credit cards accepted, bar, children's
menu, à la carte menu, car/lorry parking.
◁ᴇ *chateaux; churches; wine-cellars.*

MAGNY-LA-CAMPAGNE
Calvados, 14270

◁ᴇ LA VALLEE D'AUGE
(Mme Marie-Thérèse Sevin) ☎ 31.20.04.20
Directions: RD 40, between Caen and Saint-
Pierre-sur-Dive.
Menu: 50 to 105 Frs.
Restaurant: breakfast from 7.30. Closed Tues, and
in Jan.
Specialities: escalope Vallée d'Auge, poulet aux
écrevisses, regional menu.
Other points: children's menu, à la carte menu,
traditional decor, pets allowed, car parking.
◁ᴇ *chateaux; historic monuments; markets.*

MALE • Orne, 61260

🏠 HOTEL DE LA BELLE RENCONTRE
(M. André Carle) Le Gibet ☎ 37.49.68.85
Directions: RN 23, the Paris/Le Mans road.
Menu: 50 Frs (wine included).
Accommodation: 95 to 190 Frs.
Restaurant: breakfast from 6.00. Lunch from
11.00 until 14.30. Dinner from 19.00 until 22.00.
Closed Sat evening and Sun.
Specialities: home-cooking.
Hotel: ☆ 17 rooms. Facilities: shower, private
bathroom.
Other points: bar, traditional decor, terrace, car/
lorry parking.
◁ᴇ *chateau; Perche valley.*

MARCILLE-RAOUL
Ille-et-Vilaine, 35560

🏠 LES ROUTIERS
(M. Christian Belleperche) Le Bourg
☎ 99.73.62.14
Directions: the Combourg/Vitré road.
Menu: 45 to 75 Frs.
Accommodation: 85 to 105 Frs.
Restaurant: breakfast from 7.00. Lunch from
11.30 until 14.00. Dinner from 19.30 until 21.00.
Specialities: home-cooking.
Hotel: 7 rooms. Facilities: shower.
Other points: bar, children's menu, à la carte menu,
traditional decor, pets allowed, car/lorry parking.
◁ᴇ *Mont-Saint-Michel (30km); Combourg: chateau
(10km).*

MARIGNE-LAILLE
Sarthe, 72220

◁ᴇ AUBERGE DU BON ACCUEIL
(M. Jean-Louis Loudière) Route Nationale 138,
Laillé ☎ 43.42.12.01
Directions: RN 138, the Le Mans/Tours road.
Menu: 49 to 150 Frs.
Restaurant: breakfast from 7.00. Lunch from
12.00 until 14.30. Dinner from 19.00 until 21.30.
Closed Wed afternoon.
Specialities: home-cooking.
Other points: credit cards accepted, bar, à la carte
menu, pets allowed, car/lorry parking.

MARTIGNE-FERCHAUD
Ille-et-Vilaine, 35640

◁ᴇ LE POT D'ETAIN
(Mme Yvonne Bouteiller) 10 Grande Rue
☎ 99.47.90.12
Directions: RN 178.
Restaurant: closed Sat, and 3 weeks in Aug.
Specialities: home-cooking.
Other points: bar, traditional decor, pets allowed,
car/lorry parking.

MARZAN • Morbihan, 56130

◁ᴇ LES RIVES DE VILAINE
(M. Gilles Jouan) 13 rue de la Fontaine
☎ 99.90.63.22
Directions: RN 165, Vannes, on the right after
bridge at La Roche-Bernard.
Menu: 44 to 140 Frs.
Restaurant: breakfast from 7.30. Lunch from
12.00 until 14.00. Dinner from 19.00 until
20.00.
Specialities: fruits de mer, poissons au beurre
blanc (to order), regional menu, home-cooking.
Other points: credit cards accepted, children's
menu, traditional decor, terrace, pets allowed, car/
lorry parking.
◁ᴇ *zoo at Branféré; La Roche-Bernard; La Baule;
Gulf of Morbihan.*

MATHIEU • Calvados, 14920

◁ᴇ RELAIS DE LA COTE DE NACRE
(M. Marc Bedeau de l'Ecochère) 4 rue Augustin-
Fresnel ☎ 31.44.10.17
Directions: RD 7, Douvres-la-Délivrande.
Menu: 53 to 65 Frs.
Accommodation: 100 to 120 Frs.
Restaurant: breakfast from 7.00. Lunch from
12.00 until 15.00. Dinner from 19.30 until 21.00.
Closed Sun afternoon, and from 20th Dec to
5th Jan.
Specialities: home-cooking
Hotel: 2 rooms. Facilities: shower.
Other points: bar, traditional decor, car/lorry
parking.

MAY-SUR-ORNE • Calvados, 14320

L'AMMONITE
(Mme Maryvonne Horel) 2 rue du Canada
☎ 31.79.80.27
Directions: RD 562, the Caen/Laval road (8km
from Caen).
Languages spoken: English.
Menu: 50 to 130 Frs.
Accommodation: 130 to 170 Frs.
Restaurant: breakfast from 8.00. Lunch from
11.30 until 14.30. Dinner from 19.30 until 21.30.
Closed Sun (out of season).
Specialities: escalope normande, côte de porc au
cidre, regional menu, home-cooking.
Hotel: 8 rooms. Facilities: shower, private bathroom.
Other points: credit cards accepted, bar, children's
menu, terrace, pets allowed, car/lorry parking.
◀ *Orne valley; Caen; la Suisse normande; landing
beaches; route des fromages.*

MAYENNE • Mayenne, 53100

L'ESCALE
(M. Dominique Fortin) Route du Mans
☎ 43.04.19.14
Directions: CD 35, Le Mans.
Menu: 53 Frs (wine and coffee included).
Accommodation: 90 to 180 Frs.
Restaurant: breakfast from 5.30. Lunch from
11.00 until 14.00. Dinner from 19.00 until 21.00.
Closed Sat evening and Sun.
Specialities: home-cooking.
Hotel: 9 rooms.
Other points: credit cards accepted, bar,
children's menu, lounge area, traditional decor,
terrace, pets allowed, car/lorry parking.
◀ *Mayenne: chateau, basilica, church, chapel;
Gallo-Roman site at Jublains; musée de l'ardoise
(slate) at Renazé; musée Robert Tatin at
Cossé-le-Vivien.*

LE RELAIS DES BRUYERES
(M. Jean-Pierre Bordas) Route d'Alençon,
Aron ☎ 43.04.13.64
Directions: RN 12, between Alençon and Mayenne.
Languages spoken: German.
Menu: 55 to 138 Frs.
Accommodation: 120 to 180 Frs.
Restaurant: breakfast from 5.00. Closed Sat, and
in Aug.
Specialities: regional menu, home-cooking.
Hotel: 9 rooms. Facilities: shower, television.
Other points: credit cards accepted, bar, children's
menu, à la carte menu, lounge area, traditional
decor, terrace, pets allowed, car/lorry parking.
◀ *Bagnoles-de-l'Orne (30km).*

LE MENIL-BROUT • Orne, 61250

CHEZ GHISLAINE
(Mme Ghislaine Gautier) Route Nationale 12
☎ 33.27.10.03
Directions: RN 12, between Alençon and Dreux.

Menu: 53 Frs.
Accommodation: 100 to 120 Frs.
Restaurant: closed Sat afternoon and Sun.
Specialities: home-cooking.
Hotel: 8 rooms. Facilities: shower, private bathroom.
Other points: bar, children's menu, modern
decor, pets allowed, car/lorry parking.
◀ *Alençon; 'les alpes Manselles'; lake at Le
Mêle-sur-Sarthe.*

LE MESNIL-DURAND
Calvados, 14140

LE RELAIS DE LA FORGE
(Mme Chantale Le Rosier) Les Forges
Mézières ☎ 31.63.52.79
Directions: RD 579, between Lisieux and
Livarot.
Menu: 52 Frs.
Restaurant: breakfast from 6.00. Closed Sat and
Sun.
Specialities: home-cooking.
Other points: credit cards accepted, bar, children's
menu, traditional decor, terrace, pets allowed,
car/lorry parking.
◀ *Lisieux: basilica (12km); Auge valley.*

LES ROUTIERS
Your assurance of Quality and Value

MILLIERES • Manche, 50190

RELAIS DES TOURISTES
(M. Gérard Lunel) La Bezanterie
☎ 33.46.71.12
Directions: the Lessay/St-Lô road, between Perriers
and Lessay.
Languages spoken: English.
Restaurant: dinner until 21.00. Closed Sun.
Specialities: coq à la bière or au vin, home-cooking.
Other points: credit cards accepted, bar,
children's menu, terrace, pets allowed, car/lorry
parking.
◀ *Saint-Lô (20km); Lessay (4km); tour of cheese-
making (3km) and ham-smoking factories (with
tasting).*

LE MOLAY-LITTRY
Calvados, 14330

LA TAVERNE
(M. Alain Marie) 32 rue de Balleroy
☎ 31.22.96.36
Directions: Balleroy/Isigny and Bayeux/Lison.
Menu: 50 Frs.
Restaurant: breakfast from 8.00. Lunch from
11.30 until 14.30. Closed Wed afternoon.
Specialities: home-cooking.
Other points: bar, children's menu, pets allowed,
car/lorry parking.
◀ *forêt de Balleroy; potteries at Noron; moulin
(windmill) at Marcy; musée de la mine (mining).*

MONNAI • Orne, 61470

🏨 **LE CHEVAL BAI**
(M. Gilbert Roussel) Route Nationale 138
☎ 33.39.42.00
Directions: RN 138.
Restaurant: dinner until 23.00. Closed Sun.
Hotel: 6 rooms.
Other points: bar.

LE MONT-SAINT-MICHEL
Manche, 50116

🏨 **HOTEL MOTEL VERT**
(M. Philippe François) Route du Mont-Saint-Michel ☎ 33.60.09.33 [Fax] 33.68.22.09
Directions: RD 976, at the last crossroads before the causeway.
Languages spoken: German and English.
Menu: 55 to 200 Frs.
Accommodation: 210 to 450 Frs.
Restaurant: lunch from 12.00 until 13.30. Dinner from 19.00 until 21.00. Open 24 hours. Closed Dec and Jan.
Specialities: agneau (lamb), fruits de mer, omelette du Mont-Saint-Michel, regional menu.
Hotel: ☆ ☆ 113 rooms. Facilities: shower, private bathroom, television, telephone, open 24 hours.
Other points: credit cards accepted, bar, children's menu, à la carte menu, modern decor, car/lorry parking.
◁ *Mont-Saint-Michel; Cancale; Saint-Malo; chateau at Fougères; island of Jersey; Dinan.*

MONTAUBAN-DE-BRETAGNE
Ille-et-Vilaine, 35360

🏨 **HOTEL DE FRANCE**
(M. Gabriel Le Metayer) 34 rue du Général-de-Gaulle ☎ 99.06.40.19
Directions: Brest.
Languages spoken: English and Spanish.
Menu: 62 to 160 Frs 🍽
Accommodation: 110 to 220 Frs.
Restaurant: breakfast from 7.00. Lunch from 11.30 until 14.00. Dinner from 19.00 until 21.30. Closed Mon (out of season), and from 20th Dec to 20th Jan.
Specialities: fruits de mer, coq au Muscadet, far breton (biscuits), poissons, regional menu, home-cooking.
Hotel: ☆ ☆ 12 rooms. Facilities: shower, private bathroom, television, telephone.
Other points: credit cards accepted, bar, children's menu, à la carte menu, traditional decor, pets allowed, car parking.
◁ *forêt de Brocéliande; medieval chateau.*

🏨 **RELAIS DE LA HUCHERAIS**
(M. Alain Meheus) La Hucherais
☎ 99.06.40.29
Directions: RN 12 and 164 bis.
Languages spoken: English.
Accommodation: 100 to 170 Frs.

Restaurant: dinner until 22.00. Closed Sun.
Hotel: ☆ ☆ 14 rooms.
Other points: bar, pets allowed, car/lorry parking.

MONTAUDIN • Mayenne, 53220

🏨 **HOTEL DE PARIS**
(M. Daniel Doudard) Route d'Ernée
☎ 43.05.30.79
Directions: RN 799.
Languages spoken: English.
Menu: 44 to 48 Frs.
Accommodation: 135 to 185 Frs.
Restaurant: breakfast from 7.00. Dinner until 21.00. Closed Mon, and in Aug.
Specialities: brochet au beurre blanc, home-cooking.
Hotel: 5 rooms. Facilities: shower, private bathroom, television.
Other points: credit cards accepted, bar, children's menu, modern decor, terrace, pets allowed, car/lorry parking.
◁ *Mont-Saint-Michel; chateau at Fougères (17km); Pontmain (9km).*

MONTMARTIN-SUR-MER
Manche, 50590

🏨 **HOTELLERIE DU BON VIEUX TEMPS**
(M. Erick Bourbonnais) ☎ 33.47.54.44
[Fax] 33.46.27.12
Directions: RD 20, Granville.
Languages spoken: English.
Menu: 60 to 200 Frs.
Accommodation: 140 to 350 Frs.
Restaurant: breakfast from 8.00. Lunch from 12.00 until 14.00. Dinner from 19.30 until 21.00. Closed Sun evening (from 1st Nov to Easter).
Specialities: cider and cream-based cuisine, regional menu.
Hotel: ☆ ☆ 20 rooms. Facilities: shower, private bathroom, telephone.
Other points: credit cards accepted, bar, children's menu, à la carte menu, traditional decor, pets allowed, car/lorry parking.
◁ *Baie de la Sienne; lime-kilns; nearby manor-houses; Granville; Channel Islands excursions.*

MONTOIR-DE-BRETAGNE
Loire-Atlantique, 44550

🍴 **LES NOES**
(Mme Brigitte Liberge) Route Nationale 171, Les Noës ☎ 40.45.55.67
Directions: RN 171, the Nantes/Saint-Nazaire expressway.
Menu: 50 Frs.
Restaurant: breakfast from 6.30. Lunch from 11.45 until 14.00. Dinner from 19.00 until 21.00. Closed Sat and Sun.
Specialities: home-cooking.
Other points: credit cards accepted, bar, terrace, pets allowed, car/lorry parking.
◁ *Montoir: port; Saint-Nazaire; parc régional de Brière.*

⇌ RELAIS DU BOSCO
(M. Jean-Michel Valain) Centre International
de Frêt ☎ 40.90.18.80
Directions: between Nantes and Saint-Nazaire.
Menu: 48 Frs.
Restaurant: breakfast from 6.00. Dinner until
22.00. Closed Sat and Sun.
Specialities: home-cooking.
Other points: credit cards accepted, bar, children's
menu, lounge area, modern decor, pets allowed,
car/lorry parking.
◀ *Montoir: port; Saint-Nazaire.*

MONTREUIL-LE-CHETIF
Sarthe, 72130

⇌ AU RENDEZ-VOUS DES CHASSEURS
(Mme Françoise Bordeau) Le Grand Gué
☎ 43.33.39.90
Directions: RD 310, Sillé-le-Guillaume, at Fresnay,
on the edge of the forest.
Menu: 48 to 80 Frs.
Restaurant: breakfast from 7.00. Lunch from
12.00 until 14.00. Dinner from 19.00 until 21.00.
Specialities: regional menu, home-cooking.
Other points: credit cards accepted, bar, children's
menu, à la carte menu, traditional decor, terrace,
pets allowed, car/lorry parking.
◀ *chateau at Sainte-Suzanne; grottes (caves) de
Sauges; Fresnay; musée des coiffes (head-dresses);
abbaye de Champagne.*

MONTREUIL-SUR-ILLE
Ille-et-Vilaine, 35440

⇌ LE GRILLADIN
(M. Jean-Marc Fraizier) 10 rue Alexis-Rey
☎ 99.69.69.20
Directions: between Sens-de-Bretagne and Hédé.
Languages spoken: Arabic.
Menu: 52 to 196 Frs.
Restaurant: breakfast from 6.00. Closed Mon, and
in Aug.
Specialities: Spanish and Algerian dishes, home-
cooking.
Other points: bar, children's menu, modern
decor, terrace, pets allowed, car/lorry parking.
◀ *Mont-Saint-Michel; chateau at Combourg;
étang (pond) de Boulet.*

MORDELLES • Ille-et-Vilaine, 35310

⇌ LE RELAIS
(M. Michel Cavalier) La Croix-Ignon
☎ 99.60.02.50
Directions: RN 24, between Rennes and Lorient.
Menu: 50 Frs.
Restaurant: breakfast from 7.30. Lunch from
12.00 until 14.00. Closed Sat, Sun, and in Aug.
Specialities: home-cooking.
Other points: credit cards accepted, bar, modern
decor, pets allowed, car/lorry parking.
◀ *forêt de Brocéliande.*

MOREAC • Morbihan, 56500

⊟ LE RELAIS DU BARDERFF
(M. Jean Lamour) Zone Industrielle (Z.I.) du
Barderff ☎ 97.60.18.60 [Fax] 97.60.25.55
Directions: RN 24, between Rennes and Lorient
or Vannes and Saint-Brieuc.
Languages spoken: English.
Menu: 45 to 85 Frs.
Accommodation: 220 to 360 Frs.
Restaurant: breakfast from 5.00. Lunch from
12.00 until 14.00. Dinner from 19.00 until 22.00.
Closed Sun (out of season).
Specialities: regional menu, home-cooking.
Hotel: ✩ ✩ 20 rooms. Facilities: shower, private
bathroom, television, telephone.
Other points: credit cards accepted, bar, children's
menu, à la carte menu, lounge area, modern decor,
car/lorry parking.
◀ *the sea (30km).*

For useful expressions *à l'hôtel*, *au restaurant*
or *en route*, turn to pages 8–13.

MOREILLES • Vendée, 85450

⊟ LE CHEVAL BLANC
(M. Christian Sarraud) 9 route Nationale
☎ 51.56.11.02
Directions: RN 137, the Nantes/Bordeaux road.
Languages spoken: English and Spanish.
Menu: 58 to 69 Frs.
Accommodation: 95 to 130 Frs.
Restaurant: breakfast from 6.00. Lunch 11.30 to
14.00. Dinner 19.00 to 21.30. Closed Sun (out of
season), and from 24th Dec to 10th Jan.
Specialities: mojettes (beans), jambon vendéen
(Vendée ham), regional menu, home-cooking.
Hotel: 5 rooms.
Other points: credit cards accepted, bar, children's
menu, traditional decor, terrace, pets allowed, car/
lorry parking.
◀ *Poitou marshlands; La Rochelle; Ile de Ré;
Vendée coast.*

MORTAGNE (SAINT-LANGIS)
Orne, 61400

⊟ HOTEL DE LA GARE
(M. Belaïd Leroul) avenue de la Gare
☎ 33.25.16.10
Directions: the Bellême/Le Mans road.
Menu: 49 to 55 Frs.
Accommodation: 100 to 130 Frs.
Restaurant: breakfast from 6.00. Lunch from
12.00 until 14.30. Dinner from 19.00 until 21.30.
Closed Sat afternoon, Sun, and in Aug.
Specialities: home-cooking.
Hotel: 6 rooms. Facilities: shower, private bathroom,
telephone.
Other points: bar, modern decor, terrace, pets
allowed, car/lorry parking.
◀ *Chapelle Montlugeon.*

MORTAGNE-SUR-SEVRE
Vendée, 85290

LE PUY NARDON
(M. Gérard Duval) Zone Artisanale at Le Puy-Nardon, Route de Poitiers ☎ 51.65.19.14
Fax 51.65.19.12
Directions: RN 149, the Nantes/Poitiers road.
Languages spoken: English.
Menu: 45 Frs.
Restaurant: breakfast from 6.00. Lunch from 11.30 until 14.30. Dinner from 19.00 until 22.00.
Specialities: home-cooking.
Other points: credit cards accepted, bar, children's menu, à la carte menu, modern decor, terrace, pets allowed, car/lorry parking.
≪ le Puy du Fou; château Barbe-Bleue; la maison de l'eau at Mallièvre; musée paysan (peasant life); musée des arts at Cholet.

LE RELAIS DE LA GARE
(M. Jean-Luc Arrouet) 52 route de Cholet
☎ 51.65.11.56
Directions: RN 160
Restaurant: breakfast from 6.30. Closed Sat, Sun, and in Aug.
Other points: bar.

MORTREE • Orne, 61570

LE POINT DU JOUR
(Fabienne and Jacky Huette) 139 Grande Rue
☎ 33.35.35.22
Directions: RN 158, between Argentan and Sées.
Languages spoken: English.
Menu: 53 to 80 Frs.
Restaurant: breakfast from 7.00. Lunch from 11.45 until 14.00. Dinner from 19.00 until 21.00.
Closed Sat afternoon and Sun (except functions), and in Aug.
Specialities: bourguignon maison, emincé de volaille au calvados, regional menu, home-cooking.
Other points: credit cards accepted, bar, children's menu, à la carte menu, traditional decor, terrace, pets allowed, car/lorry parking.
≪ chateaux at Mortrée and Sassy; cathedral at Sées.

MOSLES • Calvados, 14400

RESTAURANT DE LA POSTE
(M. Jacques Lerosier) Route Nationale 13
☎ 31.22.33.79
Directions: RN 13, the Bayeux/Cherbourg road.
Menu: 50 to 70 Frs.
Restaurant: breakfast from 6.00. Lunch from 11.00 until 15.00. Dinner from 19.00 until 22.00.
Closed Sat afternoon and Sun.
Specialities: home-cooking.
Other points: credit cards accepted, modern decor, car/lorry parking.
≪ landing beaches and museum; Bayeux tapestry.

MOUZEUIL-SAINT-MARTIN
Vendée, 85370

CENTRAL ROUTIERS
(M. Jean-Marie Guilbaud) 33 rue Louis-Apraille ☎ 51.28.72.44
Directions: RN 148, between Niort and Les Sables d'Olonne.
Menu: 50 to 150 Frs ☜
Accommodation: 100 to 240 Frs.
Restaurant: breakfast from 6.30. Lunch from 12.00 until 15.00. Dinner from 20.00 until 22.00.
Specialities: anguilles (eels), couscous, regional menu, home-cooking.
Hotel: 9 rooms. Facilities: shower, private bathroom, television.
Other points: credit cards accepted, bar, children's menu, lounge area, modern decor, pets allowed, car/lorry parking.
≪ Poitou marshlands; le Puy du Fou; baie de l'Aiguillon; dam; forêt de Mervent.

MUZILLAC • Morbihan, 56190

LA CLE DES CHAMPS
(Mme Annick Melloul – Société Margann) Route de Vannes ☎ 97.41.68.74
Directions: RN 165, between Vannes and La Roche-Bernard.
Languages spoken: German, English and Spanish.
Menu: 50 Frs.
Restaurant: breakfast from 5.00. Lunch from 11.45 until 14.00. Dinner from 19.00 until 22.00.
Closed Sun evening (out of season).
Specialities: couscous, paella, choucroute, fruits de mer, regional menu, home-cooking.
Other points: credit cards accepted, bar, children's menu, à la carte menu, lounge area, modern decor, terrace, pets allowed, car/lorry parking.

NANTES • Loire-Atlantique, 44200

A L'ANCRE D'OR
(M. Serge Desmortiers) 55 boulevard Gustave-Roch ☎ 40.35.39.30
Directions: RN 43, M.I.N.
Menu: 43 to 53 Frs.
Accommodation: 75 to 130 Frs.
Restaurant: breakfast from 4.30. Meals from 6.30 until 14.30 and from 19.00 until 21.30. Closed Sat afternoon, Sun and in Aug.
Specialities: home-cooking.
Hotel: 5 rooms. Facilities: shower.
Other points: credit cards accepted, bar, à la carte menu, modern decor, car/lorry parking.
≪ Nantes: cathedral, château des ducs de Bretagne; Muscadet wine route.

L'AVENIR
(Mme Viviane Baron) 1 rue de la Pompe
☎ 40.43.46.03
Directions: RN 23, Nantes Ouest (West), La Januraie exit.
Menu: 45 to 48 Frs.

Restaurant: breakfast from 5.30. Lunch from
11.30 until 14.30. Dinner from 19.00 until 22.00.
Closed Sat, Sun, and mid-Dec.
Specialities: home-cooking.
Other points: credit cards accepted, bar, children's
menu, traditional decor, pets allowed, car/lorry
parking.
◁€ Lac de Grand-Lieu (20km); pont de Cheviré;
African safari; Port-Saint-Père.

NASSANDRES • Eure, 27550

⇒€ LE PARIS-CAEN-CHERBOURG
(M. Laurent De Nave) Route Nationale 13
☎ 32.45.00.26
Directions: RN 13, the Evreux/Lisieux road.
Menu: 54 Frs.
Restaurant: breakfast from 3.30. Closed from Sat
afternoon to Sun 22.00.
Specialities: pieds de veau, regional menu, home-
cooking.
Hotel: 4 rooms.
Other points: credit cards accepted, bar, children's
menu, traditional decor, modern decor, pets
allowed, car/lorry parking.
◁€ abbaye du Bec-Hellouin; chateau d'Harcourt.

NEUFCHATEL-EN-BRAY
Seine-Maritime, 76270

⇒€ RELAIS DES HAYONS
(M. Jean-Claude Piednoël) Esclavelles
☎ 35.93.13.15
Directions: A28, towards Forges-les-Eaux.
Menu: 50 Frs.
Restaurant: breakfast from 5.30. Lunch 11.30 to
15.00. Dinner 18.30 to 22.00. Closed Sat and Sun.
Specialities: Norman dishes, home-cooking.
Other points: credit cards accepted, bar, children's
menu, lounge area, traditional decor, pets allowed,
car/lorry parking.
◁€ Neufchâtel-en-Bray; chateau at Mesnières.

NEUFCHATEL-EN-SAOSNOIS
Sarthe, 72600

🛏 LES ROUTIERS
(Mme Christiane Chapellier) ☎ 43.97.74.10
Directions: RN 155.
Restaurant: dinner until 22.00. Closed in Aug.
Hotel: 12 rooms.
Other points: bar.

LA NEUVE-LYRE • Eure, 27330

🛏 LE RELAIS DES AMIS
(M. Jean-Claude Guyot) Hameau de Chagny
☎ 32.30.50.60
Directions: between Evreux and L'Aigle.
Accommodation: 49 Frs.
Restaurant: breakfast from 6.30. Closed Sun, and
the 1st 2 weeks in Aug.

Specialities: home-cooking.
Hotel: 5 rooms. Facilities: shower.
Other points: bar, children's menu, terrace, pets
allowed, car/lorry parking.

NIEUL-LE-DOLENT • Vendée, 85430

⇒€ CHEZ JACQUES
(M. Jacques Pinel) 8 rue de-Lattre-de-Tassigny
☎ 51.07.93.71
Directions: RD 36, between La Roche-sur-Yon
and Les Tranches-sur-Mer.
Menu: 45 to 55 Frs.
Restaurant: breakfast from 7.30. Lunch from
11.30 until 14.30. Closed Sun.
Specialities: fraise de veau, home-cooking.
Other points: credit cards accepted, bar,
traditional decor, pets allowed, car/lorry parking.
◁€ Les Sables d'Olonne.

NORT-SUR-ERDRE
Loire-Atlantique, 44390

🛏 LES 3 MARCHANDS.
(M. Yannick Briand) 3 place du Champ-de-
Foire ☎ 40.72.20.34
Menu: 48 to 78 Frs.
Accommodation: 100 to 135 Frs.
Restaurant: breakfast from 6.30. Lunch from
11.30 until 15.00. Dinner from 18.30 until 21.30.
Closed Sun.
Specialities: moules marinières, home-cooking.
Hotel: 10 rooms. Facilities: shower, private
bathroom.
Other points: credit cards accepted, bar, children's
menu, traditional decor, pets allowed, car/lorry
parking.
◁€ banks of the Erdre; le maquis de Saffré.

NOTRE-DAME-D'ALLENCON
Maine-et-Loire, 49830

⇒€ LA BOITE D'OR
(M. Fabrice Leroi) ☎ 41.54.32.85
Directions: the Angers/Niort/Poitiers road.
Menu: 48 to 135 Frs.
Restaurant: breakfast from 7.00. Dinner from
19.30 until 22.00. Closed Mon, and the first
2 weeks in Aug.
Specialities: poissons au beurre blanc, regional
menu, home-cooking.
Other points: credit cards accepted, bar, children's
menu, à la carte menu, lounge area, traditional
decor, terrace, pets allowed, car/lorry parking.
◁€ Loire chateaux; troglodyte town; vineyards.

NOTRE-DAME-DE-GRAVENCHON
Seine-Maritime, 76330

⇒€ AU COUP DE FREIN
(Mme Marie-Josée David) rue Claude-Bernard
☎ 35.38.61.35

Directions: town centre, towards Norville.
Menu: 42 Frs.
Restaurant: breakfast from 6.30. Lunch from 11.30 until 14.30. Dinner from 19.00 until 21.30. Closed Sat afternoon and Sun afternoon.
Specialities: home-cooking.
Other points: modern decor, pets allowed, car/lorry parking.

NOYAL-SUR-VILAINE
Ille-et-Vilaine, 35530

🛏 **LE RELAIS 35**
(Mme Pascale Sefelin) 20 avenue du Général-de-Gaulle ☎ 99.00.51.20
Directions: RN 157, the Paris/Rennes road.
Languages spoken: English.
Menu: 48 to 60 Frs.
Accommodation: 100 to 115 Frs.
Restaurant: breakfast from 6.00. Lunch from 11.00 until 15.00. Dinner from 18.00 until 22.00. Closed Sat afternoon, Sun and 3rd week of Aug.
Specialities: pizza, home-cooking.
Hotel: 12 rooms.
Other points: credit cards accepted, bar, children's menu, à la carte menu, modern decor, terrace, pets allowed, car parking.

OCTEVILLE • Manche, 50130

🍴 **LE VENT D'AMONT**
(M. Jacky Travers) 1 rue Jules-Ferry
☎ 33.52.16.16
Directions: RN 3 and 900.
Languages spoken: English.
Restaurant: closed Mon (after lunch).
Other points: bar, car/lorry parking.

OISSEAU-LE-PETIT • Sarthe, 72610

🍴 **HOTEL DE L'ESPERANCE**
(Mme Andrée Besnard) ☎ 33.26.81.97
Directions: RN 138, between Le Mans and Alençon.
Menu: 48 to 60 Frs.
Restaurant: breakfast from 6.00. Lunch from 12.00 until 14.00. Dinner from 19.30 until 21.00. Closed Sat, Sun, and in Aug.
Specialities: home-cooking.
Hotel: 4 rooms.
Other points: bar, children's menu, pets allowed, car/lorry parking.

OUISTREHAM • Calvados, 14150

🍴 **AU COIN DU PORT**
(Claude and Andrée Morin Notamy) 90 avenue Michel-Cabieu ☎ 31.97.15.22
Languages spoken: English.
Menu: 55 to 148 Frs.
Restaurant: breakfast from 7.30. Lunch from 12.00 until 15.00. Dinner from 19.00 until 22.00. Closed Sun (out of season), and last week in Dec.

Specialities: regional menu, home-cooking.
Other points: credit cards accepted, bar, children's menu, à la carte menu, modern decor, pets allowed.
◀ *museums; landing beaches and military cemetery.*

PACE • Orne, 61250

🍴 **LE RELAIS DU CHENE**
(M. Gilles Boutinon) Route Nationale 12
☎ 33.27.72.06
Directions: RN 12, between Alençon and Mayenne.
Menu: 49 Frs.
Restaurant: breakfast from 5.00. Closed Sat afternoon, Sun, and 1 week from Christmas Day.
Specialities: truite normande, home-cooking.
Other points: credit cards accepted, bar, children's menu, traditional decor, pets allowed, car/lorry parking.
◀ *forêt d'Ecouve; Mancelles.*

PACE-PAR-ALENCON • Orne, 61250

🍴 **LE RELAIS DES ROUTIERS**
(M. Marcel Bruneau) Damigni
☎ 33.27.70.69
Directions: RN 12, the Saint-Malo/Rennes/Alençon road.
Menu: 60 to 120 Frs.
Restaurant: breakfast from 6.30. Lunch from 11.30 until 15.00. Dinner from 19.00 until 21.00. Closed Sat afternoon and Sun afternoon.
Specialities: rillettes, paté du chef, regional menu.
Other points: credit cards accepted, bar, à la carte menu, pets allowed, car/lorry parking.

PARIGNE • Ille-et-Vilaine, 35133

🍴 **LE FRANCK'ELLE**
(M. Franck Rousset) 12 rue de la Mairie
☎ 99.97.22.90
Directions: RD 108, Flers, Fougères exit.
Menu: 51 to 120 Frs.
Restaurant: breakfast from 8.00. Lunch from 12.00 until 15.00. Dinner from 19.00 until 21.00. Closed Mon afternoon, and 1st 2 weeks in Aug.
Specialities: poulet aux écrevisses, truite hussarde, fruits de mer, regional menu.
Other points: credit cards accepted, bar, children's menu, traditional decor, pets allowed, car/lorry parking.
◀ *forêt de Fougères and chateau; Mont-Saint-Michel (23km); chateau at Fretay (2km); Rocher de Monthault; Saint-James American cemetery; Parigné: tourbière (peat-bog); Pontmain (pilgrimage).*

PARIGNY • Manche, 50600

🍴 **HOTEL DU CHEMIN DE FER**
(M. Gilbert Lecornu) La Gare ☎ 33.49.10.55
Directions: RD 977, the Caen/Rennes road, between Mortain and Saint-Hilaire.

Menu: 48 Frs.
Accommodation: 98 to 120 Frs.
Restaurant: breakfast from 6.45. Lunch from 13.00 until 15.00. Dinner from 19.00 until 21.30. Closed Sun, and 2 weeks in Aug.
Specialities: regional menu, home-cooking.
Hotel: 4 rooms. Facilities: shower, private bathroom, television.
Other points: credit cards accepted, bar, children's menu, à la carte menu, modern decor, pets allowed, car/lorry parking.
Mont-Saint-Michel (40km); lac de Vezins (8km); Villedieu-les-Poêles (city of copper) (35km).

PEDERNEC • Côtes-d'Armor, 22540

LE MAUDEZ
(M. Denis Dutillet) Maudez ☎ 96.45.31.28
Directions: Lannion.
Menu: 36 to 85 Frs.
Restaurant: breakfast from 6.45. Lunch from 11.30 until 14.00. Dinner from 19.00 until 21.00. Closed Sun, and 2 weeks in Aug.
Specialities: home-cooking.
Other points: bar, children's menu, à la carte menu.
Perrier valley; leisure park (Armoripark); Ménez-Bré.

PERCY • Manche, 50410

LE RELAIS DE LA GARE
(M. Bernard Guillotte) 4 rue de l'Ancienne Gare ☎ 33.61.20.96
Directions: RD 999, on the left as you reach Percy, coming from Saint-Lô.
Menu: 45 Frs (lunch) and 55 Frs (dinner).
Accommodation: 80 to 100 Frs.
Restaurant: lunch from 12.00. Dinner from 19.00 until 22.00. Closed Sun, public holidays, and for 1 week from 5th March.
Specialities: home-cooking.
Hotel: Facilities: shower, private bathroom.
Other points: bar, modern decor, pets allowed, car/lorry parking.
Villedieu-les-Poêles (9km); Mont-Saint-Michel (55km).

PERROS-GUIREC
Côtes-d'Armor, 22700

LE RELAIS DES CARRIERES – Chez Charly
(M. Charles Huon) 24 rue Gabriel-Viraire, La Clarté ☎ 96.91.64.00
Languages spoken: English and some German.
Menu: 55 Frs (wine and coffee included).
Restaurant: lunch from 12.00 until 15.00. Dinner from 19.00 until 22.00.
Specialities: cochon de lait (piglet), fruits de mer, regional menu, home-cooking.
Other points: bar, children's menu, à la carte menu.
church at La Clarté.

PIACE • Sarthe, 72170

LES DEUX RENARDS
(M. Jérôme Brilliet) Route Nationale 138, Le Bourg ☎ 43.97.02.16
Directions: RN 138, between Alençon (20km) and Le Mans (30km).
Menu: 48 to 55 Frs.
Restaurant: breakfast from 5.00. Lunch from 11.00 until 14.30. Dinner from 19.00 until 22.00. Closed Sat, Sun, and in Aug.
Specialities: home-cooking.
Other points: credit cards accepted, bar, traditional decor, car/lorry parking.
'les alpes Manselles' (20km).

PICAUVILLE • Manche, 50360

HOTEL DES VOYAGEURS
(Mme Fabienne Françoise) 43 rue de Périers ☎ 33.41.00.59
Directions: RN 13, Cherbourg.
Languages spoken: English.
Menu: 49 to 120 Frs.
Accommodation: 115 to 172 Frs.
Restaurant: breakfast from 6.30. Lunch from 12.00. Dinner from 19.15. Closed Sun (out of season), and 2 weeks for Christmas school holidays.
Specialities: moules marinières, soupe de poisson, home-cooking.
Hotel: 9 rooms.
Other points: credit cards accepted, bar, children's menu, à la carte menu, traditional decor, pets allowed, car/lorry parking.
Sainte-Mère-Eglise; landing beaches.

PIERREFITTE • Orne, 61160

LE PIERREFITTE
(M. Yves Delaunay) Route Nationale 158 ☎ 33.35.95.06
Directions: RN 158, the Caen/Argentan road.
Menu: 52 to 55 Frs.
Restaurant: breakfast from 6.00. Lunch from 12.00 until 14.30. Closed Sat afternoon, Sun, 2 weeks in Jan and last 2 weeks in Aug.
Specialities: home-cooking.
Other points: credit cards accepted, bar, children's menu, à la carte menu, traditional decor, pets allowed, car/lorry parking.
chateau at Falaise; memorial at Caen.

PIPRIAC • Ille-et-Vilaine, 35550

HOTEL DE LA TOUR D'AUVERGNE
(M. Michel Gérard) 7 rue de l'Avenir ☎ 99.34.41.34
Menu: 50 to 180 Frs.
Accommodation: 100 to 150 Frs (extra bed for children).
Restaurant: breakfast from 7.00. Lunch from 12.00 until 14.30. Dinner from 19.00 until 21.30. Closed Mon afternoon, and 2 weeks in Feb.

Specialities: poissons au beurre blanc, regional menu.
Hotel: ☆ 10 rooms. Facilities: shower, private bathroom, television, telephone.
Other points: credit cards accepted, bar, children's menu, traditional decor, terrace, car parking.
◖€ chateaux; glass-blowing demonstrations; craft village; excursions on the Oust; boats for hire; chapels.

PLAINTEL • Côtes-d'Armor, 22940

☞ LE SEBASTOPOL
(M. Thierry Podeur) Route de Sébastopol
☎ 96.32.15.74
Languages spoken: English.
Menu: 50 Frs.
Restaurant: breakfast from 8.00.
Specialities: choucroute, cassoulet, fer de mer, regional menu, home-cooking.
Other points: credit cards accepted, bar, children's menu, traditional decor, pets allowed, car/lorry parking.
◖€ Quintin (7km); Saint-Brieuc (12km); Loudéac (32km).

PLENEE-JUGON
Côtes-d'Armor, 22640

☞ RELAIS DES GARENNES
(M. Grant Shannod) ☎ 96.34.52.11
Directions: RN 12, between Rennes and Brest.
Languages spoken: English and Dutch.
Menu: 47 Frs.
Restaurant: breakfast from 5.00. Lunch from 11.45 until 15.00. Dinner from 19.00 until 23.30. Closed Sat evening and Sun.
Specialities: truite farcie aux cèpes, paella, couscous, cassoulet, home-cooking.
Other points: credit cards accepted, bar, children's menu, traditional decor, pets allowed, car/lorry parking.
◖€ abbaye de Bacquin; lakes at Jugon; Dinan.

PLESLIN-TRIGAVOU
Côtes-d'Armor, 22490

☞ LE MILL'PATT
(M. Lorc Renault) Le Bourg ☎ 96.27.84.14
Menu: 50 to 100 Frs.
Restaurant: breakfast from 7.00. Closed Sun (out of season), and 15th Dec to 1st Jan.
Specialities: grillades au feu de bois, saucisse du pays, regional menu, home-cooking.
Other points: bar, children's menu, à la carte menu, modern decor.

PLESTAN • Côtes-d'Armor, 22640

🏨 HOTEL DU CENTRE
(Mme Violette Méline) 5 rue de Penthièvre
☎ 96.34.10.96
Directions: RN 12, Saint-Brieuc.

Menu: 50 to 70 Frs.
Accommodation: 110 Frs.
Restaurant: breakfast from 6.30. Lunch from 11.00 until 15.00. Dinner from 19.00 until 23.00. Closed Sat evening and Sun.
Specialities: fruits de mer (to order), home-cooking.
Hotel: 11 rooms. Facilities: shower, private bathroom.
Other points: credit cards accepted, bar, à la carte menu, traditional decor, pets allowed, car/lorry parking.
◖€ lakes at Jugon; seaside.

PLEUMEUR-GAUTIER
Côtes-d'Armor, 22740

☞ CHEZ CINDY
(M. Hervé Le Foll) La Croix-Neuve
☎ 96.92.42.19
Directions: road to Tréguier-Paimpol.
Menu: 50 to 90 Frs.
Restaurant: breakfast from 9.00. Lunch from 11.30 until 14.00. Dinner from 19.00 until 21.00. Closed Sun, and 3 weeks in Aug.
Specialities: couscous (Thurs), home-cooking.
Other points: bar, children's menu, à la carte menu, traditional decor, terrace, pets allowed, car/lorry parking.
◖€ cathedral at Tréguier; Ile de Bréhat; Perros-Guirec.

PLOERMEL • Morbihan, 56800

🏨 LES ROUTIERS
(Mme Solange Rio) Route de Rennes
☎ 97.74.00.48
Directions: RN 24, after the roundabout at the entrance to Ploermel.
Menu: 50 to 140 Frs.
Accommodation: 90 to 150 Frs.
Restaurant: dinner until 22.00. Closed Sat, and in Sept.
Specialities: home-cooking.
Hotel: 11 rooms.
Other points: credit cards accepted, bar, children's menu, car/lorry parking.

PLOEUC-SUR-LIE
Côtes-d'Armor, 22150

☞ LE RELAIS DU SQUARE
(Mme Sylviane Lafon-Sagory) 5 rue d'Enfer
☎ 96.28.70.47
Directions: RN 168.
Restaurant: dinner until 21.00. Closed Sat, Aug.
Other points: bar.

PLOUAGAT • Côtes-d'Armor, 22170

🏨 CHEZ PIERRETTE
(M. Pierre Drouin) Zone Artisanale de Fournello ☎ 96.74.28.13 [Fax] 96.74.25.42
Directions: RN 12, exit at Quintin-Châtelaudren.

Menu: 56 Frs (wine and coffee included).
Accommodation: 170 Frs to 200 Frs.
Restaurant: breakfast from 5.00. Lunch from
11.30. Dinner from 19.00 until 23.00. Closed Sat
from 15.00, Sun and public holidays.
Specialities: home-cooking.
Hotel: ☆ ☆ 12 rooms. Facilities: shower, private
bathroom, television, telephone.
Other points: credit cards accepted, bar, children's
menu, lounge area, modern decor, pets allowed,
car/lorry parking.

PLOUEDERN • Finistère, 29800

☴ LE RELAIS KERIEL
(Mme Marie Gac) Keriel-Landerneau
☎ 98.20.82.53
Directions: RN 12, the Paris/Brest road.
Languages spoken: English.
Menu: 52 Frs (drink and coffee included).
Restaurant: breakfast from 6.30. Lunch from
11.30 until 13.45. Dinner from 19.00 until 21.00.
Closed from 15th Sept to 8th Oct.
Specialities: fruits de mer, regional menu, home-
cooking.
Other points: credit cards accepted, bar, children's
menu, modern decor, pets allowed, car/lorry parking.
◖ *coast of Brittany.*

PLOUER-SUR-RANCE
Côtes-d'Armor, 22490

☴ LE BON ACCUEIL
(M. Théophile Yris) La Gourbanière
☎ 96.86.91.67
Directions: RD 366, between Dinan and Saint-Malo.
Menu: 50 to 180 Frs ☜
Restaurant: breakfast from 7.30. Lunch from 12.00
until 14.00. Closed Mon afternoon, and in Aug.
Specialities: fruits de mer, saumon fumé maison,
regional menu, home-cooking.
Other points: credit cards accepted, bar, à la carte
menu, terrace, pets allowed, car/lorry parking.
◖ *Rance bridge; Dinan; Saint-Malo: marina.*

PLOUGOUMELEN
Morbihan, 56400

☴ LE KENYAH
(M. Joël Boriller) Zone Commerciale du
Kenyah ☎ 97.56.25.37
Directions: RN 165, the Vannes/Lorient road.
Languages spoken: English.
Menu: 50 Frs (all included).
Restaurant: breakfast from 6.00. Lunch from
12.00 until 14.00. Dinner from 19.00 until 22.00.
Closed Sat evening and Sun.
Specialities: grillades au feu de bois, regional
menu, home-cooking.
Other points: credit cards accepted, bar, modern
decor, terrace, pets allowed, car/lorry parking.
◖ *Auray; Vannes; Gulf of Morbihan; Quiberon;
Carnac.*

PLOUHINEC • Finistère, 29780

☴ RESTO-GRILL AN DAOL MEN
(M. Daniel Ogor) 3 rue du Général-Leclerc
☎ 98.70.76.20
Directions: RD 784, road to Audierne.
Languages spoken: English.
Menu: 49 to 150 Frs.
Restaurant: lunch from 12.00 until 15.00. Dinner
from 19.00 until 21.00. Closed Sun.
Specialities: grillades sur pierre chaude, kig-ha-fars
(biscuits), home-cooking.
Other points: credit cards accepted, traditional
decor, pets allowed, car/lorry parking.
◖ *archeological sites; pointe du Raz; pointe du Van.*

PLOUIGNEAU • Finistère, 29610

☴ BAR DES SPORTS
(M. Jean-Paul Talguen) 18 rue du 9 août
☎ 98.67.71.37
Directions: RN 12, towards the town centre.
Menu: 50 to 180 Frs.
Restaurant: breakfast from 7.00. Lunch from
12.00 until 14.30. Dinner from 19.00 until 22.00.
Closed Sun (except functions), and 2 weeks in Aug.
Specialities: fruits de mer, choucroute maison,
couscous, regional menu, home-cooking.
Other points: credit cards accepted, bar, children's
menu, lounge area, traditional decor, car/lorry
parking.
◖ *beaches; chateaux.*

PLOUNEVEZ-MOEDEC
Côtes-d'Armor, 22810

▣ RELAIS DU BEG AR C'HRA
(M. Jean-Marie Rubeus) ☎ 96.38.61.08
Directions: RN 12, between Morlaix and
Guingamp, expressway exit at Beg Ar C'Hra.
Menu: 52 Frs.
Accommodation: 115 to 170 Frs.
Restaurant: breakfast from 6.30. Lunch from
12.00 until 14.00. Dinner from 19.30 until 22.00.
Closed Sat, Sun, public holidays, 1st week in May
and mid-Aug to mid-Sept.
Specialities: home-cooking.
Hotel: 11 rooms. Facilities: shower.
Other points: credit cards accepted, bar,
traditional decor, pets allowed, car/lorry parking.
◖ *chateau at Rosambo (10km); Côte de Granit
Rose (25km).*

PLOUNEVEZ-QUINTIN
Côtes-d'Armor, 22110

☴ LES ROUTIERS
(Mme Gildas Martin) 1 place de l'Eglise
☎ 96.24.54.05
Directions: RN 790, Saint-Brieuc.
Menu: 55 to 120 Frs.
Restaurant: breakfast from 7.00. Lunch from
11.30 until 14.00. Dinner from 19.00 until 21.00.

Closed Sat, and mid-Aug to mid-Sept.
Specialities: home-cooking.
Other points: credit cards accepted, bar, children's menu, traditional decor, pets allowed, car/lorry parking.
❄ *lakes; the valley.*

PLOURAY • Morbihan, 56770

🍴 BAR-RESTAURANT LES ROUTIERS
(Mme Léandre Le Lain) 2 rue de l'Ellé
☎ 97.34.81.39
Directions: the Rennes/Quimper road.
Menu: 50 Frs.
Restaurant: breakfast from 8.00. Lunch 12.00 to 14.00. Dinner 19.30 to 20.00. Closed Sat.
Specialities: home-cooking.
Other points: bar.

POLIGNE • Ille-et-Vilaine, 35320

🍴 LE TIROUANEZ
(Mme Marylène Guillard) ☎ 99.43.73.06
Directions: RN 137, the Nantes/Rennes road.
Languages spoken: English.
Menu: 50 Frs.
Restaurant: breakfast from 7.00. Lunch from 11.30. Dinner until 24.00. Closed Sun.
Specialities: home-cooking.
Other points: credit cards accepted, bar, children's menu, modern decor, terrace, pets allowed, car/lorry parking.
❄ *Le Tertre Gris; animal park.*

PONT-AUDEMER • Eure, 27500

🍴 AU RENDEZ-VOUS DES CHAUFFEURS
(M. Renaud Pierrel) 4 rue Notre-Dame-du-Pré ☎ 32.41.04.36
Directions: RN 180
Restaurant: closed Sun.
Hotel: 3 rooms.
Other points: bar.

🍴 RELAIS DE SAINT-PAUL
(M. Claude Virfollet) Route de Saint-Paul, Les Saulniers ☎ 32.41.16.17
Directions: RN 180, between Pont-Audemer and Bernay.
Menu: 52 Frs 🍲
Restaurant: breakfast from 7.30. Lunch from 11.30 until 13.00. Closed Sat, Sun, and the first 2 weeks in Aug.
Specialities: home-cooking.
Other points: bar, traditional decor, car/lorry parking.

PONT-AVEN • Finistère, 29930

🍴 CHEZ MELANIE ET MONIQUE
(Mme Le Goc) Croissant-Kergos
☎ 98.06.03.09

Directions: between Concarneau and Quimperlé.
Menu: 🍲

PONT-HEBERT • Manche, 50880

🏨 LE MADRILENE
(Mme Marie-Thérèse Hamet) Quartier du Pont la Meauffe ☎ 33.56.44.18
Menu: 55 Frs.
Accommodation: 90 to 110 Frs.
Restaurant: breakfast from 7.00. Lunch 12.00 to 14.00. Dinner 19.00 to 21.00. Closed Sun.
Specialities: home-cooking.
Hotel: 7 rooms. Facilities: shower.
Other points: bar, pets allowed, car/lorry parking.

PONT-SAINT-MARTIN
Loire-Atlantique, 44860

🍴 LE RELAIS COTE OUEST
(M. Jean-Louis Vrignaud) Parc d'Activité de Viais ☎ 40.32.72.40
Directions: the Nantes/La Roche-sur-Yon road.
Menu: 50 to 178 Frs.
Restaurant: breakfast from 6.15. Lunch from 12.00 until 14.30. Dinner from 19.00 until 21.30. Closed Sun evening and Sat evening.
Specialities: cuisses de grenouilles, poissons au beurre blanc, home-cooking.
Other points: credit cards accepted, bar, children's menu, à la carte menu, modern decor, terrace, pets allowed, car/lorry parking.
❄ *Lac de Grand-Lieu.*

PONTCHATEAU
Loire-Atlantique, 44160

🏨 L'AUBERGE DU CALVAIRE
(Mme Gabrielle Couvrand) 6 route de la Brière, Le Calvaire ☎ 40.01.61.65
Fax 40.01.64.68
Directions: RD 33, 4km from the centre of Pontchâteau, towards Herbignac.
Languages spoken: English.
Menu: 60 to 120 Frs 🍲
Accommodation: 180 to 250 Frs.
Restaurant: breakfast from 9.00. Lunch from 12.00 until 14.00. Dinner from 19.00 until 21.00.
Specialities: anguilles (eels) au muscadet, merlan au beurre blanc, regional menu, home-cooking.
Hotel: ✰ ✰ 12 rooms. Facilities: shower, private bathroom, television, telephone.
Other points: credit cards accepted, bar, children's menu, à la carte menu, modern decor, terrace, pets allowed, car/lorry parking.
❄ *Calvaire de Pontchâteau; parc régional de Brière; Côte d'Amour; pont Saint-Nazaire; La Baule; La Roche-Bernard.*

🏨 LE RELAIS DE BEAULIEU
(Mme Louisette Praud) ☎ 40.01.60.58
Fax 40.45.60.82
Directions: RN 165, the Nantes/Vannes road.

Languages spoken: English and Italian.
Menu: 65 to 155 Frs 🍴
Accommodation: 120 to 270 Frs.
Restaurant: breakfast from 5.00. Lunch from 12.00 until 15.00. Dinner from 19.00 until 22.00. Closed Sat evening and Sun evening.
Specialities: anguilles au cidre, saumon grillé au beurre blanc, langoustes, soupe de poissons, regional menu, home-cooking.
Hotel: 15 rooms. Facilities: shower, private bathroom.
Other points: credit cards accepted, bar, children's menu, à la carte menu, pets allowed, car/lorry parking.
🗲 Calvaire de Pontchâteau; parc régional de Brière; La Baule; La Roche-Bernard; château de la Bretesche at Missillac.

PONTORSON • Manche, 50170

🏨 **LE RENOVE**
(Mme Marie-Claire Pépin) 4 rue de Rennes
☎ 33.60.00.21
Directions: RN 175.
Menu: 50 to 120 Frs.
Accommodation: 140 to 220 Frs.
Restaurant: breakfast from 7.00. Lunch from 12.00 until 15.00. Dinner from 19.00 until 22.00. Closed Sun (out of season).
Specialities: home-cooking.
Hotel: 10 rooms.
Other points: credit cards accepted, bar, children's menu, à la carte menu, modern decor, pets allowed.
🗲 Mont-Saint-Michel.

QUEVEN • Morbihan, 56530

🏨 **LE RELAIS DE LA MAIRIE**
(Mme Yvonne Legallic) rue Principale
☎ 97.05.07.50
Directions: RD 6.
Hotel: 8 rooms.
Other points: restaurant, bar.

QUIMPERLE • Finistère, 29300

🍴 **LA FOURCHE**
(Mme Solange Philipot) Route de Lorient
☎ 98.39.11.45
Directions: Quimperlé.
Menu: 50 Frs.
Restaurant: breakfast from 6.30. Lunch from 12.00 until 14.00. Dinner from 19.30 until 22.00. Closed Sat, Sun, and 1st 2 weeks in Sept.
Specialities: choucroute, couscous, andouillette chaude, home-cooking.
Other points: credit cards accepted, bar, traditional decor, pets allowed, car/lorry parking.
🗲 Forêt de Carnoët; beaches; zoo.

🍴 **TI LANIG**
(M. Alain Minec) Zone Artisanale de Keringant ☎ 98.39.16.07 [Fax] 98.39.01.28
Directions: RN 165, exit at Manoir-de-Kernault.

Languages spoken: English.
Menu: 50 to 95 Frs.
Restaurant: breakfast from 6.00. Lunch from 11.00 until 14.30. Dinner from 19.00 until 21.45. Closed Fri evening, Sat evening, Sun, and in Aug.
Specialities: regional menu, home-cooking.
Other points: credit cards accepted, bar, children's menu, à la carte menu, modern decor, terrace, pets allowed, car/lorry parking.
🗲 Forêt de Clohars-Carnoët; beaches.

RANDONNAI • Orne, 61190

🏨 **HOTEL DU GRAND CERF**
(M. Daniel Millière) 5 route Sainte-Anne
☎ 33.34.20.03
Directions: between L'Aigle and Nogent-le-Rotrou.
Menu: 46 to 60 Frs.
Accommodation: 100 to 120 Frs.
Restaurant: breakfast from 7.00. Lunch from 11.30 until 15.00. Dinner from 19.00 until 22.00. Closed Tues afternoon, and 1st 2 weeks in June.
Specialities: langue sauce piquante, rognons au madère, calmars (squid) à l'armoricaine, aile de raie (skate-wing) au vinaigre, home-cooking.
Hotel: 6 rooms. Facilities: shower, private bathroom.
Other points: credit cards accepted, children's menu, traditional decor, pets allowed, car/lorry parking.
🗲 Etoile du Perche (4km); abbey at La Trappe (8km); domaine des étands (deer-breeding).

RANES • Orne, 61150

🏨 **HOTEL DU PARC**
(M. Roger Cantin) 9 rue du Parc
☎ 33.39.73.85
Directions: RN 916, between Mont-Saint-Michel and Brittany.
Menu: 60 to 160 Frs.
Accommodation: 140 to 260 Frs.
Restaurant: breakfast from 7.30. Lunch from 12.00 until 14.00. Dinner from 19.00 until 21.00. Closed Sun evening.
Specialities: ris de veau Vallée d'Auge, coquelet au cidre, anguilles (eels) au cidre, regional menu, home-cooking.
Hotel: 7 rooms. Facilities: shower, private bathroom.
Other points: credit cards accepted, bar, children's menu, à la carte menu, traditional decor, terrace, pets allowed, car/lorry parking.
🗲 la Suisse normande; Bagnoles-de-l'Orne; le haras (stud-farm) du Pin; châteaux de Sassy and de Carrouges.

RENAC • Ille-et-Vilaine, 35660

🍴 **RESTAURANT CREPERIE BEAUREGARD**
(Mme Marie-Annick Bonno) Beauregard
☎ 99.72.07.83
Directions: RD 177, between Rennes and Redon.

Menu: 45 to 80 Frs.
Restaurant: breakfast from 9.00. Lunch from 12.00 until 14.00. Dinner from 18.00 until 21.00. Closed Mon, and 1 week in Feb.
Specialities: home-cooking.
Other points: credit cards accepted, à la carte menu, traditional decor, pets allowed, car/lorry parking.
◁€ megalithic site at Saint-Just; Redon: church.

REZE • Loire-Atlantique, 44400

⇌ RESTAURANT DES AMIS
(Mme Irène Richard) 4 place Saint-Pierre
☎ 40.75.53.29
Directions: between Pornic and Nantes.
Menu: 47 Frs.
Restaurant: breakfast from 7.00. Lunch from 11.30 until 15.00. Dinner from 19.00 until 22.00. Closed Sun.
Specialities: home-cooking.
Other points: credit cards accepted, bar, children's menu, modern decor, pets allowed, car/lorry parking.
◁€ Nantes: chateau des ducs de Bretagne, old town; route du Muscadet.

LES ROUTIERS
ACCOMMODATION DIRECTORY

This handy directory lists an extensive choice of Les Routiers-recommended places offering comfortable accommodation in relaxed surroundings throughout the British Isles.

Available from selected Les Routiers establishments or direct from the publishers, price £2.

RIAILLE • Loire-Atlantique, 44440

⇌ AU RENDEZ-VOUS DES PECHEURS
(M. Joël Aspot) place du Champ-de-Foire
☎ 40.97.80.95
Directions: D 178 and 33.
Menu: 44 to 91 Frs.
Restaurant: lunch from 11.45 until 14.30. Dinner from 19.00 until 21.00. Closed Wed afternoon, and from 28th July to 15th Aug.
Specialities: fruits de mer, home-cooking.
Other points: credit cards accepted, bar, children's menu, à la carte menu, traditional decor, terrace, car/lorry parking.
◁€ chateaux and monuments.

RICHEVILLE • Eure, 27420

⇌ RESTAURANT LE BALTO
(M. Pierre Sadok) 4 Route Nationale 14
☎ 32.27.10.55
Directions: RN 14, the Paris/Rouen road.
Languages spoken: English.
Menu: 50 to 119 Frs 🍲
Restaurant: breakfast from 5.30. Lunch from

11.00 until 15.00. Dinner from 18.30 until 21.00. Closed Sat afternoon, Sun, and in Aug.
Specialities: escalopes normandes, filet au poivre, home-cooking.
Other points: credit cards accepted, bar, children's menu, à la carte menu, traditional decor, pets allowed, car/lorry parking.
◁€ Château-Gaillard; les Andelys; Vernon; Claude Monet's house at Giverny; Gisors.

LA RIVIERE-SAINT-SAUVEUR
Calvados, 14600

⇌ LES OISEAUX DE MER
(M. Pascal Quesney) 28 route des 4 Francs
☎ 31.89.11.62
Directions: in the industrial zone (Z.I.).
Menu: 49 Frs (drink included).
Restaurant: breakfast from 5.30. Lunch from 11.00. Dinner until 21.00. Closed Sun, and in Aug.
Specialities: home-cooking.
Other points: bar, children's menu, pets allowed, car/lorry parking.
◁€ Honfleur; Deauville; Trouville.

LA ROCHE-SUR-YON
Vendée, 85000

🛏 HOTEL SULLY
(Mme Nathalie Bohy) boulevard Sully
☎ 51.37.18.21 [Fax] 51.46.09.63
Directions: RN 137, Noirmoutier.
Languages spoken: English and Spanish.
Menu: 55 Frs (drink included).
Accommodation: 150 Frs.
Restaurant: breakfast from 6.00. Lunch from 11.30 until 15.00. Dinner from 19.00 until 22.30.
Specialities: jambon de Vendée aux haricots blancs, home-cooking.
Hotel: ☆ ☆ 34 rooms. Facilities: shower, private bathroom, television, telephone.
Other points: credit cards accepted, bar, children's menu, à la carte menu, lounge area, traditional decor, terrace, pets allowed, car/lorry parking.
◁€ haras (stud-farm); dam; moulin Papon; Ecomusée de la Vendée; le Puy du Fou; Poitou marshlands.

ROMAGNY • Manche, 50140

⇌ AUBERGE DES CLOSEAUX
(M. Bernard Clouard) Les Closeaux
☎ 33.59.01.86 [Fax] 33.69.41.02
Directions: RD 977, between Rennes and Caen, towards Saint-Hilaire-du-Harcouët.
Languages spoken: English.
Menu: 54 to 145 Frs.
Accommodation: 180 to 230 Frs.
Restaurant: dinner until 20.30. Closed Sun (out of season).
Specialities: pintade (guinea-fowl) au cidre, crustacés (shellfish), poissons, regional menu.
Hotel: ☆ ☆ 10 rooms. Facilities: shower, private bathroom, television, telephone.
Other points: credit cards accepted, bar, children's

menu, à la carte menu, lounge area, modern decor, terrace, car/lorry parking.
⤞ *Mont-Saint-Michel (20km); côte de Granville.*

ROMAZY • Ille-et-Vilaine, 35490

LE RELAIS
(M. Jean-Claude Moncel) Le Bourg
☎ 99.39.50.83
Directions: RN 175, between Rennes and Mont-St-Michel.
Menu: 50 Frs.
Restaurant: breakfast from 6.30. Lunch from 11.00 until 14.30. Dinner from 19.00 until 22.00. Closed Sat and Sun.
Specialities: escalope Normande, home-cooking.
Other points: credit cards accepted, bar, pets allowed, car/lorry parking.
⤞ *Mont-Saint-Michel (30km); chateaux at Combourg (20km) and Fougères (30km); leisure park (30km).*

ROSPORDEN • Finistère, 29140

LES ROUTIERS
(Mme Maryvonne Michal) 9 pont Biais
☎ 98.59.20.40
Directions: RN 165, Quimper.
Menu: 52 Frs.
Accommodation: 160 Frs.
Restaurant: breakfast from 6.00. Lunch from 12.00 until 13.30. Dinner from 19.30 until 20.15. Closed Sat, Sun, and in Aug.
Specialities: home-cooking.
Hotel: 17 rooms.
Other points: bar, traditional decor, pets allowed, car/lorry parking.
⤞ *Concarneau (13km).*

ROTS • Calvados, 14980

LE RELAIS DU COUP DE POMPE
(M. Valentin Castander) 22 route de Caen
☎ 31.26.63.56
Directions: RN 13, Cherbourg.
Languages spoken: English and Spanish.
Restaurant: breakfast from 6.30. Lunch from 12.00 until 14.00. Dinner from 19.00 until 21.30. Closed Sat afternoon and Sun.
Specialities: home-cooking.
Hotel: 5 rooms.
Other points: bar.
⤞ *Bayeux.*

ROUANS • Loire-Atlantique, 44640

LA CHAUSSEE-LE-RETZ
(Mme Claudette Biton) La Chaussée-Le-Retz
☎ 40.64.22.23
Directions: the Paimboeuf/Saint-Brévin road.
Menu: 51 to 160 Frs.
Accommodation: 130 to 160 Frs.

Restaurant: breakfast from 7.00. Lunch from 12.00 until 15.00. Dinner from 19.30 until 22.00. Closed Sat (Oct to Easter).
Specialities: anguilles (eels) grillées, cuisses de grenouilles, home-cooking.
Hotel: 6 rooms. Facilities: shower, private bathroom.
Other points: bar, children's menu, à la carte menu, modern decor, terrace, pets allowed, car/lorry parking.
⤞ *safari at Port-Saint-Père; locks on Canal de la Martinière.*

ROUEN • Seine-Maritime, 76100

LES PLATANES
(M. Roger Sannier) 57 avenue du Mont-Riboudet ☎ 35.71.01.52 [Fax] 35.71.01.52
Menu: 55 Frs.
Accommodation: 70 to 90 Frs.
Restaurant: breakfast from 6.00. Lunch from 12.00 until 15.00. Closed public holidays, first 2 weeks in Aug and 1 week at Christmas.
Specialities: regional menu, home-cooking.
Hotel: 20 rooms. Facilities: shower.
Other points: credit cards accepted, bar, children's menu, à la carte menu, traditional decor.
⤞ *Rouen and the Seine valley; museums.*

ROUGE-PERRIERS • Eure, 27110

LE RELAIS DU PONT DE L'EURE
(Mme Colette Le Prince) 3 route d'Harcourt
☎ 32.35.05.00
Directions: RD 137, between Le Neubourg and Brionne.
Languages spoken: English.
Menu: 52 to 85 Frs.
Restaurant: breakfast from 7.00. Lunch from 12.00 until 14.30. Dinner from 19.00 until 21.00. Closed Mon.
Specialities: home-cooking.
Other points: credit cards accepted, bar, children's menu, terrace, pets allowed, car/lorry parking.
⤞ *château d'Harcourt; abbaye du Bec-Hellouin.*

ROUGEMONTIER • Eure, 27350

LE LUDO
(M. Jean-Claude Duboc) 175 Route Nationale
☎ 32.56.85.22
Directions: RN 175, the Rouen/Caen road.
Menu: 54 Frs (wine included).
Restaurant: breakfast from 4.30. Dinner until 21.30. Closed Sat from 14.30, Sun, and in Aug.
Specialities: home-cooking.
Other points: bar, à la carte menu, modern decor, pets allowed, car/lorry parking.
⤞ *Parc de Brotonne; four à pain (baker's oven) at Haye-de-Routout; musée du sabotier (clog-maker); moulin de pierre at Hauville; maison des métiers (trades) at Bourneville.*

ROZ-LANDRIEUX
Ille-et-Vilaine, 35120

LES 36 CHANDELLES
(M. Thierry Henon) 3 rue de l'Eglise
☎ 99.48.07.73
Directions: between Dol-de-Bretagne and Dinan.
Menu: 50 Frs.
Restaurant: breakfast from 7.30. Lunch from
11.30 until 14.30. Dinner from 18.30 until 21.30.
Closed Wed afternoon and evening.
Specialities: poissons, home-cooking.
Other points: bar, children's menu, traditional
decor, terrace, pets allowed, car/lorry parking.
◀€ Combourg: chateau; Cancale; Saint-Malo;
Dinan; Dinard; Mont-Saint-Michel.

LES SABLES D'OLONNE
Vendée, 85100

AU COQ HARDI
(Mlle Françoise Pajot) 7 avenue Alcide-
Cabaret ☎ 51.32.04.62
Directions: RD 949, La Rochelle.
Menu: 55 to 85 Frs.
Accommodation: 160 to 200 Frs.
Restaurant: breakfast from 8.30. Lunch from
12.00 until 15.00. Dinner from 19.00 until 20.30.
Closed Sat, Sun (out of season), and from 20th
Sept to 10th Oct.
Specialities: fruits de mer, poissons, home-cooking.
Hotel: 8 rooms.
Other points: credit cards accepted, bar,
traditional decor, terrace.
◀€ ports; beach and coastline; Atlantic coast.

LES VOYAGEURS
(M. Clément Pacory) 17 rue de la Baudière
☎ 51.95.11.49 [Fax] 51.21.50.21
Directions: RN 160 and 149.
Menu: 44 to 130 Frs.
Accommodation: 180 to 220 Frs.
Restaurant: breakfast from 7.00. Lunch from
12.00 until 14.00. Dinner from 19.15 until 21.00.
Closed Fri evening and Sat (out of season), and
3 weeks from Christmas Day.
Specialities: poissons, fruits de mer, home-cooking.
Hotel: 15 rooms. Facilities: shower, private
bathroom, television, telephone.
Other points: credit cards accepted, bar, à la carte
menu, traditional decor, pets allowed, car parking.

SACEY • Manche, 50170

LES VOYAGEURS
(Mme Marcelle Belan) Le Bourg
☎ 33.60.15.11
Directions: the Pontorson/Rennes/Fougères road.
Menu: 48 to 120 Frs.
Accommodation: 130 to 185 Frs.
Restaurant: breakfast from 6.00. Lunch from
12.00 until 15.00. Dinner from 19.00 until 22.00.
Specialities: fruits de mer, homard (lobster) à
l'américaine (to order), home-cooking.
Hotel: 7 rooms.
Other points: credit cards accepted, bar, children's

menu, traditional decor, terrace, pets allowed,
car/lorry parking.
◀€ Mont-Saint-Michel (17km); Avranches: jardin
des plantes (12km).

SAINT-AUBIN-SUR-SCIE
Seine-Maritime, 76550

LE RELAIS DE LA SCIE
(M. Roger Burgot) rue du Gouffre
☎ 35.85.44.60
Directions: RN 27, between Tôtes and Dieppe.
Menu: 53 Frs.
Restaurant: breakfast from 6.30. Lunch from
11.30 until 14.30. Closed Sun.
Specialities: home-cooking.
Other points: credit cards accepted, bar, children's
menu, lounge area, terrace, pets allowed, car parking.
◀€ Dieppe; Côte de Nacre.

SAINT-BERTHEVIN
Mayenne, 53940

L'INTERNATIONAL
(M. Henri Garnier) L'Aulne, Route Nationale
157 ☎ 43.69.31.74 [Fax] 43.69.31.74
Directions: RN 157, Rennes.
Languages spoken: English.
Menu: 57 to 110 Frs.
Accommodation: 100 to 145 Frs.
Restaurant: breakfast from 6.00. Lunch 12.00 to
15.00. Dinner 19.30 to 23.00. Closed Sun.
Specialities: home-cooking.
Hotel: ☆ ☆ 22 rooms. Facilities: shower, private
bathroom, television, telephone.
Other points: credit cards accepted, bar, children's
menu, à la carte menu, lounge area, modern decor,
terrace, pets allowed, car/lorry parking.
◀€ chateau at Laval; gardens at La Périne.

SAINT-BRANDAN
Côtes-d'Armor, 22800

RELAIS ROUTIERS
(M. Pierre Jacob) 47 rue de Launay
☎ 96.74.88.19
Directions: RD 790, on the road to Saint-Brieuc.
Menu: 50 to 75 Frs.
Restaurant: breakfast from 8.00. Lunch from
10.00 until 15.00. Dinner from 18.00 until 21.00.
Closed Sat afternoon, Sun, and in Aug.
Specialities: regional menu, home-cooking.
Other points: bar, à la carte menu, traditional
decor, car/lorry parking.
◀€ Marhalach; lac de Bosmeliac; le Chaos du Gouet.

SAINT-BREVIN-L'OCEAN
Loire-Atlantique, 44250

LA DUCHESSE ANNE
(Mme Rose-Annie Laloue) 82 avenue du
Président-Roosevelt ☎ 40.27.23.38
[Fax] 40.39.03.81
Directions: between Saint-Nazaire and Pornic.

Languages spoken: English.
Menu: 54 to 110 Frs (crêperie).
Restaurant: breakfast from 11.00. Lunch from
12.00 until 14.00. Dinner from 19.00 until 21.00.
Closed Mon/Tues after 14.30 (out of season).
Specialities: noix de Saint-Jacques à la provençale,
poisson au beurre blanc, magrets de canard, home-
cooking.
Other points: credit cards accepted, bar, à la carte
menu, traditional decor, terrace, pets allowed, car/
lorry parking.
◀ Saint-Nazaire; dolmen du Rossignol; jardin aux
Moines; musée de la marine.

SAINT-BREVIN-LES-PINS
Loire-Atlantique, 44250

≠ **LA GUINGUETTE**
   (Mme Pierrette Girault) 137 avenue du
   Maréchal-Foch, La Courance ☎ 40.27.21.95
Directions: between Saint-Nazaire and La Baule
or Pornic.
Menu: 50 Frs (winter) and 74 Frs (during the season).
Restaurant: breakfast from 6.00. Lunch 12.00 to
14.00. Dinner 19.00 to 22.00. Closed Sat, Sun
(out of season), and 1 week from Christmas Day.
Specialities: fruits de mer (in season), home-cooking.
Other points: credit cards accepted, bar, children's
menu, à la carte menu, traditional decor, terrace,
pets allowed, car/lorry parking.
◀ Pornic; le Puy du Fou.

SAINT-BROLADRE
Ille-et-Vilaine, 35120

🏠 **LE FLORIDA**
   (Mme Eliane Loas) Le Bourg ☎ 99.80.26.41
Directions: RD 797, between Pontorson and
Saint-Malo.
Menu: 49 to 65 Frs.
Accommodation: 110 to 160 Frs.
Restaurant: breakfast from 7.00. Lunch from
12.00 until 14.00. Dinner from 19.00 until 21.00.
Specialities: moules, viandes grillées, home-cooking.
Hotel: 7 rooms. Facilities: shower.
Other points: bar, children's menu, traditional
decor, terrace, pets allowed, car/lorry parking.
◀ Saint-Malo; Mont-Saint-Michel.

SAINT-COME-DU-FRESNE
Calvados, 14960

≠ **LE SANTA DE A**
   (Mme Andréa Boquet) 3 rue Panoramique
   ☎ 31.21.15.70
Menu: 52 to 140 Frs.
Restaurant: breakfast from 9.00. Closed Mon
afternoon.
Specialities: fruits de mer, home-cooking.
Other points: credit cards accepted, bar, children's
menu, à la carte menu, modern decor, terrace, pets
allowed, car/lorry parking.
◀ landing beaches; Bayeux tapestry; maison de la
mer; chateau at Saint-Côme.

SAINT-CYR-EN-PAIL
Mayenne, 53140

≠ **LES ROUTIERS**
   (Mme Antoinette Dupont) Le Bourg
   ☎ 43.03.03.21
Directions: RN 12, between Alençon and Mayenne.
Menu: 48 to 50 Frs.
Restaurant: breakfast from 6.30. Lunch from
11.30 until 14.30. Dinner from 18.30 until 21.00.
Closed Sun, and in Aug.
Specialities: home-cooking.
Other points: bar, children's menu, traditional
decor, pets allowed, car/lorry parking.
◀ Mont des Avaloirs (2km); chateau at Carrouges
(20km); Pierre-au-Loup (2km); la Corniche de Pail
(2km).

SAINT-CYR-EN-TALMONDAIS
Vendée, 85540

≠ **RESTAURANT DU CENTRE**
   (M. Jean-Claude Vaucelle) Route
   Départementale 949, Au Bourg
   ☎ 51.30.82.84
Directions: RD 949, between Fontenay-le-Comte
and Les Sables d'Olonne.
Menu: 55 to 120 Frs.
Restaurant: breakfast from 7.30. Lunch from
12.00 until 15.00. Dinner from 19.00 until 21.00.
Closed Thurs after 14.00, and 1 week in Jan.
Specialities: home-cooking.
Other points: credit cards accepted, bar, children's
menu, à la carte menu, traditional decor, car/lorry
parking.
◀ Les Sables d'Olonne (35km); Saint-Cyr: floral
park and chateau.

SAINT-DENIS-DE-MAILLOC
Calvados, 14100

≠ **LA FORGE**
   (M. Bruno Morin) ☎ 31.63.73.19
Directions: RD 519, between Lisieux and Orbec.
Menu: 51 Frs.
Restaurant: breakfast from 7.00. Lunch from 11.30
until 14.00. Closed Sat, Sun, and last 2 weeks in Aug.
Specialities: regional menu, home-cooking.
Other points: bar, children's menu, pets allowed,
car/lorry parking.
◀ basilica at Lisieux; chateau at Saint-Germain-de-
Livet; Deauville; zoo at Cerza.

SAINT-DENIS-DES-MONTS
Eure, 27520

≠ **LE LAMA**
   (M. Christian Chuette) Route Nationale 138
   ☎ 32.42.60.10
Directions: RN 138, between Rouen and Brionne.
Menu: 52 Frs.
Restaurant: breakfast from 6.00. Lunch from
11.00 until 15.00. Closed Sat, Sun, 3 weeks in Aug
and 10 days from New Year's Eve.

Specialities: home-cooking.
Other points: credit cards accepted, bar, children's menu, traditional decor, pets allowed, car/lorry parking.
◁∈ *Le Bec-Hellouin.*

SAINT-DENIS-SUR-SARTHON
Orne, 61420

🏠 HOTEL DE LA GARE – Les Amis des Routiers
(M. Guy Ellien) La Gare ☎ 33.27.30.03
Directions: RN 12.
Menu: 48 Frs (wine included).
Restaurant: breakfast from 6.00. Closed Sat, Sun.
Specialities: regional menu.
Other points: bar, à la carte menu, lorry parking.

SAINT-ERBLON
Ille-et-Vilaine, 35230

🍴 CHEZ MICHEL ET SYLVIE
(M. Michel Martin) Zone Artisanale, 3 allée des Leuzières ☎ 99.52.28.40
Directions: RD 82, Rennes/Nantes expressway.
Languages spoken: English.
Menu: 47 Frs.
Restaurant: breakfast from 9.30. Lunch from 11.30 until 14.00. Closed in Aug.
Specialities: potée, couscous, regional menu, home-cooking.
Other points: children's menu, traditional decor, pets allowed, car/lorry parking.
◁∈ *Rennes.*

SAINT-ETIENNE-DE-BRILLOUET
Vendée, 85210

🍴 LE STEPHANOIS
(Mme Marie-Thérèse Dugas)
Route Nationale 148 ☎ 51.27.63.37
Directions: RN 148, the Niort/Saint-Hermine/Nantes road.
Languages spoken: English.
Menu: 59 Frs (wine included).
Restaurant: breakfast from 6.30. Lunch from 11.30 until 14.30. Dinner from 19.00 until 22.00. Closed Thurs, 1 week in Feb and 1 week from Christmas Day.
Specialities: fruits de mer, regional menu, home-cooking.
Other points: bar, children's menu, à la carte menu, lounge area, traditional decor, terrace, car/lorry parking.
◁∈ *Poitou marshlands; le Puy du Fou (40km); chateaux.*

SAINT-EVARZEC • Finistère, 29170

🏠 AU BON REPOS
(M. Roger Guillou) Poullogoden
☎ 98.56.20.09

Directions: RD 783, between Quimper and Concarneau.
Menu: 60 to 100 Frs.
Accommodation: 130 to 200 Frs.
Restaurant: breakfast from 6.30. Lunch from 12.00 until 14.00. Dinner from 19.00 until 20.30. Closed Sat (out of season), and in Dec.
Specialities: coquilles Saint-Jacques, fruits de mer, home-cooking.
Hotel: 20 rooms. Facilities: shower, private bathroom, television, telephone.
Other points: credit cards accepted, bar, terrace, pets allowed, car/lorry parking.
◁∈ *Bénodet; beaches; Port la Forêt; Concarneau.*

SAINT-EVROULT-DE-MONTFORT
Orne, 61230

🏠 HOTEL DU RELAIS
(M. Daniel Conan) Le Bourg ☎ 33.35.60.58
Directions: RN 138, between Rouen and Alençon.
Menu: 48 Frs.
Accommodation: 80 to 150 Frs.
Restaurant: breakfast from 7.00. Lunch from 11.00 until 15.00. Dinner from 19.00 until 22.00. Closed Sun.
Specialities: home-cooking.
Hotel: 5 rooms. Facilities: shower.
Other points: bar, car/lorry parking.

SAINT-GEORGES-DE-ROUELLEY
Manche, 50720

🍴 AUBERGE DU LION D'OR
(Mme Nadia Desgaroins) Route de Domfront
☎ 33.59.35.14
Directions: RD 907, between Domfront and Saint-Mortain.
Menu: 50 Frs.
Restaurant: breakfast from 7.30. Lunch from 12.00 until 14.00
Specialities: home-cooking.
Other points: credit cards accepted, bar, traditional decor, pets allowed, car/lorry parking.
◁∈ *Fosse Arthour; Saint-Frimbault; waterfall at Mortain; abbaye de Lonlay.*

SAINT-GERMAIN-SUR-MOINE
Maine-et-Loire, 49230

🍴 LE TAILLIS DU VERGER
(M. Paul Eraud) Carrefour du Petit Lapin, Route de la Renaudière ☎ 41.64.64.61
Directions: RN 249, on the Nantes/Cholet expressway.
Menu: 55 Frs (coffee included).
Restaurant: breakfast from 6.30. Lunch from 11.30 until 14.30. Dinner from 19.00 until 22.00. Closed Sun.
Specialities: regional menu, home-cooking.
Other points: credit cards accepted, bar, children's menu, modern decor, terrace, pets allowed, car/lorry parking.

SAINT-GILDAS-DES-BOIS
Loire-Atlantique, 44530

RELAIS CASSEROLE LES ROUTIERS
(M. Michel Gaidano) 27 rue du Pont
☎ 40.01.42.15 [Fax] 40.19.60.32
Directions: RD 773, between Redon and
Pontchâteau.
Menu: 65 to 350 Frs ☜
Accommodation: 135 to 150 Frs.
Restaurant: breakfast from 7.30. Lunch from
14.00 until 14.30. Dinner from 20.00 until 21.30.
Specialities: fruits de mer, homard (lobster) grillé,
beurre blanc, regional menu.
Hotel: 10 rooms. Facilities: shower, private
bathroom, television.
Other points: credit cards accepted, bar, children's
menu, à la carte menu, traditional decor, pets
allowed, car/lorry parking.
◂ calvaire at Pontchâteau; chateau at La Bretèche.

SAINT-GILLES • Manche, 50180

CARREFOUR SAINT-GILLES
(M. Yannik Toutain) Le Bourg
☎ 33.05.24.50
Directions: between Saint-Lô and Coutances.
Menu: 50 Frs.
Restaurant: breakfast from 6.30. Closed Sat, Sun.
Specialities: home-cooking.
Other points: credit cards accepted, bar, modern
decor, terrace, pets allowed, car/lorry parking.
◂ Saint-Lô: ramparts (7km); les vieux métiers
(trades) at Remilly-sur-Lozon (10km).

SAINT-GILLES-CROIX-DE-VIE /
LE FENOUILLER • Vendée, 85800

LA MADELON
(Mme Christine Poupart) 64 rue du Centre
☎ 51.55.17.37
Directions: RN 754, from Saint-Gilles-Croix-de-
Vie, towards Nantes.
Languages spoken: English.
Menu: 49 to 110 Frs.
Accommodation: 90 to 210 Frs.
Restaurant: breakfast from 8.00. Lunch from
12.00 until 14.00. Dinner from 19.30 until 21.00.
Closed in Jan.
Specialities: fruits de mer, home-cooking.
Hotel: 15 rooms. Facilities: shower.
Other points: bar, children's menu, à la carte
menu, lounge area, pets allowed, car/lorry parking.
◂ Saint-Gilles-Croix-de-Vie; the Vendée coast:
fishing ports, marinas, beaches.

SAINT-GREGOIRE
Ille-et-Vilaine, 35760

RESTAURANT DE L'ETANG
(M. Michel Hubert) rue de l'Etang au Diable
☎ 99.38.49.43
Menu: 46 to 200 Frs.

Restaurant: breakfast from 7.30. Lunch from
11.30 until 15.00. Dinner from 19.00 until 21.00.
Closed Sat, Sun.
Specialities: home-cooking.
Other points: credit cards accepted, bar,
traditional decor, pets allowed, car/lorry parking.

SAINT-HELEN
Côtes-d'Armor, 22100

RELAIS DE LA CROIX-DU-FRENE
(M. Guy Gabillard) La Croix-du-Frêne
☎ 96.83.25.02
Restaurant: breakfast from 7.00. Lunch from
11.30 until 14.30. Dinner from 19.00 until 22.30.
Closed Sat (after 15.00), Sun, and public holidays.
Specialities: home-cooking.
Other points: bar.

SAINT-HILAIRE-DE-LOULAY
Vendée, 85600

LE RELAX
(M. Luc Van Wanghe) Les Landes-de-Roussais
☎ 51.94.02.44 [Fax] 51.94.27.25
Directions: RN 137, between Nantes and
La Rochelle, 30km from Nantes.
Languages spoken: some German and English.
Menu: 60 to 144 Frs.
Accommodation: 180 to 210 Frs.
Restaurant: breakfast from 6.00. Lunch from
11.30 until 15.00. Dinner from 19.00 until 24.00.
Closed Sat lunch, and 2 weeks in July.
Specialities: grillades au feu de bois, poissons au
beurre blanc, regional menu.
Hotel: ☆ ☆ 11 rooms. Facilities: shower, private
bathroom, television, telephone.
Other points: credit cards accepted, bar, children's
menu, à la carte menu, modern decor, terrace, pets
allowed, car/lorry parking.
◂ chateau; Muscadet wine-cellar.

SAINT-IGNEUC
Côtes-d'Armor, 22270

LES 4 ROUTES
(Mme Chantal Durand) Route Nationale 76
☎ 96.31.68.40
Directions: RN 76, the Saint-Malo/Saint-Brieuc
road.
Menu: 49 Frs.
Restaurant: breakfast from 5.00. Lunch from
11.00 until 15.00. Dinner from 19.00 until 22.30.
Closed Sat, Sun.
Specialities: couscous, Breton pâtisseries, regional
menu, home-cooking
Hotel: 4 rooms. Facilities: shower, private
bathroom, television, telephone.
Other points: credit cards accepted, bar, children's
menu, à la carte menu, pets allowed, car/lorry
parking.
◂ chateau at La Hunaudaye; Jugon; ferme
d'antan (farm of yesteryear); old Dinan.

SAINT-JACQUES-DE-LA-LANDE
Ille-et-Vilaine, 35136

⇌ LA GAITE
(M. Yannick Echelard) 26 boulevard Roger-
Dodin ☎ 99.31.27.56
Directions: RD 177, 'La Gaité' interchange on the
Redon road.
Languages spoken: some English.
Menu: 48 Frs.
Accommodation: 95 Frs per person.
Restaurant: breakfast from 7.00. Lunch from
12.00 until 14.30. Dinner from 19.30 until 22.00.
Closed Sat, Sun, and public holidays (except group
bookings).
Specialities: regional menu.
Hotel: 3 rooms. Facilities: shower, private bathroom.
Other points: credit cards accepted, bar, à la carte
menu, pets allowed, car parking.
⇇ étangs (ponds) d'Apigné; Rennes town centre.

SAINT-JEAN-BREVELAY
Morbihan, 56661

⇌ LE SAINT-YANN
(M. Rémi Verdeau) 21 rue de Rennes
☎ 97.60.30.10
Directions: between Vannes and Josselin.
Languages spoken: English and Spanish.
Menu: 45 Frs (wine included).
Restaurant: breakfast from 8.00. Lunch from
11.45 until 14.30. Closed Sun.
Specialities: home-cooking.
Other points: credit cards accepted, bar, children's
menu, traditional decor, pets allowed, car/lorry
parking.
⇇ Gulf of Morbihan (30km); chateau at Josselin.

SAINT-JEAN-DE-BEUGNE
Vendée, 85210

⇌ L'OASIS
(Mme Louisette Le Joncour) 61 route
Nationale 137 ☎ 51.27.38.80
Directions: RN 137, the Nantes/La Rochelle road.
Menu: 53 Frs.
Restaurant: breakfast from 4.30. Lunch from
11.30 until 14.30. Dinner from 18.30 until 23.00.
Closed Sat afternoon and Sun.
Specialities: regional menu, home-cooking.
Other points: credit cards accepted, bar, children's
menu, traditional decor, pets allowed, car/lorry
parking.
⇇ le Puy du Fou; chateau at Fontenay-le-Comte;
dam at Longuignard.

SAINT-JEAN-DE-COUESNON
Ille-et-Vilaine, 35140

⇌ LA JUHUELLERIE
(Mme Lucas) Route Nationale 12
☎ 99.39.11.85
Directions: RN 12, between Fougères and Rennes.
Languages spoken: English, Spanish and Italian.

Menu: 47 Frs.
Restaurant: breakfast from 7.00. Closed Sun.
Specialities: couscous, paella, pot au feu, home-
cooking.
Other points: bar, modern decor, pets allowed,
car/lorry parking.
⇇ chateau at Fougères (20km); chateau and pond
(étang) at Saint-Aubin-du-Cormier.

SAINT-JEAN-DE-DAYE
Manche, 50620

⇌ LE P'TIT TROP
(Mme Christiane Marie) rue de la Libération
☎ 33.55.48.00
Directions: RN 174, between Saint-Lô and Carentan.
Menu: 50 Frs.
Restaurant: breakfast from 7.00. Lunch from
11.30 until 14.30. Dinner from 19.00 until 21.30.
Specialities: home-cooking.
Other points: credit cards accepted, bar, children's
menu, pets allowed, car/lorry parking.
⇇ Graignes racecourse and riding school; chateau
at La Rivière.

SAINT-JEAN-DE-LA-MOTTE
Sarthe, 72510

⇌ CHEZ BEATRICE
(Mme Béatrice Collin) Route Nationale 23
☎ 43.45.72.02
Directions: RN 23, between Le Mans and Angers.
Languages spoken: English.
Restaurant: breakfast from 6.00. Lunch from
11.30 until 14.30. Dinner from 19.00 until 22.30.
Closed Sun.
Specialities: home-cooking.
Other points: credit cards accepted, bar, children's
menu, traditional decor, car/lorry parking.
⇇ Le Lude (25km); Le Mans circuit (30km);
Malicorne: potteries.

SAINT-JULIEN-LE-FAUCON
Calvados, 14140

⇌ LE CAFE DE LA GARE
(M. Robert Gallais) ☎ 31.63.62.91
Directions: RD 511, between Lisieux and Saint-
Pierre-sur-Dives.
Menu: 49 Frs (wine included).
Restaurant: breakfast from 7.00. Lunch from
12.00 until 15.00. Dinner from 20.00 until 23.00.
Closed Sun.
Specialities: home-cooking.
Other points: bar, children's menu, traditional
decor, terrace, pets allowed, car/lorry parking.
⇇ Lisieux (14km); abbey at Saint-Pierre-sur-Dives;
chateau at Saint-Germain-de-Livet.

SAINT-MALO · Ille-et-Vilaine, 35400

⇌ RESTAURANT LE PERROQUET VERT
(M. Michel Fraboulet) 2 rue Amiral-Protet
☎ 98.81.64.19

Directions: Saint-Servan exit.
Languages spoken: English.
Menu: 48 Frs.
Restaurant: breakfast from 6.30. Lunch from 11.30. Dinner from 19.00 until 20.00. Closed Sat from 16.00, Sun, and 2 weeks in Aug.
Specialities: home-cooking.
Other points: bar, children's menu, pets allowed, car/lorry parking.
◀€ Saint-Malo.

SAINT-MARS-LA-BRIERE
Sarthe, 72740

◀€ **AUBERGE DU NARAIS**
(M. Rémy Tressy) Route Nationale 157
☎ 43.89.87.30 [Fax] 43.89.87.30
Directions: RN 157, between Le Mans and Orléans.
Menu: 50 to 90 Frs.
Restaurant: breakfast from 7.00. Lunch from 12.00 until 15.00. Dinner from 19.00 until 22.00. Closed Sat after 16.00, Sun, and in Aug.
Specialities: home-cooking.
Other points: credit cards accepted, bar, children's menu, modern decor, terrace, pets allowed, car/lorry parking.
◀€ animal park; crystalline spring; chateau; forest.

SAINT-MARTIN-DES-BESACES
Calvados, 14350

🏨 **LA RENAISSANCE**
(Mme Renée Lehericey) Route Nationale 175, Le Bourg ☎ 31.68.72.65
Directions: RN 175, between Avranches and Caen.
Languages spoken: English.
Menu: 55 to 75 Frs ☕
Accommodation: 110 to 160 Frs.
Restaurant: breakfast from 7.30. Lunch from 12.00 until 14.30. Dinner from 19.00 until 21.30. Closed Mon (out of season), and in Feb.
Specialities: coquilles Saint-Jacques, rognons au vieux calvados, faux filet au poivre, regional menu.
Hotel: ☆ 8 rooms. Facilities: shower, private bathroom.
Other points: bar, à la carte menu, modern decor, terrace, pets allowed, car/lorry parking.

SAINT-MARTIN-DES-CHAMPS
Manche, 50300

◀€ **LE GRAND CHIEN**
(M. Michel Boittin) ☎ 33.58.04.52
Directions: between Pontorson and Avranches.
Menu: 45 Frs (coffee included).
Restaurant: breakfast from 5.30. Lunch from 11.30 until 15.00. Dinner from 19.00 until 21.30. Closed Sat afternoon, 2 weeks in Aug and last week in Dec.
Specialities: home-cooking.
Other points: credit cards accepted, bar,

children's menu, traditional decor, terrace, pets allowed, car/lorry parking.
◀€ musée de la 2ème guerre mondiale (Second World War); jardin des plantes; Mont-Saint-Michel.

SAINT-MEEN-LE-GRAND
Ille-et-Vilaine, 35290

◀€ **LE RELAIS DU MIDI**
(M. Christian Posnic) 25 place Patton
☎ 99.09.60.02
Directions: RN 164, Rennes/Vannes/Saint-Malo/Loudéac.
Menu: 44 Frs (weekdays) and 48 Frs (Sun).
Restaurant: breakfast from 8.00. Lunch 12.00 to 14.00. Dinner 19.30 to 21.00. Closed Sat afternoon, Sun afternoon, and last 2 weeks in Aug.
Specialities: home-cooking
Hotel: 3 rooms. Facilities: private bathroom, television, telephone.
Other points: credit cards accepted, bar, children's menu, pets allowed.

SAINT-MESMIN • Vendée, 85700

◀€ **LE RELAIS**
(M. Henry Thibault) La Boutinerie
☎ 51.91.95.00
Directions: RD 960, La Roche-sur-Yon.
Menu: 50 Frs (wine included) to 80 Frs.
Restaurant: breakfast from 6.30. Lunch from 11.30 until 15.00. Dinner from 19.00 until 21.00. Closed Sat lunch and Sun lunch (out of season).
Specialities: crêperie (at weekends), home-cooking.
Other points: credit cards accepted, bar, terrace, pets allowed, car/lorry parking.
◀€ chateau at Saint-Mesmin; le Puy du Fou.

SAINT-NAZAIRE
Loire-Atlantique, 44600

◀€ **BAR LAFAYETTE**
(M. Gilles Criaud) 7 avenue Depenhoët
☎ 40.22.53.82
Directions: chantier de l'Atlantique (Atlantic dockyard).
Menu: 45 Frs.
Restaurant: breakfast from 5.20. Closed Sat afternoon and Sun.
Specialities: home-cooking.
Other points: bar, children's menu, modern decor, terrace, pets allowed, car parking.
◀€ Saint-Nazaire; La Baule.

SAINT-NICOLAS-DE-REDON
Loire-Atlantique, 44460

◀€ **LES ROUTIERS**
(Mme Marie-Annick Hemery) 84 avenue Jean-Burel ☎ 99.71.01.96
Directions: the Nantes/Redon or Rennes/Redon road.

Menu: 48 Frs.
Restaurant: breakfast from 7.00. Lunch from 11.45. Dinner from 18.30 until 22.00. Closed Sun, and in Aug.
Specialities: couscous, home-cooking.
Other points: bar, children's menu, modern decor, pets allowed, car/lorry parking.
❦ *Redon; la Gacilly; Rochefort-en-Terre; forêt de Brocéliande.*

SAINT-NOLFF • Morbihan, 56250

🍽 LE RELAIS DE BELLEVUE
(Mme Edith Hureau) Bellevue
☎ 97.45.44.04
Directions: RN 164, via the old Rennes road.
Menu: 49 Frs (coffee included).
Restaurant: breakfast from 6.30. Lunch from 11.45 until 15.00. Dinner from 19.00 until 21.30. Closed Sun, and in Aug.
Specialities: home-cooking.
Other points: bar.

SAINT-PELLERIN • Manche, 50500

🍽 RELAIS DE LA FOURCHETTE
(Mme Nicole Le Roux) Route Nationale 13
☎ 33.42.16.56
Directions: RN 13, the Caen/Cherbourg road.
Menu: 50 to 95 Frs.
Restaurant: breakfast from 6.30. Lunch from 11.00 until 16.00. Dinner from 18.30 until 22.30. Closed Sun.
Specialities: pied de veau, rillettes, tripes, amourettes au beurre d'escargot, home-cooking.
Other points: credit cards accepted, bar, children's menu, à la carte menu, terrace, pets allowed, car/lorry parking.
❦ *landing beaches; pointe du Cotentin; ramparts.*

SAINT-PHILBERT-DE-GRAND-LIEU • Loire-Atlantique, 44310

🍴 CAFE-RESTAURANT DE LA BOULOGNE
(M. Jean-Luc Hervouet) 11 place de l'Abbatiale ☎ 40.78.70.55
Directions: RD 18 bis, between Nantes and Challans.
Menu: 49 Frs.
Accommodation: 100 to 125 Frs.
Restaurant: breakfast from 9.00. Lunch from 12.00 until 14.30. Closed Sat and Sun.
Specialities: home-cooking.
Hotel: 6 rooms.
Other points: bar, children's menu, lounge area, traditional decor, terrace, pets allowed, car parking.
❦ *9thC abbey-churches (abbatiales); Lac de Grand-Lieu.*

SAINT-PIERRE-DU-FRESNE
Calvados, 14260

🍽 CHEZ DOUDOU
(M. Loïc Lelégard) Les Haies Tigards
☎ 31.77.80.89

Directions: RN 175, between Rennes and Dinan.
Languages spoken: English.
Menu: 50 to 70 Frs.
Restaurant: breakfast from 5.00. Lunch from 11.00 until 15.00. Dinner from 19.00 until 23.00. Closed Sun.
Specialities: home-cooking.
Other points: credit cards accepted, bar, children's menu, modern decor, pets allowed, car/lorry parking.

SAINT-PIERRE-LANGERS
Manche, 50530

🍴 LA GRILLADE
(M. Marc Johan) La Havaudière
☎ 33.48.12.63
Directions: RD 973, between Cherbourg and Avranches.
Languages spoken: English.
Menu: 50 to 60 Frs.
Accommodation: 110 to 160 Frs.
Restaurant: breakfast from 6.00. Closed Sun (out of season), and between Christmas Day and New Year's Day.
Specialities: choucroute, couscous.
Hotel: 8 rooms. Facilities: shower, private bathroom.
Other points: credit cards accepted, bar, children's menu, traditional decor, car/lorry parking.
❦ *Abbaye de la Lucerne; Granville; Avranches: jardin des plantes; Mont-Saint-Michel.*

SAINT-PIERRE-LE-VIGER
Seine-Maritime, 76740

🍽 CHEZ DIDIER
(M. Didier Mouton) Route de Veules-les-Roses
☎ 35.97.43.29
Directions: RD 142, Veules-les-Roses.
Menu: 49 Frs.
Restaurant: breakfast from 5.00. Closed Sun, last week in Feb, and in July.
Specialities: home-cooking.
Other points: bar, traditional decor, pets allowed, car/lorry parking.
❦ *Veules-les-Roses; Saint-Valery-en-Caux.*

SAINT-PIERRE-LES-ELBEUF
Seine-Maritime, 76320

🍽 LA SAUVAGINE
(M. Patrick Clivaz) 611 chemin du Halage
☎ 35.78.37.70
Languages spoken: English.
Restaurant: dinner until 23.00. Closed Sun, 2 weeks in Jan/Feb and 3 weeks in Aug.
Other points: bar.

SAINT-POL-DE-LEON
Finistère, 29250

🍴 LES ROUTIERS – Le Passiflore
(M. Jean-Louis Floch) 28 rue Pen Ar Pont
☎ 98.69.00.52
Directions: Morlaix.

Languages spoken: English.
Menu: 50 to 150 Frs.
Accommodation: 160 to 200 Frs.
Restaurant: breakfast from 7.00. Lunch from 12.00 until 16.00. Dinner from 19.00 until 23.00. Closed Sun evening.
Specialities: fruits de mer (to order), home-cooking.
Hotel: ☆ 18 rooms. Facilities: shower, private bathroom.
Other points: credit cards accepted, bar, children's menu, à la carte menu, modern decor, pets allowed, car/lorry parking.
◁€ Roscoff: cathedral, port.

SAINT-QUENTIN-LES-ANGES
Mayenne, 53400

🛏 **LE RELAIS**
(Mme Marie-Annick Trottier) Le Bourg
☎ 43.06.10.62 Fax 43.06.08.41
Directions: the Rennes/Angers road, between Craon and Segré.
Languages spoken: English.
Menu: 50 Frs.
Accommodation: 90 to 125 Frs.
Restaurant: breakfast from 7.00. Lunch from 11.30 until 15.00. Dinner from 19.30 until 21.30. Closed in Aug.
Specialities: filet de canard à la craonnaise, filet de sandre (fish) au beurre blanc, regional menu, home-cooking.
Hotel: 9 rooms. Facilities: shower.
Other points: credit cards accepted, bar, children's menu, lounge area, traditional decor, pets allowed.
◁€ chateaux at Craon and Mortiercrolles; la Mine Bleue; musée Robert Tatin.

SAINT-REMY-DE-SILLE
Sarthe, 72140

🍽 **LA COQUE**
(M. Claude Rouzier) 11 bis route du Mans
☎ 43.20.11.84
Directions: RD 304, between Le Mans and Sillé-le-Guillaume.
Menu: 53 Frs.
Restaurant: breakfast from 7.00. Lunch from 12.00 until 15.00. Closed Sun, and last 3 weeks in Aug.
Specialities: home-cooking.
Other points: bar, traditional decor, pets allowed, car/lorry parking.
◁€ lake and forêt de Sillé-le-Guillaume; Sault-du-Cerf.

SAINT-REMY-SUR-ORNE
Calvados, 14570

🍽 **AU BON ACCUEIL**
(Mme Josette Benoît) ☎ 31.69.43.87
Directions: RD 562, between Condé-sur-Noireau and Thury-Harcourt.
Menu: 50 Frs.
Restaurant: breakfast from 6.30. Closed Sun (out of season).

Specialities: home-cooking.
Other points: credit cards accepted, bar, children's menu, traditional decor, terrace, pets allowed, car/lorry parking.
◁€ La Suisse normande; Saint-Rémy: musée de la mine (mining).

SAINT-ROMAIN-DE-COLBOSC
Seine-Maritime, 76430

🛏 **LE RELAIS DU FRESCOT**
(M. Jacques Chapelet) 18 Nationale
☎ 35.20.15.09
Directions: on the road to Le Havre.
Menu: 52 Frs.
Restaurant: breakfast from 5.30. Lunch from 11.30 until 14.30. Dinner until 21.00. Closed Sun.
Specialities: home-cooking.
Hotel: 7 rooms.
Other points: bar, à la carte menu, pets allowed, car/lorry parking.

SAINT-SAMSON-DE-LA-ROQUE
Eure, 27680

🍽 **RELAIS NORD BRETAGNE**
(M. Marcel Poiraud) route du Pont de Tancarville ☎ 32.57.67.30
Directions: RN 815A.
Languages spoken: English and Spanish.
Restaurant: dinner until 23.00. Closed Sat and Sun.
Other points: bar.

SAINT-SULPICE-DE-GRIMBOUVILLE • Eure, 27210

🍽 **LE RELAIS DE SAINT-SULPICE**
(Mme Christiane Pontillon) ☎ 32.42.46.27
Directions: between Pont-Audemer and Le Havre.
Menu: 52 to 125 Frs.
Restaurant: breakfast from 6.00. Lunch from 11.30 until 15.00. Dinner from 19.00 until 23.00. Closed Sun, and in July.
Specialities: home-cooking.
Other points: credit cards accepted, bar, children's menu, à la carte menu, terrace, pets allowed, car/lorry parking.

SAINT-SYMPHORIEN-DES-MONTS • Manche, 50640

🛏 **LE RELAIS DU BOIS LEGER**
(M. Raymond Pinet) Route Nationale 176, Le Bois Léger ☎ 33.49.01.43
Directions: RN 176, between Alençon and Mont-Saint-Michel.
Languages spoken: English.
Menu: 48 to 100 Frs 👌
Accommodation: 100 to 160 Frs.
Restaurant: breakfast from 6.00. Lunch from 12.00 until 14.00. Dinner from 19.00 until 21.00.

Closed Sun evening, 1 week in Feb and 3 weeks in Sept.
Specialities: pintade (guinea-fowl) aux pommes, terrine du chef, pavé au cidre, faux filet aux poivre, regional menu, home-cooking.
Hotel: 10 rooms. Facilities: shower, private bathroom.
Other points: credit cards accepted, bar, children's menu, à la carte menu, lounge area, traditional decor, terrace, pets allowed, car/lorry parking.
◄€ *Lac de Vezins; Villedieu-les-Poêles; Bagnoles-de-l'Orne; Mont-Saint-Michel; Eden Parc (300m).*

SAINT-THEGONNEC
Finistère, 29223

RESTAURANT DU COMMERCE – Les Routiers
(M. Alain Mevel) 1 rue de Paris
☎ 98.79.61.07
Directions: RN 12 to Brest, on the expressway.
Menu: 49 Frs.
Restaurant: breakfast from 7.30. Lunch from 11.30 until 14.00. Closed Sat, Sun, and beginning of Aug.
Specialities: home-cooking.
Other points: credit cards accepted, bar, children's menu, à la carte menu, traditional decor, pets allowed, car/lorry parking.
◄€ *the 'enclos' circuit.*

SAINT-VIGOR-LE-GRAND
Calvados, 14400

CHEZ PEPONNE
(Mme Marie-Annick Victoire) 3 rue du Pont-Trubert ☎ 31.92.28.39
Directions: Cherbourg.
Menu: 50 Frs.
Restaurant: breakfast from 6.00. Lunch from 11.30 until 16.00. Dinner from 18.00 until 23.00. Closed Sun, 1 week in Feb and 2 weeks in Aug.
Specialities: home-cooking.
Other points: bar, modern decor, terrace, pets allowed, car/lorry parking.
◄€ *Bayeux tapestry; landing beaches and museum; cathedral.*

SAINT-VINCENT-STERLANGES
Vendée, 85110

A L'ACCUEIL VENDEEN – Chez Dudu
(M. Auguste Baty) Route Nationale 137
☎ 51.40.23.21
Directions: RN 137, the Nantes/La Rochelle road.
Menu: 48 Frs (wine included) to 60 Frs.
Restaurant: breakfast from 6.30. Lunch from 11.30 until 14.30. Dinner from 19.30 until 22.30. Closed Sun afternoon.
Hotel: ☆ 6 rooms.
Other points: credit cards accepted, bar, modern decor, terrace, pets allowed, car/lorry parking.
◄€ *le Puy du Fou; lakes.*

SAINTE-CECILE • Manche, 50800

LE CECILIA
(M. Daniel Le Huby) Le Bourg
☎ 33.61.07.81
Directions: RD 924, Villedieu, towards Vire.
Languages spoken: English and German.
Restaurant: breakfast from 7.00. Lunch from 12.00 until 13.30. Dinner from 19.00 until 20.30. Closed Sat and Sun.
Specialities: home-cooking.
Hotel: 5 rooms.
Other points: credit cards accepted, bar, pets allowed, car/lorry parking.
◄€ *Villedieu-les-Poêles: museums.*

SAINTE-CROIX-HAGUE
Manche, 50440

LE PETIT BACCHUS
(M. Claude Le Cavelier) Le Petit Bacchus
☎ 33.52.77.53
Directions: RD 908, between Cherbourg and Baumont-Hague.
Accommodation: pension 170 Frs; demi-pension 140 Frs.
Restaurant: breakfast from 6.00. Lunch from 12.00 until 15.00. Dinner from 19.30 until 21.30. Closed Sat and Sun.
Specialities: home-cooking.
Other points: credit cards accepted, bar, children's menu, modern decor, pets allowed, car/lorry parking.
◄€ *Pointe de Jobourg; côtes de La Hague.*

SAINTE-FOY-DE-MONTGOMERY
Calvados, 14140

LE RELAIS DE MONTGOMERY
(Mme Planckeel) ☎ 31.63.53.02
Directions: RN 179.
Restaurant: closed Sun.
Hotel: 4 rooms.
Other points: bar.

SAINTE-LUCE-SUR-LOIRE
Loire-Atlantique, 44980

LA BOUGRIERE
(M. Pierre Pertue) 4 rue du Pavillon
☎ 40.25.60.84
Directions: CD 68, A11 – exit at Thouaré-Sainte-Luce Centre.
Languages spoken: English and Spanish.
Menu: 49 to 178 Frs
Restaurant: breakfast from 6.30. Lunch from 12.00 until 14.30. Dinner from 19.00 until 22.30. Closed Fri evening, Sat, Sun (except for functions), in Aug, and from Christmas Day to New Year's Day.
Specialities: fruits de mer, poissons au beurre blanc, grenouilles, anguilles (eels), grillades (grills), regional menu, home-cooking.
Other points: bar, children's menu, à la carte

menu, traditional decor, terrace, pets allowed, car/
lorry parking.
◁€ *Nantes: château des ducs de Bretagne, jardin
des plantes; tour de Bretagne (du Bouffay district
with pedestrianized streets); vineyards; banks of the
Loire; zoo at Port-Saint-Père.*

SAINTENY • Manche, 50500

⇌ LE RELAIS DES FORGES
(Mme Francine Cousin) Les Forges
☎ 33.42.39.36
Menu: 48 Frs.
Restaurant: breakfast from 7.30. Lunch from
12.00 until 14.30. Dinner from 19.00 until 20.00.
Closed Tues, and in Aug.
Specialities: home-cooking.
Other points: credit cards accepted, bar, pets
allowed, car/lorry parking.

SARGE-LES-LE-MANS
Sarthe, 72190

⇌ L'ARCHE DE SARGE-LES-LE-MANS
(M. Christian Sigler) A11, services at Sargé-Lès-
Le-Mans (accessible in both directions)
☎ 43.76.18.96 [Fax] 43.76.18.97
Restaurant: open until 23.00.
Other points: credit cards and foreign currency
accepted.

SAUMUR • Maine-et-Loire, 49400

🛏 HOTEL-RESTAURANT DE LA GARE
(Mme Thérèse Loison) 16 avenue David-
d'Angers ☎ 41.67.34.24
Directions: opposite the SNCF station.
Accommodation: 100 to 230 Frs.
Restaurant: breakfast from 7.00. Lunch from
12.00 until 14.00. Dinner from 19.00 until 21.00.
Closed Sun 13.00 to Mon 18.00 (out of season).
Specialities: cuisses de poulet 'bonne femme', rôti
à la saumuroise, sandre (fish) au beurre blanc,
magrets de canard sauce roquefort, regional menu,
home-cooking.
Hotel: ☆ ☆ 18 rooms. Facilities: shower, private
bathroom, television, telephone.
Other points: credit cards accepted, bar, children's
menu, à la carte menu, lounge area, traditional
decor, pets allowed, car/lorry parking.
◁€ *the banks of the Loire; Saumur: chateau and
countryside, troglodyte dwellings; musée des
champignons (mushrooms); musée des blindés
(armoured tanks); wine-cellars; zoo at Doué-la-
Fontaine.*

SEGRE • Maine-et-Loire, 49500

🛏 LE RELAIS DU COMMERCE
(M. Emile Georget) 1 place de la Gare
☎ 41.92.22.27
Directions: RN 775, the Cholet road.
Restaurant: breakfast from 6.30.
Specialities: home-cooking.

Hotel: 6 rooms.
Other points: bar, children's menu, lounge area,
terrace, car/lorry parking.
◁€ *la Mine Bleue; Noyant-la-Gravoyère.*

SENE • Morbihan, 56860

🛏 RELAIS ROUTIERS
(SA Penru) 46 route de Vannes, Le Poulfanc
☎ 97.47.47.97
Directions: between Vannes and Lorient.
Languages spoken: English.
Menu: 48 to 160 Frs 🍴
Accommodation: 96 to 185 Frs.
Restaurant: breakfast from 6.00. Lunch from
12.00 until 15.30. Dinner from 19.00 until 21.30.
Closed 24th Dec to 2nd Jan.
Specialities: fruits de mer, home-cooking.
Hotel: ☆ 42 rooms. Facilities: shower.
Other points: credit cards accepted, bar, children's
menu, lounge area, modern decor, terrace, pets
allowed, car/lorry parking.
◁€ *Gulf of Morbihan; marina and beaches.*

SIZUN • Finistère, 29450

🛏 HOTEL RESTAURANT
DES VOYAGEURS
(M. Joseph Corre) 2 rue de l'Argoat
☎ 98.68.80.35 [Fax] 98.24.11.49
Languages spoken: English.
Menu: 60 to 100 Frs 🍴
Accommodation: 150 to 260 Frs.
Restaurant: breakfast from 7.30. Lunch from
12.00 until 13.45. Dinner from 19.15 until 20.45.
Closed Sat evening (out of season), and from 9th
Sept to 2nd Oct.
Specialities: terrine de lapin, mousseline de truite,
fruits de mer, regional menu, home-cooking.
Hotel: ☆ ☆ 28 rooms. Facilities: shower, private
bathroom, television, telephone.
Other points: credit cards accepted, bar, children's
menu, à la carte menu, modern decor, pets allowed,
car parking.
◁€ *the 'enclos' circuit; parc régional d'Armorique.*

LES SORINIERES
Loire-Atlantique, 44840

🛏 LE RELAIS – Chez Pierrette et Jean
(M. Jean-Louis Benoît) 16 rue du Général-de-
Gaulle ☎ 40.31.22.91
Directions: RN 137 and 178, on the road to
La Roche-sur-Yon.
Menu: 43 to 110 Frs.
Accommodation: 100 Frs.
Restaurant: breakfast from 6.30. Lunch from
12.00 until 15.00. Dinner from 19.30 until 22.00.
Closed Sat evening, Sun, and 20th Dec to 15th Jan.
Specialities: couscous, entrecôte, grillades (grills),
home-cooking.
Hotel: 7 rooms.
Other points: bar, children's menu, à la carte
menu, pets allowed, lorry parking.

SOUDAN • Loire-Atlantique, 44110

☵ CAFE DE LA POSTE
(M. Claude Fruchard) 7 place Talhouët
☎ 40.28.62.36
Directions: RN 171, the Laval/Paris road.
Menu: 46 Frs (wine included).
Restaurant: lunch from 12.00 until 14.00. Closed Mon, Wed afternoon, and in Aug.
Specialities: home-cooking.
Other points: bar, traditional decor, pets allowed, car parking.
◖ Châteaubriant.

SOURDEVAL • Manche, 50150

☷ AU BON ACCUEIL – Les Routiers
(M. Daniel Delaunay) 1 place du Champ-de-Foire ☎ 33.59.62.91
Directions: RD 977, the Caen/Vire road.
Languages spoken: English.
Menu: 47 to 100 Frs.
Accommodation: 80 to 120 Frs (2 with shower).
Restaurant: breakfast from 6.00. Dinner until 22.00. Closed Sun (except bookings).
Specialities: home-cooking.
Hotel: 5 rooms.
Other points: credit cards accepted, à la carte menu, traditional decor, terrace, pets allowed, lorry parking.
◖ Mont-Saint-Michel; Avranches: musée du granit.

SOURDEVAL-LES-BOIS
Manche, 50450

☵ CHEZ COLETTE
(Mme Colette Dufour) La Croix
☎ 33.61.77.99
Directions: RN 799.
Menu: 40 Frs.
Restaurant: breakfast from 7.00. Lunch from 12.00 until 14.00.
Specialities: home-cooking.
Other points: bar, pets allowed, car/lorry parking.
◖ Abbaye d'Hambye (2km); Villedieu-les-Poêles.

SUZAY • Eure, 27420

☵ LE RELAIS MODERNE
(M. Jean-Claude Laurent) ☎ 32.55.65.01
Directions: RN 14, the Paris/Rouen road.
Menu: 55 to 60 Frs.
Restaurant: breakfast from 6.30.
Specialities: home-cooking.
Other points: bar, children's menu, modern decor, terrace, pets allowed, car/lorry parking.

TALMONT-SAINT-HILAIRE
Vendée, 85440

☷ HOTEL DU CENTRE
(M. Michel Le Blond) 1 rue du Centre
☎ 51.90.60.35

Directions: RD 949, Les Sables d'Olonne/Luçon road.
Accommodation: 100 to 180 Frs.
Restaurant: dinner till 21.00. Closed Sat, and in Oct.
Specialities: fruits de mer, regional menu, home-cooking.
Hotel: 12 rooms. Facilities: shower, private bathroom, television, telephone.
Other points: credit cards accepted, bar, children's menu, à la carte menu, terrace, pets allowed, car/lorry parking.
◖ Talmont: chateau, automobile museum.

TESSY-SUR-VIRE • Manche, 50420

☵ LES ROUTIERS
(M. Maurice Robert) place du Marché
☎ 33.56.35.25
Directions: RD 13, Granville.
Menu: 48 Frs.
Restaurant: breakfast from 7.00. Lunch from 12.00 until 15.00. Dinner from 19.00 until 21.00. Closed Thurs afternoon, Sun afternoon, and for 10 days in March.
Specialities: pieds de veau, home-cooking.
Other points: credit cards accepted, bar, children's menu, traditional decor, pets allowed, car/lorry parking.
◖ Vire river gorges; chapel at Vire; Saint-Lô; Villedieu-les-Poêles; Coutances.

THOMER-LA-SOGNE • Eure, 27240

☵ RELAIS 154
(Mme Nicole Vandecandelaere) Route d'Orléans ☎ 32.67.41.00
Directions: RN 154, between Evreux and Dreux.
Languages spoken: English.
Menu: 54 Frs.
Restaurant: breakfast from 5.00. Lunch from 11.00 until 15.00. Dinner from 19.00 until 22.30. Closed Sat and Sun.
Specialities: home-cooking.
Other points: credit cards accepted, bar, modern decor, pets allowed, car/lorry parking.
◖ cathedral at Evreux.

TIVOLY • Eure, 27320

☵ LE RELAIS EUROPEEN
(SNC Les Relais Européens) Route Nationale 154 ☎ 32.58.31.75
Directions: RN 154, the Evreux/Dreux road.
Languages spoken: English.
Menu: 53 to 55 Frs.
Restaurant: breakfast from 5.00. Closed Sat afternoon and Sun.
Specialities: fruits de mer, tartes maison, home-cooking.
Other points: credit cards accepted, bar, children's menu, traditional decor, pets allowed, car/lorry parking.
◖ Center Parc; Verneuil-sur-Avre.

TOLLEVAST • Manche, 50470

⇌ LES CHEVRES
(M. Claude Yssambourg) Route Nationale 13
☎ 33.43.77.92
Directions: RN 13.
Languages spoken: English.
Menu: 50 Frs.
Restaurant: breakfast from 7.00. Open 24 hours.
Specialities: pieds de veau, home-cooking.
Other points: credit cards accepted, bar,
traditional decor, pets allowed, car/lorry parking.
⋘ dockyard; port; Cap de la Hague.

TOTES • Seine-Maritime, 76890

⇌ LE NORMANDY
(M. Alain Montier) Route d'Yvetot
☎ 35.32.99.54
Directions: RN 27.
Menu: 55 to 100 Frs.
Restaurant: breakfast from 7.00. Lunch from
11.45 until 13.45. Dinner from 19.15 until 21.15.
Closed Sat, Sun, and the middle weeks in Aug.
Specialities: home-cooking.
Other points: credit cards accepted, bar, children's
menu, pets allowed, car/lorry parking.
⋘ zoo at Clères; Bocasse amusement park;
Dieppe; Rouen.

LE TRAIT • Seine-Maritime, 76580

⇌ LE JEAN BART – Les Routiers
(M. Jean Mahier) 488 rue Jean-Bart
☎ 35.37.22.47
Directions: RD 982, between Duclair and
Caudebec-en-Caux.
Languages spoken: German and English.
Menu: 43 Frs.
Accommodation: 80 Frs.
Restaurant: breakfast from 5.30. Lunch from 11.30
until 15.30. Dinner from 18.00 until 22.00. Closed
Sun (except functions), and last 3 weeks in Aug.
Specialities: langue sauce piquante, boudin noir
maison, onglet (beef) à l'échalotte, tripes maison,
pâtés and rillettes maison, regional menu, home-
cooking.
Hotel: Facilities: shower, private bathroom,
television, telephone.
Other points: credit cards accepted, bar, children's
menu, à la carte menu, modern decor, terrace, pets
allowed, car/lorry parking.
⋘ Abbaye de Saint-Wandrille; pont de Brotonne;
pont de Tancarville; silver cutlery factory.

TREFFENDEL • Ille-et-Vilaine, 35380

⇌ RELAIS ROUTIERS RN 24
(Mme Yvette Guillemot - SARL RN 24)
La Gare ☎ 99.61.00.62
Directions: RN 24, between Rennes and Lorient.
Menu: 47 Frs.
Restaurant: breakfast from 6.00. Lunch from

11.30 until 15.00. Dinner from 19.00 until 22.00.
Closed Sat evening and Sun.
Specialities: home-cooking.
Other points: credit cards accepted, bar, children's
menu, pets allowed, car/lorry parking.
⋘ Brocéliande valley; l'arbre en or.

TREILLIERES • Loire-Atlantique, 44119

⇌ LE PIGEON BLANC
(Mme Régine Plat) Le Pigeon Blanc
☎ 40.94.67.72 [Fax] 40.94.59.98
Directions: RN 137, Rennes.
Menu: 58 to 140 Frs.
Accommodation: 180 Frs.
Restaurant: breakfast from 5.30. Closed Sun.
Specialities: home-cooking.
Hotel: 3 rooms. Facilities: shower, private
bathroom, television.
Other points: credit cards accepted, bar, children's
menu, traditional decor, pets allowed, car/lorry
parking.
⋘ Erdre river valley.

TREMBLAY • Ille-et-Vilaine, 35460

🛏 AUBERGE BRETONNE
(M. Stéphane Louvet) La Gare
☎ 99.98.26.11
Directions: RN 155, between Antrain and
Fougères.
Languages spoken: English.
Menu: 45 to 85 Frs.
Accommodation: 110 to 185 Frs.
Restaurant: breakfast from 7.00.
Specialities: fruits de mer, home-cooking.
Hotel: 10 rooms. Facilities: shower.
Other points: bar, children's menu, à la carte
menu, terrace, pets allowed, car/lorry parking.
⋘ Mont-Saint-Michel; chateau at Fougères;
Saint-Malo.

TREMONT • Maine-et-Loire, 49310

⇌ AUBERGE DES 3 MONTS
(Mme Marie-Hélène Beau) 6 rue du Vivier,
Pont de Trémont ☎ 41.59.69.37
Directions: between Saumur and Cholet.
Menu: 50 to 85 Frs.
Restaurant: breakfast from 7.30. Lunch from
11.30 until 14.30. Dinner from 19.00 until 21.00.
Closed Wed afternoon, and 2 weeks in Aug.
Specialities: home-cooking.
Other points: credit cards accepted, bar, children's
menu, à la carte menu, modern decor, pets allowed,
car/lorry parking.
⋘ zoo at Doué-la-Fontaine; Saumur.

TREMOREL • Côtes-d'Armor, 22230

⇌ LES ROUTIERS – Chez Simone
(M. Simone Sohier) Le Bourg ☎ 96.25.21.70

Directions: RN 164 bis, between Rennes and Loudéac.
Menu: 47 to 50 Frs.
Restaurant: breakfast from 7.00. Lunch from 11.00 until 16.00. Dinner from 19.00 until 21.00. Closed Mon afternoon.
Specialities: home-cooking.
Other points: credit cards accepted, bar, children's menu, modern decor, pets allowed, car/lorry parking.

TREOGAT • Finistère, 29720

TI-GOVEL
(Mme Armelle Euzen) Le Bourg
☎ 98.87.64.37
Directions: Quimper/Ploneour-Lanvern/Audierne.
Menu: 45 Frs.
Restaurant: breakfast from 8.00. Lunch from 11.00 until 14.30. Dinner from 19.00 until 23.00.
Specialities: fruits de mer, poissons, goulash, home-cooking.
Other points: credit cards accepted, bar, children's menu, traditional decor, pets allowed, car/lorry parking.
◄ Pointe du Raz; la Torche; Quimper; Bay of Audierne: house and prehistory museum.

LE TRONQUAY • Calvados, 14490

AU ROUTIER SYMPA
(Daniel and Christine Meriel) La Commune
☎ 31.92.38.68
Directions: RD 572, between Bayeux and Saint-Lô.
Restaurant: breakfast from 5.00. Lunch from 11.30 until 14.00. Dinner from 18.30 until 21.30. Closed Sat evening and Sun.
Specialities: home-cooking.
Other points: credit cards accepted, bar, à la carte menu, pets allowed, car/lorry parking.
◄ Balleroy: chateau; musée des ballons; Bayeux: cathedral and tapestry; landing museum; pottery; musée de la mine (mining) at Le Molay-Littry.

LES ULMES • Maine-et-Loire, 49700

LA GRAPPE D'OR
(M. Pascal Conte) Le Moulin Cassé
☎ 41.67.03.31
Directions: RD 960, between Saumur and Doué-la-Fontaine.
Menu: 58 to 175 Frs.
Restaurant: breakfast from 6.30. Dinner from 19.00 until 22.00. Closed Sun from 1st Sept to 1st Apr.
Specialities: moules/frites, cuisine au chaudron, grillades (grills), home-cooking.
Other points: credit cards accepted, bar, children's menu, à la carte menu, lounge area, traditional decor, terrace, pets allowed, car/lorry parking.
◄ zoo at Doué-la-Fontaine; troglodyte sites.

UROU-ET-CRENNES • Orne, 61200

LE CLOS FLEURI
(M. Gilbert Estelle) Route de Paris

☎ 33.67.08.85 [Fax] 33.67.08.85
Directions: RN 26, the Paris/Argenton road.
Languages spoken: English and German.
Menu: 53 Frs.
Accommodation: 80 Frs.
Restaurant: breakfast from 6.30. Lunch from 12.30 until 14.00. Dinner from 19.00 until 21.30. Closed Sat and Sun.
Specialities: regional menu, home-cooking.
Hotel: 10 rooms.
Other points: credit cards accepted, children's menu, à la carte menu, traditional decor, pets allowed, car/lorry parking.
◄ haras (stud-farm) du Pin; Bagnoles-de-l'Orne.

VALLET • Loire-Atlantique, 44330

RESTAURANT DE LA GARE
(M. Michel Jouy) 43 rue Saint-Vincent
☎ 40.33.92.55 [Fax] 40.36.39.66
Directions: RD 756 and 763, on the bypass round the centre of Vallet.
Languages spoken: English.
Menu: 50 to 240 Frs.
Accommodation: 150 to 210 Frs.
Restaurant: breakfast from 6.00. Lunch from 11.30 until 14.30. Dinner from 19.00 until 21.30. Closed Sun and public holidays (except the hotel).
Specialities: fruits de mer, poisson au beurre blanc, navarin au muscadet, regional menu, home-cooking.
Hotel: 25 rooms. Facilities: shower, private bathroom, television, telephone.
Other points: credit cards accepted, bar, children's menu, à la carte menu, lounge area, terrace, pets allowed, car/lorry parking.
◄ Nantes; chateau de Clisson; zoo at La Boissière; musée Pierre Abelliard at Le Vallet.

VALOGNES • Manche, 50700

AU PETIT MONT ROUGE
(Mme Monique Le Blond) 14 boulevard de la Victoire ☎ 33.40.11.80
Directions: RN 13.
Restaurant: breakfast from 7.00. Closed Sat, Sun, and in Aug.
Specialities: home-cooking.
Other points: bar, pets allowed, car/lorry parking.

VANNES • Morbihan, 56190

L'AUBERGE VIEILLE FONTAINE
(M. Didier Le Ray) La Vieille Fontaine, La Trinité Surzur ☎ 97.42.01.01
Directions: the Nantes/Vannes road.
Languages spoken: English.
Menu: 45 to 130 Frs.
Accommodation: 120 to 200 Frs.
Restaurant: breakfast from 7.00. Lunch from 11.30 until 14.30. Dinner from 19.00 until 22.00.
Specialities: fruits de mer, regional menu, home-cooking.
Hotel: ☆ ☆ 11 rooms. Facilities: shower, private bathroom, telephone.

Other points: credit cards accepted, bar, children's menu, à la carte menu, lounge area, traditional decor, terrace, pets allowed, car/lorry parking.
◁€ *Presqu'île de Rhys; Vannes; Gulf of Morbihan.*

🚌 **LE RELAIS DE LUSCANEN**
(M. Jean-Marie Giteau) Zone Artisanale de Luscanen ☎ 97.63.45.92
Directions: RN 165, Nantes/Brest expressway, Vannes exit.
Languages spoken: English.
Menu: 48 Frs (wine included).
Accommodation: 130 Frs.
Restaurant: breakfast from 6.00. Lunch from 11.30 until 15.00. Dinner from 19.00 until 23.00. Closed Sat afternoon, Sun, and 2 weeks in Aug.
Specialities: home-cooking.
Hotel: 24 rooms. Facilities: shower, private bathroom, television.
Other points: credit cards accepted, bar, children's menu, à la carte menu, lounge area, modern decor, pets allowed, car/lorry parking.
◁€ *Breton coast; Gulf of Morbihan.*

VARVANNES • Seine-Maritime, 76890

🍴 **LE CLOS DE VARVANNES**
(M. Georges Quesnel) Le Clos de Varvannes ☎ 35.32.16.52
Directions: RN 29, between Le Havre and Tôtes.
Menu: 55 Frs.
Restaurant: breakfast from 7.30. Lunch 12.00 to 14.30. Dinner 19.00 to 21.00. Closed Sun and Aug.
Specialities: home-cooking.
Other points: credit cards accepted, bar, à la carte menu, traditional decor, terrace, pets allowed, car/lorry parking.
◁€ *Normandy.*

VENDEUVRE • Calvados, 14170

🚌 **LE RELAIS DE VENDEUVRE**
(Mme Suzanne Masson) place de la Gare ☎ 31.40.92.77
Directions: between Falaise and Lisieux.
Menu: 50 to 120 Frs.
Accommodation: 100 to 175 Frs.
Restaurant: breakfast from 7.30. Lunch 11.00 to 14.30. Dinner 19.00 to 20.30. Closed Sat.
Specialities: fruits de mer, regional menu, home-cooking.
Hotel: 11 rooms. Facilities: shower, private bathroom.
Other points: bar, children's menu, traditional decor, terrace, pets allowed, car/lorry parking.
◁€ *chateau at Vendeuvre; musée du meuble miniature (furniture); musée du fromage (cheese); chateau at Falaise.*

VERN-SUR-SEICHE
Ille-et-Vilaine, 35770

🍴 **LE WELCOME BAR**
(M. Michel Clinard) Le Clos Berquet ☎ 99.62.83.18

Directions: RD 163, between Angers and Châteaubriant.
Languages spoken: English and German.
Menu: 50 Frs.
Restaurant: breakfast from 7.30. Lunch from 11.30 until 15.00. Dinner from 19.00 until 21.00. Closed Sat afternoon, Sun and 2 weeks in Aug.
Specialities: home-cooking.
Other points: credit cards accepted, bar, à la carte menu, traditional decor, terrace, pets allowed, car/lorry parking.
◁€ *Rennes.*

VERNON • Eure, 27200

🍴 **LA BUISSONNIERE**
(Mme Michelle Bourgault) Le Petit Val ☎ 32.51.08.41
Directions: the Vernon/Paris road.
Restaurant: breakfast from 6.00. Closed Sun.
Specialities: home-cooking.
Other points: credit cards accepted, bar, children's menu, traditional decor, car/lorry parking.
◁€ *Claude Monet's house/gardens at Giverny.*

🍴 **SARL DU HAMEAU FLEURI**
(Mme Chantal Dekimpe) 88–90 avenue de Rouen ☎ 32.51.84.69
Directions: RN 15, between Bonnières and Rouen.
Menu: 55 to 82 Frs 🖐
Restaurant: breakfast from 6.30. Closed from Fri 15.00 to Mon 6.00 (out of season).
Specialities: soupe de poissons gratinée, soufflé de brochet au velouté de crustacés, suprême d'écrevisses, bavette au poivre flambée au calvados, coquilles Saint-Jacques à la provençale, boeuf stroganoff, home-cooking.
Other points: credit cards accepted, bar, children's menu, à la carte menu, traditional decor, pets allowed, car/lorry parking.
◁€ *Claude Monet's house and gardens at Giverny (8km); chateau de Bizy.*

VERTOU • Loire-Atlantique, 44120

🍴 **RESTAURANT DE LA GARE**
(M. Noël Gohaud) 10 avenue de la Gare ☎ 40.34.08.74
Directions: RN 149, between Clisson and Nantes – near Vertou station.
Menu: 46 Frs.
Restaurant: breakfast from 6.00. Lunch 11.30 to 14.00. Dinner 19.00 to 20.30. Closed Sat and Sun.
Specialities: home-cooking.
Other points: bar, children's menu, modern decor, pets allowed, car parking.
◁€ *Nantes: château des ducs de Bretagne; zoo at Doué-la-Fontaine.*

VILDE-GUINGALAN
Côtes-d'Armor, 22980

🍴 **LA BORGNETTE**
(M. Alain Lambard – SARL Mélodie) La Borgnette ☎ 96.27.61.10

Directions: the Dinan/Saint-Brieuc road, 9km from Dinan.
Menu: 47 Frs.
Restaurant: lunch from 11.00 until 15.00. Dinner from 19.00 until 22.00. Closed Sun.
Specialities: home-cooking.
Other points: credit cards accepted, bar, children's menu, pets allowed, car/lorry parking.
◁€ Dinan (9km).

VILLEBAUDON • Manche, 50410

⇌ LES ROUTIERS
(Mme Agnès Osouf) ☎ 33.61.20.52
Directions: RD 999, the Cherbourg/Rennes road.
Menu: 50 to 85 Frs.
Accommodation: 100 to 150 Frs.
Restaurant: breakfast from 6.00. Lunch from 12.00 until 15.00. Dinner from 19.00 until 21.30.
Specialities: Saint-Pierre à l'oseille, steack au poivre, home-cooking.
Hotel: 3 rooms. Facilities: shower, private bathroom.
Other points: credit cards accepted, bar, children's menu, traditional decor, terrace, car/lorry parking.
◁€ Abbaye d'Hambye; Villedieu-les-Poêles; les roches du Ham; pont de Soulenne.

VILLEDIEU-LES-POELES
Manche, 50800

⇌ HOTEL DES VOYAGEURS
(M. Bernard Magusto) 36 avenue du Maréchal-Leclerc ☎ 33.51.08.98
Directions: between Caen and Avranches.
Menu: 50 Frs.
Accommodation: 120 to 140 Frs.
Restaurant: breakfast from 6.00. Closed Sun (out of season).
Specialities: home-cooking.
Hotel: 6 rooms.
Other points: children's menu, modern decor, terrace, car/lorry parking.
◁€ Villedieu: bell-foundry, cycling and furniture museums, zoo; Granville; Mont-Saint-Michel.

VILLERS-BOCAGE • Calvados, 14310

🏨 HOTEL DE LA GARE
(Mme Martine Echivard) 6 rue Foch
☎ 31.77.39.00
Directions: RN 175, the Vire/Caen road.
Languages spoken: Spanish.
Menu: 50 to 100 Frs.
Accommodation: 160 to 260 Frs.
Restaurant: breakfast from 6.30. Lunch from 11.00 until 15.00. Dinner from 19.00 until 22.00.
Specialities: home-cooking.
Hotel: 9 rooms. Facilities: shower, private bathroom.
Other points: credit cards accepted, bar, children's menu, à la carte menu, terrace, pets allowed, car/lorry parking.
◁€ zoo at Jurques; Normandy landing beaches; Bayeux: musée de la 2ème guerre mondiale (Second World War).

VILLERS-SUR-MER • Calvados, 14640

🏨 LE NORMAND
(M. Dominique Breteau) 44 rue du Maréchal-Foch ☎ 31.87.04.23
Directions: RD 813, the Caen/Deauville road.
Menu: 52 to 89 Frs.
Accommodation: 185 Frs.
Restaurant: breakfast from 8.00. Lunch from 12.00 until 14.00. Dinner from 19.00 until 21.00. Closed Sun (out of season), from mid-Sept to mid-Oct.
Specialities: fruits de mer, regional menu, home-cooking.
Hotel: ☆ 8 rooms. Facilities: shower, television.
Other points: credit cards accepted, bar, children's menu, à la carte menu, modern decor, pets allowed, car/lorry parking.
◁€ Lisieux; Caen; Honfleur; Mont-Saint-Michel.

VIMOUTIERS • Orne, 61120

🏨 HOTEL DE LISIEUX
(Mme Yvette Larivière) 37 avenue Lyautey
☎ 33.39.02.62
Directions: RN 179.
Accommodation: 75 to 105 Frs.
Restaurant: closed Sat afternoon to Sun evening, and last 2 weeks in Aug.
Specialities: home-cooking.
Hotel: 5 rooms. Facilities: shower.
Other points: bar, modern decor.
◁€ Camembert region.

VIRE • Calvados, 14500

🏨 HOTEL DE FRANCE
(M. Roger Carnet) 4 rue d'Aignaux
☎ 31.68.00.35 Fax 31.68.22.65
Directions: the Caen/Rennes or Paris/Granville road.
Languages spoken: English.
Menu: 68 to 160 Frs ☼
Accommodation: 155 to 320 Frs.
Restaurant: breakfast from 7.00. Lunch from 12.00 until 14.00. Dinner from 19.00 until 21.30. Closed 2 weeks from 20th Dec.
Specialities: ris de veau Vallée d'Auge, tarte aux pommes flambée au Calvados, escalope normande, regional menu.
Hotel: ☆ ☆ 50 rooms. Facilities: shower, private bathroom, television, telephone.
Other points: credit cards accepted, bar, children's menu, à la carte menu, lounge area, pets allowed, car/lorry parking.
◁€ Lac de la Dathée; leisure park; forêt de Saint-Sever; zoo at Jurques; la Suisse normande.

VIVY • Maine-et-Loire, 49680

🏨 RESTAURANT SAINT-PAUL
(Mme Marie-Louise Bidet) 30 rue Nationale
☎ 41.52.50.13 Fax 41.52.58.96
Directions: RN 147, between Saumur and Le Mans via Baugé.
Languages spoken: English.

Menu: 55 to 165 Frs 🍲
Accommodation: 120 to 215 Frs.
Restaurant: breakfast from 7.00. Lunch from 12.00 until 14.30. Dinner from 17.30 until 22.00
Specialities: brochet ou sandre de Loire (fish) au beurre blanc, regional menu.
Hotel: ☆ 25 rooms. Facilities: shower.
Other points: credit cards accepted, bar, children's menu, à la carte menu, lounge area, modern decor, terrace.
◀€ Saumur: chateau, museums, wine-cellars, riding school; Loire chateaux.

LES VOIVRES • Sarthe, 72210

🍴 **RELAIS LE TAMARIS**
(M. Patrick Leguy) Route de la Suze
☎ 43.88.52.60
Directions: RD 23, exit Le Mans Sud (South).
Menu: 57 to 86 Frs.
Accommodation: 83 Frs.

Restaurant: breakfast from 6.30. Lunch from 12.00 until 15.00. Dinner from 18.00 until 22.30. Closed Sun.
Specialities: home-cooking.
Hotel: 5 rooms. Facilities: shower, telephone.
Other points: bar, children's menu, modern decor, terrace, pets allowed, car/lorry parking.
◀€ old Le Mans; racing circuit; bird park at Spay.

YVRE-L'EVEQUE • Sarthe, 72530

🍴 **LA MAISON DU BON CAFE**
(Mme Annick Simon) 25 route du Mans, Bener ☎ 43.84.54.63
Directions: RN 23, Le Mans East.
Menu: 50 to 55 Frs.
Restaurant: breakfast from 7.30. Lunch from 12.00 until 14.00. Dinner from 19.00 until 20.30. Closed Wed afternoon and in Aug.
Specialities: Le Mans rillettes, home-cooking.
Other points: bar, children's menu.

THE LOIRE

The following *départements* are included in this chapter:

Charente (16)
Charente-Maritime (17)
Cher (18)
Deux-Sèvres (79)
Eure-et-Loir (28)

Indre (36)
Indre-et-Loire (37)
Loir-et-Cher (41)
Loiret (45)
Vienne (86)

L'ABSIE • Deux-Sèvres, 79240

🍴 **RESTAURANT DE LA POSTE**
(M. Eugène Bignon) 21 rue de la Poste
☎ 49.95.90.21
Restaurant: breakfast from 8.00. Closed Sun.
Other points: bar.

AIGURANDE • Indre, 36140

🍴 **LE RELAIS DE LA MARCHE**
(M. Jean-Pierre Chambon) place du Champ-de-Foire ☎ 54.06.31.58
Directions: the Paris/Châteauroux road.
Languages spoken: English and Spanish.
Menu: 55 to 195 Frs.
Accommodation: 60 to 198 Frs.
Restaurant: breakfast from 7.00. Lunch 12.00 to 14.00. Dinner 19.00 to 21.00. Closed Sat.
Specialities: ratatouille berrichon, coq au vin,

giboulée de cerises, regional menu, home-cooking.
Hotel: ☆ ☆ 7 rooms. Facilities: shower, private bathroom, television, telephone.
Other points: credit cards accepted, bar, children's menu, à la carte menu, lounge area, terrace, pets allowed, car/lorry parking.
◀€ dam at Eguzon; vallée noire; Georges Sand's chateau; fountains at La Bouzanne.

AIRVAULT • Deux-Sèvres, 79600

🍴 **LES CHENES VERTS**
(M. Alain Rousseau) La Maucarrière
☎ 49.69.71.11
Directions: RD 938, between Parthenay and Thouars.
Menu: 50 to 92 Frs.
Accommodation: 70 to 150 Frs.
Restaurant: breakfast from 6.30. Lunch from 12.00 until 14.00. Dinner from 19.00 until 21.00. Closed Sun, and 15th Sept to 15th Oct.

Specialities: home-cooking.
Hotel: 10 rooms.
Other points: credit cards accepted, bar, children's menu, à la carte menu, traditional decor, terrace, pets allowed, car/lorry parking.
◄ Airvault: church, museum, dam.

LES AIX D'ANGILLON • Cher, 18220

🍴 LE PARISIEN
(M. Jacques Blanchet) 20 place du Général-de-Gaulle ☎ 48.64.43.62
Directions: Bourges, towards Sancerre.
Menu: 50 to 75 Frs.
Accommodation: 90 to 140 Frs.
Restaurant: breakfast from 7.00. Lunch from 12.00 until 14.00. Dinner from 19.30 until 20.30. Closed Sun, and in Aug.
Specialities: home-cooking.
Hotel: 6 rooms.
Other points: bar, traditional decor, pets allowed.
◄ chateaux: Menetou-Salon (9km) at Maupas (7km); Bourges (20km).

ALLOGNY • Cher, 18110

CAFE-RESTAURANT DE LA MAIRIE
(M. Noël Hellegouarch) place de la Mairie ☎ 48.64.00.71
Directions: RD 944, between Salbris and Bourges.
Languages spoken: English.
Menu: 58 Frs.
Restaurant: breakfast from 7.00. Lunch 12.00 to 14.30. Dinner 19.00 to 22.00. Closed Thurs.
Specialities: game (according to season), coq au vin, regional menu, home-cooking.
Other points: credit cards accepted, bar, children's menu, à la carte menu, traditional decor, pets allowed, car/lorry parking.
◄ Bourges cathedral; pottery.

AMBOISE • Indre-et-Loire, 37400

LE CHANTECLERC
(M. Eric Boitelle) 34 avenue de Tours ☎ 47.57.11.94
Directions: between Tours and Blois.
Menu: 50 Frs.
Accommodation: 80 to 120 Frs.
Restaurant: breakfast from 6.30. Lunch 12.00 to 14.00. Dinner 19.30 to 21.00. Closed Sun.
Specialities: home-cooking.
Hotel: 4 rooms. Facilities: shower.
Other points: credit cards accepted, bar, modern decor, pets allowed, car/lorry parking.
◄ chateau at Amboise; postal museum; pagoda at Chanteloup.

ARDENTES • Indre, 36120

🍴 CAFE DES SPORTS
(Mme Cécile Pascaud) 21 avenue de Verdun ☎ 54.36.21.19

Directions: the Châteauroux/Montluçon road.
Menu: 55 to 70 Frs.
Accommodation: 75 to 140 Frs.
Restaurant: breakfast from 7.00. Lunch from 12.00 until 14.00. Dinner from 19.00 until 20.30. Closed Sat evening, Sun (except the bar), and first 2 weeks in Aug.
Specialities: home-cooking.
Hotel: 5 rooms. Facilities: shower, private bathroom.
Other points: credit cards accepted, bar, children's menu, traditional decor, car/lorry parking.
◄ Georges Sand's chateau at Nohant (15km); chateau at Mers-sur-Indre (15km).

🍴 LE RELAIS DE CLAVIERES
(Mme Pascale Portrait) Route de Montluçon, Clavières ☎ 54.26.98.46
Directions: Montluçon.
Menu: 48 to 68 Frs.
Accommodation: 75 to 100 Frs.
Restaurant: breakfast from 7.00. Lunch from 12.00 until 13.30. Dinner from 20.00 until 20.30. Closed Sun.
Specialities: home-cooking.
Hotel: 4 rooms. Facilities: shower.
Other points: bar, terrace, pets allowed, car parking.
◄ Georges Sand's chateau.

ARGENT-SUR-SAULDRE Cher, 18410

AUBERGE DES BRUYERES
(M. Jean-Yves Muelle) 10 rue Nationale ☎ 48.73.60.20
Restaurant: breakfast from 9.00. Lunch from 12.00 until 14.00. Dinner from 19.00 until 21.00. Closed Sun (out of season), and in Oct.
Specialities: home-cooking.
Other points: credit cards accepted, bar, à la carte menu, traditional decor, pets allowed.
◄ Musée des métiers (trades/crafts).

ASCOUX • Loiret, 45300

🍴 AUBERGE SAINT-ELOI
(SDF Robillard-Daroux) 1 rue de Pithiviers ☎ 38.33.00.20
Directions: RN 721.
Accommodation: 130 Frs.
Restaurant: dinner until 21.00. Closed Sun.
Specialities: home-cooking.
Hotel: 10 rooms.
Other points: credit cards accepted, bar, traditional decor, car parking.

ATHEE-SUR-CHER Indre-et-Loire, 37270

L'ESCALE
(M. Henry Le Roy) ☎ 47.50.67.29
Directions: RN 76, between Tours and Vierzon.

Menu: 55 Frs (wine included).
Restaurant: Open 11.00 until 15.00. Dinner from 18.30 until 21.30. Closed Sun.
Specialities: galette de pomme de terre, home-cooking.
Other points: credit cards accepted, bar, traditional decor, terrace, pets allowed, car/lorry parking.
◄€ Tours; Bléré; Loire chateaux.

LES AUBIERS • Deux-Sèvres, 79250

⊨ HOTEL DU CHEVAL BLANC
(Mme Marcelle Sauer) 9 place Saint-Mélaine
☎ 49.65.60.51
Restaurant: breakfast from 9.00. Lunch from 12.00 until 14.00. Closed Sat, Sun, and in Aug.
Specialities: home-cooking.
Other points: bar, car/lorry parking.

AUBIGNY-SUR-NERE • Cher, 18700

🚗 LES ROUTIER
(M. Bernard Ollier) 17 avenue Charles-Lefèbvre ☎ 48.58.01.42
Directions: RN 940, the Gien/Vierzon road.
Menu: 50 Frs.
Accommodation: 80 to 104 Frs.
Restaurant: breakfast from 7.00. Lunch from 11.00 until 13.30. Dinner from 19.30 until 21.30. Closed Sat afternoon, Sun, public holidays, Aug, and one week at Christmas.
Specialities: sanglier (boar), chevreuil (venison) (in season), regional menu.
Hotel: 9 rooms. Facilities: shower.
Other points: credit cards accepted, bar, traditional decor, pets allowed, car/lorry parking.
◄€ chateaux; Sancerre vineyards.

AUNEAU • Eure-et-Loir, 28700

🚗 AUX TROIS MARCHES
(Régine and Christian Séttaoui-Gasnier) 2 rue Emile-Labiche ☎ 37.31.70.49
Directions: A11 (Ablis exit) or A10 (Allainville exit).
Menu: 54 to 58 Frs.
Accommodation: 120 to 180 Frs.
Restaurant: breakfast from 6.00. Lunch from 11.00 until 14.30. Dinner from 19.00 until 20.30. Closed Sat evening, Sun, in Aug and last week in Dec.
Specialities: home-cooking.
Hotel: 8 rooms.
Other points: credit cards accepted, bar, children's menu, traditional decor, pets allowed, car parking.
◄€ chateau at Auneau.

AUSSAC-VADALLE
Charente, 16560

⊨ LA BELLE CANTINIERE
(Mme Claudy Judes) Route Nationale 10
☎ 45.20.66.89 Fax 45.20.71.99
Directions: RN 10, the Poitiers/Bordeaux road.
Languages spoken: English and Spanish.
Menu: 55 Frs.

Restaurant: breakfast from 5.00. Lunch from 11.30 until 15.00. Dinner from 19.00 until 23.00. Closed Sat evening and Sun.
Specialities: fruits de mer, home-cooking.
Other points: credit cards accepted, bar, children's menu, traditional decor, terrace, pets allowed, car/lorry parking.

AZAY-LE-FERRON • Indre, 36290

⊨ L'UNION
(M. Thierry Audoin) place de l'Eglise
☎ 54.39.20.88
Menu: 50 to 110 Frs.
Restaurant: breakfast from 8.00. Dinner from 20.00 until 21.00. Closed Mon afternoon.
Specialities: fruits de mer, game, home-cooking.
Other points: credit cards accepted, bar, children's menu, à la carte menu, traditional decor, pets allowed, car/lorry parking.
◄€ chateau at Azay-le-Ferron; wildlife park at La Haute-Touche.

AZAY-LE-RIDEAU
Indre-et-Loire, 37190

⊨ RESTAURANT DE LA GARE
(M. Didier Chevallier) 63 avenue de la Gare
☎ 47.45.40.60
Directions: between Chinon and Tours.
Menu: 48 Frs (wine included) to 200 Frs.
Restaurant: breakfast from 7.30. Lunch 12.00 to 14.30. Dinner 19.00 to 22.00. Closed Sun.
Specialities: home-cooking.
Other points: credit cards accepted, bar, children's menu, terrace, pets allowed, car/lorry parking.
◄€ Chinon; Musée Dufresne; Cadillac museum.

BARBEZIEUX • Charente, 16360

⊨ LA CAMBROUSSE
(M. Jean-Claude Pichon) Le Pont du Noble – La Tâtre ☎ 45.78.52.83
Directions: RN 10, between Angoulême and Bordeaux.
Menu: 57 Frs.
Accommodation: 90 to 110 Frs.
Restaurant: lunch from 12.00 until 14.00. Dinner from 19.00 until 24.00. Open 24 hours. Closed Sat 10am to Sun 11pm.
Specialities: home-cooking.
Hotel: 13 rooms. Facilities: shower, private bathroom.
Other points: credit cards accepted, bar, traditional decor, car/lorry parking.

BARBEZIEUX-SAINT-HILAIRE
Charente, 16120

⊨ RELAIS DE LA BILLETTE
(Mme Danielle Houdusse) Ladiville
☎ 45.78.57.09 Fax 45.78.35.33
Directions: RN 10, 20km south of Angoulême, 10km north of Barbezieux.

Menu: 68 to 120 Frs 🍽️
Restaurant: lunch from 12.00 until 13.00. Dinner from 19.00 until 22.30. Open 24 hours. Closed Sun, and 1 week in Aug.
Specialities: confit de canard, escalope à la charentaise, magret de canard, lapin au pineau des Charentes, escalope à la charentaise, filet de canard, regional menu, home-cooking.
Other points: credit cards accepted, bar, à la carte menu, traditional decor, pets allowed, car/lorry parking.
◁€ *church at Ladiville; chateau at Barbezieux; Angoulême: hôtel-de-ville and old quarters, le Maine Girand.*

LA BAZOCHE-GOUET
Eure-et-Loir, 28330

🍴 **LA BONNE AUBERGE**
(M. Jean-Paul Thierry) 54 avenue du Général-Leclerc ☎ 37.49.21.61
Directions: RD 927, the Chartres/Le Mans road.
Menu: 45 to 75 Frs.
Restaurant: breakfast from 7.00. Closed Sun, 2 weeks in Feb and 2 weeks in July.
Specialities: regional menu, home-cooking.
Other points: bar, children's menu, traditional decor, car/lorry parking.
◁€ *Perche hills; chateau at Nogent-le-Rotrou; open-air centre at Brou; numerous étangs (ponds).*

BAZOCHES-EN-DUNOIS
Eure-et-Loir, 28140

🍴 **AU BON ACCUEIL**
(Mme Marie-Claude Boucher) 7 rue de l'Eglise ☎ 37.22.08.30
Directions: RN 927, Chartres/Orléans/Châteaudun.
Menu: 51 to 120 Frs.
Restaurant: breakfast from 7.30. Lunch from 11.00 until 15.00. Dinner from 19.30 until 22.00.
Specialities: truites à l'oignon, potée beauceronne, rognons (kidneys) au vin rouge, pot au feu sauce tomate, tarte à la rhubarbe, home-cooking.
Other points: bar, children's menu, traditional decor, pets allowed, car/lorry parking.
◁€ *Chartres cathedral; Châteaudun; Orléans; Loire chateaux; grottes (caves) du Foulon.*

BEAUNE-LA-ROLANDE
Loiret, 45340

🏠 **HOTEL DE LA GARE**
(Mme Jacqueline Todesco) Gare d'Auxy ☎ 38.96.70.44 [Fax] 38.96.70.44
Directions: the Orléans/Paris road.
Languages spoken: English.
Menu: 55 Frs (wine and coffee included) to 98 Frs.
Accommodation: 100 to 150 Frs.
Restaurant: breakfast from 7.00. Lunch from 12.00 until 15.00. Dinner from 19.00 until 22.00.
Specialities: regional menu, home-cooking.
Hotel: 10 rooms.

Other points: credit cards accepted, bar, children's menu, à la carte menu, traditional decor, terrace, pets allowed, car/lorry parking.
◁€ *Montargis; Pithiviers; Nemours; Gien.*

BEAUVOIR-SUR-NIORT
Deux-Sèvres, 79360

🍴 **L'ETAPE**
(Mme Annick Duverne) 7 place de l'Hôtel-de-Ville ☎ 49.09.70.17
Directions: RN 150, between Saint-Jean d'Angély and Niort.
Languages spoken: some English.
Menu: 53 Frs (wine and coffee included) and 70 Frs.
Restaurant: lunch from 12.00 until 14.00. Dinner from 19.00 until 21.00. Closed Sun afternoon.
Specialities: regional menu, home-cooking.
Other points: bar, à la carte menu, terrace, pets allowed, car/lorry parking.
◁€ *zoo at Chizé (10km); Rimbaud's windmill (1km); churches (10km).*

BEDENAC • Charente-Maritime, 17210

🍴 **ESCAGRILL**
(Mme Maryline Hudelot) Route Nationale 10 ☎ 46.04.45.42
Directions: RN 10, the Angoulême/Bordeaux road.
Languages spoken: German, English, Spanish, Italian.
Menu: 57 (wine included) to 105 Frs.
Restaurant: breakfast from 5.00. Dinner until 24.00.
Specialities: grillade de charolais, fruits de mer, regional menu, home-cooking.
Other points: credit cards accepted, bar, children's menu, à la carte menu, modern decor, terrace, pets allowed, car/lorry parking.

BEURLAY • Charente-Maritime, 17250

🍴 **LE RELAIS D'ARY**
(M. Yves Mariaud) 1 route de Rochefort ☎ 46.95.01.39
Directions: RN 137, between Rochefort and Saintes.
Languages spoken: Spanish.
Menu: 30 to 60 Frs.
Restaurant: breakfast from 6.30. Lunch 10.00 to 15.00. Dinner 19.00 to 24.00. Closed Sun.
Specialities: home-cooking.
Other points: credit cards accepted, bar, à la carte menu, traditional decor, terrace, car/lorry parking.
◁€ *chateau at La Rochecourbon.*

LE BLANC • Indre, 36300

🍴 **LE REFLET DES ILES**
(M. Serge Marie) Visais ☎ 54.37.04.33
Menu: 49 to 120 Frs.
Restaurant: dinner until 21.00. Closed Mon.
Specialities: exotic dishes.
Other points: bar, car/lorry parking.

BLERE • Indre-et-Loire, 37150

🍽 LE RELAIS
(Mme Paulette Rossignol) 48 rue de Tours
☎ 47.57.92.31
Directions: RN 76, the Tours/Vierzon road.
Menu: 60 to 85 Frs.
Restaurant: breakfast from 8.00. Lunch from
12.00 until 14.30. Dinner from 19.00 until 21.30.
Specialities: home-cooking.
Other points: credit cards accepted, bar, children's
menu, à la carte menu, modern decor, terrace, pets
allowed, car/lorry parking.
🍴 chateaux at Chenonceaux, Amboise and
Loches; musée des poids-lourds (HGVs); abbey at
Pontlevoy.

BLOIS • Loir-et-Cher, 41000

🍽 BAR DE LA CITE
(M. Didier Moreau) 55 avenue de Vendôme
☎ 54.43.48.54
Directions: RD 951, Vendôme.
Menu: 50 Frs (wine and coffee included).
Restaurant: breakfast from 5.00. Lunch from
12.00 until 14.30. Dinner from 19.00 until 21.00.
Closed Sat and Sun.
Specialities: home-cooking.
Other points: bar, children's menu, lounge area,
modern decor, terrace, pets allowed, car/lorry
parking.
🍴 Loire chateaux at Blois, Chambord, Cheverny;
the town of Blois.

For the very best in food and drink
while travelling in Britain,
why not become a member of
Club Bon Viveur,
Les Routiers' Ultimate Dining Scheme?
See back of book for further details.

🍽 L'ARCHE DE BLOIS
(M. Vincent Staelens) A10, services at Blois –
Villerbon (accessible in both directions)
☎ 54.46.81.71 [Fax] 54.46.84.77
Restaurant: open 24 hours.
Other points: credit cards and foreign currency
accepted.

BOIS-DE-FEUGERES
Eure-et-Loir, 28800

🍽 RELAIS ROUTIER DU-BOIS-DE-FEUGERES
(M. Alain Laurent) 26 Route Nationale
☎ 37.96.33.01
Directions: RN 10, between Chartres and
Châteaudun.
Languages spoken: English and German.
Menu: 52 to 66 Frs.
Restaurant: breakfast from 4.00. Closed Sat
evening and Sun.
Specialities: home-cooking.

Other points: credit cards accepted, bar,
children's menu, à la carte menu, traditional decor,
pets allowed, car/lorry parking.
🍴 Chartres cathedral.

BORDS • Charente-Maritime, 17430

🍽 CAFE DU CENTRE
(M. Martial Perrocheau) place de l'Eglise
☎ 46.83.84.31
Directions: RN 137, between Rochefort and
Saintes.
Restaurant: breakfast from 7.00.
Specialities: home-cooking.
Other points: bar, traditional decor, pets allowed.

BOSSEE • Indre-et-Loire, 37240

🍽 AUX DELICES ANTILLAIS
(Mme Nicole Le Lain) Route Départementale
760 ☎ 47.92.88.27
Directions: RN 10, between Loches and Chinon.
Languages spoken: English and Spanish.
Menu: 56 Frs (wine included) to 135 Frs.
Restaurant: breakfast from 7.00. Lunch from
12.00 until 15.00. Dinner from 19.00 until 1.00.
Closed Mon, and in Feb.
Specialities: dishes from the Antilles, regional
menu, home-cooking.
Other points: credit cards accepted, bar, children's
menu, à la carte menu, modern decor, terrace, pets
allowed, car/lorry parking.
🍴 Loire chateaux; cellars at Nourray, Montlouis
and Chinon.

BOULAY-LES-BARRES
Loiret, 45140

🍽 AUBERGE DE LA ROUTE – Chez Jacky
(M. Jacky Gasnot) 21 route d'Orléans
☎ 38.75.34.90
Directions: RN 155.
Restaurant: breakfast from 6.30. Lunch from
12.00 until 14.00. Closed Sat, and in Aug.
Other points: bar.

BOURGES • Cher, 18000

🏨 LES AILES
(SARL Les Ailes) 147 avenue Marcel-Haegelen
☎ 48.21.57.86
Directions: RN 151, Châteauroux.
Languages spoken: English.
Menu: 46 to 75 Frs.
Accommodation: 100 to 170 Frs.
Restaurant: breakfast from 6.00. Lunch from
12.00 until 14.00. Dinner from 19.30 until 22.00.
Closed Sat evening, Sun, 2 weeks in Aug and
1 week at Christmas.
Specialities: home-cooking.
Hotel: 16 rooms.

Other points: credit cards accepted, bar, à la carte menu, pets allowed, car/lorry parking.
◄£ *Bourges: old town and cathedral, Jacques Coeurs palace.*

BOURRAS • Charente, 16200

⊨ RELAIS DES VIGNES
(Mme Monique Delavoie)
☎ 45.35.81.62
Directions: RN 141, between Cognac and Royan.
Menu: 50 to 53 Frs.
Restaurant: breakfast from 7.30. Lunch from 11.30 until 14.30. Dinner from 19.30 until 22.00. Closed Sun, and 15th Aug to 15th Sept.
Specialities: home-cooking.
Other points: credit cards accepted, bar, children's menu, terrace, pets allowed, car/lorry parking.
◄£ *distillery buildings, cooper's workshop.*

BRECHES
Indre-et-Loire, 37330

⊨ RESTAURANT ROUTIERS
(Mme Anita Vaillant) Le Bel Air
☎ 47.24.13.03
Directions: RD 766, between Angers (80km) and Blois (75km).
Menu: 58 Frs.
Restaurant: breakfast from 6.00. Closed Sat, Sun, and in Aug.
Specialities: home-cooking.
Other points: credit cards accepted, bar, traditional decor, lorry parking.
◄£ *Loire chateaux.*

LE BREUIL
Loir-et-Cher, 41330

⊨ LE CONCORDE
(Mme Andrée Gehanno) L'Aérodrome
☎ 54.20.12.04
Directions: RD 957.
Languages spoken: Italian.
Restaurant: dinner until 22.00. Closed Sat, and in Aug.
Other points: bar.

BRIARE • Loiret, 45250

⊨ LE RELAIS
(M. Eric Bourgoin) Gare de Châtillon-sur-Loire
☎ 38.31.44.42
Directions: RN 7.
Accommodation: 75 to 85 Frs.
Restaurant: breakfast from 5.00. Closed Sat evening and Sun.
Specialities: home-cooking.
Hotel: 9 rooms. Facilities: shower.

Other points: bar, children's menu, traditional decor, pets allowed, car/lorry parking.

BRIE • Charente, 16590

⊨ L'AUBERGE DES ROUTIERS
(SARL Doré et Fils) Les Rassats
☎ 45.65.90.24
Directions: RN 141, the Limoges/Bordeaux road.
Menu: 55 to 65 Frs.
Restaurant: breakfast from 4.30. Closed Sat evening, Sun, and in Aug.
Specialities: Charentais dishes, home-cooking.
Other points: credit cards accepted, bar, children's menu, lounge area, traditional decor, pets allowed, car/lorry parking.
◄£ *chateau at La Rochefoucauld; Angoulême; Cognac.*

BRION-PRÈS-THOUET
Deux-Sèvres, 79290

⊨ LE RELAIS DE BRION
(M. Alain Bruneleau) 39 rue Principale
☎ 49.67.73.34
Directions: RD 938, the Saumur/Thouars road.
Languages spoken: German and English.
Menu: 52 to 90 Frs.
Accommodation: 100 to 150 Frs.
Restaurant: breakfast from 6.15. Lunch from 11.30 until 14.00. Dinner from 19.00 until 21.00. Closed Sun, public holidays, and the last 3 weeks of Aug.
Specialities: magret de canard (duck) à l'orange, home-cooking.
Hotel: 2 rooms. Facilities: shower.
Other points: credit cards accepted, bar, children's menu, à la carte menu, traditional decor, terrace, pets allowed, car/lorry parking.
◄£ *Saumur (25km); Montreuil-Bellay (7km); Thouars (old town).*

BRIOUX-SUR-BOUTONNE
Deux-Sèvres, 79170

⊨ AUBERGE DU CHEVAL BLANC
(Mme Pierrette André) 23 place du Champ-de-Foire ☎ 49.07.52.08
Directions: between Poitiers and Saint-Jean d'Y (d'Angély).
Menu: 55 Frs (wine included) to 150 Frs.
Accommodation: 100 to 180 Frs.
Restaurant: breakfast from 7.00. Lunch from 12.00 until 15.00. Dinner from 19.00 until 21.00.
Specialities: pigeonneau au pineau, chevreau (kid) aux oignons, farci, home-cooking.
Hotel: 4 rooms. Facilities: shower, private bathroom.
Other points: credit cards accepted, bar, children's menu, à la carte menu, lounge area, traditional decor, terrace, pets allowed, car/lorry parking.
◄£ *Niort; Melle; silver mines.*

BROU · Eure-et-Loir, 28160

🛏 HOTEL DE LA GARE
(M. Alain Duparc) 76 avenue du Général-de-
Gaulle ☎ 32.44.00.81
Directions: RD 955, between Alençon and
Orléans.
Menu: 50 Frs.
Accommodation: 130 to 148 Frs.
Restaurant: breakfast from 6.00. Lunch from
11.00 until 14.00. Dinner from 19.00 until 21.00.
Closed Sun, and in Dec.
Specialities: home-cooking.
Hotel: 8 rooms. Facilities: shower.
Other points: credit cards accepted, bar, children's
menu, traditional decor, pets allowed, car/lorry
parking.
❧ chateaux at Nogent and Châteaudun.

For useful expressions à l'hôtel, au restaurant
or en route, turn to pages 8–13.

LA CELLE-SAINT-AVANT
Indre-et-Loire, 37160

🛏 LA CARAVANE
(M. Jacky Baudouin) Route Nationale 10
☎ 47.65.07.82
Directions: RN 10, between Poitiers and Tours.
Menu: 55 (wine included) to 65 Frs.
Accommodation: 60 to 150 Frs.
Restaurant: breakfast from 5.00. Lunch from
11.30 until 15.00. Dinner from 19.00 until
23.00.
Specialities: home-cooking.
Hotel: 8 rooms.
Other points: credit cards accepted, bar, children's
menu, traditional decor, pets allowed, car/lorry
parking.
❧ Loire chateaux; Futuroscope.

CELON · Indre, 36200

🍴 LES ROUTIERS
(M. Maurice Dufour) ☎ 54.25.32.08
Directions: RN 20, the Paris/Toulouse road.
Menu: 60 to 90 Frs.
Restaurant: closed Sun (out of season).
Specialities: sauté de veau à l'ancienne, regional
menu, home-cooking.
Other points: credit cards accepted, bar, children's
menu, modern decor, pets allowed, car/lorry parking.
❧ Vallée de la Creuse; lac d'Eguzon.

CHAINGY · Loiret, 45161

🍴 LE RELAIS DE FOURNEAUX
(M. Carlos De Sousa) Route Nationale 152
☎ 38.80.69.12
Languages spoken: English.
Restaurant: closed Sun.
Other points: bar.

CHAMPAGNE-MOUTON
Charente, 16350

🛏 HOTEL PLAISANCE
(Mme Nathalie Cambien) place du Château
☎ 45.31.80.52
Directions: RN 740, between Confolens and
Ruffec.
Languages spoken: German, English and
Spanish.
Menu: 60 to 250 Frs.
Accommodation: 130 to 200 Frs.
Restaurant: breakfast from 7.00. Lunch from
12.00 until 14.00. Dinner from 19.00 until
22.00.
Specialities: daube en croute, cassoulet, raviole de
Saint-Jacques (scallops), petit salé (pickled pork)
aux lentilles, regional menu, home-cooking.
Hotel: 15 rooms. Facilities: shower.
Other points: credit cards accepted, bar,
children's menu, à la carte menu, lounge area,
traditional decor, terrace, pets allowed, car/lorry
parking.
❧ Confolens; Nanteuil-en-Vallée; Angoulême.

LA CHAPELLE-D'ANGILLON
Cher, 18380

🍴 LE RELAIS DES ROUTIERS
(Mme Georgette Champion) Route
Départementale 30 ☎ 48.58.06.36
Directions: RN 30
Restaurant: closed Sat.
Other points: bar.

LA CHAPELLE-SAINT-LAURENT
Deux-Sèvres, 79430

🍴 CAFE DES SPORTS
(Louisette and André Guérin) 6 route de
Bressuire ☎ 49.72.05.64
Directions: RD 748, between Niort and Angers.
Menu: 51 Frs.
Restaurant: breakfast from 7.00. Lunch from
12.00 until 14.00. Dinner from 19.00 until 20.30.
Closed Sat (restaurant only), and a few days in
Aug.
Specialities: regional menu, home-cooking.
Other points: credit cards accepted, bar,
children's menu, traditional decor, pets allowed,
car/lorry parking.
❧ Futuroscope; Le Puy du Fou; Poitou
marshlands; moulin (windmill) des Mothes.

LA CHAPELLE-SAINT-SEPULCRE
Loiret, 45210

🍴 LA POTENCE
(Mme Liliane Visier) Route Nationale 60
☎ 38.92.03.10
Directions: RN 60.
Restaurant: closed Sat and Sun, 2 weeks in June.
Other points: bar.

LA CHAPELLE-SUR-LOIRE
Indre-et-Loire, 37140

🛏 LE RELAIS DE LA MAIRIE
(M. Jacques Joyeau) place Albert-Ruelle
☎ 47.97.34.07
Directions: RN 152, the Tours/Saumur road.
Menu: 50 to 98 Frs.
Accommodation: 130 to 190 Frs.
Restaurant: breakfast from 6.00. Lunch from 12.00 until 15.00. Dinner from 19.00 until 22.00.
Specialities: coq au vin de Chinon, truite au vin de Bourgueil, rillons (crackling), rillettes (potted pork), regional menu, home-cooking.
Hotel: 12 rooms. Facilities: private bathroom, television, telephone.
Other points: credit cards accepted, bar, children's menu, à la carte menu, traditional decor, terrace, car/lorry parking.
◁€ Loire chateaux; Saumur.

⧉ LE ZEBRE A CARREAUX
(M. Raymond Noël) Le Bourg
☎ 47.97.45.50
Directions: RN 152.
Languages spoken: German, English and Flemish.
Menu: 45 Frs.
Restaurant: breakfast from 6.00
Other points: bar, car/lorry parking.

CHARENTON-DU-CHER
Cher, 18210

⧉ LA BONNE TABLE
(Mme Antoinette Frège) 36 rue Nationale
☎ 48.60.72.73
Directions: RN 151 bis.
Restaurant: breakfast from 6.30. Dinner until 22.00. Closed Tues evening, and in Aug.
Specialities: home-cooking.
Other points: bar, pets allowed, car/lorry parking.

⧉ LE FAISAN DORE
(Mme Carmen Ville) Laugère ☎ 48.60.75.38
Directions: Châteauroux/Bourges/Moulins.
Languages spoken: Spanish.
Menu: 56 Frs (wine and coffee included) to 100 Frs.
Restaurant: breakfast from 7.00. Lunch from 11.00 until 14.30. Dinner from 19.00 until 21.00. Closed Sat.
Specialities: home-cooking.
Other points: credit cards accepted, bar, à la carte menu, traditional decor, pets allowed, car/lorry parking.
◁€ forêt de Tronçais; étang (pond) de Gould.

CHARSONVILLE • Loiret, 45130

⧉ LES ROUTIERS
(M. Patrick Billard) 15 rue de la Libération
☎ 38.74.23.00
Directions: RN 157, the Orléans/Le Mans road.
Menu: 45 Frs.

Restaurant: breakfast from 5.00. Lunch 11.45 to 14.15. Closed Sun, Mon afternoon, and in Aug.
Specialities: regional menu, home-cooking.
Other points: credit cards accepted, bar, traditional decor, terrace, pets allowed, car/lorry parking.
◁€ Loire chateaux.

CHARTRES • Eure-et-Loir, 28000

🛏 RELAIS BEAUCERON
(M. Lucien Lichet) Route Nationale 10, Mignières ☎ 37.26.46.21 [Fax] 37.26.30.64
Directions: RN 10, the Chartres/Tours road, Thivars exit.
Languages spoken: English and Spanish.
Menu: 69 to 138 Frs ⌣
Restaurant: breakfast from 5.00. Lunch from 11.45 until 14.30. Dinner from 18.45 until 22.30. Closed Sat evening (out of season) and Sun.
Specialities: oeufs à la Chartres, côte de boeuf au gris meunier, home-cooking.
Hotel: ✰ ✰ 30 rooms. Facilities: shower, private bathroom, television, telephone.
Other points: credit cards accepted, bar, children's menu, à la carte menu, lounge area, traditional decor, pets allowed, car/lorry parking.
◁€ Chartres cathedral; moulin du bois de Feugère; church at Meslay-le-Grenet; banks of the river Loir; Loire and Châteaudun chateaux.

⧉ RESTAURANT LE PALMIER
(M. Boussad Naar) 20 rue Saint-Maurice
☎ 37.21.13.89
Directions: RN 10, 250m from the station.
Menu: 48 to 98 Frs ⌣
Restaurant: breakfast from 9.00. Lunch from 11.30 until 15.00. Dinner from 19.00 until 23.00.
Specialities: couscous, paella, grillades, regional menu, home-cooking.
Other points: credit cards accepted, bar, children's menu, à la carte menu, traditional decor.
◁€ Chartres cathedral.

CHARTRES-SUR-CHER
Loir-et-Cher, 41320

⧉ LES ROUTIERS
(Mme Gérard Coutaud) 60 rue du 11 novembre ☎ 54.98.01.93
Directions: RN 76, between Tours and Vierzon.
Menu: 55 Frs.
Restaurant: breakfast from 7.00. Lunch from 12.00 until 14.00. Closed Sun, and last 2 weeks in Aug.
Specialities: home-cooking.
Other points: credit cards accepted, bar, children's menu, traditional decor, pets allowed, car parking.

CHASSENEUIL • Charente, 16260

⧉ AUBERGE DU BON ACCUEIL
(Mme Hélène Giraudeau) 20 rue Bir Hacheim ☎ 45.22.27.34
Directions: RN 141, the Limoges/Angoulême road.
Menu: 55 Frs (wine included).
Restaurant: breakfast from 7.00. Lunch from

12.00 until 14.30. Dinner from 19.00 until 22.00.
Specialities: tripes, daube, coq au vin, home-cooking.
Other points: bar, children's menu, traditional decor, pets allowed, car/lorry parking.
≪ *Résistance memorial; chateau at La Rochefoucauld.*

CHATEAU-GAILLARD-SANTILLY
Eure-et-Loir, 28310

AU ROUTIER GAILLARD – Chez Lili
(Mme Liliane Boidrou) 1 rue Charles-Péguy
☎ 37.90.07.03
Languages spoken: Dutch, Polish and Russian.
Restaurant: dinner until 24.00. Closed Sat evening and Sun.
Specialities: home-cooking.
Other points: credit cards accepted, children's menu, pets allowed, car/lorry parking.
≪ *sugar refinery; Artenay.*

LE RELAIS 20
(Messieurs Dahmani Frères) 33 rue Charles-Péguy ☎ 37.90.07.33 [Fax] 37.90.07.33
Languages spoken: Spanish, Portuguese and Kabyle.
Menu: 56 Frs.
Restaurant: breakfast from 4.00. Closed Sat afternoon and Sun.
Specialities: couscous (Thurs and Fri).
Other points: credit cards accepted, bar, lounge area, modern decor, pets allowed, car/lorry parking.
≪ *Toury.*

CHATEAU-LA-VALLIERE
Indre-et-Loire, 37330

LE GRAND CERF
(M. Jean Meunier) La Porrorie
☎ 47.24.11.06 [Fax] 47.24.18.95
Directions: RD 959, the Tours/Laval road between Le Lude and Château-la-Vallière.
Languages spoken: English.
Menu: 54 to 280 Frs.
Accommodation: 130 to 240 Frs.
Restaurant: breakfast from 7.00. Lunch from 12.00 until 14.00. Dinner from 19.00 until 21.00. Closed Sat (in winter), Sun evening, and from 25th Oct to 15th Nov.
Specialities: rillette de la Sarthe, ris de veau, aiguillette de canard, regional menu, home-cooking.
Hotel: ☆ ☆ 24 rooms. Facilities: shower, private bathroom, television, telephone.
Other points: credit cards accepted, bar, children's menu, à la carte menu, modern decor, terrace, pets allowed, car/lorry parking.
≪ *Lude chateaux; lac de Rille; zoo; La Flèche.*

CHATEAUBERNARD
Charente, 16100

PENSION DU CAMP
(M. Jean-Louis Bruno) Route de Barbezieux
☎ 45.82.09.47

Directions: between Barbezieux and Bordeaux.
Languages spoken: English.
Menu: 60 to 85 Frs.
Accommodation: 100 to 175 Frs.
Restaurant: breakfast from 6.00. Dinner until 23.00. Closed Fri after 15.00, Sat and Sun.
Specialities: home-cooking.
Hotel: 3 rooms. Facilities: shower.
Other points: credit cards accepted, bar, children's menu, lounge area, modern decor, terrace, car/lorry parking.
≪ *Cognac; Saint-Gobin.*

CHATEAUNEUF-SUR-LOIRE
Loiret, 45110

HOTEL DE LA PLACE
(Jacky and Christiane Maillard) 2 route de Châteauneuf, Germigny des Prés
☎ 38.58.21.33
Directions: RN 60, between Orléans and Montargis.
Menu: 55 to 150 Frs ☜
Accommodation: 130 to 200 Frs.
Restaurant: breakfast from 7.00. Lunch from 12.00 until 14.00. Dinner from 20.00 until 21.30. Closed Fri (out of season).
Specialities: fricassée de pintade (guinea-fowl) angevine, home-cooking.
Hotel: 11 rooms. Facilities: shower, private bathroom, television, telephone.
Other points: bar, children's menu, à la carte menu, lounge area, traditional decor, terrace, pets allowed, car/lorry parking.
≪ *valley of kings; Carlovingian church; Saint-Benoît monastery; chateau at Sully-sur-Loire; Gien; musée de la marine (maritime museum) at Châteauneuf-sur-Loire.*

CHATEAUROUX • Indre, 36000

BAR DE L'AVENUE
(M. Laurent Guillot) 1 avenue de la Manufacture ☎ 54.34.09.27
Directions: RN 20.
Languages spoken: English.
Restaurant: closed Sun.
Other points: bar.

CHATELLERAULT • Vienne, 86100

L'ARCHE DE CHATELLERAULT – ANTRAN
(M. Daniel Ricou) A10, services at Châtellerault – Antran (accessible in both directions) ☎ 49.02.72.04 [Fax] 49.02.69.80
Restaurant: open 24 hours.
Other points: credit cards and foreign currency accepted.

L'ARCHE DE CHATELLERAULT – USSEAU
(M. Dominique Robert) A10, services at Châtellerault – Usseau (accessible Bordeaux/Paris direction) ☎ 49.02.72.03
[Fax] 49.02.66.15

Restaurant: open until 24.00.
Other points: credit cards and foreign currency accepted.

CHATILLON-LE-ROI • Loiret, 45480

☲ LE DAGOBERT
(Mme Léone Roullet) 41 rue du Château
☎ 38.39.97.12
Directions: RD 927, between Pithiviers and Toury.
Menu: 55 Frs (wine included).
Restaurant: breakfast from 6.30. Lunch from 11.30. Dinner from 19.00.
Specialities: home-cooking.
Other points: bar, children's menu, à la carte menu, traditional decor, pets allowed, car/lorry parking.
◀ *chateau at Chamarolles; museums.*

CHATILLON-SUR-INDRE
Indre, 36700

☷ AUBERGE DE LA PROMENADE
(M. Pascal Bouquin) 88 rue Grande
☎ 54.38.80.79
Directions: RN 143, between Tours and Châteauroux.
Languages spoken: English.
Menu: 55 Frs.
Accommodation: 150 to 190 Frs.
Restaurant: breakfast from 6.15. Lunch from 11.30 until 14.00. Dinner from 19.00 until 21.00. Closed Sun.
Specialities: home-cooking.
Hotel: ☆ 7 rooms. Facilities: shower, private bathroom, telephone.
Other points: bar, traditional decor, pets allowed, car/lorry parking.
◀ *Loire chateaux; wildlife park at La Brenne; nature reserve at La Haute-Touche.*

☷ LE RELAIS DU MAIL
(Mme Huguette Soret) boulevard du Général-Leclerc ☎ 54.38.71.21
Directions: RN 143.
Menu: 48 Frs.
Accommodation: 90 to 190 Frs.
Restaurant: lunch from 12.00 until 14.00. Dinner from 19.00 until 21.00. Closed for 10 days in early Nov.
Specialities: home-cooking.
Hotel: 5 rooms. Facilities: shower.
Other points: bar, traditional decor, pets allowed, car/lorry parking.
◀ *chateau at Azay-le-Ferron (20km).*

CHAUNAY-BOURG • Vienne, 86510

☷ LE COMMERCE
(M. Patrick Le Roux) ☎ 49.59.02.71
Directions: RN 10, the Poitiers/Bordeaux road, 40km from Poitiers.
Languages spoken: English.

Menu: 55 Frs (wine included) to 98 Frs.
Accommodation: 120 to 180 Frs.
Restaurant: breakfast from 6.00. Lunch from 12.00 until 14.30. Dinner from 19.00 until 22.30.
Specialities: regional menu, home-cooking.
Hotel: ☆ 8 rooms. Facilities: shower.
Other points: credit cards accepted, children's menu, à la carte menu, lounge area, traditional decor, terrace, pets allowed, car/lorry parking.
◀ *Civray, Ruffec.*

CHAUVIGNY • Vienne, 86300

☲ RESTAURANT DU MARCHE
(M. Joël Torsat) 8 place du Marché
☎ 49.46.32.34
Directions: RN 151, the Poitiers/Châteauroux road.
Menu: 46 to 58 Frs.
Restaurant: breakfast from 7.30. Lunch from 12.00 until 14.00. Dinner from 19.30 until 21.00. Closed Thurs, and from 15th Sept to 15th Oct.
Specialities: home-cooking.
Other points: credit cards accepted, bar, modern decor, terrace, pets allowed, car/lorry parking.
◀ *Chauvigny (medieval city); Civaux (Merovingian cemetery).*

CHICHE • Deux-Sèvres, 79350

☲ CHEZ JACQUES
(M. Jacques Vincent) 27 place Saint-Martin
☎ 49.72.40.51
Directions: RN 149, the Poitiers/Nantes road.
Menu: 47 to 57 Frs.
Restaurant: breakfast from 7.30. Lunch from 11.45 until 14.00. Dinner from 19.00 until 21.30. Closed Wed afternoon, 2 weeks in Aug, and 1 week at Christmas.
Specialities: home-cooking.
Other points: bar, children's menu, traditional decor, terrace, pets allowed, car/lorry parking.

CHIERZAC-PAR-BEDENAC
Charente-Maritime, 17210

☲ LES ROUTIERS
(Mme Mireille Bertaud) ☎ 46.04.44.24
Directions: RN 10, Bordeaux.
Menu: 50 to 60 Frs.
Restaurant: breakfast from 7.00. Lunch from 12.00 until 14.30. Dinner from 19.00 until 21.00. Closed Sat, and one week in July.
Specialities: home-cooking.
Other points: bar, pets allowed, lorry parking.

CIVRAY • Vienne, 86400

☲ LE RELAIS DES USINES
(Mme Brigitte Nicoulaud) 19 rue Norbert-Portejoie ☎ 49.87.04.33
Directions: the Niort/Limoges road.

Menu: 52 Frs.
Restaurant: breakfast from 6.45. Lunch from 11.30 until 15.00. Dinner from 19.00 until 21.00. Closed Sat afternoon and Sun.
Specialities: home-cooking.
Other points: bar, traditional decor, pets allowed, car/lorry parking.
⊄ church at Civray; Saint-Nicolas; Charroux.

CIVRAY-DE-TOURAINE
Indre-et-Loire, 37150

≈ LE MARECHAL
(M. Jean Jabveneau) 1 rue de Bléré
☎ 47.23.92.16
Directions: RN 76, the Tours/Vierzon road.
Menu: 55 to 62 Frs.
Restaurant: breakfast from 6.00. Lunch from 12.00 until 14.00. Dinner from 19.00 until 22.00. Closed Sat afternoon, Sun, public holidays and 21st Aug to 11th Sept.
Specialities: regional menu.
Other points: credit cards accepted, bar, children's menu, à la carte menu, lounge area, traditional decor, terrace, pets allowed, car/lorry parking.
⊄ chateaux at Chenonceaux, Amboise and Loches.

CLION-SUR-INDRE • Indre, 36700

≊ AUBERGE DU PIED DE BOURGES
(Mme Nicole Chamton) 31 rue Nationale
☎ 54.38.60.90
Menu: 55 Frs (wine included).
Accommodation: 100 Frs (30% for extra bed)
Restaurant: breakfast from 6.00. Lunch from 11.00 until 13.30. Dinner from 19.00 until 21.00.
Specialities: home-cooking.
Hotel: 6 rooms. Facilities: shower.
Other points: credit cards accepted, bar.
⊄ chateaux.

LA CLOTTE
Charente-Maritime, 17360

≈ LE SABLIER
(Mme Sylvie Hubert) Route Départementale 910 bis ☎ 46.04.72.80
Directions: RD 910, between Libourne and Mont-Guyon.
Menu: 55 Frs (wine and coffee included).
Restaurant: breakfast from 7.00. Lunch from 12.00 until 14.00. Dinner from 19.00 until 22.00.
Specialities: home-cooking.
Other points: bar, traditional decor, terrace, pets allowed, car/lorry parking.
⊄ Mont-Guyon; Mont-Tendre.

CLUIS • Indre, 36340

≈ CHEZ VALERIE
(Mme Valérie Mazure) 6 rue des Parc
☎ 54.31.26.06
Languages spoken: English.
Menu: 50 Frs.

Restaurant: closed Wed afternoon.
Specialities: escargots.
Other points: bar.

CONFOLENS • Charente, 16500

≈ RELAIS DES CIGOGNES
(M. Saïd Yassa) Brillac ☎ 45.89.45.90
Directions: CD 951, between Bellac and Angoulême.
Menu: 60 to 70 Frs.
Restaurant: breakfast from 6.00. Lunch 11.00 to 14.00. Dinner 18.00 to 22.00. Closed Mon.
Specialities: home-cooking.
Other points: credit cards accepted, bar, children's menu, traditional decor, pets allowed, car/lorry parking.
⊄ Ouradour-sur-Glane; chateau at Saint-Germain-de-Confolens.

CORME-ROYAL
Charente-Maritime, 17600

≊ L'AUBERGE CORNILLONNE
(Mme Arlette Bellet) 1 rue du Grand-Pré
☎ 46.94.72.48
Directions: RD 137, between Marennes and Ile d'Oléron.
Menu: 54 Frs (wine included) to 98 Frs.
Accommodation: 140 to 180 Frs.
Restaurant: breakfast from 7.00. Lunch from 12.00 until 13.00. Dinner from 19.00 until 20.00. Closed Mon afternoon (out of season).
Specialities: escargots à la charentaise, mouclade (mussels in curry sauce), regional menu, home-cooking.
Hotel: ☆ 7 rooms. Facilities: shower, television, telephone.
Other points: bar, children's menu, à la carte menu, lounge area, traditional decor, pets allowed, car/lorry parking.
⊄ 12thC church; chateau at La Roche-Courbon.

CORMENON • Loir-et-Cher, 41170

≈ AUBERGE DU PARC
(M. André Touffu) 86 rue de la Poterie
☎ 54.80.92.04
Directions: RN 157, Le Mans.
Menu: 57 to 120 Frs.
Restaurant: breakfast from 7.00. Closed Sun and last 2 weeks in Aug.
Specialities: home-cooking.
Other points: credit cards accepted, bar, children's menu, à la carte menu, traditional decor, terrace, pets allowed, car/lorry parking.
⊄ Mondoubleau; Loir valley; musée des poids-lourds (HGVs).

CORMERY • Indre-et-Loire, 37320

≈ RESTAURANT LA CHAUMIERE
(M. Dominique Goron) 1 avenue de la Gare, Tauxigny ☎ 47.43.40.26

Directions: RN 143, Tours/Loches/Châteauroux.
Menu: 48 to 100 Frs.
Accommodation: 80 Frs (1 bed) to 160 Frs
(2 beds).
Restaurant: breakfast from 7.30. Lunch from
11.55 until 14.15. Dinner from 19.00 until 20.30.
Closed Wed after 14.30, and 2 weeks in Aug.
Specialities: fruits de mer (to order), coquillages
farcis, home-cooking.
Hotel: 3 rooms. Facilities: shower.
Other points: credit cards accepted, bar, children's
menu, terrace, pets allowed, car parking.
◄ *Loire chateaux.*

COULOMBIERS • Vienne, 86600

⇶ LE RELAIS DE LA PAZIOTERIE
(Mme Yvonne Barrusseau) Lusignan
☎ 49.60.90.59
Directions: RN 11, between Poitiers and Saintes.
Restaurant: breakfast from 5.00.
Specialities: home-cooking.
Other points: bar.

COURTENAY • Loiret, 45320

🚗 LE RELAIS DES SPORTS
(M. Gérard Martin) 38 rue de Villeneuve
☎ 38.97.32.37
Directions: RD 60, between Sens and
Montargis.
Languages spoken: German and English.
Menu: 57 Frs (plat du jour 42 Frs).
Accommodation: 70 to 120 Frs.
Restaurant: breakfast from 7.30. Lunch from
12.00 until 14.00. Dinner from 19.00 until 21.00.
Closed Sat evening, Sun, 15th to 30th March and
15th Aug to 7th Sept.
Specialities: home-cooking.
Hotel: 6 rooms. Facilities: shower, private
bathroom.
Other points: credit cards accepted, bar,
traditional decor, pets allowed, car parking.

COZES • Charente-Maritime, 17120

⇶ STATION SERVICE SHELL
(M. Jacques Gadiou) Route de Royan, Grezac
☎ 46.90.84.12
Restaurant: open until 24.00.

CREVANT-MONTIERCHAUME
Indre, 36130

⇶ AU CHEZ SOI
(Mme Yvonne Belouin-Ferré) Route Nationale
151 ☎ 54.26.00.19
Directions: RN 151, between Châteauroux and
Bourges.
Menu: 45 Frs (drink and coffee included).
Restaurant: breakfast from 11.00. Lunch from
11.00 until 15.00. Closed Sat, Sun, and in Aug.

Specialities: home-cooking.
Other points: children's menu, pets allowed.

CROIX-CHAPEAU
Charente-Maritime, 17220

⇶ CAFE DE PARIS
(M. Claude Blanche) 60 avenue de la
Libération ☎ 46.35.81.20
Directions: between Surgères and La Rochelle.
Menu: 50 Frs (wine included).
Restaurant: breakfast from 6.00. Lunch from
11.30 until 15.00. Dinner from 18.30 until 21.30.
Specialities: home-cooking.
Other points: credit cards accepted, bar,
traditional decor, pets allowed, car/lorry parking.
◄ *La Rochelle.*

DAMPIERRE-EN-CROT • Cher, 18260

🏠 LES TILLEULS
(M. André Paris) Route Départementale 923
☎ 48.73.81.04
Directions: RD 923, between Aubigny and Cosnes.
Menu: 48 Frs (wine included) to 130 Frs.
Accommodation: 80 Frs.
Restaurant: breakfast from 5.30. Lunch from
12.00 until 14.30. Dinner from 18.30 until 21.00.
Specialities: home-cooking.
Hotel: 5 rooms.
Other points: bar, children's menu, à la carte
menu, traditional decor, terrace, pets allowed,
car/lorry parking.
◄ *Sancerre; musée de la sorcellerie (sorcery);
chateaux.*

DARVOY • Loiret, 45150

⇶ LES ROUTIERS
(Mme Gwénola Guyomarc'h) 4 route
d'Orléans ☎ 38.59.71.00
Directions: RN 751, between Orléans and Jargeau.
Menu: 55 to 60 Frs.
Restaurant: breakfast from 6.30. Lunch from
11.45 until 14.30. Closed Sun.
Specialities: home-cooking.
Other points: bar, traditional decor, pets allowed,
car/lorry parking.

DEOLS • Indre, 36130

⇶ L'ESCALE VILLAGE
(M. Jean-Claude Sergent) Route Nationale 20
☎ 54.22.03.77 [Fax] 54.22.56.70
Directions: RN 20, the Paris/Limoges road.
Languages spoken: English and Spanish.
Menu: 49 to 120 Frs.
Restaurant: lunch from 11.30 until 14.00. Dinner
from 18.30 until 22.00.
Specialities: fruits de mer, regional menu.
Other points: credit cards accepted, bar,
children's menu, à la carte menu, modern decor,

pets allowed, car/lorry parking.
◄ *chateau at Valençay; Georges Sand's chateau; nature reserve at La Haute-Touche; region of 1,000 étangs (ponds).*

☷ LE RELAIS DE L'INTER
(M. Boubekeur Abderrahmane) Route d'Issoudun ☎ 54.27.20.07
Languages spoken: English, Spanish and Arabic.
Menu: 49 to 98 Frs.
Restaurant: breakfast from 5.00. Lunch from 10.30 until 15.30. Dinner from 18.30 until 23.30.
Specialities: couscous, grillades (grills), regional menu, home-cooking.
Other points: credit cards accepted, bar, children's menu, à la carte menu, modern decor, terrace, pets allowed, car/lorry parking.

DIGNY
Eure-et-Loir, 28250

☷ AUBERGE DE LA VALLEE
(M. Claude Doré) 35 rue du Maréchal-Leclerc ☎ 37.29.01.04
Directions: RD 928, Le Mans.
Menu: 40 to 90 Frs.
Restaurant: breakfast from 6.30. Lunch from 11.30 until 14.30. Dinner from 19.00 until 21.00. Closed Sun afternoon.
Specialities: couscous, paella, choucroute, home-cooking.
Other points: credit cards accepted, bar, children's menu, à la carte menu, traditional decor, terrace, pets allowed, car parking.
◄ *Chartres cathedral; La Ferté-Vidaure (chateau and museum); museum of miniatures.*

DREUX
Eure-et-Loir, 28100

☷ LE MARCEAU
(M. Jean-Pierre Parent) 40–42 avenue du Général-Marceau ☎ 37.46.05.57
Directions: RN 12 and 154, between Chartres and Le Mans.
Menu: 54 Frs.
Restaurant: breakfast from 6.30. Lunch from 12.00 until 14.00. Closed Sun, and in Aug.
Specialities: home-cooking.
Other points: credit cards accepted, bar, modern decor, terrace, pets allowed, car/lorry parking.
◄ *royal chapel; ancient belfry.*

LES EGLISES D'ARGENTEUIL
Charente-Maritime, 17400

☲ CHEZ VEVETTE
(M. Joël Pillot) ☎ 46.59.94.21
Directions: CD 950, the Poitiers/Saintes road.
Menu: 65 Frs.
Accommodation: 110 to 150 Frs.
Restaurant: breakfast from 7.00. Lunch from

12.00 until 14.00. Dinner from 19.30 until 21.00. Closed Fri and Sat evenings, Sun and from 15th Aug to 1st Sept.
Specialities: home-cooking.
Hotel: 5 rooms.
Other points: bar, children's menu, car/lorry parking.

EPANNES
Deux-Sèvres, 79270

☲ RELAIS SUISSE OCEAN
(M. Jacky Guilloteau) ☎ 49.04.80.01
Directions: RN 11, the Niort/La Rochelle road, exit 23.
Menu: 55 to 135 Frs.
Accommodation: 100 to 150 Frs.
Restaurant: breakfast from 7.00. Lunch from 11.30 until 14.30. Dinner from 19.30 until 21.00. Closed Sat evening, Sun, and 1st 2 weeks in Sept.
Specialities: fruits de mer, poissons, regional menu, home-cooking.
Hotel: 9 rooms. Facilities: shower, private bathroom, television.
Other points: bar, children's menu, à la carte menu, traditional decor, pets allowed, car/lorry parking.
◄ *Poitou marshlands; forêt de Chizé; La Rochelle.*

EPERNON
Eure-et-Loir, 28230

☷ LA GUINGUETTE
(Mme Gislaine Das Dores) 47 rue du Grand-Pont ☎ 37.83.51.25
Directions: RD 306, between Chartres and Rambouillet.
Menu: 55 to 90 Frs.
Restaurant: breakfast from 8.00. Lunch from 11.30 until 14.00. Dinner from 19.00 until 21.00.
Specialities: home-cooking.
Other points: credit cards accepted, bar, children's menu, lounge area, modern decor, pets allowed, car/lorry parking.
◄ *chateau at Maintenon; wine-presses at Epernon.*

ESVRES-SUR-INDRE
Indre-et-Loire, 37520

☷ LE SAINT-MALO
(Mme Marie-Claire Bouvard) La Pommeraie, Route Nationale 143 ☎ 47.65.77.58
Directions: RN 143.
Languages spoken: English.
Menu: 48 Frs.
Restaurant: closed Sat and Sun.
Specialities: home-cooking.
Other points: bar, children's menu, à la carte menu, traditional decor, pets allowed, car/lorry parking.
◄ *Loire chateaux.*

ETAGNAC • Charente, 16150

🍴 RELAIS D'ETAGNAC
(M. Louis Labrousse) ☎ 45.89.21.38
Directions: RN 141/948.
Languages spoken: English.
Hotel: 10 rooms.
Other points: bar.

LA FERRIERE • Deux-Sèvres, 79390

🍴 AU BON ACCUEIL
(Mmes Bilheu-Berger) 10 avenue de Poitiers
☎ 49.63.03.01
Directions: RN 149, the Poitiers/Nantes road.
Menu: 53 to 60 Frs.
Restaurant: breakfast from 8.30. Lunch from
12.00 until 14.00. Dinner from 19.30 until 21.00.
Closed Thurs evening, 2 weeks in Jan and last 3
weeks in Aug.
Specialities: home-cooking.
Other points: credit cards accepted, bar, car/lorry
parking.
◁€ Futuroscope (at Poitiers); Jaunay.

FLEURE • Vienne, 86340

🍴 AUX AMIS DE LA ROUTE
(Mme Michèle Guionnet) ☎ 49.42.60.25
Directions: RN 147, the Poitiers/Limoges road.
Menu: 50 to 80 Frs.
Restaurant: breakfast from 6.00. Lunch from
12.00 until 14.30. Dinner from 19.00 until 22.00.
Specialities: home-cooking.
Other points: credit cards accepted, bar, children's
menu, à la carte menu, traditional decor, pets
allowed, car/lorry parking.
◁€ Futuroscope; le Puy du Fou.

FONDETTES • Indre-et-Loire, 37230

🍴 LE BEAU MANOIR
(Mme Edith Bourreau) 6 quai de la Guignière
☎ 47.42.01.02
Directions: RN 152, the Angers/Nantes road.
Menu: 51 Frs.
Restaurant: breakfast from 7.00. Lunch from
12.00 until 14.00. Dinner from 19.00 until 21.30.
Closed Sat afternoon, Sun, and the 1st 2 weeks in
May.
Specialities: home-cooking.
Other points: credit cards accepted, bar, children's
menu, traditional decor, terrace, pets allowed, car/
lorry parking.
◁€ Loire chateaux (radius 10–30km).

FONTAINE-EN-SOLOGNE
Loir-et-Cher, 41250

🍴 LE RELAIS DE SOLOGNE
(M. Guy Normand) Route Départementale
765, La Chaucherie ☎ 54.79.98.85

Directions: RD 765, the Blois/Romorantin/Vierzon
road.
Menu: 54 Frs (wine included) to 75 Frs.
Restaurant: breakfast from 6.00. Lunch from
11.00 until 14.30. Dinner from 19.00 until 22.00.
Closed Sat afternoon and Sun.
Specialities: home-cooking.
Other points: credit cards accepted, bar,
children's menu, traditional decor, terrace, pets
allowed, car/lorry parking.
◁€ chateaux at Cheverny and Chambord.

FONTAINE-LE-COMTE
Vienne, 86240

🍴 AUBERGE DE LA GARENNE
(Mme Michelle Guérin) allée des Cerfs
☎ 49.57.01.22
Directions: the Niort/Bordeaux road.
Menu: 60 to 112 Frs.
Restaurant: breakfast from 6.00. Lunch from
11.30 until 14.00. Dinner from 19.00 until 22.00.
Closed Sun, public holidays, and in Aug.
Specialities: regional menu, home-cooking.
Other points: credit cards accepted, bar, children's
menu, à la carte menu, traditional decor, terrace,
pets allowed, car/lorry parking.
◁€ Futuroscope (10km).

FONTAINE-SIMON
Eure-et-Loir, 28240

🍴 AU BON COIN
(Mme Sergine Durand) 1 rue de la Mairie
☎ 37.81.84.98
Directions: Dreux-Rémalard.
Menu: 48 Frs.
Restaurant: breakfast from 7.00. Lunch from
12.00 until 14.00. Dinner from 19.00 until 20.30.
Closed Fri, and in Aug.
Specialities: home-cooking.
Hotel: 10 rooms. Facilities: shower, private
bathroom.
Other points: credit cards accepted, bar,
traditional decor, car/lorry parking.
◁€ chateau at La Loupe; La Fontaine-Simon;
chateau at Les Vaux.

FONTENAY-SUR-LOING
Loiret, 45210

🍴 LES 100 BORNES
(M. Guy Martin) Route Nationale 7
☎ 38.95.82.06
Directions: RN 7, between Montargis and
Dordives.
Menu: 53 to 90 Frs.
Restaurant: lunch from 11.45 until 15.00. Dinner
from 19.00 until 24.00. Open 24 hours. Closed
2 weeks in Aug.
Specialities: home-cooking.
Other points: credit cards accepted, bar, pets
allowed, car/lorry parking.

FOSSE • Loir-et-Cher, 41330

⇥ BAR DE L'ESPERANCE
(Mme Brigitte Chauvin-Sala) 7 rue de Saint-Sulpice ☎ 54.20.01.77
Directions: RN 153, between Vendôme and Le Mans.
Menu: 56 Frs.
Restaurant: breakfast from 7.15. Lunch from 11.30 until 14.30. Dinner from 19.00 until 21.30. Closed Sat and Sun.
Specialities: home-cooking.
Other points: credit cards accepted, bar, children's menu.

FRANCUEIL • Indre-et-Loire, 37150

🏠 LE RELAIS DES CHATEAUX
(M. Pierre-Jean Rafel) 'Les Perrières' ☎ 47.23.85.86
Directions: RN 76.
Languages spoken: English.
Menu: 58 to 130 Frs.
Accommodation: 160 to 210 Frs.
Restaurant: breakfast from 6.30. Lunch from 12.00 until 14.30. Dinner from 19.00 until 22.30. Closed Sun evening.
Specialities: regional menu, home-cooking.
Hotel: 4 rooms. Facilities: shower, private bathroom.
Other points: credit cards accepted, bar, children's menu, à la carte menu, traditional decor, terrace, pets allowed, car/lorry parking.
◁€ Loire chateaux (Chenonceaux and Amboise); parc de Beauval; Tours.

FRETEVAL
Loir-et-Cher, 41160

⇥ SARL LE PLESSIS
(Mlle Isabelle Thebault) Route Nationale 10 ☎ 54.82.64.28
Directions: RN 10, between Vendôme (20km) and Châteaudun (24km).
Languages spoken: German, English and Spanish.
Menu: 54 to 90 Frs.
Restaurant: lunch from 12.00 until 14.00. Dinner from 19.00 until 22.00. Closed from Sat 10am to Sun 10am, and 1 week at Christmas.
Specialities: home-cooking.
Other points: credit cards accepted, bar, traditional decor, pets allowed, car/lorry parking.
◁€ Vendôme; Loir valley.

GIDY • Loiret, 45520

⇥ L'ARCHE PORT DU VAL DE LOIRE
(M. Frédéric Rio) A10, services at Orléans – Gidy (accessible in both directions)
☎ 38.73.31.02 Fax 38.81.80.50
Other points: credit cards and foreign currency accepted.

GIEN • Loiret, 45500

⇥ CAFE DU NORD
(Mme Suzanne Botineau) 51 place de la Victoire ☎ 38.67.32.98
Directions: RN 140 and CD 952.
Languages spoken: English.
Restaurant: closed Sun, and 1st 2 weeks in Aug.
Other points: bar.

🏠 SARL LE RELAIS NORMAND
(M. Pierre Montceau) 64 place de la Victoire ☎ 38.67.28.56
Directions: opposite the faïencerie (pottery).
Languages spoken: English.
Menu: 54 Frs.
Accommodation: 120 to 150 Frs.
Restaurant: breakfast from 5.45. Lunch from 11.30 until 14.30. Dinner from 19.30 until 21.00. Closed Sat and Sun (except groups of 30+).
Specialities: home-cooking.
Hotel: 12 rooms.
Other points: bar, children's menu, modern decor, terrace, car/lorry parking.
◁€ Gien: pottery, musée de la chasse (hunting).

GIEVRES • Loir-et-Cher, 41130

⇥ SARL RELAIS DE NORAY
(Mme Christiane Laithier) Route de Vierzon ☎ 54.98.64.00
Directions: RN 76, Vierzon.
Menu: 57 Frs.
Restaurant: breakfast from 7.00. Lunch from 11.00 until 14.30. Dinner from 19.00 until 22.30. Closed Sat evening, Sun, and in Aug.
Specialities: home-cooking.
Other points: bar, children's menu, traditional decor, terrace, car/lorry parking.
◁€ chateau at Selles-sur-Cher.

HUISSEAU-EN-BEAUCE
Loir-et-Cher, 41310

⇥ LES PLATANES
(M. Hubert Breton) Route Nationale 10 ☎ 54.82.81.46
Directions: RN 10, between Vendôme and Châteaurenault.
Menu: 58 Frs.
Restaurant: breakfast from 6.30. Lunch from 12.00 until 15.00. Dinner from 19.00 until 22.30. Closed Sat evening, Sun, and early Sept.
Specialities: home-cooking.
Other points: credit cards accepted, bar, children's menu, pets allowed, car/lorry parking.
◁€ Loir valley.

INTVILLE-LA-GUETARD
Loiret, 45300

⇥ LE RELAIS D'INTVILLE
(M. Philippe Robillard) ☎ 38.39.71.70

Directions: between Etampes and Pithiviers.
Languages spoken: English.
Menu: 55 Frs (wine included).
Restaurant: breakfast from 5.30. Closed Sun.
Specialities: home-cooking.
Other points: credit cards accepted, bar, traditional decor, terrace, pets allowed, car/lorry parking.
⋖≡ Pithiviers.

ISDES • Loiret, 45620

≅ HOTEL DU DAUPHIN
(M. Lucien Laurent) 11 Grande Rue
☎ 38.29.10.29
Directions: RD 83, between La Motte-Beuvron and Sully.
Menu: 55 to 120 Frs.
Accommodation: 60 to 120 Frs.
Restaurant: breakfast from 6.30. Lunch from 11.30 until 14.00. Dinner from 19.00 until 20.30. Closed Mon afternoon.
Specialities: regional menu, home-cooking.
Hotel: 11 rooms. Facilities: shower.
Other points: bar, children's menu, traditional decor, terrace, pets allowed, car/lorry parking.
⋖≡ chateau at Sully; musée de la chasse (hunting) at Gien; canal bridge at Briare; chateau at Chambord; Jeanne d'Arc's house at Orléans.

ISSOUDUN • Indre, 36100

≅ LE RELAIS DE LA CROIX ROUGE
(M. Claude Grosyeux) 14 faubourg de la Croix-Rouge ☎ 54.21.04.91
Directions: RN 151.
Languages spoken: English, German, Italian, Turkish.
Restaurant: dinner until 21.00. Closed Sat, Sun, mid-Aug.
Hotel: 5 rooms.
Other points: bar.

≅ LE RELAIS ISSOLDUNOIS
(M. Hervé De Sa) 8 route de Bourges
☎ 54.03.04.05 [Fax] 54.03.01.00
Directions: RN 151, between Châteauroux (27km) and Bourges (27km).
Languages spoken: English.
Menu: 50 Frs.
Accommodation: 160 to 230 Frs.
Restaurant: breakfast from 6.00. Lunch from 11.45 until 14.30. Dinner from 19.00 until 22.00.
Specialities: regional menu, home-cooking.
Hotel: 16 rooms. Facilities: shower, private bathroom, television, telephone.
Other points: credit cards accepted, bar, children's menu, à la carte menu, modern decor, terrace, car/lorry parking.
⋖≡ Issoudun; Bourges.

JARNAC • Charente, 16200

⇌ LES ROUTIERS
(Mme Maryse Bouffinie) 77 rue Pasteur
☎ 45.81.02.40

Directions: RN 141, between Angoulême and Royan.
Menu: 55 Frs.
Restaurant: breakfast from 7.00. Lunch from 12.00 until 14.00. Dinner from 19.00 until 22.00. Closed Sun (except bookings).
Specialities: home-cooking.
Other points: bar, children's menu, pets allowed, car/lorry parking.
⋖≡ Cognac distillery buildings (Courvoisier).

LADON • Loiret, 45270

≅ LE RELAIS DE LADON
(M. Pierre Guillaumin) 400 avenue du 24 Novembre ☎ 38.95.51.32
Directions: RN 60, between Montargis and Orléans.
Menu: 50 to 70 Frs.
Accommodation: 72 to 110 Frs.
Restaurant: breakfast from 5.30. Closed Sun, 28th June to 19th July, 2 weeks after Christmas.
Specialities: home-cooking.
Hotel: 7 rooms. Facilities: shower.
Other points: bar, terrace, pets allowed, car/lorry parking.
⋖≡ windmill.

LAGEON • Deux-Sèvres, 79200

⇌ LE SAMPIERO
(M. Christian Garandeau) Route Départementale 938 ☎ 49.69.82.11
Directions: RD 938, between Parthenay and Thouars.
Languages spoken: English and Italian.
Menu: 55 Frs (wine included) to 175 Frs.
Restaurant: breakfast from 6.15. Lunch from 11.30 until 15.00. Dinner from 19.30 until 23.00. Closed Sun evening.
Specialities: regional menu, home-cooking.
Other points: bar, children's menu, à la carte menu, modern decor, terrace, pets allowed, car/lorry parking.
⋖≡ Parthenay; Thouars; Poitou marshlands.

LANDES
Charente-Maritime, 17380

≅ AUX AMIS DE LA ROUTE
(M. Eric Prestavoine) rue d'Aunis
☎ 46.59.73.37
Directions: between Saint-Jean d'Y (d'Angély) and Surgères.
Menu: 55 Frs (wine included).
Accommodation: 90 to 150 Frs.
Restaurant: breakfast from 7.00. Lunch from 11.30 until 14.30. Dinner from 18.30 until 21.30.
Specialities: home-cooking.
Hotel: 4 rooms.
Other points: bar, children's menu, traditional decor, pets allowed, car/lorry parking.
⋖≡ Saint-Jean d'Angély; Surgères.

LENCLOITRE • Vienne, 86140

AU 14 ANNE ANDRE
(M. André Pernelle) 2 place du Champ-de-Foire ☎ 49.90.71.29
Directions: between Châtellerault and Nantes.
Menu: 50 to 60 Frs.
Restaurant: breakfast from 7.00. Lunch from 11.00 until 15.00. Dinner from 19.00 until 23.00. Closed Sun.
Specialities: couscous (to order), home-cooking.
Other points: credit cards accepted, bar, lounge area, modern decor, pets allowed, car/lorry parking.
❦ *Futuroscope; Poitou marshlands; Loire chateaux: Azay-le-Rideau, Villandry, Chinon, Saumur.*

LINGE • Indre, 36220

CHEZ FRANCOISE ET JACKY
(Mme Françoise Bechgaoui) Le Bourg ☎ 54.28.03.94
Directions: between Le Blanc and Châteauroux.
Menu: 55 Frs (wine included) to 70 Frs.
Restaurant: breakfast from 7.00.
Specialities: couscous and paella, home-cooking.
Other points: credit cards accepted, bar, children's menu, traditional decor, terrace, pets allowed, car/lorry parking.
❦ *Azay-le-Ferron; Le Blanc; La Brenne nature reserve.*

LISSAY-LOCHY
Cher, 18340

AUBERGE DES MAISONS ROUGES
(M. Robert Léger) Les Maisons Rouges ☎ 48.64.76.07
Directions: intersection of RD 28 and 73.
Menu: 60 to 160 Frs.
Restaurant: breakfast from 6.00. Lunch from 12.00 until 14.00. Closed Sat morning.
Specialities: home-cooking.
Other points: credit cards accepted, bar, à la carte menu, traditional decor, terrace, pets allowed, car/lorry parking.
❦ *Noirlac; Châteauneuf; Bourges.*

LOGRON • Eure-et-Loir, 28200

AUBERGE SAINT-NICOLAS
(M. Bruno Hubert) 2 rue des Buissonnots ☎ 37.98.98.02
Directions: between Orléans and Alençon.
Menu: 50 to 105 Frs.
Restaurant: breakfast from 8.00. Lunch from 11.30 until 14.00. Dinner from 19.00 until 21.00. Closed Sun evening and Mon.
Specialities: home-cooking.
Other points: bar, children's menu, pets allowed, car/lorry parking.

LORRIS • Loiret, 45260

AUBERGE DE LA CROIX ROUGE
(Mme Lisiane Berlin) 28 rue Guillaume ☎ 38.92.47.03
Directions: RD 961.
Restaurant: breakfast from 8.00. Closed Sun afternoon.
Specialities: home-cooking.
Other points: bar, children's menu, à la carte menu.

LOULAY • Charente-Maritime, 17330

CHEZ JO
(M. Georges Mahdid) 10 place du Général-de-Gaulle ☎ 46.33.80.59
Directions: RN 150, between Saint-Jean d'Angély and Niort.
Menu: 55 to 65 Frs.
Accommodation: 100 to 145 Frs.
Restaurant: breakfast from 8.00. Lunch from 12.00 until 14.00. Dinner from 19.30 until 21.00. Closed Sun.
Specialities: home-cooking.
Hotel: 5 rooms.
Other points: bar, children's menu, traditional decor, pets allowed, car/lorry parking.
❦ *La Rochelle (40km); Poitou marshlands; forêt de Chizé; Neolithic museum; chateaux.*

LUCAY-LE-MALE • Indre, 36360

LE DAUPHIN
(M. Patrick Bruneau) 7 place de Verdun ☎ 54.40.41.17
Directions: between Valençay and Loches.
Menu: 55 Frs (wine included) to 75 Frs.
Restaurant: breakfast from 8.00. Lunch from 11.30 until 15.00. Dinner from 19.30 until 23.00. Closed Wed, and the last 2 weeks in Aug.
Specialities: home-cooking.
Other points: credit cards accepted, bar, traditional decor, terrace, pets allowed, car/lorry parking.
❦ *Valençay.*

LUNERY • Cher, 18400

BAR DU CENTRE
(M. Michel Porcheron) 1 place Jacques-Georges ☎ 48.68.98.71
Directions: RD 27, between Bourges and Châteauneuf-sur-Cher.
Menu: 50 Frs (with wine and coffee included) to 100 Frs.
Restaurant: breakfast from 6.30. Lunch from 12.00 until 14.00. Dinner from 19.00 until 22.00. Closed Tues, 2 weeks in Feb and 2 weeks in Sept.
Specialities: paté aux pommes de terre, magret de canard, home-cooking.
Other points: bar, children's menu, à la carte menu, traditional decor, pets allowed, car/lorry parking.
❦ *Bourges (20km).*

LUSSAC-LES-CHATEAUX
Vienne, 86320

☞ LE CHENE VERT
(Mme Nadia Homaërt) 14 route de Limoges
☎ 49.48.40.30
Directions: RN 147, the Poitiers/Limoges road.
Menu: 57 to 68 Frs.
Restaurant: breakfast from 6.30. Lunch from
12.00 until 15.00. Dinner from 19.00 until 22.30.
Closed Sun.
Specialities: magrets, confits, salade landaise,
home-cooking.
Other points: bar, children's menu, à la carte
menu, traditional decor, terrace, pets allowed,
car/lorry parking.
◖ *Vienne valley; La Rigaudière dungeon at
Bouresse; caves and prehistory museums.*

LUTZ-EN-DUNOIS
Eure-et-Loir, 28200

🛏 LA RENCONTRE
(M. Francis Berrier) ☎ 37.45.18.08
Directions: D 955, between Châteaudun and
Orléans.
Menu: 58 Frs.
Accommodation: 70 to 110 Frs.
Restaurant: breakfast from 5.30. Lunch from
11.00 until 15.00. Dinner from 19.00 until 21.30.
Closed Sat evening, Sun, public holidays and
mid-Feb to 1st March.
Specialities: home-cooking.
Hotel: 5 rooms. Facilities: shower, private
bathroom.
Other points: credit cards accepted, bar,
traditional decor, terrace, pets allowed, car/lorry
parking.
◖ *Châteaudun: chateau, caves, windmills; Loir
valley.*

MAINVILLIERS • Eure-et-Loir, 28300

☞ L'ARCHE DE CHARTRES NORD
(M. Jean-Jacques Bigot) A11, services at
Chartres – Gasville (accessible in both
directions) ☎ 37.31.62.42 [Fax] 37.31.61.99
Restaurant: open 24 hours.
Other points: credit cards and foreign currency
accepted.

☞ L'ARCHE DE CHARTRES SUD
(M. Olivier Plot) A11, services at Chartres –
Bois-Paris (accessible in both directions)
☎ 37.31.62.41 [Fax] 37.31.90.51
Other points: credit cards and foreign currency
accepted.

MANTHELAN • Indre-et-Loire, 37240

☞ LE RELAIS DE LA CROIX VERTE
(Mme Christiane Martin) 25 rue Nationale
☎ 47.92.80.16

Languages spoken: English.
Other points: bar, car/lorry parking.

MARANS • Charente-Maritime, 17230

☞ LE POINT DU JOUR
(Mme Sylviane Gérard) 2 rue des Moulins
☎ 46.01.14.54
Directions: RN 137, Nantes.
Menu: 55 to 75 Frs.
Restaurant: breakfast from 5.30. Lunch from
11.30 until 16.00. Dinner from 19.00 until 23.00.
Closed Sat and Sun (out of season).
Specialities: mouclade (mussels in curry sauce),
home-cooking.
Other points: credit cards accepted, bar,
children's menu, traditional decor, pets allowed,
car/lorry parking.
◖ *Poitou marshlands; La Rochelle.*

MAROLLES • Eure-et-Loir, 28260

☞ AU RELAIS DE MAROLLES
(Mme Viviane Beauvais) 44 rue Georges-
Bréant ☎ 37.43.20.50
Directions: RN 12.
Menu: 55 to 85 Frs 🥄
Restaurant: dinner until 24.00. Closed Sat, Sun
(except functions), and 1st 2 weeks in Aug.
Specialities: escalope normande, omelette aux
pleurottes, grillades (grills).
Other points: bar, car/lorry parking.

MARVILLE-MOUTIERS-BRULE
Eure-et-Loir, 28500

☞ LE RELAIS
(Mme Raymonde Lesch) ☎ 37.38.36.20
Directions: between Chartres and Dreux.
Menu: 50 to 65 Frs.
Restaurant: breakfast from 6.00. Closed Mon
afternoon, Sat, and 1 week at Christmas.
Specialities: home-cooking.
Other points: credit cards accepted, bar, à la carte
menu, modern decor, pets allowed, car/lorry
parking.
◖ *Chartres cathedral (27km); royal chapel at
Dreux (4km).*

MERY-SUR-CHER • Cher, 18100

🛏 LE RELAIS BERRY SOLOGNE
(M. Claude Carré) Route Nationale 76
☎ 48.75.20.34
Directions: RN 76, between Vierzon and Tours.
Menu: 65 Frs.
Accommodation: 85 to 145 Frs.
Restaurant: breakfast from 5.00. Dinner from
19.00 until 22.00. Closed Sat and Sun.
Specialities: Berry regional dishes, home-cooking.
Hotel: 11 rooms. Facilities: shower.
Other points: credit cards accepted, bar,

children's menu, traditional decor, pets allowed, car/lorry parking.
◀ Loire chateaux.

MEZIERES-EN-BRENNE
Indre, 36290

🍴 CAFE DES SPORTS –
Chez Sylviane
(M. Henri Peuvion) 11 rue de l'Ouest
☎ 54.38.11.62
Directions: RD 925, at the entrance to Mézières coming from Leblanc.
Menu: 50 to 80 Frs.
Accommodation: 90 to 220 Frs.
Restaurant: breakfast from 7.30. Lunch from 12.00 until 14.30. Dinner from 19.00 until 21.00.
Specialities: home-cooking.
Hotel: 6 rooms. Facilities: shower.
Other points: bar, children's menu, traditional decor, terrace, pets allowed, car/lorry parking.
◀ La Brenne nature reserve; les 1,000 étangs (ponds).

MIGNERES • Loiret, 45490

🍴 LE RELAIS DE MIGNERES
(M. Romain Cousin) 3 rue de la Gare
☎ 38.87.85.57
Directions: RD 94, between Auxy and Montargis.
Menu: 53 Frs (wine and coffee included) to 100 Frs.
Accommodation: 80 to 120 Frs.
Restaurant: breakfast from 6.30. Lunch from 11.00 until 14.00. Dinner from 19.30 until 21.30. Closed Sun.
Specialities: regional menu, home-cooking.
Hotel: 7 rooms. Facilities: shower.
Other points: bar, children's menu, lounge area, traditional decor, pets allowed, car/lorry parking.

MONNAIE • Indre-et-Loire, 37380

🍴 L'ARCHE DE TOURS – VAL DE LOIRE
(M. Christophe Ozenne) A10, services at Tours – Val de Loire (accessible in both directions) ☎ 47.56.15.49 [Fax] 47.56.12.17
Restaurant: open 24 hours.
Other points: credit cards and foreign currency accepted.

🍴 LA BONNE ETAPE
(Mme Claudette Thauvin) 67 rue Nationale
☎ 47.56.10.64
Menu: 50 to 85 Frs.
Accommodation: 130 to 150 Frs.
Restaurant: lunch from 12.00 until 14.00. Dinner from 19.00 until 21.00. Closed Sun, and Christmas Day.
Hotel: 6 rooms.
Other points: bar, car/lorry parking.

MONTARGIS • Loiret, 45200

🍴 LE PARIS-MONTARGIS
(M. Darbier) 221 rue Emile-Mangin
☎ 38.85.63.04
Languages spoken: English.
Restaurant: closed Sun.
Hotel: 10 rooms.
Other points: bar.

MONTBAZON
Indre-et-Loire, 37250

🍴 LA GRANGE BARBIER
(M. William Laborde) Route Nationale 10
☎ 47.26.01.69
Directions: RN 10, Montbazon southern exit, towards Poitiers.
Menu: 54 to 110 Frs.
Accommodation: 105 to 160 Frs.
Restaurant: breakfast from 7.15. Lunch from 11.30 until 14.00. Dinner from 19.00 until 21.30. Closed Sun evening, and the last 2 weeks in Aug.
Specialities: home-cooking.
Hotel: 5 rooms. Facilities: shower.
Other points: credit cards accepted, bar, children's menu, à la carte menu, traditional decor, terrace, pets allowed, car/lorry parking.
◀ Loire chateaux.

LES MONTILS
Loir-et-Cher, 41120

🚳 LES DEUX ROUES
(M. Jean-Pierre Levaux) 28 rue de Bel-Air
☎ 54.44.02.40
Directions: RN 764, between Blois and Montrichard.
Restaurant: breakfast from 7.00. Lunch from 11.30 until 14.00. Dinner from 19.30 until 20.30. Closed Sun.
Specialities: home-cooking.
Other points: bar, traditional decor, car/lorry parking.
◀ tower and ancient porchway at Les Montils.

MONTLANDON
Eure-et-Loir, 28240

🚳 LE RELAIS DE LA PERRUCHE
(M. André Baudelin) Route Nationale 23
☎ 37.37.30.95
Directions: RN 23.
Menu: 58 Frs.
Restaurant: breakfast from 4.00.
Specialities: home-cooking.
Other points: credit cards accepted, bar, children's menu, modern decor, terrace, pets allowed, car/lorry parking.
◀ chateau at Nogent-le-Rotrou (20km); church at Montlandon; La Fontaine-Simon (12km).

MONTMOREAU • Charente, 16190

🍴 LES ROUTIERS
(Mme Ernestine Ferrier) 14 avenue de
l'Angoumois ☎ 46.60.21.17
Directions: RN 674, the Angoulême/Libourne
road.
Restaurant: breakfast from 8.00.
Specialities: coq au vin, escargots, home-cooking.
Hotel: 6 rooms. Facilities: shower.
Other points: bar, modern decor, terrace.
◀€ Aubeterre.

MORNAY-SUR-ALLIER
Cher, 18600

🍴 L'ETAPE DU RIVAGE
(M. Christian Moret) Le Rivage
☎ 48.74.59.17
Directions: RN 76, between Bourges and
Moulins.
Menu: 50 Frs.
Accommodation: 80 to 140 Frs.
Restaurant: closed Sat, Sun, and in Aug.
Specialities: home-cooking.
Hotel: 4 rooms. Facilities: shower, private
bathroom.
Other points: credit cards accepted, bar, children's
menu, lounge area, traditional decor, pets allowed,
car/lorry parking.
◀€ animal park at Saint-Augustin; floral park and
chateau at Apremont-sur-Allier; river Allier.

🍴 LE RELAIS DE LA ROUTE
(Mme Jacqueline Chevrot) Route Nationale 76
☎ 48.74.53.54
Directions: RN 76.
Languages spoken: German and English.
Menu: 52 to 90 Frs.
Accommodation: 60 to 90 Frs.
Restaurant: open 24 hours. Closed from Sat 15.00
to Mon 1.00.
Specialities: home-cooking.
Hotel: 5 rooms. Facilities: private bathroom.
Other points: credit cards accepted, bar, pets
allowed, car/lorry parking.
◀€ Apremont (15km); parc de Saint-Augustin
(7km).

MOULISMES • Vienne, 86500

🍴 LA TABLE OUVERTE
(SARL Gransagne-Baudet) Route Nationale 147
☎ 49.91.90.68
Directions: RN 147, between Poitiers (50km) and
Limoges (70km).
Menu: 50 to 120 Frs.
Accommodation: 115 to 205 Frs.
Restaurant: breakfast from 6.00. Lunch from
12.00 until 14.30. Dinner from 19.30 until 21.30.
Closed Sat and Sun afternoon (out of season).
Specialities: home-cooking.
Hotel: ☆ 7 rooms. Facilities: shower, private
bathroom, television, telephone.

Other points: credit cards accepted, bar, à la carte
menu, traditional decor, pets allowed, car/lorry
parking.
◀€ Gartempe and Vienne valleys; Futuroscope;
Oradour-sur-Glane; nuclear power station at
Civaux.

NAINTRE • Vienne, 86530

🍴 LA HALTE
(Henni Houas) Nationale 10
☎ 49.90.09.69
Directions: RN 10, Châtellerault southern exit, on
Aquitaine autoroute.
Languages spoken: English, Arabic, Spanish,
German.
Restaurant: closed Sat and Sun.
Other points: bar.

NEUVY • Loir-et-Cher, 41250

🍴 LA CHEMINEE
(M. Philippe Masclet) Le Bourg
☎ 54.46.42.70
Directions: RD 923, the Paris/Angoulême
road.
Languages spoken: English, Spanish and
Portuguese.
Menu: 55 Frs (with wine and coffee included) to
140 Frs 🍵
Accommodation: 170 to 260 Frs.
Restaurant: breakfast from 7.00. Lunch from
12.00 until 14.00. Dinner from 19.00 until 21.00.
Closed Wed, and 2 weeks in Sept.
Specialities: escargots, salade de gésiers (chicken
gizzards), feuilleté de chèvre, rognons de veau, filet
de canard, darne de saumon, coquille Saint-
Jacques, cuisses de grenouilles, regional menu,
home-cooking.
Hotel: 9 rooms.
Other points: credit cards accepted, bar,
children's menu, à la carte menu, lounge area,
traditional decor, terrace, pets allowed, car/lorry
parking.
◀€ Chambord (10km); Cheverny (15km); Blois
(20km); Villesavin (10km).

NEUVY-BOUIN
Deux-Sèvres, 79300

🍴 BAR DES SPORTS
(M. Bernard Benechère) 20 rue du
Commerce ☎ 49.63.76.22
Directions: RD 948, between Bressuire and
Niort.
Menu: 50 Frs (wine included).
Restaurant: breakfast from 7.30. Lunch from
12.00 until 14.00. Dinner from 19.00 until 21.00.
Closed one week in Aug.
Specialities: home-cooking.
Other points: bar, traditional decor, terrace, pets
allowed, car/lorry parking.
◀€ Niort; Bressuire.

NEUVY-SAINT-SEPULCHRE
Indre, 36230

🍴 **LA CHARRETTE**
(M. Nicolas Pavlicevic) 21 place du Champ-de-Foire ☎ 54.30.84.77
Directions: RD 927, between La Châtre and Montluçon.
Languages spoken: Italian, Yugoslavian, Polish, Russian.
Menu: 64 and 80 Frs.
Accommodation: 140 to 190 Frs.
Restaurant: lunch from 12.30 until 14.00. Dinner from 19.00 until 22.00
Specialities: coq au vin, boeuf bourguignon, blanquette de veau (to order), home-cooking.
Hotel: 7 rooms. Facilities: shower.
Other points: bar, children's menu, à la carte menu, lounge area, traditional decor, car/lorry parking.
◁€ *Georges Sand's chateau; château de Nohan-Vic; château de Sarsay; basilica.*

NIORT • Deux-Sèvres, 79000

🍴 **LE BON ACCUEIL**
(Mme Thérèse Denibaud) 424 avenue Saint-Jean-d'Angély ☎ 49.79.27.60
Directions: RN 150, the Niort/Bordeaux road.
Menu: 55 to 70 Frs.
Restaurant: breakfast from 6.00. Lunch from 12.00 until 14.00. Dinner from 19.30 until 22.30. Closed Sat afternoon, Sun, and 3 weeks in Aug.
Specialities: home-cooking.
Other points: credit cards accepted, bar, children's menu, modern decor, car/lorry parking.
◁€ *Poitou marshlands (15km); zoo; forêt de Chizé (20km).*

NOGENT-LE-PHAYE
Eure-et-Loir, 28630

🍴 **LE RELAIS DU MOULIN ROUGE**
(M. Christian Bru) Le Moulin Rouge, Route Nationale 10 ☎ 37.31.62.68
Directions: RN 10, Chartres exit, towards Paris.
Menu: 55 Frs (coffee included).
Restaurant: breakfast from 5.00. Lunch from 11.30 until 14.30. Dinner from 19.00 until 21.45. Closed Sat, Sun, and in Aug.
Specialities: home-cooking.
Other points: credit cards accepted, bar, traditional decor, pets allowed, car/lorry parking.

NOHANT-EN-GOUT
Cher, 18390

🍴 **RELAIS DU BERRY**
(SARL Ligot) Route Nationale 151 ☎ 48.30.42.90
Directions: RN 151, the La Charité-sur-Loire/Auxerre road.
Languages spoken: German, English and Spanish.

Menu: 50 to 110 Frs.
Restaurant: lunch from 11.00 until 15.30. Dinner from 19.00 until 23.00. Closed Mon from 15.00, and 2 weeks in Feb.
Specialities: Berry regional dishes, feuilleté de ris de veau, regional menu, home-cooking.
Other points: credit cards accepted, bar, children's menu, à la carte menu, traditional decor, terrace, pets allowed, car/lorry parking.
◁€ *Bourges and environs.*

NOYANT-DE-TOURAINE
Indre-et-Loire, 37800

🍴 **CHEZ MIMI**
(Mme Annick Giret) Route de Chinon ☎ 47.65.82.26
Directions: l'Ile Bouchard.
Languages spoken: English.
Menu: 50 Frs (wine and coffee included).
Restaurant: breakfast from 5.00. Closed Sat from 14.00 and Sun.
Specialities: rillons maisons, rognons flambés au cognac, fruits de mer, gratin de fruits rouges au Sabayon, home-cooking.
Other points: credit cards accepted, bar, children's menu, traditional decor, terrace, pets allowed, car/lorry parking.
◁€ *chateaux at Chinon and Azay-le-Rideau (44km); Maillé.*

NOYERS-SUR-CHER
Loir-et-Cher, 41140

🍴 **RELAIS SAVOIE MEDITERRANEE BRETAGNE**
(M. Christian Florentin) 131 Route Nationale 76 ☎ 54.32.46.77
Languages spoken: German.
Menu: 50 Frs (wine included).
Restaurant: breakfast from 7.00. Lunch from 11.00 until 15.00. Dinner from 19.00 until 23.30. Closed Sun, and the 2nd and 3rd weeks in Aug.
Specialities: tripes à la mode de Caen, rognons au madère, boeuf bourguignon, home-cooking.
Other points: credit cards accepted, bar, children's menu, modern decor, pets allowed, car/lorry parking.

PARANCAY
Charente-Maritime, 17330

🍴 **LE RELAIS D'AUNIS**
(M. Jean-Paul Ferru) ☎ 46.33.94.67
Languages spoken: English.
Menu: 52 to 118 Frs.
Restaurant: lunch from 11.30 until 14.30. Dinner from 19.30 until 21.00. Closed Sat, and the last 2 weeks in Dec.
Specialities: escargots, anguilles (eels).
Other points: bar, à la carte menu, car/lorry parking.

PELLEVOISIN • Indre, 36180

⟐ LE RELAIS DES ROUTIERS – Chez Babette
(Mme Elisabeth Petit) 30 rue Jean-Giraudoux
☎ 54.39.03.78
Directions: RD 11, between Buzançais and Ecueillé.
Languages spoken: English.
Menu: 50 Frs.
Accommodation: 135 Frs.
Restaurant: breakfast from 10.00. Lunch from 12.00 until 14.00. Dinner from 19.30 until 21.30. Closed Sun, and in Aug.
Specialities: salade de chèvre chaud, salade de gésiers (chicken gizzards), grillades, home-cooking.
Hotel: 4 rooms. Facilities: shower, private bathroom, telephone.
Other points: credit cards accepted, bar, à la carte menu, traditional decor, terrace, car parking.
⟐ chateaux at Valençay and Argy.

PERRUSSON
Indre-et-Loire, 37600

⟐ LES ROUTIERS
(M. Kléber Lanchais) 3 rue de l'Indre
☎ 47.59.04.34
Directions: RN 143, the Tours/Châteauroux road.
Restaurant: breakfast from 7.30. Lunch from 12.00 until 15.00. Dinner from 19.00 until 22.00. Closed Sun evening, and 2 weeks in Aug.
Specialities: home-cooking.
Hotel: 7 rooms. Facilities: shower.
Other points: credit cards accepted, bar, children's menu, à la carte menu, pets allowed, car/lorry parking.
⟐ chateau at Loches.

LA PERUSE • Charente, 16370

⟐ LES ROUTIERS
(M. André Troussieux) Route Nationale 141
☎ 45.71.11.73
Directions: RN 141, the Limoges/Angoulême road.
Menu: 50 to 60 Frs.
Restaurant: breakfast from 5.30. Lunch from 11.00 until 14.00. Dinner from 19.00 until 21.00. Closed Sun.
Specialities: home-cooking.
Other points: credit cards accepted, bar, traditional decor, pets allowed, lorry parking.

PEZOU • Loir-et-Cher, 41100

⟐ RELAIS D'ARGENTEUIL
(M. Pierre Hauville) 'Fontaine'
☎ 54.23.42.47
Directions: RN 10.
Menu: 60 Frs.
Accommodation: 88 to 178 Frs.
Restaurant: breakfast from 5.00. Lunch from 11.30 until 14.00. Dinner from 18.30 until 22.30.

Closed Sat after 11am, Sun, public holidays, Aug, and 1 week at end of Dec.
Specialities: home-cooking.
Hotel: 6 rooms. Facilities: shower.
Other points: credit cards accepted, bar, children's menu, traditional decor, pets allowed, car/lorry parking.

PITHIVIERS • Loiret, 45300

⟐ LA PORTE DE BEAUCE
(M. Christian Collard) 6 Mail Ouest
☎ 38.30.02.52
Directions: RN 152.
Languages spoken: English and Polish.
Restaurant: breakfast from 6.30. Lunch from 12.00 until 14.00. Closed Mon, and in Sept.
Specialities: grillades, home-cooking.
Other points: credit cards accepted, bar, à la carte menu, traditional decor, modern decor, terrace, pets allowed, car/lorry parking.
⟐ transport museum; fortified chateau; narrow-gauge steam train tourist circuit.

POMPAIRE • Deux-Sèvres, 79200

⟐ LA CLE DES CHAMPS
(Mme Yolande Dubin) Route de Saint-Maixent ☎ 49.95.20.75
Directions: in the commercial centre.
Menu: 52 to 110 Frs.
Restaurant: breakfast from 7.00. Lunch from 11.00 until 15.00. Dinner from 19.00 until 21.30. Closed Sun (except groups).
Specialities: cuisses de grenouilles, anguille (eel) provençale, plateau de fruits de mer, regional menu, home-cooking.
Other points: credit cards accepted, bar, children's menu, à la carte menu, modern decor, pets allowed, car/lorry parking.
⟐ Parthenay (medieval city); Poitou marshlands.

PONS • Charente-Maritime, 17800

⟐ L'ARCHE DE SAINTES – SAINT-LEGER
(M. Didier Jacques) A10, services at Saint-Léger (accessible in both directions)
☎ 46.91.95.30 Fax 46.91.93.82
Other points: credit cards and foreign currency accepted.

PRESSAC • Vienne, 86460

⟐ LE RELAIS ROUTIER
(Mme Francine Bouyer) place de l'Eglise
☎ 49.48.56.99
Directions: RN 148, Niort/Poitiers/Limoges/Guéret.
Menu: 54 Frs (wine and coffee included).
Restaurant: breakfast from 5.00. Lunch from 10.00 until 16.00. Dinner from 19.00 until 24.00. Closed Sat, and last 2 weeks in Aug.
Specialities: farcis poitevin, home-cooking.

PRUNAY-LE-GILLON
Eure-et-Loir, 28360

☲ LA GERBE D'OR
(M. Henri Gosset) 10 rue du Pavillon, Fainville ☎ 37.25.72.38
Directions: RN 154, between Chartres and Orléans.
Menu: 55 Frs (wine included) to 120 Frs.
Accommodation: 140 to 160 Frs.
Restaurant: breakfast from 7.00. Lunch from 11.00 until 15.00. Dinner from 18.00 until 22.00. Closed Sat evening and Sun evening (in winter).
Specialities: home-cooking.
Hotel: 10 rooms.
Other points: credit cards accepted, bar, children's menu, à la carte menu, traditional decor, terrace, pets allowed, car/lorry parking.
◀€ Chartres cathedral; museum.

REFFANNES • Deux-Sèvres, 79420

☲ LE CHEVAL BLANC
(M. Didier Chevalier) avenue de la Grande-Auberge, Le Bourg ☎ 49.70.25.18
Directions: RD 938, Saint-Maixent or Parthenay.
Menu: 52 to 60 Frs.
Restaurant: breakfast from 7.30. Lunch from 10.00 until 15.00. Dinner from 19.00 until 21.00. Closed Sat, and 15th to 31st Aug.
Specialities: home-cooking.
Other points: bar, children's menu, traditional decor, pets allowed, car/lorry parking.
◀€ Parthenay.

RHODES • Indre, 36170

☲ RELAIS ROUTIERS DE RHODES
(M. Jean-Pierre Pérez) Mouhet ☎ 54.47.65.26
Directions: RN 20, between Limoges and Châteauroux.
Menu: 56 Frs.
Restaurant: breakfast from 6.00. Dinner until 22.30. Closed Sat, Sun, and in Aug.
Specialities: home-cooking.
Other points: bar, à la carte menu, lounge area, traditional decor, pets allowed, car/lorry parking.
◀€ Gallo-Roman sites; Lac d'Eguzon; Creuse valley.

ROCHECORBON
Indre-et-Loire, 37210

☲ RELAIS DE PATYS
(M. Jean-Marc Nourry) 1 rue de Patys ☎ 47.52.61.75

Directions: RN 152, between Tours and Blois.
Languages spoken: English and Spanish.
Menu: 51 to 62 Frs.
Accommodation: 105 to 135 Frs.
Restaurant: breakfast from 6.30. Lunch from 12.00 until 14.00. Dinner from 19.00 until 21.00. Closed Sun, and in Aug.
Specialities: home-cooking.
Hotel: 4 rooms. Facilities: shower, private bathroom.
Other points: bar, children's menu, à la carte menu, lounge area, modern decor, pets allowed, car/lorry parking.
◀€ Loire chateaux; numerous wine-cellars.

LA ROCHELLE
Charente-Maritime, 17000

☲ L'AQUARELLE
(Mme Muriel Parente) 26 boulevard du Maréchal-Lyautey ☎ 46.43.00.27
Directions: Ile de Ré.
Languages spoken: English and Portuguese.
Menu: 51 Frs (wine included).
Accommodation: 125 to 165 Frs.
Restaurant: breakfast from 7.30. Lunch from 11.30 until 14.30. Dinner from 19.30 until 21.30. Closed Sun afternoon.
Specialities: home-cooking.
Hotel: ☆ 10 rooms. Facilities: shower, private bathroom.
Other points: credit cards accepted, bar, modern decor, terrace, pets allowed, car/lorry parking.
◀€ La Rochelle; the Ile de Ré.

☲ L'OCEANIC
(M. Philippe Alzin) place du Marché-de-la-Pallice ☎ 46.42.62.37
Directions: between Ile de Ré and La Pallice.
Menu: 50 to 80 Frs.
Accommodation: 80 to 120 Frs.
Restaurant: breakfast from 6.30. Lunch from 11.30 until 14.00. Dinner from 19.30 until 22.00. Closed Sat and Sun.
Specialities: couscous, paella, cassoulet, choucroute, home-cooking.
Hotel: 5 rooms. Facilities: shower, private bathroom.
Other points: credit cards accepted, bar, traditional decor, terrace, pets allowed, car/lorry parking.
◀€ La Rochelle: old town, marina, museums.

☲ LE DELMAS BAR
(Mme Jeanine Francson) 32 boulevard Emile-Delmas ☎ 46.42.60.23
Directions: between La Rochelle and Ile de Ré.
Other points: bar, modern decor, pets allowed, car/lorry parking.
◀€ Ile d'Oléron; Aix; Ré; Poitou marshlands.

☲ LE GOELAND
(M. Jacques Durandeau) 15 rue du Docteur-Bigois ☎ 46.42.05.29
Languages spoken: English.

Other points: bar, children's menu, traditional decor, terrace, pets allowed, car/lorry parking.
◀€ Futuroscope; driving tours of the Vienne and Vigeant rivers; Clain valley.

Menu: 50 Frs.
Accommodation: 150 to 200 Frs.
Restaurant: breakfast from 6.30. Closed Sat afternoon and Sun afternoon.
Specialities: home-cooking.
Hotel: 6 rooms. Facilities: shower.
Other points: credit cards accepted, bar, children's menu, à la carte menu, traditional decor, terrace, pets allowed, car/lorry parking.
⋐ La Rochelle (port); Ile de Ré; maritime museum; museum of automata.

⋽ LES EMBRUNS

(René and Fabienne Poultier) 413 avenue Jean-Guiton ☎ 46.42.61.88
Directions: port de la Pallice, head of the bay.
Languages spoken: English.
Menu: 48 to 120 Frs.
Restaurant: breakfast from 6.00. Lunch from 11.30 until 15.00. Dinner from 19.00 until 21.00. Closed Sat and Sun.
Specialities: couscous, paella, choucroute (every Fri) Portuguese and Spanish dishes, fruits de mer, regional menu, home-cooking.
Other points: credit cards accepted, bar, children's menu, traditional decor, pets allowed, car/lorry parking.
⋐ Port de la Pallice (new fishing port).

LA ROCHELLE-PALLICE
Charente-Maritime, 17000

⋽ CHEZ ANNIE

(Mme Annie Bernelas) rue de l'Ile de Ré ☎ 46.42.53.61
Menu: 56 Frs.
Restaurant: breakfast from 6.00. Lunch from 12.00 until 15.00. Dinner from 19.00 until 21.30. Closed Sun, and 1st 2 weeks in Aug.
Specialities: home-cooking.
Other points: credit cards accepted, bar, modern decor, pets allowed, car/lorry parking.
⋐ the Ile de Ré; La Rochelle (commercial and fishing port).

ROMORANTIN-LANTHENAY
Loir-et-Cher, 41200

⊟ LES AUBIERS

(Mme Boivin) 1 avenue de Blois ☎ 54.76.05.59
Directions: RN 722 and 765, town centre.
Menu: 54 to 180 Frs.
Accommodation: 150 to 200 Frs.
Restaurant: breakfast from 6.30. Lunch from 12.00 until 14.00. Dinner from 19.30 until 21.00.
Specialities: home-cooking.
Hotel: ☆ 19 rooms. Facilities: shower, private bathroom, television, telephone.
Other points: credit cards accepted, bar, children's menu, à la carte menu, traditional decor, car/lorry parking.
⋐ chateaux at Chambord, Romorantin, Lassay and Blois.

⋽ RELAIS DE L'AVENIR

(Mme Jocelyne Breton) 44 avenue de Villefranche ☎ 54.76.14.28
Menu: 50 Frs.
Restaurant: breakfast from 7.15. Lunch from 11.45 until 15.00. Closed Sat, Sun, and 2 weeks in Aug.
Specialities: home-cooking.
Other points: traditional decor, pets allowed.

RORTHAIS • Deux-Sèvres, 79700

⋽ CHEZ FANFAN

(M. Marie-Françoise Simonnet) 10 place Saint-Hilaire ☎ 49.81.44.42
Directions: RN 149, the Poitiers/Nantes road.
Menu: 49 Frs.
Restaurant: breakfast from 5.30. Lunch from 11.30 until 14.30. Dinner from 19.00 until 22.00. Closed Sun, and 2 weeks from Christmas.
Specialities: home-cooking.
Other points: credit cards accepted, bar, children's menu, modern decor, pets allowed, car/lorry parking.

ROUILLAC • Charente, 16170

⊟ LA BOULE D'OR

(Mme Elisabeth Lhermite) 56 rue du Général-de-Gaulle ☎ 45.96.50.45
Directions: RN 939, between La Rochelle and Angoulême.
Languages spoken: German.
Menu: 56 Frs (wine and coffee included).
Accommodation: 140 to 260 Frs.
Restaurant: breakfast from 6.30. Lunch from 11.30 until 15.00. Dinner from 18.30 until 22.00. Closed Sun, and 2 weeks in Aug.
Specialities: home-cooking.
Hotel: 10 rooms. Facilities: shower.
Other points: credit cards accepted, bar, children's menu, à la carte menu, traditional decor, pets allowed, car/lorry parking.
⋐ chateau at Lignière (5km); Cognac (25km); Angoulême (25km).

ROUILLE • Vienne, 86480

⊟ CHEZ MARYSE

(Mme Maryse Tellier) Le Grand Breuil ☎ 49.43.93.75
Directions: RD 950, between Poitiers and Royan.
Menu: 60 Frs.
Accommodation: 120 Frs.
Restaurant: breakfast from 7.00. Lunch from 12.00 until 14.00. Dinner from 19.00 until 21.00. Closed Sun, and the last 2 weeks in May.
Specialities: home-cooking.
Hotel: 6 rooms. Facilities: shower, private bathroom.
Other points: credit cards accepted, bar, modern decor, terrace, pets allowed, car/lorry parking.
⋐ Gallo-Roman ruins; Futuroscope at Poitiers.

ROULLET SAINT-ESTEPHE
Charente, 16440

🍽 **LES VALLEES**
(M. Jean-Jacques Faudry) Les Vallées
☎ 45.66.30.31
Directions: RN 10, the Paris/Bordeaux road.
Menu: 55 to 85 Frs.
Accommodation: 100 to 130 Frs.
Restaurant: breakfast from 7.00. Lunch from
11.00 until 15.00. Dinner from 18.30 until 22.00.
Closed Sat evening and Sun evening (out of season).
Specialities: terrine maison au cognac, lapin
(rabbit) au pineau des charentes, regional menu,
home-cooking.
Hotel: 5 rooms.
Other points: bar, children's menu, à la carte
menu, terrace, pets allowed, car/lorry parking.
◁€ cognac distillery; Angoulême (ramparts, hôtel-
de-ville, cathedral); chocolate-making factory.

ROUMAZIERES • Charente, 16370

🍽 **LES ROUTIERS**
(M. Claude Harout) 122 route Nationale
☎ 45.71.10.88
Directions: RN 141, between Limoges and
Angoulême.
Menu: 50 Frs (wine included).
Restaurant: breakfast from 6.00. Lunch from
11.30 until 16.00. Dinner from 19.00 until 22.00.
Closed Sun.
Specialities: home-cooking.
Other points: bar, traditional decor, pets allowed,
car/lorry parking.
◁€ La Rochefoucauld; Confolens; dam at Lavaud.

ROUMAZIERES-LOUBERT
Charente, 16270

🍽 **LES ROUTIERS**
(M. Raymond Bisserier) Les 3 Chênes
☎ 45.71.71.83
Directions: Angoulême/Montluçon.
Menu: 59 Frs (wine and coffee included) to 75 Frs.
Accommodation: 110 Frs.
Restaurant: breakfast from 5.30. Lunch from
10.30 until 15.30. Dinner from 18.30 until 22.30.
Closed Sat, Sun, and the last 2 weeks in Aug.
Specialities: home-cooking.
Hotel: 7 rooms. Facilities: shower.
Other points: bar, traditional decor, terrace, pets
allowed, car/lorry parking.
◁€ chateaux at Nieul and Confolens; Angoulême;
La Rochefoucauld.

ROYAN • Charente-Maritime, 17200

🍽 **LE SYMPATIC**
(M. Yves Boinard) 30 avenue de la Libération
☎ 46.05.67.21
Directions: on the outskirts of Royan, coming from
Bordeaux.

Menu: 54 to 72 Frs.
Accommodation: 150 to 220 Frs.
Restaurant: breakfast from 6.00. Lunch from
12.00 until 14.00. Dinner from 19.00 until 21.00.
Closed Sun (out of season), and 1 week at
Christmas.
Specialities: home-cooking.
Hotel: 15 rooms. Facilities: shower.
Other points: credit cards accepted, bar,
children's menu, traditional decor, pets allowed,
car/lorry parking.
◁€ museum; zoological gardens; forests.

ROZIERES-EN-BEAUCE
Loiret, 45130

🍽 **LA BAGATELLE**
(Mme Sylvie Bihel) 1 rue Bagatelle
☎ 38.74.22.03
Directions: RN 157, between Orléans and
Le Mans.
Menu: 50 to 70 Frs.
Accommodation: 120 to 150 Frs.
Restaurant: breakfast from 6.00. Lunch from
11.00 until 15.00. Dinner from 18.30 until 23.00.
Closed Sat.
Specialities: home-cooking.
Hotel: 4 rooms. Facilities: shower, private
bathroom.
Other points: credit cards accepted, bar,
children's menu, modern decor, pets allowed,
car/lorry parking.
◁€ Orléans; Loire chateaux.

RUFFEC • Charente, 16700

🍽 **LE LANDAIS**
(M. Jean-Michel Lapegue)
34 avenue Célestin-Sieur
☎ 45.31.04.16
Directions: at the Ruffec exit, towards
Angoulême.
Menu: 55 to 80 Frs.
Restaurant: breakfast from 6.00. Lunch from
12.00 until 14.30. Dinner from 19.00 until 21.30.
Closed Sun, and 2 weeks in Dec.
Specialities: home-cooking.
Other points: credit cards accepted, bar,
children's menu, à la carte menu, traditional decor,
pets allowed, car/lorry parking.
◁€ old Angoulême; Futuroscope at Poitiers.

🍽 **PARIS IRUN**
(M. Jacky Sommier) Les Adjots
☎ 45.31.02.44
Directions: RN 10, between Poitiers and
Angoulême.
Menu: 50 to 80 Frs.
Restaurant: breakfast from 6.00. Lunch from
12.00 until 14.30. Closed Sun, and in Aug.
Specialities: regional menu, home-cooking.
Other points: bar, children's menu, traditional
decor, terrace, pets allowed, car/lorry parking.
◁€ driving tour of the river valleys.

RUFFEC-LE-CHATEAU
Indre, 36300

🍴 **CHEZ P'TIT JEAN**
(Mme Micheline Marandon) Route Nationale
151 ☎ 54.37.70.05
Directions: RN 151, the Châteauroux/Poitiers road.
Menu: 50 to 100 Frs.
Accommodation: 150 Frs.
Restaurant: breakfast from 6.00. Lunch from
11.30 until 14.30. Dinner from 19.00 until 22.00.
Closed 2 weeks in Sept.
Specialities: regional menu, home-cooking.
Hotel: 5 rooms. Facilities: shower.
Other points: credit cards accepted, bar,
children's menu, à la carte menu, traditional decor,
terrace, pets allowed, car/lorry parking.
◀ *La Brenne wildlife park; Futuroscope.*

SAINT-AGNANT
Charente-Maritime, 17260

🍴 **AU RENDEZ-VOUS DES AMIS**
(Mme Muriel Chautard) Le Pont
☎ 46.83.30.36
Languages spoken: German and English.
Menu: 58 to 60 Frs.
Restaurant: lunch from 11.30 until 14.00. Dinner
from 19.00 until 22.00. Closed Mon evening, Sat
morning, and in Oct–Nov.
Specialities: marmite de poissons aux petits légumes.
Other points: bar, car/lorry parking.

SAINT-AIGNAN-LE-JAILLARD
Loiret, 45600

🍴 **LES ROUTIERS SAINT-AIGNAN**
(Mme Claudine Gasnier) 78 rue Nationale
☎ 38.36.38.21
Directions: between Sully and Gien.
Menu: 53 to 120 Frs.
Restaurant: breakfast from 7.30. Lunch from
11.30 until 15.00. Dinner from 19.00 until 23.00.
Closed Wed, Feb school holiday, last 2 weeks in
Aug.
Specialities: coq au vin, couscous, choucroute,
grillades (grills), home-cooking.
Other points: bar, children's menu, traditional
decor, terrace, pets allowed, car/lorry parking.
◀ *chateaux at Gien, Chambord and Sully; La
Sologne; Saint-Benoist basilica; pottery at Gien;
trout-breeding.*

SAINT-ARNOULT-DES-BOIS
Eure-et-Loir, 28190

🍴 **TY KORN**
(M. Daniel Le Cam) 40 Grande Rue
☎ 37.22.53.17
Accommodation: 90 Frs.
Restaurant: breakfast from 6.30. Lunch from
12.00 until 14.00. Dinner from 19.30 until 22.00.
Closed Sun, and in Aug.

Specialities: regional menu, home-cooking.
Hotel: 5 rooms.
Other points: bar.

SAINT-AUGUSTIN-SUR-MER
Charente-Maritime, 17570

🍴 **LA MARINA**
(M. Jacky Dussaillant) Centre Commercial
☎ 46.23.28.22
Directions: between Royan and La Tremblade.
Languages spoken: English and Spanish.
Menu: 55 (wine and coffee included) to 110 Frs.
Restaurant: breakfast from 7.00. Lunch from
11.30 until 14.00. Dinner from 18.30 until 22.00.
Closed 3 weeks in Oct.
Specialities: regional menu, home-cooking.
Other points: credit cards accepted, bar,
children's menu, à la carte menu, modern decor,
terrace, pets allowed, car/lorry parking.
◀ *Royan; zoo at La Palmyre; Ile d'Oléron.*

SAINT-EUGENE
Charente-Maritime, 17520

🍴 **LES DEUX CHARENTES**
(Mme Marcelle Blanchard) La Maison de Bois
☎ 46.49.13.28
Directions: RD 731, Cognac/Royan/Barbezieux.
Menu: 53 to 180 Frs 🍴
Restaurant: breakfast from 6.30. Lunch from
11.00 until 14.30. Dinner from 19.15 until 21.00.
Closed Wed afternoon, and mid-Feb.
Specialities: regional menu, home-cooking.
Other points: credit cards accepted, bar,
children's menu, à la carte menu, traditional decor,
terrace, pets allowed, car/lorry parking.
◀ *distilleries at Brie and Archiac; dolmen at Saint-
Fort; Cognac; Jarnac.*

SAINT-FLORENT-SUR-CHER
Cher, 18400

🍴 **L'IMPREVU**
(M. Bernard Ruellan) 60 rue Jean-Jaurès
☎ 48.55.12.00
Directions: RN 151, between Bourges and
Châteauroult.
Menu: 52 Frs.
Restaurant: breakfast from 5.00. Dinner from
19.00 until 21.30. Closed Sun.
Specialities: galettes bretonnes, home-cooking.
Other points: credit cards accepted, bar,
children's menu, modern decor, pets allowed,
lorry parking.

SAINT-GENIS-DE-SAINTONGE
Charente-Maritime, 17240

🍴 **LE RELAIS DE SAINTONGE**
(Roux SA) Route Nationale 137
☎ 46.49.00.95

Directions: RN 137, the Saintes/Bordeaux road.
Languages spoken: English.
Menu: 60 (wine and coffee included) to 130 Frs.
Accommodation: 95 to 120 Frs.
Restaurant: lunch from 12.00 until 14.00. Dinner from 19.00 until 23.00. Open 24 hours.
Specialities: escargots à la charentaise, regional menu, home-cooking.
Hotel: ☆ 10 rooms.
Other points: credit cards accepted, bar, children's menu, à la carte menu, lounge area, traditional decor, terrace, pets allowed, car/lorry parking.
◀€ *Saintes (30km); Cognac (30km); Royan (35km); Jonzac-les-Thermes (10km).*

SAINT-GEORGES-SUR-EURE
Eure-et-Loir, 28190

🛏 **AU RENDEZ-VOUS DES PECHEURS**
(Henri and Monique Hubert) 9 rue Raymond-Bataille ☎ 37.26.81.90
Directions: RN 23, between Chartres and Le Mans.
Languages spoken: English.
Menu: 50 Frs.
Accommodation: 130 to 170 Frs.
Restaurant: breakfast from 6.30. Lunch from 12.00 until 14.00. Dinner from 19.00 until 20.30. Closed Sun, and 1 week at Christmas.
Specialities: coq au vin, pieds panés, choucroute, cassoulet, home-cooking.
Hotel: 9 rooms. Facilities: shower, private bathroom, television.
Other points: credit cards accepted, bar, children's menu, à la carte menu, traditional decor, terrace, pets allowed, car/lorry parking.
◀€ *Chartres: cathedral (8km); sailing lakes.*

SAINT-GERMAIN-LA-GATINE
Eure-et-Loir, 28300

🍽 **LE RELAIS DE SAINT-GERMAIN**
(M. Pierre Picard) 1 route de Chartres
☎ 37.22.80.31
Directions: RN 154, between Dreux and Chartres.
Menu: 49 Frs.
Restaurant: breakfast from 5.00. Lunch from 11.30 until 14.30. Dinner from 19.00 until 21.00. Closed Sat and Sun.
Specialities: home-cooking.
Other points: credit cards accepted, bar, children's menu, traditional decor, modern decor, pets allowed, car/lorry parking.
◀€ *Chartres cathedral.*

SAINT-HILAIRE-LA-GRAVELLE
Loir-et-Cher, 41160

🍽 **AUBERGE DU LOIR**
(M. Sylvain Pierdos) 10 rue Léon-Cibié
☎ 54.82.65.00
Directions: RD 19, the Orléans/Le Mans road.
Languages spoken: English.
Menu: 60 to 62 Frs.

Accommodation: 220 Frs.
Restaurant: breakfast from 7.00. Lunch from 12.00 until 14.00. Dinner from 19.00 until 22.00. Closed Wed, and in Sept.
Specialities: home-cooking.
Hotel: 2 rooms. Facilities: shower.
Other points: credit cards accepted, bar, children's menu, lounge area, traditional decor, terrace, pets allowed, car/lorry parking.

SAINT-MAURICE-SUR-FESSARD
Loiret, 45700

🍽 **CAFE DE LA GARE**
(Mme Colette Jehl) Route Nationale 60
☎ 38.97.81.00
Directions: RN 60, the Paris/Orléans road.
Languages spoken: English.
Menu: 55 to 65 Frs.
Restaurant: breakfast from 6.15. Lunch from 11.30 until 14.00. Dinner from 17.00 until 21.00. Closed from Sat 16.00 to Mon 6.30 (out of season).
Specialities: coq au vin, civet de gibier, home-cooking.
Other points: credit cards accepted, bar, children's menu, modern decor, terrace, pets allowed, car/lorry parking.

🍽 **LE RELAIS DE SAINT-MAURICE**
(M. Pascal Crouvisier) Route Nationale 60
☎ 38.97.80.59
Directions: RN 60, the Montargis/Orléans road.
Menu: 57 Frs.
Restaurant: breakfast from 6.30. Lunch from 12.00 until 14.00. Dinner from 19.15 until 21.30. Closed Sat evening and Sun.
Specialities: regional menu, home-cooking.
Other points: credit cards accepted, bar, traditional decor, terrace, car parking.

SAINT-NICOLAS-DE-BOURGUEIL
Indre-et-Loire, 37140

🍽 **LE RELAIS**
(M. Joël Joulin) place de l'Eglise
☎ 47.97.75.39
Directions: RD 35, the Tours/Angers road, via Bourgueil.
Menu: 52 to 77 Frs.
Accommodation: 130 to 180 Frs.
Restaurant: breakfast from 7.00. Lunch from 11.30 until 14.00. Dinner from 19.30 until 21.00. Closed Sat, Sun, public holidays, and in Aug.
Specialities: home-cooking.
Hotel: 3 rooms. Facilities: shower, private bathroom.
Other points: credit cards accepted, bar, à la carte menu, traditional decor, pets allowed, car/lorry parking.

SAINT-PIERRE-DES-CORPS
Indre-et-Loire, 37700

🍽 **LE GRILLON**
(M. Patrick Vitel) 9 quai de la Loire
☎ 47.44.74.90

Menu: 58 to 100 Frs.
Restaurant: breakfast from 6.00. Lunch from
11.30 until 14.30. Dinner from 18.00 until 22.00.
Closed Sun, and 2 weeks in Aug.
Specialities: home-cooking.
Other points: credit cards accepted, bar, modern
decor, pets allowed, car/lorry parking.
◁€ chateaux at Tours, Amboise and Chenonceau;
numerous museums.

SAINT-SAVINIEN
Charente-Maritime, 17350

🏠 LE SAINT-SAVINIEN
(Mlle Elisabeth Dieu) 27 rue de Champeroux
☎ 46.90.20.33
Directions: RD 18, between Saintes (12km) and
Saint-Jean d'Angély (10km).
Menu: 60 Frs (wine and coffee included).
Accommodation: 120 to 210 Frs.
Restaurant: breakfast from 7.30. Lunch from
12.00 until 14.00. Dinner from 19.30 until 22.00.
Closed Wed afternoon.
Specialities: regional menu, home-cooking.
Hotel: 9 rooms.
Other points: credit cards accepted, bar, children's
menu, à la carte menu, traditional decor, pets
allowed, car/lorry parking.
◁€ Saintes (12km); Saint-Jean d'Angély (10km);
miniature port; Saint-Savinien (visitor site).

SAINT-SORNIN
Charente, 16220

🍴 LES ROUTIERS
(M. Thérèse Dubois) Le Bourg
☎ 45.23.12.83
Directions: between La Rochefoucauld and
Montbron.
Menu: 58 Frs.
Restaurant: breakfast from 6.30. Lunch from
12.00 until 14.00. Dinner from 19.00 until 21.00.
Closed Mon after 14.00, and 2 weeks in Aug.
Specialities: home-cooking.
Other points: bar, children's menu, traditional
decor, terrace, pets allowed, car/lorry parking.

SAINT-SYMPHORIEN
Eure-et-Loir, 28700

🍴 LE RELAIS DES ESSARS
(M. Alain Nau) Route Nationale 10, Essars
☎ 37.31.18.30
Directions: RN 10, between Rambouillet and
Chartres.
Languages spoken: English.
Menu: 51 Frs.
Restaurant: breakfast from 6.00.
Specialities: home-cooking.
Other points: credit cards accepted, bar,
children's menu, modern decor, terrace, car/lorry
parking.
◁€ chateau at Maintenon; Rambouillet (18km).

SAINT-VICTOR-DE-BUTHON
Eure-et-Loir, 28240

🍴 CHEZ MIMI
(M. Faveris) La Hurie ☎ 37.81.34.60
Directions: RN 23, between Nogent-le-Rotrou
and Chartres.
Menu: 55 to 115 Frs.
Restaurant: breakfast from 6.30. Lunch from
12.00 until 15.00. Dinner from 19.00 until 22.30.
Closed Sun.
Specialities: home-cooking.
Other points: bar, children's menu, pets allowed,
car/lorry parking.

SAINTE-MAURE-DE-TOURAINE
Indre-et-Loire, 37800

🏠 L'ETOILE DU SUD
(M. Norhislem Medjahed) Route Nationale 10
☎ 47.65.40.61
Directions: RN 10, the Tours/Poitiers road.
Languages spoken: German, English and Arabic.
Menu: 55 Frs (wine included).
Accommodation: 100 to 250 Frs.
Restaurant: breakfast from 4.00. Lunch from
12.00 until 14.30. Dinner from 19.00 until 22.30.
Specialities: oriental dishes, regional menu, home-
cooking.
Hotel: ☆ 25 rooms. Facilities: shower, private
bathroom.
Other points: credit cards accepted, bar, children's
menu, à la carte menu, lounge area, modern decor,
terrace, pets allowed, car/lorry parking.
◁€ Chinon; Azay-le-Rideau; caves at Savonnières;
Villandry.

SAINTES • Charente-Maritime, 17100

🍴 L'OASIS
(M. Guy Fumoleau) Route de Rochefort
☎ 46.93.07.20
Directions: RN 137, Saintes centre.
Menu: 45 to 95 Frs.
Restaurant: breakfast from 6.00. Lunch from
12.00 until 14.00. Dinner from 19.15 until 21.15.
Closed Sat, Sun, from 3rd to 25th Aug and 1 week
at Christmas.
Specialities: home-cooking.
Other points: bar, à la carte menu, lounge area,
traditional decor, terrace, pets allowed, car/lorry
parking.
◁€ Gallo-Roman town, with arenas, baths,
chateaux, museums.

SANCERGUES • Cher, 18140

🍴 LE BON LABOUREUR
(Mme Martine Dubois) 54 Grande Rue
☎ 48.72.76.13
Directions: RN 151, between La Charité-sur-Loire
and Bourges.
Languages spoken: German and Italian.

Menu: 56 to 150 Frs.
Accommodation: 90 to 100 Frs.
Restaurant: breakfast from 7.30. Lunch from
11.45 until 13.45. Dinner from 19.00 until
20.30. Closed Tues afternoon, and from 5th July
to 5th Aug.
Specialities: fruits de mer, poissons, choucroute,
home-cooking.
Hotel: 4 rooms. Facilities: shower, private
bathroom, telephone.
Other points: bar, children's menu, traditional
decor, pets allowed, car parking.
◀€ Sancerre (25km); Bourges cathedral (40km);
abbey at Noirlac (60km); floral park at Apremont.

SARGE-SUR-BRAYE
Loir-et-Cher, 41170

⇛ **RELAIS DE MONPLAISIR**
(M. Michel Moujeard) Route Nationale 157
☎ 54.72.72.21
Directions: RN 157, Le Mans/Orléans/
Mondoubleau/Montoire.
Languages spoken: English, Spanish and Italian.
Menu: 51 Frs.
Restaurant: breakfast from 6.00. Lunch from
11.30 until 15.00. Dinner from 19.00 until 22.30.
Closed Sat, Sun, and in Aug.
Specialities: home-cooking.
Other points: credit cards accepted, bar,
traditional decor, terrace, car/lorry parking.
◀€ Loir and Braye valleys; chateau des Templiers at
Arville (15km).

SAUJON • Charente-Maritime, 17600

🏠 **HOTEL DE LA GARE**
(Mme Mellot) 2 rue Clemenceau
☎ 46.02.80.33
Directions: RN 150, between Saintes and Royan.
Languages spoken: English.
Menu: 35 to 65 Frs.
Accommodation: 140 to 210 Frs.
Restaurant: breakfast from 6.30. Lunch from
12.00 until 14.00. Dinner from 19.30 until 21.00.
Closed Sun, and end Dec.
Specialities: home-cooking.
Hotel: ✫ 12 rooms. Facilities: shower, private
bathroom, television, telephone.
Other points: credit cards accepted, bar, lounge
area, traditional decor, terrace, pets allowed, car/
lorry parking.
◀€ Saujon environs and beach.

SAUZE-VAUSSAIS
Deux-Sèvres, 79190

⇛ **LE RELAIS DES ROUTIERS**
(M. Joël Quintard) Chaignepain
☎ 49.29.34.61
Directions: RD 948.
Menu: 50 Frs.
Restaurant: breakfast from 7.00. Lunch from

11.30 until 14.30. Dinner from 19.00 until 22.00.
Closed Sat, and in Aug.
Specialities: home-cooking.
Other points: bar, lounge area, traditional decor,
car/lorry parking.

SAZILLY • Indre-et-Loire, 37220

⇛ **RELAIS DE LA PROMENADE**
(Mme Jocelyne Bigot) Le Bourg
☎ 47.58.55.50
Directions: RN 760, towards Chiron.
Menu: 50 Frs.
Restaurant: breakfast from 7.00. Lunch from
11.45 until 14.00. Dinner from 19.00 until 20.30.
Closed Sun.
Specialities: home-cooking.
Other points: bar, traditional decor, terrace, pets
allowed, car/lorry parking.
◀€ Loire chateaux.

SCOURY • Indre, 36300

🏠 **LE RELAIS ROUTIERS**
(Mme Roselyne Pilet) ☎ 54.37.98.09
Directions: RN 151, between Châteauroux and
Poitiers.
Menu: 54 Frs.
Accommodation: 90 Frs.
Restaurant: breakfast from 5.30. Closed Sat
afternoon, Sun (except by arrangement), the week
of the 15th Aug national holiday, and Christmas
week.
Specialities: home-cooking.
Hotel: 5 rooms. Facilities: shower, private
bathroom, television.
Other points: credit cards accepted, bar,
children's menu, modern decor, pets allowed,
car/lorry parking.
◀€ La Brenne wildlife park (20km).

SECONDIGNY • Deux-Sèvres, 79130

🏠 **LES ROUTIERS**
(M. Noël Duranceau) 43 rue de la Vendée
☎ 49.95.61.35
Directions: RD 949, La Roche-sur-Yon.
Languages spoken: English.
Menu: 55 to 150 Frs 🍽
Accommodation: 110 to 160 Frs.
Restaurant: breakfast from 7.00. Lunch from
11.30 until 14.00. Dinner from 19.00 until 21.00.
Closed Mon, 1 week in Feb and 1 week in Sept.
Specialities: farcis poitevin, moules marinières,
escargots farcis, salade gourmande, regional menu,
home-cooking.
Hotel: 5 rooms. Facilities: shower, television,
telephone.
Other points: credit cards accepted, bar,
children's menu, à la carte menu, traditional decor,
terrace, car/lorry parking.
◀€ Romanesque churches; chateau at Saint-Loup;
Mervent (forest); Futuroscope at Poitiers.

SERAZEREUX 'LE PEAGE'
Eure-et-Loir, 28170

🍽 **AU BON ACCUEIL**
(Mme Eliane Hérisson) Route Nationale 154
☎ 37.65.22.49
Directions: RN 154, between Chartres and Dreux.
Menu: 51 to 90 Frs.
Restaurant: breakfast from 4.30. Closed Sat evening, Sun, and 3 weeks in Aug.
Specialities: home-cooking.
Other points: credit cards accepted, bar, children's menu, modern decor, pets allowed, car/lorry parking.
◀ *Chartres cathedral.*

SERIGNY • Charente-Maritime, 17230

🍽 **CHEZ JOHAN**
(M. Johan Mercier) Route Nationale 137
☎ 46.01.40.43
Directions: Nantes.
Restaurant: dinner until 24.00. Closed Sun.
Other points: bar.

SOLTERRE • Loiret, 45700

🍽 **AUBERGE DE LA ROUTE BLEUE**
(M. Claude Baudouin) Route Nationale 7,
La Commodité ☎ 38.94.90.04
Directions: RN 7, the Paris/Nevers/Bourges/Lyon road.
Menu: 58 Frs (wine included) to 85 Frs.
Restaurant: breakfast from 4.30.
Specialities: ris de veau normand, escalope cordon bleu, escargots roquefort, home-cooking.
Other points: credit cards accepted, bar, children's menu, à la carte menu, traditional decor, terrace, pets allowed, car/lorry parking.
◀ *Gien; Montargis; Briare; Rogny-les-Sept-Ecluses.*

SOMMIERES-DU-CLAIN
Vienne, 86160

🏨 **AUBERGE DES 3 PILLIERS**
(M. Martial Richard) place de l'Eglise
☎ 49.87.70.09
Menu: 45 to 120 Frs.
Accommodation: 65 Frs.
Restaurant: breakfast from 6.00. Lunch from 12.00 until 15.00. Dinner from 19.00 until 23.00. Closed Mon, and 2 weeks in Feb.
Specialities: Poitou regional dishes, home-cooking.
Hotel: 5 rooms. Facilities: shower.
Other points: bar, children's menu, à la carte menu, traditional decor, terrace, pets allowed, car/lorry parking.

SUEVRES • Loir-et-Cher, 41500

🏨 **LE RELAIS DE LA PROVIDENCE**
(M. Michel Grosse) 1 place de la Mairie
☎ 54.87.80.88

Directions: RN 152, between Orléans and Tours.
Languages spoken: English and Spanish.
Menu: 55 to 125 Frs 🍲
Accommodation: 100 to 180 Frs.
Restaurant: breakfast from 6.00. Lunch from 12.00 until 15.00. Dinner from 19.00 until 22.00. Closed Sat evening and Sun evening.
Specialities: home-cooking.
Hotel: 7 rooms. Facilities: shower.
Other points: credit cards accepted, bar, children's menu, à la carte menu, traditional decor, pets allowed, car/lorry parking.
◀ *Loire chateaux; Poulain chocolate-making factory; nuclear power station at Saint-Laurent; wine-making cellars.*

SULLY-SUR-LOIRE • Loiret, 45600

🏨 **CHEZ LIONEL**
(M. Lionel Funten) 47–49 avenue de la Gare
☎ 38.36.26.11
Directions: Gare/Gendarmerie.
Menu: 58 Frs (wine included).
Accommodation: 100 to 190 Frs.
Restaurant: breakfast from 6.00. Dinner until 21.30. Closed Sat afternoon, Sun, and from 8th to 23rd Aug.
Specialities: rognons à l'ancienne, lapin aux 4 moutardes, home-cooking.
Hotel: ☆ 10 rooms. Facilities: shower, private bathroom.
Other points: credit cards accepted, bar, children's menu, lounge area, traditional decor, terrace, pets allowed, car/lorry parking.
◀ *chateau at Sully; Saint-Benoît basilica; 9thC church at Germiny.*

🏨 **LE SAINT-GERMAIN – Le Cercle d'Or**
(Bernard and Patricia Schwartz) 2 place Saint-Germain ☎ 38.36.27.02
Directions: RN 152, as you leave Sully, in the direction of Orléans.
Menu: 52 to 102 Frs.
Accommodation: 130 to 155 Frs.
Restaurant: breakfast from 6.30. Lunch from 11.30 until 13.45. Dinner from 19.00 until 21.00. Closed Fri evening, Sun evening, and the last 2 weeks in Dec.
Specialities: andouillette de Jargeou, coq au vin maison, fish, regional menu.
Hotel: 6 rooms. Facilities: shower.
Other points: bar, children's menu, à la carte menu, traditional decor, pets allowed, car/lorry parking.
◀ *chateau at Sully-sur-Loire; Saint-Benoît basilica; Gien: pottery; musée de la chasse (hunting); valley of kings.*

SURY-AUX-BOIS • Loiret, 45530

🍽 **LE RELAIS DU PONT DES BEIGNERS**
(M. Jean-Pierre Gueru) Pont des Beigners
☎ 38.55.97.72
Directions: RN 60, between Orléans and Montargis.
Menu: 59 to 70 Frs 🍲

Restaurant: breakfast from 6.00. Lunch from 11.30 until 14.30. Dinner from 18.30 until 22.00. Closed Sat afternoon, Sun, and from mid-Aug to mid-Sept.
Specialities: coq au vin de l'Orléanais, poulet sauté à la provençale, home-cooking.
Other points: credit cards accepted, bar, à la carte menu, traditional decor, terrace, pets allowed, car/lorry parking.
◁€ *Sully-sur-Loire; Montargis.*

TAVERS • Loiret, 45190

⊨ LA PIERRE TOURNANTE
(M. Daniel Lecoq) 36 Route Nationale 152
☎ 38.44.92.25
Directions: RN 152.
Restaurant: closed Sun.
Other points: bar.

TENDU • Indre, 36200

⊟ LE RELAIS
(M. André Luneau) Route Nationale 20
☎ 54.24.14.10
Menu: 60 to 160 Frs 🍲
Accommodation: 120 to 180 Frs.
Restaurant: lunch from 11.30 until 14.00. Dinner from 19.30 until 21.00. Closed Tues afternoon and Wed (out of season), 2 weeks end Sept/early Oct.
Specialities: regional menu, home-cooking.
Hotel: 9 rooms. Facilities: shower.
Other points: credit cards accepted, bar, à la carte menu, traditional decor, pets allowed.
◁€ *dam at Eguzon (25km); La Brenne (25km); Creuse valley; Argenton.*

THEILLAY • Loir-et-Cher, 41300

⊟ RELAIS DE LA LOGE
(M. Guy Paillaud) Route Nationale 20
☎ 54.83.37.20
Directions: RN 20, 13km from Vierzon.
Languages spoken: English.
Accommodation: 100 to 150 Frs.
Specialities: game (in season), home-cooking.
Hotel: ☆ 35 rooms. Facilities: shower, private bathroom.
Other points: credit cards accepted, bar, pets allowed, car/lorry parking.

THIVARS • Eure-et-Loir, 28630

⊟ LE RESTAURANT DU STADE
(M. Patrick Petit) 15 Route Nationale
☎ 37.26.40.05
Directions: RN 10, 5km from Chartres.
Menu: 50 to 68 Frs.
Accommodation: 140 Frs (+ 35 Frs for extra bed).
Restaurant: breakfast from 6.30. Lunch from 12.00 until 14.30. Dinner from 19.00 until 21.30. Closed Sat evening and Sun, and 1st 3 weeks in Aug.

Specialities: home-cooking.
Hotel: 8 rooms. Facilities: shower, private bathroom.
Other points: credit cards accepted, bar, modern decor, pets allowed, car/lorry parking.
◁€ *Chartres cathedral.*

THOU • Loiret, 45420

⊨ AU LIT ON DORT
(M. Solange Bertrand) ☎ 38.31.62.07
Directions: RD 965.
Restaurant: lunch from 11.30 until 14.30. Closed Mon afternoon, and in Aug.
Specialities: vol-au-vent, filet de boeuf and charlotte au chocolat, home-cooking.
Other points: traditional decor, pets allowed, car/lorry parking.

THOUARS • Deux-Sèvres, 79100

⊨ LE MILLE PATTES
(Mme Martine Valleau) 17 route de Launay
☎ 49.56.36.53
Directions: RN 1.
Languages spoken: English and German.
Other points: bar.

TONNAY-CHARENTE
Charente-Maritime, 17430

⊨ L'OASIS
(Mme Geneviève Vachon) 27 rue de Lattre-de-Tassigny ☎ 46.88.70.84
Directions: between Rochefort-sur-Mer and Saintes.
Restaurant: breakfast from 8.00. Lunch from 12.00 until 14.00. Closed Sun.
Specialities: couscous, home-cooking.
Other points: bar, pets allowed, car/lorry parking.

⊨ LES FONTAINES
(M. Jean-Paul Revelaud) 110 avenue d'Aunis
☎ 46.83.79.11
Directions: RN 137, between Nantes and Bordeaux, Rochefort exit.
Menu: 50 Frs.
Restaurant: lunch from 11.30 until 14.30. Dinner from 19.00 until 21.00. Closed Sun.
Specialities: home-cooking.
Other points: bar, children's menu, traditional decor, terrace, pets allowed, car/lorry parking.
◁€ *Rochefort: Corderie Royale (royal ropeworks); Pierre Loti's house.*

TOURY • Eure-et-Loir, 28390

⊨ LE RELAIS DE LA CHAPELLE
(Mme Claudine Comarlot) 60 avenue de la Chapelle ☎ 37.90.64.96
Menu: 59 to 62 Frs (coffee included).
Restaurant: breakfast from 4.00. Lunch from

12.00 until 14.30. Dinner from 19.30 until 23.00.
Closed Sat, Sun, 1 week in May and 1 week at
Christmas.
Specialities: home-cooking.
Other points: bar, traditional decor, terrace, car/
lorry parking.

TOUVERAC • Charente, 16360

☵ LE RELAIS DE TOUVERAC

(Mme Marylin Hudelot) Route Nationale 10
☎ 45.78.63.53
Directions: RN 10, the Angoulême/Bordeaux road.
Languages spoken: English, Spanish, Portuguese.
Menu: 63 to 80 Frs.
Restaurant: breakfast from 5.00. Lunch from
11.30 until 15.00. Dinner from 19.00 until 23.00.
Specialities: home-cooking.
Other points: credit cards accepted, bar,
children's menu, à la carte menu, lounge area,
modern decor, terrace, pets allowed, car/lorry
parking.
◁€ Cognac (30km); Aubeterre.

TREON • Eure-et-Loir, 28500

⊟ LE RELAIS DE TREON

(Mme Paulette Cuvellier) 20 rue de
Châteauneuf ☎ 37.82.62.35
Directions: RN 928, between Le Mans and
Nogent-le-Rotrou.
Menu: 57 Frs.
Restaurant: breakfast from 6.30. Lunch from
11.30 until 14.30. Dinner from 19.30 until 21.00.
Closed Sat, Sun and 2 weeks in Aug.
Specialities: home-cooking.
Hotel: 8 rooms. Facilities: shower, private
bathroom, television.
Other points: credit cards accepted, bar, lounge
area, lorry parking.
◁€ Chartres cathedral; royal chapel at Dreux;
chateau at Maintenon.

LA TRIMOUILLE
Vienne, 86290

⊟ L'AUBERGE FLEURIE

(Mme Monique Dufour) 30 rue
Octave-Bernard ☎ 49.91.60.64
Directions: RN 675, towards Blois/Périgueux.
Menu: 55 to 100 Frs ☜
Accommodation: 90 to 160 Frs.
Restaurant: breakfast from 7.00. Lunch from
12.00 until 14.00. Closed Sun and public holidays
after lunch.
Specialities: moules au vert, médaillon de ris de
veau à la Trimouillaise, home-cooking.
Hotel: 5 rooms. Facilities: shower.
Other points: bar, traditional decor, pets allowed,
car/lorry parking.
◁€ Futuroscope (70km); abbey at Villesalem; church
at Saint-Savin; chateau/town of Archambault-
Guillaume.

VALENCAY • Indre, 36600

⊟ SARL AUBERGE DU CHATEAU

(M. Vincent Coulon) 1 route de Blois
☎ 54.00.02.94
Directions: RN 156.
Menu: 50 Frs.
Accommodation: 60 to 110 Frs.
Restaurant: breakfast from 6.00. Lunch from
11.30 until 14.30. Dinner from 19.30 until 22.00.
Closed Sun (from 1st Oct to 31st March), 2 weeks
in Sept and 3 weeks in Feb.
Specialities: home-cooking.
Hotel: 5 rooms.
Other points: credit cards accepted, bar,
traditional decor, pets allowed, car/lorry parking.
◁€ chateau at Valençay.

VATAN • Indre, 36150

⊟ LE CHENE VERT

(Mme Andrée Lahaye) 13 avenue de Paris
☎ 54.49.76.56
Menu: 55 Frs.
Restaurant: breakfast from 7.45. Lunch from
12.00 until 14.00. Dinner from 19.30 until 21.00.
Closed Sat evening, Sun and in Sept.
Specialities: home-cooking.
Hotel: 6 rooms. Facilities: shower, private
bathroom.
Other points: credit cards accepted, bar, modern
decor, pets allowed, car/lorry parking.
◁€ Bourges; Valençay.

VENDOEUVRES • Indre, 36500

☵ CAFE DES SPORTS

(Mlle Isabelle Ferrand) 9 place Saint-Jean
☎ 54.38.33.82
Languages spoken: German, English and Dutch.
Menu: 55 Frs.
Other points: bar.

VERGNE • Charente-Maritime, 17330

☵ CHEZ PAPOU ET NADINE

(Mme Nadine Sabourin) Route Nationale 150 –
Tout-y-Faut ☎ 46.24.62.05
Directions: RN 150, the Niort/Bordeaux road.
Languages spoken: English.
Menu: 55 Frs (wine included).
Restaurant: breakfast from 6.00. Lunch from
11.30 until 15.00. Dinner from 18.30 until 22.00.
Specialities: home-cooking.
Other points: bar, traditional decor, pets allowed,
car/lorry parking.
◁€ Dampierre, Saint-Jean d'Y (d'Angély), Niort.

VERRUE • Vienne, 86420

⊟ LA BALBINIERE

(Paulette and Rémy Nativelle) La Balbinière
☎ 49.22.84.01

Directions: RN 147, the Poitiers/Angers road.
Menu: 57 to 85 Frs.
Accommodation: 110 to 200 Frs.
Restaurant: breakfast from 7.30. Lunch from
12.00 until 14.00. Dinner from 19.30 until 22.00.
Closed Sun evening, Mon, mid-Jan to mid-Feb and
one week in Aug.
Specialities: home-cooking.
Hotel: 8 rooms. Facilities: shower.
Other points: credit cards accepted, bar, modern
decor, pets allowed, car/lorry parking.
◀€ *Futuroscope at Poitiers.*

VIERZON • Cher, 18100

☕ AUX MILLE PATTES
(M. Ludwig Jakubik) 85 route de Tours
☎ 48.75.46.38
Directions: RN 76, the Vierzon/Tours road.
Menu: 53 Frs.
Restaurant: breakfast from 7.00. Closed Sun.
Other points: bar, pets allowed, car/lorry parking.
◀€ *Bourges.*

☕ MODERN'SPORT
(Mme Jeanine Madeleine) 141 avenue
Edouard-Vaillant ☎ 48.75.13.63
Directions: RN 20.
Restaurant: breakfast from 6.30. Lunch from
12.00 until 14.00. Dinner from 19.00 until 22.00.
Closed Sat, and in Aug.
Specialities: home-cooking.
Other points: bar, traditional decor, car/lorry
parking.

VILLARS-LES-BOIS
Charente-Maritime, 17770

☕ MOULIN DE POPEGRAIN
(Mme Maria Izel) Route Départementale 731
☎ 46.94.55.08
Directions: RD 731, between Cognac and Saint-
Jean d'Y (d'Angély).
Languages spoken: English, Spanish and
Portuguese.
Menu: 55 Frs (wine included) to 120 Frs.
Restaurant: breakfast from 6.00. Lunch from
11.00 until 15.00. Dinner from 19.00 until 22.00.
Specialities: morue (salt cod), tripes portugaises,
caldeirada, regional menu, home-cooking.
Other points: credit cards accepted, bar, children's
menu, à la carte menu, traditional decor, pets
allowed, car/lorry parking.
◀€ *museum and cellars at Cognac; glassworks;
abbey at Font-Douce.*

VILLEDOMER
Indre-et-Loire, 37110

☕ LE GAI PRINTEMPS
(Mme Luce Mounissens) Route Nationale 10
☎ 47.55.02.02
Languages spoken: English.

Menu: 50 to 150 Frs.
Restaurant: breakfast from 6.00. Closed Sat, Sun,
public holidays and in Aug.
Specialities: home-cooking.
Other points: credit cards accepted, bar,
children's menu, à la carte menu, lounge area,
traditional decor, terrace, pets allowed, car/lorry
parking.
◀€ *Loire chateaux.*

🏠 LES GRANDS VINS DE TOURAINE
(M. Claude Romian) Route Nationale 10
La Grande Vallée ☎ 47.55.01.05
Directions: RN 10, between Châteaurenault and
Monnaie.
Menu: 58 to 130 Frs ☕
Accommodation: 85 to 190 Frs.
Restaurant: breakfast from 7.00. Lunch from
11.45 until 14.00. Dinner from 19.00 until 21.30.
Closed Wed, and the last 2 weeks in July.
Specialities: andouillette and cuisse de lapin au
Vouvray, cuisses de grenouille, coq au vin, home-
cooking.
Hotel: 4 rooms. Facilities: shower.
Other points: credit cards accepted, bar, à la carte
menu, modern decor, pets allowed, car/lorry
parking.
◀€ *chateaux at Amboise and Tours; wine-cellars at
Vouvray.*

VILLEROMAIN • Loir-et-Cher, 41100

☕ AU BON COIN
(Mme Isabelle Renouf) 13 Grande Rue
☎ 54.23.81.17
Directions: RD 957, between Vendôme and Blois.
Languages spoken: English and Spanish.
Menu: 54 to 150 Frs.
Restaurant: breakfast from 7.30. Lunch from
11.30 until 14.30. Dinner from 19.30 until 21.00.
Closed Sun, and in Feb or March.
Specialities: poissons, gibier (game) (in season),
regional menu, home-cooking.
Other points: credit cards accepted, bar, children's
menu, à la carte menu, modern decor, pets allowed,
car/lorry parking.
◀€ *chateaux of Loir-et-Cher; Loir valley.*

VIVONNE • Vienne, 86370

☕ LE ROUTIERS
(M. Serge Judes) Route Nationale 10
☎ 49.43.41.03 [Fax] 49.43.42.36
Directions: RN 10, the Paris/Bordeaux road.
Languages spoken: Spanish.
Menu: 60 Frs (wine included) to 70 Frs.
Restaurant: lunch from 12.00 until 16.00. Dinner
from 19.00 until 23.00.
Specialities: entrecôtes aux échalottes, home-
cooking.
Other points: credit cards accepted, bar, children's
menu, modern decor, terrace, pets allowed, car/lorry
parking.
◀€ *Futuroscope at Poitiers.*

YMONVILLE • Eure-et-Loir, 28150

🍴 A L'ETOILE
(Mme Thérèse Brulé) 31 rue du Haut-Chemin
☎ 37.32.25.67
Directions: RN 154, between Chartres and Orléans.
Menu: 90 to 160 Frs.
Accommodation: 140 to 195 Frs.
Restaurant: breakfast from 7.00. Lunch from
12.00 until 13.30. Dinner from 19.30 until 21.00.
Closed Mon, 2 weeks in Jan and 10 days in Nov.
Specialities: poulet de Beauce à la saveur de
truffe, tourte de petit gris, home-cooking.
Hotel: ☆ 10 rooms. Facilities: shower, private
bathroom.
Other points: credit cards accepted, bar, children's
menu, à la carte menu, lounge area, traditional

decor, pets allowed, car parking.
◖€ *windmill; demeure beauceronne (Beauce
dwelling); Chartres: cathedral (25km).*

🍴 LE RELAIS DE BEAUCE
(Mme Martine Millochau) La Michellerie,
Route Nationale 154 ☎ 37.32.26.34
Directions: RN 154, the Orléans/Chartres road.
Menu: 58 Frs.
Restaurant: breakfast from 5.30. Lunch from
11.30 until 14.30. Dinner from 19.00 until 22.00.
Closed Sat, Sun, public holidays, and in Aug.
Specialities: home-cooking.
Other points: credit cards accepted, bar, modern
decor, pets allowed, car/lorry parking.
◖€ *Chartres: cathedral, maison de Picassiette;
windmill.*

CENTRAL FRANCE

The following *départements* are included in this chapter:

Allier (03)
Cantal (15)
Corrèze (19)
Creuse (23)

Haute-Loire (43)
Haute-Vienne (87)
Puy-de-Dôme (63)

AIXE-SUR-VIENNE
Haute-Vienne, 87700

🍴 LA CHAUMIERE
(M. Jean-Louis Péchalat) 5 avenue de la Gare
☎ 55.70.12.12
Directions: RN 21, Limoges/Périgueux road.
Menu: 55 to 120 Frs.
Accommodation: 95 to 130 Frs.
Restaurant: breakfast from 7.00. Lunch from
12.00 until 14.00. Dinner from 19.00 until 21.00.
Closed Wed evening, Sun evening and the last
2 weeks in Aug.
Specialities: coq au vin, confit de canard, entrecôte
bordelaise, regional menu, home-cooking.
Hotel: 5 rooms. Facilities: shower.
Other points: credit cards accepted, bar,
traditional decor, pets allowed, car parking.
◖€ *Limoges (12km); Ouradour-sur-Glane (20km);
porcelain factory tours.*

ARFEUILLES • Allier, 03640

🍴 LE RELAIS DES CHEVREAUX
(M. Joseph Bernard) Route Nationale 7,
Chatelus ☎ 70.55.03.80

Directions: RN 7.
Languages spoken: English, Spanish.
Menu: 55 to 60 Frs.
Restaurant: open 24 hours. Closed Sat
evenings.
Specialities: home-cooking.
Other points: credit cards accepted, bar,
children's menu, traditional decor, pets allowed,
car/lorry parking.
◖€ *chateau at Lapalisse; leisure park.*

ARGENTAT • Corrèze, 19400

🍴 CHEZ RAYMOND
(Mme Monique Pouzaud) place du 14 juillet
☎ 55.28.01.97
Directions: Tulle.
Menu: 65 to 100 Frs (wine included).
Accommodation: 115 to 160 Frs.
Restaurant: breakfast from 6.00. Lunch from
12.00 until 14.00. Dinner from 19.00 until 21.00.
Closed Sun (except bookings).
Specialities: home-cooking.
Hotel: 7 rooms. Facilities: shower.
Other points: bar, modern decor, pets allowed,
car/lorry parking.

AUBUSSON • Creuse, 23200

≒ LE RELAIS VERT ET BLEU
(Mme Murielle Magnat) in the Zone
Industrielle (Z.I.) du Mont ☎ 55.83.85.45
Directions: between Montluçon and Ussel.
Menu: 52 Frs (wine included) to 95 Frs.
Restaurant: breakfast from 7.00.
Specialities: regional menu, home-cooking.
Other points: credit cards accepted, bar,
children's menu, à la carte menu, traditional decor,
terrace, pets allowed, car/lorry parking.
◁ Aubusson.

≒ SPORT BAR
(M. Patrice Picquette) 15 avenue de la
République ☎ 55.83.80.60
Directions: RN 141, Limoges/Clermont-Ferrand
road.
Menu: 55 Frs (wine included) to 85 Frs.
Restaurant: breakfast from 7.00. Lunch from
11.30 until 15.00. Dinner from 19.00 until 21.00.
Closed Sun.
Specialities: home-cooking.
Other points: bar, children's menu, traditional
decor, pets allowed, car/lorry parking.
◁ Aubusson.

AURILLAC • Cantal, 15000

≒ BAR L'ESCUDILLIERS
(M. Robert Montourcy) place du 8 Mai
☎ 71.63.79.30
Directions: between Rodez and Brive-la-
Gaillarde.
Menu: from 55 Frs (wine and coffee included).
Restaurant: breakfast from 6.00. Lunch from
11.00 until 14.00. Closed Sun.
Specialities: coq au vin, regional menu, home-
cooking.
◁ Saint-Flour; Salers; Conques.

⌂ L'ETAPE DE LA MAISON NEUVE
(Mme Corinne Muller) Giou de Mamou
☎ 71.64.58.42
Directions: RN 122, 4km from Aurillac, towards
Clermont-Ferrand.
Menu: 52 Frs (wine included) to 65 Frs.
Accommodation: 100 to 120 Frs.
Restaurant: breakfast from 6.30. Lunch from
11.30 until 14.30. Dinner from 18.30 until 22.00.
Closed Sun (except in July and Aug).
Specialities: regional menu, home-cooking.
Hotel: 10 rooms.
Other points: credit cards accepted, bar,
children's menu, à la carte menu, lounge area,
traditional decor, terrace, pets allowed, car/lorry
parking.
◁ Puy Mary; Super Lioran.

≒ LE RELAIS DE LA SABLIERE
(Mme Jeanine Delort) Route Nationale 122,
La Sablière ☎ 71.64.51.80
Directions: RN 122, Montauban/Toulouse.
Languages spoken: English and Spanish.

Menu: from 55 Frs.
Restaurant: breakfast from 7.00. Lunch from
12.00 until 13.00. Dinner from 18.30 until 21.00.
Closed Sun, and in Aug.
Specialities: regional menu, home-cooking.
Other points: bar, terrace, pets allowed, car/lorry
parking.

BEAUNE-LES-MINES
Haute-Vienne, 87280

⌂ LA TERRASSE DE BEAUNE
(Mme Janine Malterre) ☎ 55.39.90.58
Fax 55.39.47.55
Directions: RN 20, at the Limoges exit.
Languages spoken: English.
Menu: from 52 Frs (with wine and coffee
included) ⌣
Accommodation: 140 to 260 Frs.
Restaurant: breakfast from 6.30. Lunch from
11.30 until 15.00. Dinner from 19.00 until 22.00.
Closed Sun, and 2 weeks in Aug.
Specialities: home-cooking.
Hotel: 9 rooms. Facilities: shower, private
bathroom.
Other points: credit cards accepted, bar, lounge
area, modern decor, terrace, pets allowed, car/
lorry parking.
◁ Limoges.

BELLEVUE-LA-MONTAGNE
Haute-Loire, 43350

⌂ HOTEL DES VOYAGEURS
(Mme Odette Chapon) ☎ 77.00.60.15
Directions: RD 906.
Menu: 50 to 90 Frs.
Accommodation: 100 Frs.
Restaurant: open 24 hours.
Specialities: home-cooking.
Hotel: 7 rooms.
Other points: bar, lounge area, terrace, pets
allowed, car/lorry parking.
◁ Le Puy-en-Velay (25km); la Chaise-Dieu (17km).

BESSAY-SUR-ALLIER
Allier, 03340

≒ LE BAR DE LA ROUTE BLEUE
(M. Francis Blanche) rue Charles-Louis-
Philippe ☎ 70.43.01.59
Directions: RN 7, between Moulins and
Varennes.
Languages spoken: English.
Menu: from 58 Frs (wine included).
Restaurant: breakfast from 6.30. Lunch from
12.00 until 14.30. Dinner from 19.00 until 23.00.
Closed Sat, Sun, and last 2 weeks in Aug and
1 week at Christmas.
Specialities: pieds de veau, regional menu, home-
cooking.
Other points: bar, children's menu, traditional
decor, pets allowed, car/lorry parking.

BORT-LES-ORGUES • Corrèze, 19110

🛏 LE RELAIS DES ROUTIERS

(Mme Antoinette Chereix) 9 place du Champ-de-Foire ☎ 55.72.00.42
Directions: RN 122.
Hotel: 5 rooms.
Other points: bar, restaurant.

BOURGANEUF • Creuse, 23400

🍴 LA BERGERIE

(Mme Brigitte Belz) Montboucher
☎ 55.64.20.18
Directions: RN 141, between Limoges and Clermont-Ferrand.
Menu: 51 to 200 Frs.
Restaurant: breakfast from 7.00. Lunch from 11.00 until 15.00. Dinner from 19.00 until 23.00. Closed Mon night to Tues 19.00.
Specialities: civet de gibier (game stew), fish, home-cooking.
Other points: credit cards accepted, bar, children's menu, traditional decor, terrace, pets allowed, car/lorry parking.
◀ Lac de Vassivière (25km); Aubusson tapestries (30km); Oradour-sur-Glane; museum at Lévêché.

BRIOUDE • Haute-Loire, 43100

🍴 LES ROUTIERS

(M. Roger Devins) Route de Clermont
☎ 71.50.14.39
Directions: RN 102, Le Puy-en-Velay/Clermont road.
Menu: 55 to 70 Frs.
Restaurant: breakfast from 6.00. Lunch from 12.00 until 14.00. Dinner from 19.30 until 21.30. Closed Sun, and from 15th–31st Aug.
Specialities: home-cooking.
Other points: credit cards accepted, bar, children's menu, modern decor, terrace.
◀ basilica; maison du saumon; the Allier valley.

BRIVE-LA-GAILLARDE
Corrèze, 19100

🛏 LE NOUVEL HOTEL

(Mme Patrick Mongin) 2 avenue Desgenettes
☎ 55.86.01.66
Directions: RN 89, between Périgueux and Clermont-Ferrand.
Languages spoken: English.
Menu: from 55 Frs (wine included).
Accommodation: 90 to 140 Frs.
Restaurant: breakfast from 6.30. Lunch from 12.00 until 14.30. Dinner from 19.00 until 22.00. Closed Sat afternoon and Sun.
Specialities: home-cooking.
Hotel: 12 rooms.
Other points: credit cards accepted, bar, traditional decor, terrace, pets allowed, car/lorry parking.
◀ caves of Lascaux; Les Eyziers de Tayac; Rocamadour; Padirac.

BRIVES-CHARENSAC
Haute-Loire, 43700

🛏 LE RELAIS DU COMMERCE

(Mme Elie Masson-Ferret) 2 route de Lyon
☎ 71.09.16.16
Directions: Valence/Saint-Etienne road.
Menu: 55 to 65 Frs.
Accommodation: 90 to 130 Frs.
Restaurant: breakfast from 6.00. Lunch from 11.30 until 14.00. Dinner from 19.00 until 21.00.
Specialities: home-cooking.
Hotel: 10 rooms. Facilities: shower.
Other points: credit cards accepted, bar, children's menu, traditional decor, car/lorry parking.
◀ Le Puy-en-Velay (3km); Loire chateaux (25km); source of the Loire (45km).

BROUT-VERNET • Allier, 03110

🛏 SARL CENTRE ROUTIER

(Mme Georgette Roux) Route Nationale 9
☎ 70.58.24.61 [Fax] 70.58.25.16
Directions: RN 9, between Gannat and Saint-Pourcain-sur-Sioule.
Menu: 59 to 64 Frs.
Accommodation: 120 to 150 Frs.
Restaurant: breakfast from 5.30. Lunch from 12.00 until 14.30. Dinner from 19.00 until 23.30. Closed Sat afternoon and Sun.
Specialities: home-cooking.
Hotel: 9 rooms.
Other points: credit cards accepted, bar, children's menu, traditional decor, terrace, pets allowed, car/lorry parking.
◀ La Sioule.

CHAMALIERE-SUR-LOIRE
Haute-Loire, 43800

🍴 LES ROUTIERS

(Mme Marie-Line Roure) rue Nationale
☎ 71.03.42.10
Directions: RD 103, between Le Puy-en-Velay and Saint-Etienne.
Menu: from 48 Frs.
Restaurant: breakfast from 7.30. Lunch from 11.45 until 14.30. Dinner from 19.00 until 20.30. Closed Wed.
Specialities: home-cooking.
Other points: bar, modern decor, pets allowed, car parking.
◀ Loire valley and chateaux.

CHAMBORET
Haute-Vienne, 87140

🍴 LA BERGERIE

(SARL Albenque/Moreau) ☎ 55.53.44.16
[Fax] 55.53.57.41
Directions: RN 147, between Limoges and Poitiers.
Menu: 58 to 125 Frs.

Restaurant: breakfast from 6.00. Lunch from 12.00 until 14.00. Dinner from 19.00 until 23.00. Closed Sun.
Specialities: home-cooking.
Other points: credit cards accepted, bar, children's menu, à la carte menu, traditional decor, pets allowed, car/lorry parking.
◀ Oradour-sur-Glane; lac de Saint-Pardoux; le Mont de Blond.

LA CHAPELAUDE • Allier, 03380

🍽 LE RELAIS DES TARTASSES
(Mme Colette Boutillon) Huriel
☎ 70.06.45.06
Directions: RD 143, Châteauroux.
Menu: 65 to 100 Frs.
Accommodation: 130 to 180 Frs.
Restaurant: breakfast from 6.00. Lunch from 12.00 until 14.00. Dinner from 19.00 until 22.00.
Specialities: pâté de pommes de terre, home-cooking.
Hotel: 7 rooms.
Other points: credit cards accepted, bar, children's menu, car/lorry parking.

LA CHAPELLE-D'AUREC
Haute-Loire, 43120

🍽 LE RELAIS DE LA CHAPELLE
(M. Gabriel Colombet) La Mioulaterre
☎ 71.66.53.55
Directions: RN 88, Le Puy-en-Velay.
Menu: 55 to 120 Frs.
Accommodation: 120 to 180 Frs.
Restaurant: breakfast from 6.30. Lunch from 12.00 until 14.00. Dinner from 19.30 until 21.00.
Specialities: home-cooking.
Hotel: 4 rooms. Facilities: shower, private bathroom.
Other points: credit cards accepted, bar, children's menu, à la carte menu, lounge area, modern decor, terrace, pets allowed, car/lorry parking.

CHATEAUNEUF-LA-FORET
Haute-Vienne, 87130

🍽 AUX CEPS
(M. Philippe Le Gorbelec) La Veytisou
☎ 55.69.33.38
Directions: RD 979, between Limoges and Eymoutiers.
Languages spoken: English.
Menu: 53 Frs (wine included) to 80 Frs.
Accommodation: 85 to 150 Frs.
Restaurant: breakfast from 6.30.
Specialities: potée limousine, ceps, poissons, home-made desserts, home-cooking.
Hotel: 8 rooms. Facilities: shower.
Other points: bar, children's menu, traditional decor, terrace, pets allowed, car/lorry parking.
◀ Vassivière; Montgargon.

🍽 LA BELLE ETOILE
(M. Jean-Christophe Biaujou) rue des Tilleuls
☎ 55.69.76.12
Directions: 9 km from Eymouthiers.
Menu: 53 Frs (wine included).
Restaurant: breakfast from 7.00. Closed Sun.
Other points: bar, modern decor, pets allowed, car/lorry parking.

LA CHOMETTE • Haute-Loire, 43230

🍽 LE COQ HARDI
(Mme Marie-Louise Meyronneinc) Route Nationale 102 ☎ 71.76.62.29
Directions: RN 102, between Clermont-Ferrand and Le Puy-en-Velay.
Menu: 50 to 80 Frs.
Accommodation: 90 Frs.
Restaurant: breakfast from 8.00. Lunch from 12.00 until 14.00. Dinner from 20.00 until 22.00. Closed Sat, and in Oct.
Specialities: regional Auvergnat specialities, saucisses-lentilles, potée, home-cooking.
Hotel: 2 rooms.
Other points: bar, lounge area.
◀ Le Puy-en-Velay; the Allier valley; museum of paleontology; Résistance museum; church at La Chomette.

LES ROUTIERS
Your assurance of Quality and Value

CLERMONT-FERRAND
Puy-de-Dôme, 63000

🍽 AUVERGNE PYRENEES – Les Routiers
(Mme Marie-Louise Laborde) 12 bis place des Carmes ☎ 73.92.35.73
Directions: RN 9, in town centre.
Languages spoken: English and Spanish.
Menu: 54 to 95 Frs.
Accommodation: 145 to 270 Frs.
Restaurant: breakfast from 6.30. Lunch from 12.00 until 14.00. Dinner from 19.30 until 21.00.
Specialities: coq au vin, regional menu, home-cooking.
Hotel: ☆ ☆ 15 rooms. Facilities: shower, private bathroom, telephone.
Other points: bar, lounge area, modern decor, terrace, pets allowed, car/lorry parking.
◀ Puy de Dôme; Chamalières; Royat; Montferrand; lakes; chateaux.

🍽 LE ROUTIER
(Mme Jocelyne Sausseau) 12 rue d'Estaing
☎ 73.90.15.24
Menu: from 43 Frs (wine included).
Restaurant: breakfast from 7.00. Closed Sat and Sun.
Specialities: home-cooking.
Other points: bar, traditional decor, pets allowed, car/lorry parking.
◀ Clermont-Ferrand.

COSNE-D'ALLIER • Allier, 03430

L'ESCALE
(Mme Marie-Joseph Sauvat-Majdoub) 2 place de la Liberté ☎ 70.07.21.10
Directions: A74, between Montluçon and Villefranche-d'Allier.
Languages spoken: English and Spanish.
Menu: from 55 Frs (wine and coffee included).
Accommodation: 100 Frs.
Restaurant: breakfast from 6.45. Lunch from 11.00 until 15.30. Dinner from 17.00 until 22.30.
Specialities: regional menu, home-cooking.
Hotel: 6 rooms. Facilities: shower.
Other points: credit cards accepted, bar, à la carte menu, modern decor, terrace, pets allowed, car/lorry parking.
⫷ chateaux and forest.

COSTAROS • Haute-Loire, 43490

LES ROUTIERS
(Mme Thérèse Rossello) rue Principale ☎ 71.57.16.04
Directions: RN 88, Le Puy-en-Velay/Marseille road.
Languages spoken: Spanish.
Menu: 60 to 90 Frs ⌣
Accommodation: 90 Frs.
Restaurant: breakfast from 7.00. Lunch from 12.00 until 14.30. Dinner from 19.30 until 21.00. Closed Sat (out of season), and from end Dec to mid-Jan.
Specialities: grenouilles, mousse de brochet, avocat farci, lapin chasseur, truite meunière, caille flambée, rognons au madère, regional menu.
Hotel: 17 rooms. Facilities: shower.
Other points: bar, à la carte menu, traditional decor, terrace, pets allowed, car/lorry parking.

COUSSAC-BONNEVAL
Haute-Vienne, 87500

LE GAI COUSSAC
(Mme Colette Renaudin) avenue du 11 Novembre ☎ 55.75.21.59
Directions: RD 901, between Pompadour and Saint-Yrieix-la-Perche.
Menu: 52 Frs (with wine and coffee included) to 120 Frs.
Accommodation: 90 to 190 Frs.
Restaurant: lunch from 12.00 until 14.00. Dinner from 19.00 until 22.30.
Specialities: home-cooking.
Hotel: 6 rooms. Facilities: shower.
Other points: credit cards accepted, bar, children's menu, à la carte menu, lounge area, modern decor, pets allowed, car/lorry parking.
⫷ chateau; haras de Pompadour.

CREUZIER-LE-VIEUX • Allier, 03300

CHEZ LA MERE RIBOULIN (SARL)
(M. Marcel Joly) 10 rue des Ailes
☎ 70.98.44.88

Directions: Zone Industrielle (Z.I.) at Vichy Rhue.
Restaurant: breakfast from 5.30.
Specialities: home-cooking.
Hotel: ☆ 16 rooms. Facilities: shower.
Other points: credit cards accepted, bar, à la carte menu, terrace, pets allowed, car/lorry parking.
⫷ Vichy.

CUSSAC • Haute-Vienne, 87150

BAR RESTAURANT HOTEL TABAC
(Mme Denise Barrière) Route Départementale 699 – Le Bourg
☎ 55.70.94.84
Directions: RD 699, Limoges/Angoulême road.
Menu: 45 Frs (wine included) to 85 Frs.
Accommodation: 120 to 160 Frs.
Restaurant: breakfast from 7.00. Lunch from 11.00 until 15.00. Dinner from 18.30 until 21.30.
Specialities: ris de veau, omelette aux ceps, regional menu, home-cooking.
Hotel: 10 rooms. Facilities: shower, private bathroom.
Other points: credit cards accepted, bar, children's menu, traditional decor, pets allowed, car/lorry parking.
⫷ Richard Coeur de Lion circuit; chateaux.

CUSSET • Allier, 03300

HOTEL DE LA GARE
(M. Jean Laroque) 1 route de Paris
☎ 70.98.26.10
Menu: from 55 Frs.
Accommodation: 90 Frs.
Restaurant: breakfast from 6.30. Lunch from 12.00 until 13.30. Closed Sun, and in July.
Specialities: home-cooking.
Hotel: 2 rooms. Facilities: shower.
Other points: bar, traditional decor, car parking.

LES MONTAGNARDS
(M. Roger Pol) 20 rue du Général-Raynal
☎ 70.98.38.60
Directions: at the Cusset exit, towards Lapalisse.
Menu: 50 to 55 Frs.
Restaurant: breakfast from 7.00. Lunch from 11.30 until 14.00. Closed Sun, and in Aug.
Specialities: home-cooking.
Other points: bar, traditional decor, pets allowed, car/lorry parking.
⫷ Bourbonnais mountains (20km); Vichy (3km).

DEUX-CHAISES • Allier, 03240

LE RELAIS DE L'AMITIE
(Mme Brigitte Bordier) Route Nationale 145
☎ 70.47.14.83 [Fax] 70.47.14.83
Directions: RN 145, between Moulins and Bellac.
Languages spoken: English, Spanish and Italian.
Menu: 56 Frs (wine included).
Restaurant: breakfast from 5.30. Lunch from

12.00 until 14.00. Dinner from 19.30 until 22.00.
Closed Sat afternoon, Sun.
Specialities: home-cooking.
Other points: bar, traditional decor, pets allowed,
car/lorry parking.

DOMPIERRE-SUR-BESBRE
Allier, 03290

LE RELAIS DE LA BESBRE
(M. Jean-Pierre Marossa) 207 avenue de
la Gare ☎ 70.34.53.69
Directions: RN 79, between Moulins and Mâcon.
Menu: 52 to 72 Frs.
Restaurant: breakfast from 6.00. Lunch from
12.00 until 14.00. Dinner from 19.00 until 21.00.
Closed Sat afternoon, Sun, and from mid-Sept to
beginning of Oct.
Specialities: home-cooking.
Other points: bar, traditional decor, pets allowed,
car/lorry parking.
◁≡ *Besbre valley.*

DURDAT-LAREQUILLE
Allier, 03310

**RESTAURANT DES SPORTS –
Chez Gérard et Nathalie**
(Gérard and Nathalie Lombardi) Route
Nationale 144 ☎ 70.51.07.28
Directions: RN 144, Montluçon/Clermont-Ferrand
road.
Languages spoken: English, Spanish and Italian.
Menu: from 55 Frs.
Restaurant: breakfast from 6.00. Lunch from
11.30 until 14.00. Dinner from 19.00 until 20.00.
Closed Sun, and in Aug.
Specialities: home-cooking.
Other points: bar, modern decor, terrace, car/
lorry parking.
◁≡ *Sioule gorges (30km); chateau at Chouvigny
(35km).*

EYMOUTIERS • Haute-Vienne, 87120

LE SAINT PSALMET
(M. Michel Le Petit) place du Champ de Foire
☎ 55.69.10.06 Fax 55.69.23.92
Directions: CD 940 and 941, Limoges/Ussel or
Guéret/Tulle roads.
Languages spoken: English and Spanish.
Menu: 45 (wine included) to 120 Frs.
Accommodation: 125 to 180 Frs.
Restaurant: breakfast from 6.00. Lunch from
12.00 until 15.00. Dinner from 19.00 until 22.00.
Specialities: gigot de lotte aux cèpes, regional
menu, home-cooking.
Hotel: ☆ ☆ 38 rooms. Facilities: shower, private
bathroom, telephone.
Other points: credit cards accepted, bar,
children's menu, à la carte menu, lounge area,
terrace, pets allowed, car/lorry parking.
◁≡ *Lac de Vassivière.*

GENOUILLAC • Creuse, 23350

AU PETIT BONHEUR
(Mme Monique Gouvet) 36 Grande Rue,
Le Bourg ☎ 55.80.81.69
Directions: RD 145, between Guéret and La Châtre.
Restaurant: breakfast from 6.00.
Specialities: regional menu, home-cooking.
Other points: credit cards accepted, bar, children's
menu, à la carte menu, car/lorry parking.

ISSOIRE • Puy-de-Dôme, 63500

AU REPOS DES ROUTIERS
(Mme Ginette Clauzin) Veneix
☎ 73.96.62.01
Directions: A 75, Clermont/Montpellier road.
Menu: from 54 Frs (wine included).
Accommodation: 100 to 185 Frs.
Restaurant: breakfast from 6.00.
Specialities: home-cooking.
Hotel: 7 rooms. Facilities: shower.
Other points: bar, traditional decor, terrace, pets
allowed, car/lorry parking.
◁≡ *Issoire; Montpeyrou.*

AUBERGE DU CHAPEAU ROUGE
(M. Marc Olives) route de Saint-Germain
☎ 73.89.14.74
Directions: exit 14, for aérodrome.
Menu: from 50 Frs.
Restaurant: breakfast from 5.00. Lunch from
11.30 until 15.00. Dinner from 19.00 until 23.00.
Closed Sat evening, Sun, and in Aug.
Specialities: home-cooking.
Other points: credit cards accepted, bar, modern
decor, pets allowed, car/lorry parking.
◁≡ *Auvergne volcanic park.*

LAPALISSE • Allier, 03120

LE CHAPON DORE
(M. Jean-Luc Lalauze) 1 avenue du 8 Mai 1945
☎ 70.99.09.51
Directions: RN 7, Vichy/Paris/Moulins road.
Menu: from 55 Frs.
Accommodation: 65 to 180 Frs.
Restaurant: breakfast from 6.30. Lunch from
11.30 until 14.00. Dinner from 19.00 until 21.00.
Closed Sun.
Specialities: home-cooking.
Hotel: ☆ 8 rooms. Facilities: shower.
Other points: bar, children's menu, traditional
decor, terrace, pets allowed, car/lorry parking.
◁≡ *zoo; chateaux; amusement and leisure parks.*

LIMOGES • Haute-Vienne, 87000

CHEZ BICHON
(M. Roland Houard) 68 avenue du Maréchal-
de-Lattre-de-Tassigny ☎ 55.30.68.83
Directions: RN 20, Toulouse/Lyon road.
Languages spoken: English and Spanish.

Menu: from 55 Frs (children under 10 half-price).
Restaurant: breakfast from 6.00. Lunch from 12.00 until 14.00. Dinner from 18.00 until 21.00. Closed Sat.
Specialities: specialities to order, home-cooking.
Other points: bar, traditional decor, pets allowed.
⊰€ *cathedral; factory and museum of porcelain; Oradour-sur-Glane (20km).*

⊐€ LES LILAS
(Mme Gilberte Broussas) 233 avenue Baudin
☎ 55.34.35.67
Directions: RN 21, on the outskirts of Limoges coming from Périgueux direction.
Menu: 50 to 68 Frs.
Restaurant: dinner until 24.00.
Specialities: lotte, beignet de gambas, potée limousine, home-cooking.
Other points: credit cards accepted, bar, children's menu, à la carte menu, traditional decor, terrace, car parking.
⊰€ *Limoges.*

MALEMORT • Corrèze, 19360

⊐€ CHEZ PAULETTE
(Mme Paulette Vergne) 2 avenue Pierre-et-Marie-Curie ☎ 55.92.28.14
Directions: RN 89, Brive-la-Gaillarde/Tulle/Clermont-Ferrand road.
Menu: 55 to 60 Frs.
Restaurant: breakfast from 7.00. Lunch from 12.00 until 14.30. Closed Sun, and 2 weeks in Aug.
Specialities: petit salé (pickled pork), choux farci, pâté de pommes de terre, home-cooking.
Other points: bar, car/lorry parking.
⊰€ *Collonge-la-Rouge; tower at Brénige-Malemont.*

LES ROUTIERS GUIDE TO BRITAIN AND IRELAND

Whether on business or pleasure, the *Les Routiers* guide to Britain and Ireland lists an unrivalled choice of over 1,500 carefully selected hotels, restaurants, guesthouses and inns, where you can dine and stay in comfort. All have been inspected and personally recommended and offer the ultimate in hospitality.

Available from all good bookshops, or direct from the publishers, price £10.99.

MARSAC-EN-LIVRADOIS
Puy-de-Dôme, 63940

🏠 LE KALLISTE
(SDF Vialle-Barrier) Route Départementale 906
☎ 73.95.62.58
Directions: RD 906, between Thiers and Le Puy-en-Velay.
Menu: 55 Frs (wine included) to 85 Frs.
Accommodation: 130 to 230 Frs.
Restaurant: breakfast from 7.30. Lunch from 12.00 until 14.30. Dinner from 19.00 until 22.30.

Specialities: home-cooking.
Hotel: 18 rooms. Facilities: shower, private bathroom.
Other points: credit cards accepted, bar, children's menu, à la carte menu, lounge area, terrace, pets allowed, car/lorry parking.
⊰€ *Richard le Bas windmill; museum of lace-making; musée Fourme.*

MAURIAC • Cantal, 15200

🏠 LES ROUTIERS – Chez Brigitte
(SARL Laroche-Rongier) 27 rue Saint-Mary
☎ 71.68.00.79
Directions: RD 678, Ussel.
Menu: 68 to 100 Frs.
Accommodation: 95 to 140 Frs.
Restaurant: breakfast from 7.30. Lunch from 12.00 until 13.30. Dinner from 19.00 until 20.30. Closed from Fri Sat 6pm.
Specialities: Auvergnat specialities, home-cooking.
Hotel: ☆ 10 rooms. Facilities: shower, private bathroom.
Other points: credit cards accepted, bar, children's menu, à la carte menu, traditional decor, car parking.
⊰€ *Puy Mary; chateau at Val; Salers; Dordogne valley; golf-course at Saint-Jean; Val-Saint-Jean pool at Mauriac.*

MERINCHAL • Creuse, 23420

🏠 HOTEL DU MIDI
(M. José Bartolo) 12 Létrade Gare
☎ 55.67.23.63
Directions: RN 141, Clermont-Ferrand/Limoges road.
Languages spoken: English, Spanish and Portuguese.
Menu: 50 to 146 Frs.
Accommodation: 110 to 230 Frs.
Restaurant: breakfast from 7.30. Lunch from 12.00 until 14.00. Dinner from 19.30 until 22.30.
Specialities: cassoulet au confit, feuilleté de fruits de mer, home-cooking.
Hotel: 10 rooms. Facilities: shower.
Other points: bar, children's menu, à la carte menu, lounge area, traditional decor, terrace, pets allowed, car/lorry parking.
⊰€ *lakes; chateaux.*

MOLOMPIZE • Cantal, 15500

🏠 HOTEL DU CENTRE
(Mme Françoise Dubois) ☎ 71.73.61.97
Languages spoken: English.
Menu: 50 to 80 Frs.
Accommodation: 100 to 150 Frs.
Restaurant: breakfast from 7.00. Lunch from 12.00 until 13.30. Dinner from 19.30 until 21.00.
Specialities: regional menu, home-cooking.
Hotel: 15 rooms. Facilities: private bathroom.
Other points: credit cards accepted, bar, lounge

area, traditional decor, terrace, pets allowed, car/
lorry parking.
⋐ *Garabit (viaduct); Chaudes-Aigues; Salers;
Saint-Flour.*

MONESTIER-MERLINE
Corrèze, 19340

⊟ **LE RELAIS DU VIEUX CHENE**
(Mme Lebon and M. Dumaille) Route
Nationale 89 ☎ 55.94.39.89
Directions: RN 89, Bordeaux/Lyon road.
Menu: 55 Frs (wine and coffee included) to 128 Frs.
Restaurant: breakfast from 5.30. Lunch from
11.30 until 15.00. Dinner from 18.30 until 24.00.
Specialities: home-cooking.
Other points: bar, children's menu.
⋐ *Puy de Sancy; Le Mont-Dore.*

MONTLUCON • Allier, 03100

⊟ **LE CADET ROUSSEL**
(M. Edouard Gawron) 53 rue de Pasquis
☎ 70.29.32.27
Directions: RN 145, Pasquis industrial zone (Z.I.).
Languages spoken: Polish, Russian and Czech.
Menu: 50 to 60 Frs.
Accommodation: 75 to 120 Frs.
Restaurant: breakfast from 7.00. Lunch from
12.00 until 14.00. Dinner from 19.00 until 21.30.
Closed Sun.
Specialities: home-cooking.
Hotel: 8 rooms. Facilities: shower, private bathroom,
television.
Other points: bar, à la carte menu, modern decor,
terrace, car parking.

MONTMARAULT • Allier, 03390

⇇ **RELAIS DE L'ETAPE**
(M. Robert Legal) route de Moulins
☎ 70.07.36.03
Directions: RN 145 expressway; 100 metres from
exit A71.
Menu: 60 Frs (coffee included) to 80 Frs.
Restaurant: breakfast from 5.00. Closed Sat
evening and Sun.
Specialities: home-cooking.
Other points: credit cards accepted, bar, children's
menu, à la carte menu, modern decor, terrace, pets
allowed, car/lorry parking.

MOULINS • Allier, 03000

⇇ **LES TROIS RUBANS**
(M. Pierre Molinie) route de Paris
☎ 70.44.08.51
Directions: RN 7, Lyon.
Menu: from 55 Frs.
Restaurant: breakfast from 6.30. Lunch from
11.30 until 14.00. Dinner until 20.00. Closed Sun,
and in Aug.

Specialities: home-cooking.
Other points: bar.

NEBOUZAT • Puy-de-Dôme, 63210

⊟ **AU RENDEZ-VOUS DES ROUTIERS**
(M. Pascal Menot) ☎ 73.87.10.04
Directions: RN 89, Lyon/Bordeaux road.
Menu: 55 to 75 Frs.
Accommodation: 120 to 150 Frs.
Restaurant: breakfast from 7.00. Closed Sun.
Specialities: regional menu, home-cooking.
Hotel: 10 rooms.
Other points: bar, children's menu, à la carte
menu, modern decor, pets allowed, car/lorry
parking.
⋐ *Auvergne regional volcanic park; the Puy-de-
Dôme.*

NEUSSARGUES • Cantal, 15170

⇇ **AUBERGE DES BRANQUES**
(Mme Jeanine Terrisse) rue du Calvaire
☎ 71.20.53.92
Directions: RN 122, between Aurillac and
Clermont-Ferrand.
Menu: 50 to 70 Frs.
Restaurant: breakfast from 7.00. Lunch from
12.00 until 15.00. Dinner from 19.00 until 22.00.
Closed Sun.
Specialities: home-cooking.
Other points: bar, children's menu, modern
decor, terrace, pets allowed, car/lorry parking.
⋐ *Garabit viaduct; Saint-Flour; Puy Mary.*

NOAILLES • Corrèze, 19600

⊟ **RELAIS D'ANTAN**
(M. Patrick Lomey) Route Nationale 20
☎ 55.85.85.76 [Fax] 55.85.15.82
Directions: RN 20, between Brive-la-Gaillarde
and Toulouse.
Languages spoken: Spanish and Portuguese.
Menu: from 59 Frs (wine included).
Accommodation: 120 to 150 Frs.
Restaurant: breakfast from 6.00. Lunch from
11.30 until 14.00. Dinner from 19.00 until 22.00.
Closed Sat evening and Sun.
Specialities: home-cooking.
Hotel: 16 rooms.
Other points: credit cards accepted, bar,
traditional decor, terrace, pets allowed, car/lorry
parking.
⋐ *Turenne; Rocamadour; Padirac; Souillac.*

OBJAT • Corrèze, 19130

⊟ **RELAIS DU PARC**
(Mme Monique Richard) 1 avenue Poincaré
☎ 55.84.11.11
Menu: from 55 Frs.
Restaurant: breakfast from 7.00.

Specialities: omelette aux cèpes, foie gras, confit de canard, regional menu, home-cooking.
Hotel: 14 rooms.
Other points: bar, children's menu, à la carte menu.

OLLIERGUES • Puy-de-Dôme, 63880

⇶ LA SAPINIERE
(M. Bernard Somma) Route Départementale 906, Giroux Gare ☎ 73.53.56.58
Directions: RD 906, between Thiers and Ambert.
Menu: from 50 Frs (wine and coffee included).
Restaurant: breakfast from 7.00.
Specialities: home-cooking.
Other points: bar, children's menu, traditional decor, pets allowed, car/lorry parking.
◀€ Olliergues.

PERIGNY • Allier, 03120

🏠 LE RELAIS DE PERIGNY
(M. Patrice Cardinaud) Le Bourg
☎ 70.99.84.57
Directions: RN 7, 3km from Lapalisse.
Languages spoken: English.
Menu: 57 to 60 Frs.
Accommodation: 100 to 120 Frs.
Restaurant: Open 24 hours. Closed Sat and Sun.
Specialities: home-cooking.
Hotel: ☆ 6 rooms.
Other points: credit cards accepted, bar, lounge area, traditional decor, pets allowed, car/lorry parking.
◀€ Vichy; chateau at Lapalisse.

LE PERTUIS • Haute-Loire, 43260

🏠 LE RELAIS DU COL
(Mme Odile Diétrich) Route Nationale 88
☎ 71.57.60.06
Menu: 55 to 65 Frs.
Accommodation: 100 to 200 Frs.
Restaurant: breakfast from 5.00. Lunch from 12.00 until 14.30. Dinner from 19.00 until 22.00. Closed Sat.
Specialities: home-cooking.
Hotel: 8 rooms.
Other points: bar, car/lorry parking.

PIERREFITTE-SUR-LOIRE
Allier, 03470

⇶ STATION TOTAL
(M. Michel Ray) Route Nationale 79
☎ 70.42.91.91
Directions: RN 79, between Moulins (50km) and Mâcon (100km).
Languages spoken: English, German and Italian.
Specialities: home-cooking. Facilities: open 24 hours.
Other points: credit cards accepted, à la carte

menu, traditional decor, terrace, pets allowed, car/lorry parking.

PINOLS • Haute-Loire, 43300

🏠 HOTEL DES VOYAGEURS
(Mme Jacqueline Cornet) ☎ 71.74.11.42
Directions: RN 590.
Menu: 65 to 80 Frs.
Accommodation: 60 to 75 Frs.
Restaurant: breakfast from 7.00. Dinner from 19.00 until 21.00
Specialities: potée auvergnate, ris de veau aux champignons, home-cooking.
Hotel: 6 rooms. Facilities: shower.
Other points: bar, children's menu, traditional decor, pets allowed.
◀€ Le Puy-en-Velay; le Mont Mouchet.

PONT-DE-MENAT
Puy-de-Dôme, 63560

🏠 CHEZ ROGER
(Mme Marie Pinel) Menat ☎ 73.85.50.17
Directions: RN 144, Montluçon/Clermont-Ferrand road.
Menu: 60 to 140 Frs 🍳
Accommodation: 100 to 160 Frs.
Restaurant: breakfast from 9.00. Lunch from 12.00 until 14.00. Dinner from 19.00 until 21.00. Closed Tues.
Specialities: jambon d'Auvergne, potée auvergnate, trout, regional menu, home-cooking.
Hotel: 8 rooms. Facilities: shower, private bathroom.
Other points: bar, children's menu, à la carte menu, traditional decor, terrace, pets allowed, car/lorry parking.

PONTAUMUR • Puy-de-Dôme, 63380

⇶ CHEZ LUCETTE
(Mme Lucette Condon) Puy Maury
☎ 73.79.00.40
Directions: between Pontaumur and Aubusson.
Menu: 55 to 110 Frs.
Restaurant: breakfast from 6.30. Lunch from 12.00 until 14.30. Dinner from 19.30 until 21.00. Closed last 2 weeks in Aug.
Specialities: home-cooking.
Other points: bar, à la carte menu, terrace, car/lorry parking.
◀€ summit of the Puy-de-Dôme (50km); viaduct at Fades; dam at Sauret-Bessève; Auvergne regional volcanic park.

LE PUY-EN-VELAY
Haute-Loire, 43000

🏠 LA TAVERNE
(M. René Rolland) 50 boulevard Carnot
☎ 71.09.35.16

Menu: 65 to 80 Frs.
Accommodation: 130 to 220 Frs.
Restaurant: breakfast from 7.00. Lunch from 12.00 until 14.00. Dinner from 19.00 until 21.00. Closed in Sept.
Specialities: regional menu, home-cooking.
Hotel: 10 rooms. Facilities: shower.
Other points: credit cards accepted, bar, traditional decor.
◁€ cathedral.

RIOM • Puy-de-Dôme, 63200

⇌ AU STAND
(Mme Janine Dassaud) 24 avenue de Clermont ☎ 73.38.04.06
Directions: RN 9, Riom Sud (South).
Languages spoken: English.
Menu: 55 to 75 Frs.
Restaurant: breakfast from 7.00. Lunch 11.30 to 14.00. Closed Sun, public holidays, and in Aug.
Specialities: home-cooking.
Other points: credit cards accepted, bar, children's menu, traditional decor, pets allowed, lorry parking.
◁€ Auvergne regional volcanic park; museums and monuments at Riom.

RIS • Puy-de-Dôme, 63290

🏠 HOTEL DE LA GARE
(M. Jean-Claude Védrines) Gare de Ris ☎ 73.94.68.68
Directions: CD 906, between Vichy and Thiers.
Menu: 40 to 55 Frs (wine and coffee included).
Accommodation: 75 to 160 Frs.
Restaurant: breakfast from 5.30. Lunch from 11.30 until 15.00. Dinner from 19.00 until 21.00. Closed Sat afternoon, Sun.
Specialities: home-cooking.
Hotel: 10 rooms. Facilities: shower, private bathroom.
Other points: credit cards accepted, bar, children's menu, traditional decor, terrace, pets allowed, car/lorry parking.
◁€ Vichy; Thiers; Clermont-Ferrand; mountains of the Bourbonnais; park at Livradois; Auvergne regional volcanic park.

ROFFIAC • Cantal, 15100

⇌ AUBERGE DE LA VALLEE
(M. Pierre Farges) ☎ 71.60.04.50
Directions: RD 826, St-Flour, towards Aurillac.
Restaurant: closed Sat, Sun, and last 2 weeks in Aug.
Specialities: regional menu, home-cooking.
Other points: bar.

SAINT-BONNET
Puy-de-Dôme, 63200

🏠 LE BON COIN
(M. Jean Levadoux) 2 rue de la République ☎ 73.63.31.14

Directions: RN 143.
Restaurant: closed 15th Sept–10th Oct.
Hotel: 10 rooms.
Other points: bar.

SAINT-FLOUR • Cantal, 15100

🏠 LE PROGRES
(M. Alain Mourgues) 61 rue des Lacs ☎ 71.60.03.06
Languages spoken: English and Spanish.
Menu: 55 to 220 Frs 🍽
Accommodation: 150 to 220 Frs.
Restaurant: breakfast from 7.00. Lunch from 12.00 until 14.00. Dinner from 19.30 until 22.00.
Specialities: Auvergnat specialities, regional menu.
Hotel: ✰ ✰ 10 rooms. Facilities: shower, private bathroom, television, telephone.
Other points: credit cards accepted, bar, children's menu, à la carte menu, modern decor, pets allowed, car/lorry parking.
◁€ Garabit viaduct; circus at Mallet; cascade at Le Sailhant; plentiful rambling.

🏠 LES ROUTIERS
(Mme Liliane Teissèdre) 49 place de la Liberté ☎ 71.60.23.00
Directions: RN 9.
Languages spoken: English and Spanish.
Menu: 60 to 100 Frs.
Accommodation: 100 Frs.
Restaurant: breakfast from 7.30. Lunch from 12.00 until 16.00. Dinner from 19.00 until 22.00. Closed Mon (out of season), and in Jan and Feb.
Specialities: tripoux de Saint-Flour, regional menu, home-cooking.
Hotel: 7 rooms. Facilities: shower.
Other points: credit cards accepted, à la carte menu, traditional decor, pets allowed.
◁€ Garabit viaduct; circus at Mallet; Chaudes-Aigues; chateau at Alleuze-du-Sailbant; Desierres; Mont-Mouchet; cathedral at Saint-Flour.

SAINT-GENCE • Haute-Vienne, 87510

⇌ LE CAMPANELLE
(M. Albert Denardou) Campanelle ☎ 55.48.02.83
Directions: between Limoges and Bellegarde.
Menu: from 60 Frs.
Restaurant: breakfast from 8.00. Lunch from 12.00 until 14.00. Dinner from 19.00 until 21.00. Closed Sat, and in Aug.
Specialities: home-cooking.
Other points: bar, traditional decor, car/lorry parking.

SAINT-GEORGES-D'AURAC
Haute-Loire, 43230

🏠 LES TILLEULS
(M. Eric Crouzet) Route Nationale 102 ☎ 71.77.50.75

Directions: RN 102, between Le Puy-en-Velay and Clermont-Ferrand.
Menu: from 52 Frs (wine and coffee included).
Accommodation: 90 to 100 Frs.
Restaurant: breakfast from 6.00. Lunch from 11.30 until 14.30. Dinner from 19.00 until 22.00.
Specialities: home-cooking.
Hotel: 8 rooms.
Other points: bar, children's menu, modern decor, terrace, pets allowed, car/lorry parking.
☞ chateau at Chavagnac-la-Fayette.

SAINT-JULIEN-CHAPTEUIL
Haute-Loire, 43260

🍴 **AUBERGE DU MEYCAL**
(M. René Chapuis) Boussoulet
☎ 71.08.71.03
Directions: RD 15, Le Puy-en-Velay/Valence road.
Menu: 50 to 90 Frs.
Accommodation: 120 to 150 Frs.
Restaurant: breakfast from 8.00. Lunch from 12.00 until 13.15. Dinner from 19.00 until 20.30.
Specialities: truite, omelette norvégienne, grenouilles, home-cooking.
Hotel: ☆ 12 rooms. Facilities: shower, private bathroom, telephone.
Other points: bar, lounge area, traditional decor, terrace, pets allowed, car/lorry parking.
☞ chateau; 4 lakes (25km).

SAINT-JUNIEN • Haute-Vienne, 87200

🍴 **L'ETOILE**
(M. Alain Noble) 8 avenue Henri-Barbusse
☎ 55.02.15.19 Fax 55.02.92.64
Directions: RN 141, Angoulême/Limoges road.
Languages spoken: English.
Menu: 55 to 180 Frs.
Accommodation: 120 to 220 Frs (overnight stop 170 Frs).
Restaurant: breakfast from 6.30. Lunch from 11.00 until 16.00. Dinner from 19.30 until 22.00. Closed Sun and 20th Dec to 6th Jan.
Specialities: home-cooking.
Hotel: 10 rooms. Facilities: shower, private bathroom.
Other points: credit cards accepted, bar, à la carte menu, traditional decor, terrace, pets allowed, car parking.

SAINT-JUST-LE-MARTEL
Haute-Vienne, 87590

🍴 **LE PETIT SALE**
(M. Jean-Pierre Teyti) Les Chabanes
☎ 55.09.21.14
Directions: RD 141, Clermont-Ferrand.
Menu: 58 to 160 Frs 🍳
Accommodation: 140 to 280 Frs.
Restaurant: breakfast from 7.00. Lunch from 12.00 until 15.00. Dinner from 19.00 until 22.00.
Specialities: truite meunière aux amandes,

saumon à l'oseille, raie aux câpres, magret de canard au poivre, pintade rôtie, ris de veau sauce madère, boeuf limousin, regional menu.
Hotel: ☆ ☆ 10 rooms. Facilities: shower, private bathroom, television, telephone.
Other points: credit cards accepted, bar, children's menu, à la carte menu, lounge area, traditional decor, terrace, pets allowed, car/lorry parking.
☞ Limoges; porcelain factories; Aubusson tapestries; Saint-Léonard; Lac de Vassivière; chateau at Peyrat.

SAINT-MATHIEU
Haute-Vienne, 87440

🍴 **LA GRANGE DU LAC**
(M. Franck Varachaut) Les Champs
☎ 55.00.35.84
Directions: RN 699, Limoges road, via Cussac.
Languages spoken: English.
Menu: 50 to 140 Frs.
Accommodation: 110 to 200 Frs.
Restaurant: breakfast from 8.00. Lunch from 11.00 until 15.00. Dinner from 19.00 until 24.00. Closed Tues evening.
Specialities: magret, confits, cèpes, moules, gésiers, foie gras, regional menu.
Hotel: 6 rooms. Facilities: shower.
Other points: credit cards accepted, bar, children's menu, à la carte menu, lounge area, traditional decor, terrace, pets allowed, car/lorry parking.
☞ chateau at Rochechouart; Monbrun; Oradour-sur-Glane; Bandiat-Tardoire valley; tower at Chalus.

SAINT-POURCAIN • Allier, 03500

🍴 **LE BELVEDERE**
(Mme Jeannine Lacaussade) Les Plachis
☎ 70.42.09.58
Directions: RN 9, Moulins.
Menu: 60 to 145 Frs.
Restaurant: breakfast from 8.00. Lunch from 11.00 until 14.00. Dinner from 19.00 until 22.00. Closed Wed afternoon.
Specialities: coq au vin, paté bourbonnais, fritures (whitebait, in season), home-cooking.
Other points: credit cards accepted, bar, children's menu, à la carte menu, modern decor, terrace, pets allowed, car/lorry parking.

SAINT-SORNIN-LEULAC
Haute-Vienne, 87290

🍴 **HOTEL DU CENTRE**
(M. Patrick Gaillac) ☎ 55.76.32.54
Directions: RN 145, between La Croisière and Bellac.
Languages spoken: English.
Menu: from 50 Frs (wine and coffee included).
Restaurant: breakfast from 7.00.
Specialities: home-cooking.

Other points: credit cards accepted, bar, children's menu, traditional decor, terrace, pets allowed, car/lorry parking.
⋖ Lac de Saint-Pardoux; Le Dordat.

SAINT-VICTURNIEN
Haute-Vienne, 87420

🏨 LE PUIS MALAIS
(M. Moum – SARL MBR) Route Nationale 141, La Malaise ☎ 55.03.87.03
Directions: RN 141, Limoges/Angoulême road.
Menu: 56 Frs (wine included) to 130 Frs.
Restaurant: breakfast from 6.00.
Specialities: regional menu, home-cooking.
Hotel: 8 rooms. Facilities: shower.
Other points: credit cards accepted, bar, traditional decor, terrace, pets allowed, car/lorry parking.
⋖ Oradour-sur-Glane (8km).

SAINT-YORRE • Allier, 03270

🏨 NOUVEL HOTEL
(M. Hubert Chesnel) 17 avenue de Vichy ☎ 70.59.41.97
Directions: CD 906, between Thiers and Vichy.
Languages spoken: English.
Menu: 48 to 120 Frs.
Accommodation: 110 to 150 Frs.
Restaurant: breakfast from 6.30. Lunch from 11.45 until 14.30. Dinner from 17.45 until 21.30. Closed Sat, and in Feb.
Specialities: home-cooking.
Hotel: 12 rooms. Facilities: shower, private bathroom, television.
Other points: credit cards accepted, bar, children's menu, à la carte menu, lounge area, modern decor, pets allowed, car parking.
⋖ chateau at Busset; Vichy: spa, park; crystallery; butterfly farm.

SAUVIAT-SUR-VIGE
Haute-Vienne, 87400

🏨 HOTEL DE LA POSTE
(M. Pierre Chassagne) ☎ 55.75.30.12
Directions: RN 141.
Accommodation: 130 to 180 Frs.
Restaurant: dinner until 22.00. Closed Wed, and in Sept.
Hotel: ☆ 10 rooms. Facilities: shower, private bathroom, telephone.
Other points: credit cards accepted, bar, traditional decor, pets allowed, car/lorry parking.
⋖ Lac de Vassivière.

SEREILHAC • Haute-Vienne, 87620

🏨 AUBERGE DES ROUTIERS
(Mme Denise Vignaud) Route Nationale 21 ☎ 55.39.10.46

Languages spoken: English.
Restaurant: dinner until 23.00.
Hotel: 6 rooms.
Other points: bar.

LA SOUTERRAINE
Creuse, 23300

🏨 LES ROUTIERS
(M. Raymond Boutet) La Croisière-Saint-Maurice ☎ 55.63.77.55
Directions: RN 145, between Limoges and Guéret.
Menu: from 52 Frs.
Accommodation: 80 to 130 Frs.
Restaurant: breakfast from 5.00. Lunch from 12.00 until 15.00. Dinner from 19.00 until 23.00. Closed Sun, and 1 week at Christmas.
Specialities: rognons au porto, coq au vin, potée auvergnate, home-cooking.
Hotel: 15 rooms. Facilities: shower.
Other points: credit cards accepted, bar, traditional decor, terrace, pets allowed, car/lorry parking.
⋖ étang de la Cazine; étang du Cheix.

TENCE • Haute-Loire, 43190

🍴 BAR-RESTAURANT DES CARS
(M. David Bonnet) 13 Grande Rue ☎ 71.59.84.01
Directions: RN 88, town centre.
Menu: 45 to 70 Frs.
Restaurant: breakfast from 7.00. Lunch from 11.30 until 15.00. Dinner from 19.00 until 21.00.
Specialities: home-cooking.
Other points: bar, children's menu, à la carte menu, traditional decor, pets allowed, car/lorry parking.
⋖ chateaux; dam at La Valette.

TOULON-SUR-ALLIER
Allier, 03400

🍴 LE FLAMBEAU
(SARL Le Flambeau) Route Nationale 7 ☎ 70.20.90.28
Directions: RN 7.
Menu: 60 to 80 Frs.
Restaurant: breakfast from 8.00. Lunch from 11.00 until 15.00. Dinner from 19.00 until 23.00. Closed Sun.
Specialities: home-cooking.
Other points: children's menu, à la carte menu, car/lorry parking.

🍴 LE RELAIS FLEURI
(M. Belain) Route Nationale 7 ☎ 70.44.47.16
Directions: RN 7.
Restaurant: closed Sun, and in Aug.
Other points: bar.

USSEL • Cantal, 15300

LE RELAIS DE LA PLANEZE
(Mme Gilberte Esbrat) Route
Départementale 926 ☎ 71.73.20.52
[Fax] 71.23.11.99
Directions: RD 926, between Murat and Saint-Flour.
Menu: 55 to 70 Frs.
Restaurant: breakfast from 7.15. Lunch from
12.00 until 14.00. Closed Sun, last week in Aug
and 1st week in Sept, one week at Christmas.
Specialities: home-cooking.
Other points: credit cards accepted, bar,
traditional decor, terrace, pets allowed, car/lorry
parking.
◀ *Salers; Garabit viaduct; Murat; Saint-Flour.*

VARENNES-SUR-ALLIER
Allier, 03150

LA RENAISSANCE
(Mme Rose Gardel) Bellevue
☎ 70.45.62.86
Directions: RN 7.
Languages spoken: Portuguese.
Restaurant: dinner until 21.00.
Other points: bar.

LES TOURISTES
(M. André Juniet) 1 rue des Halles
☎ 70.45.00.51
Directions: RN 7, Lyon.
Menu: 60 to 90 Frs ☞
Accommodation: 130 to 250 Frs.
Restaurant: breakfast from 6.00. Lunch from
12.00 until 14.00. Dinner from 19.30 until 21.00.
Closed Sat from Oct to May.
Specialities: home-cooking.
Hotel: 9 rooms.
Other points: credit cards accepted, bar,
traditional decor, pets allowed, car parking.
◀ *Gayette dungeon; Vichy; sport/leisure centre.*

LE VERNET-LA-VARENNE
Puy-de-Dôme, 63580

HOTEL DU CHATEAU
(SNC – Bernard and Denis Charnay-Magaud)
☎ 73.71.31.79
Directions: RD 999, Issoire.
Languages spoken: English.
Menu: 45 to 90 Frs.
Accommodation: 70 to 115 Frs.
Restaurant: breakfast from 7.30. Lunch from
12.00 until 14.00. Dinner from 19.30 until 21.00.
Closed Mon afternoon (from 3pm).
Specialities: pôtée auvergnate, terrines maison,
regional menu, home-cooking.
Hotel: 7 rooms. Facilities: shower.
Other points: credit cards accepted, bar,
children's menu, traditional decor, terrace, pets
allowed, car/lorry parking.
◀ *La Chaise-Dieu; Ambert; amethyst mines.*

VICHY • Allier, 03200

RELAIS DE LA PASSERELLE
(M. Jean-Pierre Pesce) 1 rue de Bordeaux
☎ 70.98.57.70
Directions: towards Thiers and Le Puy-en-Velay.
Menu: from 50 Frs.
Accommodation: 80 to 140 Frs.
Restaurant: breakfast from 6.30. Lunch from
12.00 until 14.00. Dinner from 19.00 until 20.00.
Closed Sun, and in Aug.
Specialities: home-cooking.
Hotel: 4 rooms. Facilities: shower, telephone.
Other points: bar, modern decor.
◀ *Vichy: spa and parks; pool; dam; salmon ladders.*

> For the very best in food and drink
> while travelling in Britain,
> why not become a member of
> **Club Bon Viveur**,
> Les Routiers' Ultimate Dining Scheme?
> See back of book for further details.

VIEILLE-BRIOUDE
Haute-Loire, 43100

LES GLYCINES
(Mme Viviane Chardonnal) avenue de
Versailles ☎ 71.50.91.80
Directions: RN 102, between Clermont-Ferrand
and Le Puy-en-Velay.
Languages spoken: English and Spanish.
Menu: 62 to 250 Frs.
Accommodation: 195 to 320 Frs.
Restaurant: breakfast from 7.00. Lunch from 12.00
until 14.00. Dinner from 19.30 until 21.00. Closed
from Fri afternoon to Sat afternoon, and in Jan.
Specialities: saumon, gibier (game) (in season).
Hotel: ✰ ✰ 13 rooms. Facilities: shower, private
bathroom, television, telephone.
Other points: credit cards accepted, bar, à la carte
menu, lounge area, modern decor, terrace, pets
allowed, car/lorry parking.
◀ *valley of the Allier; basilica; house of salmon;
museum of lace-making; abbey at Lavandieu.*

VOLVIC • Puy-de-Dôme, 63530

HOTEL DE LA NUGERE
(Mme Elisabeth Ternisien-Bourdon)
Le Cratère ☎ 73.33.50.47
Directions: between Clermont-Ferrand and Limoges.
Menu: 55 to 85 Frs.
Accommodation: 80 to 110 Frs.
Restaurant: breakfast from 6.00. Lunch from
12.00 until 14.30. Dinner from 19.00 until 22.30.
Specialities: specialities of Périgord, couscous,
paella, regional menu, home-cooking.
Hotel: 16 rooms. Facilities: shower.
Other points: bar, children's menu, à la carte
menu, terrace, pets allowed, car/lorry parking.
◀ *the Puy de Dôme; maison de la pierre; chateau
at La Tour Noël.*

VOREY-SUR-ARZON
Haute-Loire, 43800

☎ RESTAURANT DE LA BASCULE
(M. Serge Hilaire) place des Moulettes
☎ 71.03.41.67
Directions: RN 103, between Saint-Etienne and
Le Puy-en-Velay.
Languages spoken: Italian.
Accommodation: 80 to 100 Frs.
Restaurant: breakfast from 6.30. Lunch from
11.45 until 15.00. Dinner from 19.00 until
21.30.
Specialities: home-cooking.
Hotel: 5 rooms.
Other points: bar, children's menu, pets allowed,
car/lorry parking.
◀€ Loire valley; Le Puy-en-Velay.

YSSINGEAUX • Haute-Loire, 43200

☎ LA PETITE AUBERGE
(M. Yves Drevet) 'La Guide' ☎ 71.65.57.75
Directions: RN 88, Saint-Etienne/Le Puy-en-Velay
road.
Menu: 53 to 130 Frs.
Accommodation: 75 to 130 Frs.
Restaurant: breakfast from 6.00. Lunch from
12.00 until 15.00. Dinner from 19.30 until 22.00.
Closed Sat afternoon and Sun afternoon.
Specialities: regional menu, home-cooking.
Hotel: 5 rooms.
Other points: credit cards accepted, bar, children's
menu, à la carte menu, traditional decor, terrace,
pets allowed, car/lorry parking.
◀€ Le Puy-en-Velay; volcanic mountains in the
Velay region; forêt du Meygal; dams; chateaux.

SOUTH-WEST FRANCE

The following *départements* are included in this chapter:

Ariège (09)
Aude (11)
Aveyron (12)
Dordogne (24)
Gard (30)
Gers (32)
Gironde (33)
Haute-Garonne (31)
Hautes-Pyrénées (65)

Hérault (34)
Landes (40)
Lot (46)
Lot-et-Garonne (47)
Lozère (48)
Pyrénées-Atlantiques (64)
Pyrénées-Orientales (66)
Tarn (81)
Tarn-et-Garonne (82)

ABZAC • Gironde, 33230

☶ LE GAULOIS
(M. Jacques Lacoux) Tripoteau ☎ 57.49.07.34
Directions: RN 84, road to Lyon.
Menu: 50 to 75 Frs.
Restaurant: breakfast from 5.00.
Specialities: regional menu, home-cooking.
Other points: credit cards accepted, bar,
children's menu, à la carte menu, terrace, pets
allowed, car/lorry parking.
◀€ Saint-Emilion; Pomerol.

AGUESSAC • Aveyron, 12520

☎ LE BALLON ROND
(M. Guy Pailhas) Route Nationale 9
☎ 65.59.80.18
Directions: Millau/Gorges du Tarn.
Menu: 55 to 110 Frs.
Accommodation: 120 to 180 Frs.

Restaurant: breakfast from 7.30. Lunch from
12.00 until 14.00. Dinner from 19.30 until 21.00.
Specialities: tripoux, daube, regional menu.
Hotel: 6 rooms.
Other points: credit cards accepted, bar,
children's menu, à la carte menu, lounge area,
traditional decor, pets allowed, car/lorry parking.
◀€ gorges of the Tarn; Millau; Roquefort; La
Couvertoirade; grottes (caves) de l'Aven Armand
and Dargilan; lac du Levezou.

AIRE-SUR-L'ADOUR
Landes, 40800

☎ LES ROUTIERS
(M. Joël Daste) 15 rue du 4 Septembre
☎ 58.71.63.01 [Fax] 58.71.63.01
Directions: RN 134, Mont-de-Marsan/Tarbes.
Restaurant: breakfast from 7.00. Lunch from
12.00 until 14.00. Dinner from 19.30 until 22.00.
Closed Sat (out of season).

Specialities: magret de canard, foie gras, regional menu, home-cooking.
Hotel: ☆ 7 rooms. Facilities: shower.
Other points: credit cards accepted, bar, children's menu, à la carte menu, traditional decor, terrace, pets allowed, car/lorry parking.

ALBAN • Tarn, 81250

⇛ RESTAURANT DU MIDI
(M. Patrick Daurelle) 9 place des Tilleuls
☎ 63.55.82.24
Directions: RD 999, between Albi and Millau.
Languages spoken: Spanish.
Menu: 60 Frs (wine included).
Restaurant: lunch 12.00 to 14.00. Dinner 19.00 to 21.00. Closed Tues after 15.00, last week in Aug.
Specialities: daube, tripoux, regional menu, home-cooking.
Other points: credit cards accepted, bar, children's menu, lounge area, traditional decor, terrace, pets allowed, car/lorry parking.
⇚ Roquefort; Albi; Castres; Cordes; gorges of the Tarn.

ALBI • Tarn, 81000

⇛ AUBERGE LANDAISE DE CHEZ MARCEL
(M. Marcel Gauzère) Route de Montplaisir, La Rivayrolle ☎ 63.45.03.11
Restaurant: closed Sun.
Other points: bar.

⇚ LE RELAIS CATALAN
(Mme Virginie Campin) Barrière de Montplaisir, Route de Millau ☎ 63.60.27.00
Directions: RD 999, the Albi/Millau road.
Languages spoken: English.
Menu: 60 Frs.
Accommodation: 110 Frs.
Restaurant: breakfast from 5.00. Lunch 11.30 to 15.00. Dinner 19.00 to 21.30. Closed Sat and Sun.
Specialities: home-cooking.
Hotel: 8 rooms.
Other points: credit cards accepted, bar, children's menu, traditional decor, terrace, pets allowed, car/lorry parking.
⇚ Albi; Cordes-sur-Ciel; Monesties; Ambialet.

⇛ LE RELAIS FLEURI
(M. Pédro Casado) 25 avenue François-Verdier ☎ 63.54.07.09
Directions: RN 88, on the outskirts of Albi, coming from Toulouse.
Languages spoken: Spanish.
Menu: 55 to 120 Frs.
Accommodation: 120 to 150 Frs.
Restaurant: breakfast from 7.30. Lunch 11.00 to 15.00. Dinner 19.00 to 22.00. Closed Sun.
Specialities: paella (to order), regional menu, home-cooking.
Hotel: 3 rooms. Facilities: shower, private bathroom.
Other points: bar, à la carte menu, traditional decor, terrace, pets allowed, car parking.
⇚ cathedrals; musée Toulouse-Lautrec; musée de cire (wax); gorges of the Tarn.

ALBINE • Tarn, 81240

⇛ LA GRILLE
(Mme Odile Mayer) 1 avenue de la Ribaute
☎ 63.98.39.11
Menu: 55 Frs.
Restaurant: lunch from 11.30 until 15.00. Dinner from 19.00 until 23.00
Other points: bar, car/lorry parking.

AMBRES • Tarn, 81500

⇚ AUBERGE DES POMMIERS
(M. Alain Sore) Le Grès ☎ 63.58.05.56
Directions: RD 87, on the Gaillac road.
Languages spoken: English, Spanish.
Menu: 57 to 180 Frs.
Accommodation: 100 to 220 Frs.
Restaurant: breakfast from 7.00. Lunch 12.00 to 14.00. Dinner 20.00 to 21.00. Closed Fri evening.
Specialities: home-cooking.
Hotel: ☆ 6 rooms. Facilities: shower.
Other points: credit cards accepted, bar, lounge area, terrace, car/lorry parking.

AMOU • Landes, 40330

⇚ AU FEU DE BOIS
(M. Joël Martinet) avenue des Pyrénées
☎ 58.89.00.86
Directions: RD 15, between Dax and Pau.
Menu: 45 to 130 Frs.
Accommodation: 100 to 270 Frs.
Restaurant: breakfast from 8.00. Lunch 12.00 to 14.30. Dinner 19.30 to 21.30. Closed Fri evening, Sat lunch (out of season), 3 weeks in Jan, 2 weeks in Sept.
Specialities: foie gras, confit, magret de canard, Saint-Pierre à l'oseille, regional menu.
Hotel: ☆ ☆ 16 rooms. Facilities: shower, private bathroom.
Other points: credit cards accepted, bar, children's menu, à la carte menu, traditional decor, terrace, pets allowed, car/lorry parking.
⇚ circuit de la Chalosse; Dax (30km); Pau (40km); Lourdes (60km); Basque country (80km); montagne de la Heure.

ANGLET • Pyrénées-Atlantiques, 64600

⇚ LES MOUETTES
(M. Jean-Claude Motta) 5 avenue de l'Adour
☎ 59.52.46.08
Languages spoken: Italian.
Menu: 52 Frs (wine and coffee included).
Accommodation: 80 to 160 Frs.
Restaurant: breakfast from 6.30. Lunch from 12.00 until 14.00. Dinner from 19.30 until 22.30. Closed Sat, Sun, and the last 2 weeks of Aug.
Specialities: home-cooking.
Hotel: 11 rooms. Facilities: shower, private bathroom.
Other points: bar, traditional decor, pets allowed, car parking.
⇚ the Basque coast.

ANTONNE-ET-TRIGONANT
Dordogne, 24420

⫤ LE RELAIS DE LAURIERE
(M. Jean-Claude Condaminas) Laurière
☎ 53.06.17.92
Directions: RN 21, between Périgueux and Limoges.
Languages spoken: English.
Menu: 58 Frs (wine and coffee included).
Accommodation: 80 Frs.
Restaurant: closed Sun, and 2 weeks in Aug.
Specialities: terrine, rillette maison, petit salé (pickled pork), regional menu, home-cooking.
Hotel: 4 rooms.
Other points: credit cards accepted, bar, children's menu, à la carte menu, lounge area, traditional decor, terrace, pets allowed, car/lorry parking.
◁ *Périgueux (10km): Renaissance chateau (1km); Hautefort (20km).*

L'ARDOISE • Gard, 30290

⫿ LE CHALET
(Mme Sylvie Barrez) Route Nationale 580
☎ 66.50.22.22
Languages spoken: English, Spanish, Italian.
Menu: 90 Frs.
Accommodation: 150 to 190 Frs.
Restaurant: breakfast from 6.30. Closed Sat evening, Sun evening.
Specialities: croûte morille, poulet au sang (vin de Bourgogne), regional menu.
Hotel: 7 rooms. Facilities: shower.
Other points: bar, car/lorry parking.
◁ *gorges of the Ardèche (30km); Nîmes (35km); Avignon (25km).*

ASTAFFORT • Lot-et-Garonne, 47220

⫤ LE RELAIS DES PYRENEES
(M. Claude Parma) Barbonvièle
☎ 53.67.14.57
Directions: RN 21, the Agen/Lourdes road.
Languages spoken: Spanish, Italian.
Menu: 60 to 90 Frs.
Restaurant: breakfast from 5.30. Lunch from 11.00 until 15.00. Dinner from 19.00 until 21.00. Closed Sun, and 1 weeks at end Aug.
Specialities: magrets de canard aux cèpes (to order), regional menu, home-cooking.
Other points: credit cards accepted, traditional decor, terrace, pets allowed, car/lorry parking.
◁ *chateaux; Armagnac cellars (25-km radius).*

AUCAMVILLE
Haute-Garonne, 31140

⫤ LE TOIT
(M. Jean-Pierre Lablanche) 50 chaussée des Mazuries ☎ 61.70.46.37
Languages spoken: Spanish.
Restaurant: dinner until 24.00
Other points: bar.

AUSSILLON-MAZAMET
Tarn, 81200

⫤ CHEZ LOULOU
(M. Philippe Barreau) 21 avenue Charles-Sabatier ☎ 63.61.26.16
Directions: RN 112, the Albi/Beziers road.
Languages spoken: English, Spanish.
Menu: 60 Frs.
Restaurant: breakfast from 6.15. Lunch 12.00 to 14.30. Dinner 19.30 to 21.30. Closed Sun.
Specialities: regional menu, home-cooking.
Other points: credit cards accepted, bar, traditional decor, car/lorry parking.
◁ *la montagne noire.*

AUZITS • Aveyron, 12390

⫤ IGUE DU MOULIN
(SARL Igue du Moulin) Route Nationale 140
☎ 65.63.90.90
Directions: RN 140, the Brive/Mediterranean road.
Menu: 55 Frs.
Restaurant: breakfast from 7.00. Lunch from 11.30 until 14.30. Dinner from 19.00 until 22.00. Closed Sun (Nov to March).
Specialities: stockfish, soupe au fromage, regional menu, home-cooking.
Other points: bar, à la carte menu, traditional decor, terrace, pets allowed, car/lorry parking.
◁ *Conques; Decazeville: 'la Découverte' mine.*

AVIGNONET-LAURAGAIS
Haute-Garonne, 31290

⫤ LA PERGOLA
(M. Etienne Batan) Route Nationale 113
☎ 61.81.63.54 [Fax] 61.27.82.76
Directions: RN 113, between Villefranche and Castelnaudary.
Languages spoken: Spanish.
Menu: 59 to 125 Frs.
Accommodation: 120 to 170 Frs.
Restaurant: breakfast from 7.00. Lunch 12.00 to 14.30. Dinner 19.30 to 21.30. Closed Sat evening, Sun evening, and in Feb (school holidays).
Specialities: cassoulet, confits, regional menu, home-cooking.
Hotel: 3 rooms. Facilities: shower.
Other points: credit cards accepted, bar, à la carte menu, terrace, pets allowed, car/lorry parking.
◁ *Port Lauragais: musée Pierre-Paul Riquet; canal du Midi watershed.*

AZERAT • Dordogne, 24210

⫤ LE RELAIS D'AZERAT – Chez Annie
(Mme Annie Debord) ☎ 53.05.21.05
Directions: RN 89, between Périgueux and Brive-la-Gaillarde.
Restaurant: breakfast from 7.00. Lunch from 12.00. Dinner 19.00 to 21.00. Closed Sat and Sun (except by arrangement), and last 2 weeks in Aug.

Specialities: home-cooking.
Hotel: 4 rooms.
Other points: bar, car/lorry parking.
◁€ *grottes (caves) de Lascaux (12km); château d'Hautefort (20km).*

LES BACCARETS
Haute-Garonne, 31550

🚗 **LA CHAUMIERE**
(M. Daniel Laroche) Route Nationale 20, Cintegabelle ☎ 61.08.90.70
Directions: RN 20, the Toulouse/Foix road.
Menu: 60 Frs.
Accommodation: 85 to 115 Frs.
Restaurant: breakfast from 6.00. Closed Sun, and one week from Christmas Day.
Specialities: home-cooking.
Hotel: 12 rooms.
Other points: credit cards accepted, bar, children's menu, traditional decor, pets allowed, car/lorry parking.

BAGNAC-SUR-CELE • Lot, 46270

🚛 **RELAIS ROUTIERS LA PLANQUETTE**
(Mme Micheline Claudon) Route d'Aurillac
☎ 65.34.93.50
Directions: RN 122, between Aurillac and Figeac.
Menu: 55 to 65 Frs.
Accommodation: 120 to 140 Frs.
Restaurant: breakfast from 7.00. Lunch 11.30 to 14.00. Dinner 19.00 to 21.00. Closed Mon afternoon.
Specialities: home-cooking.
Hotel: 4 rooms.
Other points: bar, children's menu, traditional decor, car/lorry parking.

BAIGTS-EN-CHALOSSE
Landes, 40380

🚛 **LE CARREFOUR**
(M. Jean Bonnot) Le Carrefour
☎ 58.95.63.05
Directions: RD 2, between Dax and Saint-Sever.
Menu: 55 to 190 Frs.
Accommodation: 60 to 70 Frs.
Restaurant: breakfast from 7.00. Lunch from 12.30 until 14.00. Dinner from 20.00 until 21.00. Closed Mon.
Specialities: Burgundian dishes, home-cooking.
Hotel: 4 rooms. Facilities: shower, private bathroom.
Other points: credit cards accepted, bar, children's menu, à la carte menu, modern decor, terrace, car/lorry parking.

BALARUC-LE-VIEUX
Hérault, 34540

🚗 **LA SOURCE**
(M. Paul Amidieu) Issanka ☎ 67.78.72.85
[Fax] 67.78.65.19

Directions: Gigean.
Languages spoken: German, English, Spanish.
Menu: 59 to 95 Frs.
Restaurant: breakfast from 5.30. Lunch 11.30 to 15.00. Dinner 19.00 to 22.00. Closed Sun.
Specialities: rouille sétoise, bourride de merlu, regional menu, home-cooking.
Hotel: 9 rooms. Facilities: shower, private bathroom.
Other points: credit cards accepted, bar, children's menu, à la carte menu, traditional decor, terrace, pets allowed, car/lorry parking.
◁€ *étang de Thau; Mont Saint-Clair; cimetière marin (sailors' cemetery); musée George-Brassens; abbaye de Valmagne; parc à huîtres (oyster beds).*

BARAQUEVILLE • Aveyron, 12160

🚗 **LE PALOUS**
(M. Cluzel, Druilhe and Palous) 184 avenue du Centre ☎ 65.69.01.89 [Fax] 65.69.10.80
Directions: at the crossroads of the Albi/Montauban/Millau/Rodez roads.
Languages spoken: English.
Menu: 50 to 135 Frs.
Accommodation: 200 to 216 Frs.
Restaurant: breakfast from 6.30. Lunch from 11.30 until 14.00. Dinner from 19.30 until 21.30. Closed for 1 week at Christmas.
Specialities: tripoux, magret, confit de canard, foie gras, regional menu.
Hotel: ☆ ☆ 16 rooms. Facilities: shower, private bathroom, television, telephone.
Other points: credit cards accepted, bar, children's menu, à la carte menu, lounge area, traditional decor, modern decor, terrace, pets allowed, car/lorry parking.
◁€ *Sauveterre-de-Rouergue; viaduct at Le Viaur; lac de Pareloup; Conques.*

LA BASTIDE-L'EVEQUE
Aveyron, 12200

🚛 **RELAIS DE L'HERMET**
(M. Yvan Bourdoncle) Route Départementale 911 ☎ 65.65.61.41
Directions: RD 911.
Restaurant: closed Sat and Sun evening.
Other points: bar, car/lorry parking.

BEAUCHALOT
Haute-Garonne, 31360

🚗 **AU BEARNAIS**
(M. René Fréchou) Saint-Martory
☎ 61.90.23.44
Directions: RN 117, the Toulouse/Bayonne road.
Languages spoken: English, Spanish.
Menu: 50 to 180 Frs.
Accommodation: 120 to 170 Frs.
Restaurant: breakfast from 7.00. Lunch from 12.00 until 14.00. Dinner from 19.30 until 21.00. Closed Mon, and in Sept.
Specialities: garbure (thick soup) béarnaise, foie gras, confit de canard, civet de chevreuil (venison), regional menu, home-cooking.

Hotel: 5 rooms.
Other points: bar, à la carte menu, traditional decor, terrace, pets allowed, car/lorry parking.
⊄ *Saint-Bernard-de-Comminges.*

BELARGA • Hérault, 34230

🚆 LA GAITE
(Mme Danielle Aussel) 34 avenue du Grand-Chemin ☎ 67.25.00.82
Directions: RD 32, between Pezenas and Gignac.
Menu: 55 Frs.
Accommodation: 130 Frs.
Restaurant: breakfast from 6.30. Lunch from 11.30. Dinner 19.00 to 23.00. Closed Sun (in winter).
Specialities: home-cooking.
Hotel: 5 rooms. Facilities: shower, private bathroom.
Other points: credit cards accepted, bar, children's menu, modern decor, pets allowed, car/lorry parking.
⊄ *chateau.*

BELLEGARDE • Gard, 30127

🚆 LOU FELIBRE
(Mme Sabeline Raffi) Route Nationale 113 ☎ 66.01.15.21
Directions: RN 113, between Arles and Nîmes.
Languages spoken: German, English, Italian, Spanish.
Menu: 55 Frs.
Restaurant: breakfast from 5.00. Lunch from 12.00 until 14.30. Dinner from 19.15 until 22.00. Closed on public holidays, and last 2 weeks in Aug.
Specialities: regional menu, home-cooking.
Other points: credit cards accepted, bar, children's menu, modern decor, terrace, pets allowed, car/lorry parking.
⊄ *Nîmes (15km); Arles (11km); Saint-Gilles (10km); l'abbaye de Saint-Romain 'Beaucaire' (11km); Pont du Gard (26km).*

BERGERAC • Dordogne, 24100

🚆 LOU PETITOU
(M. Gérard Bornerie) Route de Fleix – Gala ☎ 53.57.93.93
Directions: RD 32, Bergerac/Le Fleix.
Menu: 55 Frs (wine included).
Restaurant: breakfast from 7.30. Lunch from 11.30 until 15.00. Dinner from 18.30 until 21.00. Closed Sat and Sun.
Specialities: home-cooking.
Other points: bar, traditional decor, terrace, pets allowed, car/lorry parking.
⊄ *Bergerac.*

BERNOS-BEAULAC • Gironde, 33430

🚆 LE RESTORELAIS
(SARL Lamy-Lefèvre) Bois de Fond ☎ 56.25.45.05
Directions: RD 932, Pau.
Menu: 55 to 90 Frs.

Restaurant: breakfast from 5.00. Closed Sat afternoon and Sun.
Specialities: confit de canard, entrecôte, foie gras, regional menu, home-cooking.
Other points: credit cards accepted, bar, children's menu, lounge area, traditional decor, terrace, pets allowed, car/lorry parking.
⊄ *châteaux de Roquetaillade and de Préchacq.*

BERTHOLENE • Aveyron, 12310

🚆 HOTEL BANCAREL
(M. Jean Brun) Route Nationale 88 ☎ 65.69.62.10 [Fax] 65.70.72.88
Directions: RN 88, between Rodez and Millau.
Menu: 55 to 150 Frs ✎
Accommodation: 150 to 240 Frs.
Restaurant: breakfast from 7.00. Lunch 12.00 to 14.00. Dinner 19.30 to 21.00. Closed from 25th Sept to 15th Oct, and last 2 weeks in Jan.
Specialities: choux farci à la paysanne, confit de canard, feuilleté au roquefort, regional menu.
Hotel: ☆ 13 rooms. Facilities: shower, private bathroom, television.
Other points: credit cards accepted, bar, children's menu, à la carte menu, traditional decor, pets allowed, car/lorry parking.
⊄ *lac du Levezou; trou de Bozouls; gorges of the Tarn and the Lot; lacs de Pareloup; forêt des Palanges; rivers (fishing).*

BESSIERE • Haute-Garonne, 31660

🚆 LE RELAIS BESSIERAIN
(M. André Beccarelli) 18 route de Montauban ☎ 61.84.00.95
Directions: RD 630, between Montauban (30km) and Castres (45km).
Languages spoken: Spanish, Italian.
Menu: 52 Frs (wine and coffee included).
Accommodation: 120 Frs.
Restaurant: breakfast from 6.30.
Specialities: home-cooking.
Hotel: 12 rooms.
Other points: bar, children's menu, traditional decor, terrace, pets allowed, car/lorry parking.
⊄ *Toulouse (27km); Corde (40km).*

BEZIERS • Hérault, 34000

🚆 L'OPPIDUM
(M. Alain Cherrier) Route Nationale 113 ☎ 67.28.30.34
Directions: RN 113, exit Béziers Ouest (West) (3km).
Languages spoken: English.
Menu: 58 Frs (wine and coffee included).
Accommodation: 90 to 160 Frs.
Restaurant: breakfast from 6.30. Dinner from 19.00 until 22.00. Closed Sat afternoon and Sun.
Hotel: 16 rooms. Facilities: shower.
Other points: bar, traditional decor, pets allowed, lorry parking.
⊄ *Sète; Roman site; les 7 écluses (locks).*

🍴 LE CANTAGAL
(M. Christian Mourier) Route de Pézenas
☎ 67.31.25.47
Languages spoken: English, Spanish.
Menu: 60 to 65 Frs.
Restaurant: breakfast from 6.30. Closed Sat
evening and Sun (out of season).
Specialities: regional menu, home-cooking.
Other points: credit cards accepted, modern
decor, terrace, pets allowed, car/lorry parking.

BIARS-SUR-CERE • Lot, 46130

🍴 CHEZ ALAIN
(M. Alain Cavalhac) 16 avenue de la
République ☎ 65.38.42.30
Directions: RN 140.
Restaurant: lunch from 12.00 until 15.00. Dinner
from 19.00 until 22.30. Closed Sun, and in Aug.
Specialities: home-cooking.
Other points: bar, modern decor.
◀€ Rocamadour; gouffre de Padirac; chateau at
Castelnau.

BLAYE-LES-MINES • Tarn, 81400

🏨 LE RELAIS SAINTE MARIE
(Mme Marie-Louise Bernier) 53 avenue d'Albi
☎ 63.76.53.81
Menu: 55 Frs.
Accommodation: 70 Frs.
Restaurant: breakfast from 7.00. Lunch 12.00 to
14.00. Dinner 20.00 to 22.00. Closed Sat and Sun.
Specialities: regional menu.
Hotel: 7 rooms. Facilities: shower, private bathroom.
Other points: bar, modern decor, pets allowed,
car/lorry parking.
◀€ open-cast mines.

BONLOC
Pyrénées-Atlantiques, 64240

🏨 RELAIS LILIPEAN
(Mme Charlotte Fouché) ☎ 59.29.51.48
Directions: RD 21, 3km from Hasparren.
Languages spoken: English.
Menu: 55 to 150 Frs.
Accommodation: 100 to 150 Frs.
Restaurant: breakfast from 9.00. Lunch from
11.30 until 15.00. Dinner from 19.30 until 20.30.
Closed Sat, and mid-Dec to mid-Jan.
Specialities: regional menu, home-cooking.
Hotel: 6 rooms.
Other points: bar, children's menu, à la carte
menu, traditional decor, terrace, pets allowed,
car/lorry parking.
◀€ grottes d'Oxolaya; château d'Arnaga; abbaye
de Bellocq.

BONSECOURS • Aveyron, 12560

**🍴 RESTAURANT BONSECOURS –
LA FERME**
(Mme Thérése Vayssie) ☎ 65.47.64.77

Restaurant: breakfast from 7.00. Lunch until
15.00. Dinner from 19.00 until 23.30. Closed Sat
evening.
Specialities: regional menu, home-cooking.
Other points: credit cards accepted, bar, lounge
area, traditional decor, terrace, pets allowed,
car/lorry parking.
◀€ medieval château de Séverac; gorges of the
Tarn; medieval village; cave (cellar) de Roquefort.

BORDEAUX
Gironde, 33800

🍴 AU BON ACCUEIL
(M. Fidel Gonzalez) 12 quai de la Monnaie
☎ 56.91.05.26
Directions: on the quays.
Languages spoken: Spanish, Italian and
Portuguese.
Menu: 46 to 90 Frs.
Restaurant: breakfast from 7.00. Lunch from
12.00 until 15.00. Dinner from 19.30 until 23.30.
Closed Sun, and in Aug.
Specialities: home-cooking.
Other points: bar, traditional decor, pets allowed,
car/lorry parking.
◀€ Blaye; Saint-Emilion; old Bordeaux.

🍴 B.R.I.R. INTER DES ROUTIERS
(M. Orlando Gonçalves) 295 cours Balguerie-
Stuttenber ☎ 56.43.15.47
Directions: RN 10
Languages spoken: Portuguese, Spanish.
Restaurant: dinner until 23.00. Closed Sat
afternoon and Sun, and in Aug.
Other points: bar.

🍴 LE BON COIN
(Mme Sandrine Nouts) 142 rue Lucien-Faure
☎ 56.39.40.13 [Fax] 56.39.40.13
Directions: RN 10, after the pont d'Aquitaine
(bridge), towards Toulouse.
Languages spoken: a little English.
Menu: 58 Frs (coffee included).
Restaurant: breakfast from 6.00. Closed Fri
evening, Sat, Sun, 3 weeks in Aug and 1 week in
Dec.
Specialities: escargots à la bordelaise, home-
cooking.
Other points: credit cards accepted, bar,
children's menu, traditional decor, pets allowed,
car/lorry parking.
◀€ Bordeaux: museum, monuments, ruins.

🍴 RESTAURANT DE L'UNION
(M. Dominique Depeyris) 116 rue Lucien-
Faure ☎ 56.50.05.77
Directions: RN 10, Bordeaux centre.
Languages spoken: English.
Menu: 50 Frs.
Restaurant: breakfast from 6.00. Closed Sat, Sun,
and in Aug.
Specialities: home-cooking.
Other points: bar, à la carte menu, traditional
decor, pets allowed, car/lorry parking.

BORDEAUX-BASTIDE
Gironde, 33100

🛏 **LE PORTO**
(Mme Rosa-Maria Pereira) 202 bis quai de
Brazza ☎ 56.86.15.93
Directions: RN 10, Bordeaux right bank, towards
Lormont.
Languages spoken: Spanish, Portuguese.
Menu: 55 Frs.
Accommodation: 100 to 150 Frs.
Restaurant: breakfast from 6.30. Closed Sat, Sun,
and in Aug.
Specialities: Portuguese dishes, home-cooking.
Hotel: 12 rooms. Facilities: shower, private bathroom.
Other points: credit cards accepted, bar,
traditional decor, pets allowed, car/lorry parking.
❦ *Bordeaux: place des Quinconces, cathedral,
grand théâtre.*

BRAM • Aude, 11150

🛏 **CHEZ ALAIN**
(M. Alain Albecq) Route Nationale 113
☎ 68.76.12.75
Directions: RN 113, between Carcassonne and
Toulouse.
Languages spoken: Spanish.
Menu: 65 Frs.
Accommodation: 150 Frs.
Restaurant: breakfast from 5.00. Lunch from
11.00 until 15.00. Dinner from 19.00 until 23.00.
Closed Sat, Sun, and in Aug.
Specialities: cassoulet, escargots, tripes, blanquettes,
civets (game stew), regional menu, home-cooking.
Hotel: 11 rooms. Facilities: shower, private
bathroom, television, telephone.
Other points: credit cards accepted, bar, traditional
decor, terrace, pets allowed, car/lorry parking.
❦ *Carcassonne; cathedral at Montréal (8km);
Ariège; Andorra.*

BRESSOLS • Tarn-et-Garonne, 82710

🍽 **L'ATHENA**
(Mme Marie-Thérèse Correggia) Route de
Montauban ☎ 63.02.18.44
Languages spoken: English, German, Italian.
Menu: 57 Frs.
Restaurant: lunch from 11.00 until 15.00. Dinner
from 17.00 until 24.00. Closed Sun.
Other points: bar, car/lorry parking.

BURLATS • Tarn, 81100

🍽 **AUBERGE DE L'OUSTALOU**
(M. Daniel Rebours) Route Départementale
622, Les 7 Faux ☎ 63.35.98.66
Directions: between Castres and Brassac/Lacaune.
Languages spoken: English.
Menu: 60 Frs (wine and coffee included) to 140 Frs.
Restaurant: breakfast from 6.30. Lunch from
12.00 until 14.30. Dinner from 19.00 until 21.30.
Closed Mon evening.

Specialities: daube provençale, tripes à la mode
de Caen, regional menu, home-cooking.
Other points: bar, children's menu, à la carte
menu, traditional decor, terrace, car/lorry parking.
❦ *Sidobre region: le rocher tremblant (peyro-
clabado: rocking stone); monts de Lacaune; La
Salvetat.*

BUZIET • Pyrénées-Atlantiques, 64000

🛏 **LE BELLEVUE**
(Mme Marcelle Lorry) Belair ☎ 59.21.76.03
Directions: the Pau/Oloron road.
Languages spoken: Spanish and a little English.
Menu: 60 to 110 Frs.
Accommodation: 170 to 200 Frs.
Restaurant: breakfast from 8.30. Lunch from
12.00 until 14.30. Dinner from 19.30 until 21.00.
Closed Sat, and one week at Christmas.
Specialities: confit, garbure béarnaise, regional
menu, home-cooking.
Hotel: 6 rooms. Facilities: shower.
Other points: bar, à la carte menu, terrace, car/
lorry parking.
❦ *Pyrenees; Ossau and Aspe valleys; Lourdes;
Pau; wine route; Jurançon.*

CAHORS-PERN • Lot, 46170

🛏 **LE RELAIS DES CIGALES**
(M. José-Manuel Fernandez) Route Nationale
20, Saint-Barthelemy ☎ 65.21.97.49
Fax 65.21.86.66
Directions: RN 20, the Cahors/Toulouse road.
Languages spoken: English, Spanish.
Menu: 55 to 120 Frs.
Accommodation: 150 Frs.
Restaurant: breakfast from 5.00. Lunch 12.00 to
15.00. Dinner 19.00 to 23.00. Closed Sun.
Specialities: magrets, cassoulet au confit d'oie, foie
gras, regional menu, home-cooking.
Hotel: 12 rooms. Facilities: shower, private
bathroom, television.
Other points: credit cards accepted, bar, children's
menu, à la carte menu, lounge area, modern decor,
terrace, pets allowed, car/lorry parking.
❦ *Cahors; Lot valley; caves at Rocamadour;
gouffre de Padirac; gorges of the Aveyron.*

LA CALMETTE • Gard, 30190

🍽 **LE RELAIS DE L'ESCALETTE**
(M. Georges Apostolakis) Route Nationale 6
☎ 66.63.13.63
Directions: RN 6.
Languages spoken: English.
Restaurant: dinner until 24.00.
Other points: bar.

CAMPSEGRET • Dordogne, 24140

🛏 **LES TAMARIS**
(M. Alain Thomas) La Croix, Route Nationale
32 ☎ 53.24.21.75

Directions: RN 21, between Bergerac and Périgueux.
Languages spoken: English.
Menu: 55 to 150 Frs 🍳
Accommodation: 150 to 180 Frs.
Restaurant: breakfast from 6.00. Dinner from 19.00 until 23.00. Closed Sun evening (out of season).
Specialities: foie gras mi-cuit, salade du Périgord, noix de Saint-Jacques à la crème de crevettes, filet de saumon, magret aux trois poivres, tournedos aux cèpes, regional menu, home-cooking.
Hotel: ☆ 11 rooms. Facilities: shower, private bathroom, television, telephone.
Other points: credit cards accepted, bar, children's menu, à la carte menu, lounge area, traditional decor, terrace, pets allowed, car/lorry parking.

CASTELNAU-D'ESTREFONDS
Haute-Garonne, 31620

🍴 **L'ARCHE DE TOULOUSE – FRONTONNAIS**
(M. M Gilles Dubarry) A62, services at Le Frontonnais (accessible in both directions)
☎ 61.74.65.65 [Fax] 61.74.32.09
Other points: credit cards and foreign currency accepted.

CASTELNAU-RIVIERE-BASSE
Hautes-Pyrénées, 65700

🍴 **LE RELAIS DE MADIRAN**
(M. Michel Ducasse) Route de Bordeaux
☎ 62.31.97.99
Directions: RD 935, between Aire-sur-l'Adour and Tarbes.
Languages spoken: Spanish, Italian and Portuguese.
Menu: 55 to 105 Frs.
Restaurant: breakfast from 6.30. Lunch from 11.30 until 14.00. Dinner from 19.30 until 21.00. Closed Sun (out of season) evenings in summer.
Specialities: gambas à la crème, magret grillé, regional menu, home-cooking.
Other points: bar, children's menu, à la carte menu, traditional decor, terrace, pets allowed, car/lorry parking.
◀€ vine-growing region; Madiran; Pachrenc; les courses landaises (entertaining and bloodless mock bullfights).

CASTELSARRASIN
Tarn-et-Garonne, 82100

🏠 **CHEZ MAURICE**
(M. Jean-Pierre Boissier) 35 route de Toulouse
☎ 63.32.30.83
Directions: RN 113, the Toulouse/Bordeaux road.
Menu: 49 to 80 Frs.
Accommodation: 95 to 165 Frs.
Restaurant: breakfast from 5.00. Lunch from

12.00 until 15.00. Dinner from 19.00 until 23.00. Closed Sat evening, Sun, and 3 weeks in Aug.
Specialities: cassoulet, magrets de canard, confits, foie gras maison, blanquette de veau, regional menu, home-cooking.
Hotel: ☆ 15 rooms. Facilities: shower.
Other points: bar, à la carte menu, lounge area, terrace, pets allowed, car/lorry parking.
◀€ Moissac; Auvillar; canal du Midi; Saint-Antonin-Noble-Val.

CASTETS-DES-LANDES
Landes, 40260

🍴 **CENTRE ROUTIER**
(M. Fernand Judes) ☎ 58.55.01.67
Directions: RN 10.
Menu: 60 Frs (wine included).
Restaurant: breakfast from 5.00.
Specialities: regional menu, home-cooking.
Other points: credit cards accepted, bar, children's menu, lounge area, terrace, pets allowed, car/lorry parking.

🍴 **LE STUC**
(Mme Danièle Calleja) ☎ 58.89.40.62
Directions: RN 10.
Languages spoken: Portuguese and Spanish.
Menu: 50 Frs.
Restaurant: breakfast from 7.00. Lunch from 12.00 until 14.30. Closed Sun (out of season), and 15th Oct to 15th Nov.
Specialities: home-cooking.
Other points: credit cards accepted, bar, traditional decor, car/lorry parking.
◀€ lakes.

CASTRES • Tarn, 81100

🍴 **LES ROUTIERS**
(M. Michel Labessouille) 247 avenue Charles-de-Gaulle ☎ 63.35.54.38
Directions: RN 622, the Mazamet road.
Menu: 65 Frs.
Restaurant: breakfast from 6.30. Lunch from 12.00 until 14.30. Dinner from 19.30 until 22.00. Closed Sun afternoon.
Specialities: couscous, cassoulet, home-cooking.
Hotel: 8 rooms.
Other points: credit cards accepted, bar, children's menu, à la carte menu, lounge area, traditional decor, terrace, pets allowed, car/lorry parking.
◀€ Sidobre region; musée Goya; jardin de l'Exéché.

CAUNEILLE • Landes, 40300

🍴 **AU HAOU**
(Mme Henriette Lalanne) Route Nationale 117
☎ 58.73.04.60
Directions: RN 117.
Restaurant: dinner until 23.00. Closed from 20th Dec for 2 weeks.
Other points: bar.

CAUSSADE • Tarn-et-Garonne, 82300

🏠 RELAIS D'AUVERGNE
(M. Antoine Noualhac) Zone Industrielle (Z.I.)
de Meaux ☎ 63.93.03.89
Directions: RN 20, between Montauban and Cahors.
Menu: 53 to 105 Frs.
Accommodation: 95 to 135 Frs.
Restaurant: breakfast from 6.00. Lunch from
11.30 until 14.00. Dinner from 19.00 until 21.00.
Specialities: cassoulet, grillades (grills), confit de
canard, home-cooking.
Hotel: 14 rooms. Facilities: shower, private
bathroom.
Other points: credit cards accepted, bar, children's
menu, à la carte menu, lounge area, modern decor,
terrace, pets allowed, car/lorry parking.
◀ gorges of the Tarn; Saint-Antonin; Bruniquel.

CENAC • Dordogne, 24250

➡ LA PROMENADE
(M. Pascal Thomas) Route Nationale 703
☎ 53.28.36.87
Directions: RN 703, Sarlat/Domme.
Menu: 55 to 150 Frs 🍴
Accommodation: 120 to 170 Frs.
Restaurant: breakfast from 7.00. Lunch from
12.00 until 14.00. Dinner from 19.00 until 21.00.
Specialities: regional menu.
Other points: credit cards accepted, bar,
children's menu, à la carte menu, pets allowed,
car/lorry parking.
◀ the heart of 'Périgord noir'.

CHAUDEYRAC • Lozère, 48170

🏠 HOTEL DE FRANCE
(M. Yves Trémoulet) Route Nationale 88
☎ 66.47.91.00 [Fax] 66.47.93.29
Directions: RN 88, the Lyon/Toulouse road.
Languages spoken: Spanish.
Menu: 55 Frs (wine and coffee included) to 120 Frs.
Accommodation: 180 to 230 Frs.
Restaurant: breakfast from 6.00. Lunch from
12.00 until 15.00. Dinner from 18.00 until 22.00.
Specialities: regional menu, home-cooking.
Hotel: ☆ 12 rooms. Facilities: shower, private
bathroom, telephone.
Other points: credit cards accepted, bar,
children's menu, à la carte menu, lounge area,
modern decor, terrace, car/lorry parking.
◀ lac de Naussac; Notre-Dame-des-Neiges;
gorges of the Tarn.

COLOMBIERS • Hérault, 34440

🏠 LA GRILLADE
(M. Lionel Gilhodes) Route de Narbonne
☎ 67.37.26.01 [Fax] 67.37.66.94
Directions: RN 113, Narbonne.
Languages spoken: English.
Menu: 60 Frs (wine and coffee included) to
128 Frs.

Accommodation: 175 to 225 Frs.
Restaurant: breakfast from 6.00. Lunch 12.00 to
14.00. Dinner 19.30 to 22.00. Closed Sun.
Specialities: home-cooking.
Hotel: ☆ ☆ 30 rooms. Facilities: shower, private
bathroom, television, telephone.
Other points: credit cards accepted, children's
menu, à la carte menu, lounge area, modern
decor, pets allowed, car/lorry parking.
◀ canal du Midi; beach (14km).

CONILHAC-LES-CORBIERES
Aude, 11200

➡ L'ONCLE ET LE NEVEU
(M. Franck Raynaud) Route Nationale 113
☎ 68.27.08.05
Directions: RN 13.
Languages spoken: Spanish.
Restaurant: breakfast from 5.15.
Specialities: soupe de poissons, cassoulet, regional
menu, home-cooking.
Other points: credit cards accepted, bar,
children's menu, traditional decor, pets allowed,
car/lorry parking.

LA COQUILLE • Dordogne, 24450

➡ LES PORTES DU PERIGORD VERT
(M. Didier Fontaine) Route Nationale 21
☎ 53.52.83.46
Directions: the Périgueux/Limoges road.
Languages spoken: German and English.
Menu: 50 to 125 Frs.
Restaurant: breakfast from 6.00. Lunch from 11.00
until 15.00. Dinner from 19.00 until 22.00. Closed
Sat evening, Sun.
Specialities: Périgord dishes, regional menu, home-
cooking.
Other points: credit cards accepted, bar,
children's menu, à la carte menu, lounge area,
terrace, pets allowed, car/lorry parking.
◀ grottes (caves) de Villard; Jumilhac-le-Grand;
Puiguilhem.

CUQ-TOULZA • Tarn, 81470

🏠 LE RELAIS CHEZ ALAIN
(M. Alain Pratviel) La Bombardière
☎ 63.75.70.36
Directions: RD 621, between Toulouse and Castres.
Languages spoken: English.
Menu: 60 to 300 Frs.
Accommodation: 120 to 240 Frs.
Restaurant: lunch from 11.00 until 16.00. Dinner
from 19.00 until 23.00.
Specialities: bouillabaisse, regional menu.
Hotel: ☆ ☆ 9 rooms. Facilities: shower, private
bathroom, telephone.
Other points: credit cards accepted, bar, children's
menu, à la carte menu, lounge area, traditional
decor, terrace, pets allowed, car/lorry parking.
◀ lac de Saint-Ferréol; Sidobre region; chateau
and circuit de Pastel.

CUXAC-CABARDES • Aude, 11390

🍴 LA MONTAGNE NOIR – Chez Jojo
(M. Harry Hovinga) Route Départementale 118
☎ 68.26.50.03
Directions: RD 118, between Carcassonne and
Mazamet.
Languages spoken: German, English, Dutch.
Restaurant: lunch from 12.00 until 14.00.
Specialities: home-cooking.
Other points: credit cards accepted, bar,
children's menu, traditional decor, terrace, pets
allowed, car/lorry parking.
◀ *Carcassonne; grottes (caves) du Limousis;
Catharist chateaux.*

DAX • Landes, 40100

🏨 AUBERGE DE LA CHALOSSE
(M. Christian Richaud) 157 avenue Georges-
Clemenceau ☎ 58.74.23.08
Directions: Orthez.
Menu: 52 Frs.
Accommodation: 90 to 160 Frs.
Restaurant: breakfast from 6.00. Lunch 12.00 to
14.00. Dinner 20.00 to 22.00. Closed Sun, Aug.
Specialities: home-cooking.
Hotel: 6 rooms.
Other points: bar, modern decor, terrace, pets
allowed, car/lorry parking.
◀ *hot springs; museum.*

DECAZEVILLE • Aveyron, 12300

🍴 A L'AUBERGE DE SAINT-JULIEN
(Mme Yvette Carrière) Route Départementale
963, Saint-Julien-de-Piganiol
☎ 65.64.05.92 [Fax] 65.64.05.92
Directions: the Aurillac/Rodez road.
Menu: 45 to 100 Frs.
Restaurant: breakfast from 8.30. Lunch from
12.00 until 14.00. Closed Mon.
Specialities: stockfish, aligot, poule farcie, regional
menu.
Other points: bar, traditional decor, pets allowed,
car/lorry parking.

DOUZENS • Aude, 11700

🏨 LES ROUTIERS
(Mme Monique Hulin) 98 avenue des
Corbières ☎ 68.79.19.99
Directions: RD 2113, between Narbonne and
Carcassonne.
Languages spoken: English.
Menu: 53 to 150 Frs.
Accommodation: 120 to 200 Frs.
Specialities: regional menu, home-cooking.
Hotel: 8 rooms. Facilities: shower, private bathroom.
Other points: credit cards accepted, bar,
children's menu, à la carte menu, traditional decor,
terrace, pets allowed, car parking.
◀ *musée des oiseaux (birds); numerous abysses
(gouffres) and abbeys in a radius of 50km.*

ESCOURCE • Landes, 40210

🏨 AU ROUTIER
(M. Jean-Pierre Fortinon) Cap de Pin
☎ 58.07.20.54
Directions: RN 10, Sabres, exit 15.
Menu: 65 to 200 Frs 🍽
Accommodation: 160 to 300 Frs.
Restaurant: breakfast from 6.30. Lunch from
12.00 until 14.30. Dinner from 19.30 until 22.30.
Closed Sun, and 2 weeks from 20th Dec.
Specialities: salade de foie de canard frais, ris de
veau madère, magret grillé, regional menu.
Hotel: 15 rooms. Facilities: shower.
Other points: credit cards accepted, bar,
children's menu, à la carte menu, modern decor,
terrace, car/lorry parking.
◀ *musée de Marquèze (18km); beach at Mimizan
(30km).*

ESPALION • Aveyron, 12500

🍴 RELAIS DES QUATRE ROUTES
(M. Michel Molinier) Les Quatre Routes,
Route Départementale 920 ☎ 65.44.05.14
Directions: RD 920, Clermont-Ferrand.
Menu: 50 to 95 Frs.
Accommodation: 80 to 130 Frs.
Restaurant: breakfast from 6.30. Lunch from
12.00 until 14.00. Dinner from 19.30 until 22.00.
Closed Sun (out of season).
Specialities: regional menu, home-cooking.
Hotel: ☆ 4 rooms. Facilities: shower, private
bathroom.
Other points: bar, children's menu, modern
decor, terrace, car/lorry parking.
◀ *Lot valley; château de Calmont; historic
monuments.*

FABREGUES • Hérault, 34690

🍴 L'ARCHE DE FABREGUES
(M. François Tillier) A9, services at
Montpellier – Fabrègues (accessible in both
directions) ☎ 67.85.15.06 [Fax] 67.85.15.29
Restaurant: facilities: open 24 hours.
Other points: credit cards accepted.

🍴 RESTAURANT LE 113
(Mme Josette Avignon) ☎ 67.85.12.86
Directions: RN 113.
Restaurant: closed Sun, and in Oct.
Specialities: regional menu, home-cooking.
Other points: credit cards accepted, bar,
children's menu.
◀ *Bouzique; Mèze; Saint-Guilhem-le-Desert;
le Grau-du-Roi.*

LES FARGUETTES • Tarn, 81190

🍴 RELAIS DE LA PLAINE
(Mme Marie-France Mouget) Route Nationale
88 ☎ 63.76.65.89
Directions: RN 88, the Albi/Rodez road.
Languages spoken: English.

Menu: 55 to 120 Frs.
Restaurant: breakfast from 5.00. Lunch from 11.00 until 15.00. Dinner from 19.00 until 22.00. Closed Wed morning.
Specialities: regional menu, home-cooking.
Other points: credit cards accepted, bar, children's menu, à la carte menu, modern decor, terrace, pets allowed, car/lorry parking.
◀ Cordes; viaduct at Le Viaur; Carmaux; Albi; monts d'Aubrac; Rodez; Toulouse.

FIGEAC • Lot, 46100

🏠 RELAIS DES CHASSEURS
(Mme Véronique Noyer) Route de Capdenac, La Vayssière ☎ 65.34.12.33
Directions: RN 140, the Brive/Montpellier road, Figeac exit towards Rodez.
Languages spoken: English.
Menu: 60 Frs (wine and coffee included).
Accommodation: 120 to 180 Frs.
Restaurant: breakfast from 6.00. Lunch from 11.30 until 14.00. Dinner from 18.30 until 21.30. Closed Sun.
Specialities: regional menu, home-cooking.
Hotel: 8 rooms. Facilities: shower.
Other points: credit cards accepted, bar, children's menu, lounge area, traditional decor, terrace, pets allowed, car/lorry parking.
◀ Figeac; Capdenac-le-Haut; valleys of the Lot and Célé.

FIRBEIX • Dordogne, 24450

🍴 RELAIS DES SPORTS
(M. René Beaubatit) Route Nationale 21 ☎ 53.52.82.53
Directions: RN 21.
Restaurant: closed in Oct.
Other points: bar.

FITOU • Aude, 11510

🏠 LE RELAIS SAINT-ROCH
(M. Roland Durand) 39 Route Nationale 9 ☎ 68.45.71.75
Directions: RN 9, between Narbonne and Perpignan.
Languages spoken: Spanish.
Accommodation: 80 to 110 Frs.
Restaurant: breakfast from 4.00. Dinner from 16.30 until 24.00.
Specialities: home-cooking.
Hotel: 10 rooms. Facilities: shower, private bathroom.
Other points: credit cards accepted, bar, à la carte menu, traditional decor, terrace, pets allowed, car/lorry parking.
◀ Sigean African reserve; château de Salses; le Lidia (ship).

FLEURANCE • Gers, 32500

🍴 RESTAURANT DU STADE
(M. Alphonse Pujade) place de l'Eglise ☎ 62.06.02.23

Directions: RN 21.
Menu: 55 to 140 Frs.
Restaurant: breakfast from 10.00. Lunch 12.00 to 14.00. Dinner 19.00 tol 21.00. Closed Sat, mid-June to mid-July and 1 week at Christmas.
Specialities: home-cooking.
Other points: bar, children's menu, à la carte menu, traditional decor, terrace, pets allowed, car/lorry parking.

FOIX • Ariège, 09000

🏠 LE SOLEIL D'OR
(M. Jean Coumes) 57 avenue du Général-Leclerc ☎ 61.65.01.33
Directions: RN 20.
Menu: 40 to 65 Frs.
Accommodation: 80 to 120 Frs.
Restaurant: breakfast from 6.30. Lunch from 12.00 until 14.00. Dinner from 20.00 until 21.00. Closed Sat and Sun (except bookings).
Specialities: home-cooking.
Hotel: 7 rooms. Facilities: shower.
Other points: bar, pets allowed, car/lorry parking.
◀ château de Foix; grottes (caves).

FONTCOUVERTE • Tarn, 81430

🍴 RESTAURANT CHEZ PAPA
(Mme Anne-Marie Scalia) ☎ 63.55.38.23
Languages spoken: Italian and Arabic.
Menu: 55 to 130 Frs.
Restaurant: breakfast from 8.00
Specialities: bouillabaisse, couscous, paella (to order), regional menu, home-cooking.
Other points: credit cards accepted, bar, children's menu, à la carte menu, pets allowed, car/lorry parking.

FUMEL • Lot-et-Garonne, 47500

🍴 BAR ROUTIER DE LA SOIERIE
(Mme Liliane Lafon) 88 avenue de l'Usine ☎ 53.71.34.22
Menu: 50 Frs.
Restaurant: breakfast from 6.00. Dinner from 18.00 until 20.00. Closed Sun.
Specialities: home-cooking.
Other points: bar, terrace, pets allowed, car/lorry parking.
◀ château de Bonaguil; Périgord.

GAGES • Aveyron, 12630

🏠 LE RELAIS DE LA PLAINE
(Mme Yvonne Dallo) ☎ 65.42.29.03
Directions: RN 88, the Brive/Mediterranean road, 10km from Rodez.
Menu: 65 to 95 Frs.
Accommodation: 100 to 220 Frs.
Restaurant: breakfast from 6.30. Lunch from 12.00 until 14.00. Dinner from 19.30 until 21.00. Closed weekends (out of season), 2 weeks in Nov and 1 week at New Year.

Specialities: tripoux, confit de canard, salade de gésiers (chicken gizzards), regional menu, home-cooking.
Hotel: 22 rooms. Facilities: shower, private bathroom.
Other points: credit cards accepted, bar, children's menu, à la carte menu, lounge area, modern decor, terrace, pets allowed, car/lorry parking.
◈ *gorges of the Tarn; Lot valley; grottes (caves) de l'Aubrac; lacs de Pareloup; Rodez: cathedral.*

GAILLAN-LESPARRE
Gironde, 33340

◀ **MARIE-FRANCE**
(Mme Marie-France Dupuy) place des Ecoles
☎ 56.41.20.53
Directions: RN 215, between Bordeaux and Soulac.
Menu: 58 to 170 Frs.
Restaurant: breakfast from 8.00. Lunch from 11.30 until 15.00. Dinner from 19.00 until 21.00. Closed Sun (out of season), last 2 weeks in Aug and one week at Christmas.
Specialities: gibiers (game), poissons, regional menu.
Other points: bar, children's menu, à la carte menu, traditional decor, terrace, car/lorry parking.
◈ *Médoc chateaux.*

GAN • Pyrénées-Atlantiques, 64290

◀ **AUX PETITS BEARNAIS**
(M. Laurent Courtadiou) Route de Rebenacq
☎ 59.05.51.07
Directions: between Pau and Gourette.
Menu: 50 to 80 Frs.
Restaurant: breakfast from 7.00. Lunch from 12.00 until 15.00. Dinner from 19.00 until 23.00.
Specialities: home-cooking.
Other points: bar, modern decor, terrace, pets allowed, car/lorry parking.
◈ *the Pyrenees.*

GARANOU-LUZENAC
Ariège, 09250

🍴 **LES ROUTIERS**
(Mme Marie Pirès) avenue de la Gare
☎ 61.64.47.13
Directions: RN 20, between Toulouse and Andorra.
Languages spoken: Spanish, Portuguese.
Menu: 60 Frs.
Accommodation: 110 to 140 Frs.
Restaurant: breakfast from 8.00. Lunch 12.00 to 14.00. Dinner 20.00 to 22.00. Closed Sun, Aug.
Specialities: home-cooking.
Hotel: 9 rooms. Facilities: shower, private bathroom, telephone.
Other points: credit cards accepted, bar, children's menu, traditional decor, terrace, pets allowed, car/lorry parking.
◈ *soapstone quarries; caves and subterranean streams; château de Foix; Andorra.*

GER
Pyrénées-Atlantiques, 64530

◀ **A LA CLE D'OR**
(M. Alain Coudert) Route Nationale 117
☎ 62.31.50.56
Directions: RN 117, the Pau (28km)/Tarbes (12km) road.
Languages spoken: Spanish.
Menu: 55 Frs.
Accommodation: 75 to 100 Frs.
Restaurant: breakfast from 6.00. Lunch from 12.00 until 14.00. Closed Sat, Sun, and 3 weeks from 15th Aug.
Specialities: home-cooking.
Other points: bar, modern decor, car/lorry parking.
◈ *Pau; Lourdes; the Pyrenees.*

GOURDON • Lot, 46300

🛏 **HOTEL DE LA MADELEINE**
(M. Jean Barbes) boulevard de la Madeleine
☎ 61.41.02.63
Directions: RD 673, between Souillac and Sarlat.
Menu: 60 Frs (wine included) to 135 Frs.
Accommodation: 165 to 250 Frs.
Restaurant: breakfast from 7.30. Lunch from 12.00 until 15.30. Dinner from 20.00 until 22.00. Closed weekends (out of season), and in Oct.
Specialities: regional menu, home-cooking.
Hotel: 13 rooms. Facilities: shower, private bathroom, television, telephone.
Other points: credit cards accepted, bar, children's menu, à la carte menu, lounge area, traditional decor, terrace, pets allowed, car/lorry parking.
◈ *Gourdon; Rocamadour; Padirac; Sarlat.*

GRAMAT • Lot, 46500

🛏 **HOTEL DU CENTRE**
(M. André Grimal) place de la République
☎ 65.38.73.37 [Fax] 65.38.73.66
Directions: RN 140, between Brive-la-Gaillarde and Rodez.
Languages spoken: English.
Menu: 75 to 200 Frs 🍽
Accommodation: 230 to 350 Frs.
Restaurant: breakfast from 7.00. Lunch from 12.00 until 14.00. Dinner from 19.30 until 21.00. Closed Sat (out of season), 3rd week of Nov and Feb school holidays.
Specialities: foie gras, confits de canard, cèpes, tripoux, gésiers (chicken gizzards), cassoulet, regional menu, home-cooking.
Hotel: ☆ ☆ 14 rooms. Facilities: shower, private bathroom, television, telephone.
Other points: credit cards accepted, bar, children's menu, à la carte menu, lounge area, modern decor, terrace, pets allowed, car/lorry parking.
◈ *Rocamadour; gouffre de Padirac; gorges of the Antoire.*

GRAYAN-L'HOPITAL
Gironde, 33590

☎ LE COQ ROUGE
(Mme Jocelyne Lavigne) Route de Soulac-sur-Mer ☎ 56.09.48.65
Directions: RD 101, Pointe de Grave, Bordeaux.
Menu: 55 Frs (wine included) to 140 Frs.
Restaurant: breakfast from 7.30.
Specialities: confits, fruits de mer, home-cooking.
Other points: credit cards accepted, bar, children's menu, à la carte menu, terrace, pets allowed, car/lorry parking.
◀ the Médoc region; pointe de Grave.

GRISOLLES • Tarn-et-Garonne, 82170

☎ LE RELAIS DE LA GARE
(Laurence and Jean-Gilbert Moroni) Route Nationale 20 ☎ 63.67.37.63
Directions: RN 20.
Languages spoken: English.
Menu: 58 to 130 Frs.
Restaurant: lunch from 11.30 until 15.00. Dinner from 19.15 until 22.30.
Specialities: regional menu.
Other points: bar, car/lorry parking.

HENDAYE
Pyrénées-Atlantiques, 64700

☎ RELAIS ROUTIERS – Chez Mongobert
(M. Alain Mongobert) 11 avenue d'Espagne ☎ 59.70.78.95
Directions: RN 10, near the Spanish border.
Languages spoken: German.
Menu: 58 Frs.
Restaurant: breakfast from 7.00. Closed Sun, Aug.
Specialities: home-cooking.
Other points: bar.

HOSTENS • Gironde, 33125

☎ AU BON ACCUEIL
(SARL Au Bon Accueil) ☎ 56.88.50.63
Restaurant: closed Sat and Sun, Aug.
Other points: bar, car/lorry parking.

L'ISLE-JOURDAIN • Gers, 32600

☎ L'OLYMPIA – Les Routiers
(M. Michel Amour) 5 rue de la République ☎ 62.07.01.35
Directions: RN 124, between Toulouse and Auch.
Menu: 47 Frs.
Restaurant: breakfast from 9.00. Lunch from 11.00 until 14.00. Dinner from 19.00 until 21.00. Closed Mon evening, Sun, public holidays, and in Aug.
Specialities: regional dishes according to season, home-cooking.
Other points: credit cards accepted, bar, à la carte menu, lounge area, traditional decor, pets allowed, car/lorry parking.

◀ Auch: (ancient city) cathedral; numerous chateaux and lakes.

ISSANKA • Hérault, 34540

☎ LE GARRIGOU
(Mme Danyelle Hohmann) Le Garrigou ☎ 67.78.71.30
Directions: RN 113, Sète exit, towards Gigean.
Languages spoken: English, Spanish.
Menu: 60 to 120 Frs.
Accommodation: 150 Frs.
Restaurant: breakfast from 5.30. Lunch from 12.00 until 16.00. Dinner from 18.00 until 23.00. Closed Sat evening and Sun evening.
Specialities: seiche à la rouille, poissons, regional menu, home-cooking.
Hotel: ☆ ☆ 8 rooms. Facilities: shower, telephone.
Other points: children's menu, lounge area, modern decor, pets allowed, car/lorry parking.
◀ Mont Saint-Clair; abbaye de Saint-Félix.

LABATUT • Landes, 40300

☎ LA GUINGUETTE
(M. Christian Begu) Route Nationale 117 ☎ 58.98.18.82
Directions: RN 117, between Toulouse and Bayonne.
Languages spoken: some English and Spanish.
Menu: 55 to 180 Frs.
Accommodation: 130 to 250 Frs.
Restaurant: breakfast from 7.00. Lunch from 11.30 until 14.30. Dinner from 18.30 until 21.30. Closed Sun evening.
Specialities: garbure (thick soup), salade landaise, foie gras, confits, salade de kiwi, regional menu.
Hotel: 5 rooms. Facilities: shower.
Other points: credit cards accepted, bar, children's menu, à la carte menu, lounge area, terrace, pets allowed, car/lorry parking.
◀ lake; le Gave-de-Pau.

LABRUGUIERE • Tarn, 81290

☎ LA MARMITE
(M. René Ozanne) 35 avenue Henri-Simon ☎ 63.50.21.19
Directions: RN 621.
Menu: 58 to 70 Frs.
Accommodation: 100 Frs.
Restaurant: breakfast from 7.00. Closed Sat, Sun.
Specialities: home-cooking.
Hotel: 16 rooms.
Other points: pets allowed, car/lorry parking.

LACAPELLE-MARIVAL • Lot, 46120

☎ LA MARMITE
(Mme Muriel Mivielle) place de Larroque ☎ 65.40.98.07
Directions: RN 140, between Brive-la-Gaillarde and Figeac.

Languages spoken: English, Spanish.
Menu: 50 (wine included) to 75 Frs.
Restaurant: breakfast from 7.30. Lunch 11.00 to 15.00. Dinner 18.30 to 23.00. Closed Sat.
Specialities: home-cooking.
Other points: bar, children's menu, à la carte menu, lounge area, traditional decor, terrace, pets allowed, car/lorry parking.
◁€ *Rocamadour; Padirac; Gramat.*

LACAUNE • Tarn, 81230

🛏 **LE CHALET**
(M. Joseph Delpino) 14 rue André-Theron
☎ 63.37.08.91
Directions: RN 81, the Albi/Castres road.
Languages spoken: English, Spanish.
Menu: 40 to 180 Frs.
Accommodation: 150 to 180 Frs.
Restaurant: breakfast from 7.00. Lunch 12.00 to 14.30. Dinner 19.30 to 21.30. Closed Sun, Dec.
Specialities: paella, couscous, cassoulet, home-cooking.
Hotel: 10 rooms. Facilities: shower.
Other points: bar, children's menu, à la carte menu, traditional decor, terrace, car/lorry parking.
◁€ *Sidobre region; cave de Roquefort; leisure activities: walks, fishing, sailboarding.*

LAFITTE-SUR-LOT
Lot-et-Garonne, 47320

🍴 **LES AMIS DE LA ROUTE**
(M. Max Briot) Route de Villeneuve
☎ 53.84.08.98
Directions: RD 666, Villeneuve-sur-Lot.
Languages spoken: English, Spanish.
Restaurant: breakfast from 7.00. Lunch 12.00 to 14.00. Dinner 19.00 to 22.00. Closed Sat, Sun.
Specialities: home-cooking.
Other points: credit cards accepted, bar, terrace, pets allowed, car/lorry parking.

LAFOX • Lot-et-Garonne, 47270

🛏 **LES ROUTIERS – Le Toulousain**
(M. René André) Route Nationale 113
☎ 53.68.54.83
Directions: RN 113, the Bordeaux/Toulouse road.
Languages spoken: Spanish.
Menu: 57 to 110 Frs.
Restaurant: breakfast from 4.30. Closed Sun, 2 weeks in Aug and 2 weeks in Dec.
Specialities: regional menu, home-cooking.
Hotel: ☆ 27 rooms. Facilities: shower.
Other points: credit cards accepted, bar, children's menu, à la carte menu, lounge area, traditional decor, pets allowed, car/lorry parking.

LAGARRIGUE • Tarn, 81090

🛏 **RESTAURANT BIGUES**
(Mme Josiane Bigues) 2 avenue de Mazamet
☎ 63.35.12.25

Directions: RN 112, between Castres and Mazamet.
Menu: 60 Frs.
Accommodation: 180 to 200 Frs.
Restaurant: breakfast from 7.00. Lunch from 12.00 until 14.00. Dinner from 19.30 until 21.30. Closed Sat evening, Sun, and in Aug.
Specialities: cassoulet, soupe au fromage, regional menu, home-cooking.
Hotel: 8 rooms. Facilities: shower, private bathroom, television, telephone.
Other points: credit cards accepted, bar, children's menu, modern decor, pets allowed, car/lorry parking.
◁€ *Castres; Sidobre region.*

LALOUBERE • Hautes-Pyrénées, 65310

🛏 **HOTEL DES PYRENEES**
(Mme Michèle Cazamayou) 13 rue du Maréchal-Foch ☎ 62.45.29.62
Directions: RD 135, between Bagnères-de-Bigorre and La Mongie.
Languages spoken: English, Spanish.
Menu: 65 to 85 Frs.
Accommodation: 115 to 145 Frs.
Restaurant: breakfast from 7.00. Lunch from 12.00 until 14.00. Dinner from 19.30 until 21.00. Closed Sun, and in Aug.
Specialities: regional menu.
Hotel: ☆ 13 rooms. Facilities: shower.
Other points: credit cards accepted, bar, children's menu, lounge area, modern decor, terrace, pets allowed, car/lorry parking.
◁€ *Lourdes (17km); Pic du Midi; cirque de Gavarnie.*

LAMAGISTERE
Tarn-et-Garonne, 82360

🍴 **CHEZ BOMPA**
(M. Gilbert Bompa) 56 avenue Saint-Michel
☎ 63.39.91.56
Directions: RN 113, the Bordeaux/Toulouse road.
Languages spoken: Spanish.
Menu: 55 to 80 Frs.
Restaurant: breakfast from 6.00. Lunch from 12.00 until 15.00. Dinner from 19.00 until 22.00. Closed Sat, and 2 weeks in Aug.
Specialities: magret, foie gras, gambas flambées, cuisses de canard, regional menu, home-cooking.
Other points: credit cards accepted, bar, children's menu, à la carte menu, lounge area, traditional decor, terrace, pets allowed, car/lorry parking.
◁€ *Centrale (power station) Golfech; Auvillar; Moissac; échelles à poissons (fish-ladders).*

LAMONZIE-SAINT-MARTIN
Dordogne, 24680

🍴 **RELAIS LA POMME D'OR**
(M. Jean-Louis Gonthier) ☎ 53.24.04.00
Directions: RD 936, Bergerac towards Bordeaux.
Languages spoken: English, Spanish.
Menu: 65 to 160 Frs.
Restaurant: breakfast from 6.00. Lunch from

12.00 until 14.30. Dinner from 19.30 until 21.30. Closed Sat, Sun evening, and in Aug.
Specialities: omelette aux cèpes, pavé au poivre vert, regional menu.
Other points: bar, children's menu, à la carte menu, car/lorry parking.

LANGON • Gironde, 33210

🛏 HOTEL-RESTAURANT DARLOT
(M. Jean-Paul Darlot) 10 rue Dotézac
☎ 56.63.01.36
Directions: RN 113, A62 autoroute, Langon exit.
Languages spoken: English, Spanish.
Menu: 60 to 200 Frs 🍽
Accommodation: 120 to 160 Frs.
Restaurant: breakfast from 7.00. Lunch from 12.00 until 15.00. Dinner from 19.00 until 22.00. Closed Sun, and in Aug.
Specialities: civet de lièvre, cèpes à la bordelaise, salmis de palombe (dove), regional menu, home-cooking.
Hotel: 11 rooms. Facilities: shower, private bathroom.
Other points: bar, children's menu, à la carte menu, lounge area, traditional decor, terrace, pets allowed, car/lorry parking.
◀ Verdelais basilica and calvary; grottes (caves) de Sainte-Croix-du-Mont; château de Roquetaillade; Bazas: cathedral; Saint-Macaire; Montesquieu's chateau de la Brède; Graves wines (30km).

🍽 LE PASSAGER
(Gérard and Nadine Barcelona) Route de Pau, Mazères ☎ 56.63.15.22
Directions: CD 932, at the Langon exit (3km), towards Pau.
Menu: 56 Frs (wine and coffee included).
Restaurant: breakfast from 5.00. Lunch from 11.30 until 14.30. Dinner from 19.30 until 22.00. Closed Sat, Sun, and last 2 weeks in Aug.
Specialities: home-cooking.
Other points: credit cards accepted, bar, lounge area, traditional decor, terrace, pets allowed, car/lorry parking.
◀ Bazas (10km); Saint-Macaire (6km); Sauternes (10km); Roquetaillade (3km); Graves vineyards; chateaux of Toulouse-Lautrec and François Mauriac.

LANGOGNE • Lozère, 48300

🛏 HOTEL DU LUXEMBOURG
(Mme Adrienne Chabalier) place de la Gare
☎ 66.69.00.11
Directions: RN 88, between Le Puy-en-Velay and Nîmes.
Languages spoken: English.
Menu: 60 to 120 Frs.
Accommodation: 120 to 200 Frs.
Restaurant: breakfast from 7.30. Lunch from 12.00 until 14.00. Dinner from 19.30 until 21.00 and Jan.
Specialities: champignons, truites, tripes, home-cooking.
Hotel: ☆ 14 rooms. Facilities: shower, private bathroom, television.

Other points: credit cards accepted, bar, children's menu, lounge area, traditional decor, terrace, pets allowed, car/lorry parking.
◀ Notre-Dame-des-Neiges; lac du Bouchet and lac d'Issarlès; dam at Noussac.

LANNEMEZAN
Hautes-Pyrénées, 65300

🛏 HOSTELLERIE DU CHATEAU
(Monique and Virginio Vassiliou-Rodriguez) 133 place du Château ☎ 62.98.06.29
Directions: between Auch (70km) and Tarbes (35km).
Languages spoken: Spanish.
Menu: 55 Frs (wine and coffee included) to 100 Frs.
Accommodation: 80 to 120 Frs.
Restaurant: lunch from 11.30 until 14.30. Dinner from 19.00 until 21.00. Closed Sun.
Specialities: paella, regional menu, home-cooking.
Hotel: 7 rooms.
Other points: credit cards accepted, bar, children's menu, à la carte menu, traditional decor, terrace, pets allowed, car/lorry parking.
◀ caves; chateaux.

LANUEJOULS • Aveyron, 12350

🍽 CHEZ HUGUETTE
(Mme Huguette Couderc) 25 avenue du Rouergue ☎ 65.81.95.10
Directions: between Rodez and Villefranche-de-Rouergue.
Menu: 55 to 85 Frs (wine included).
Restaurant: breakfast from 6.00. Lunch 12.00 to 13.30. Dinner 19.00 to 21.00. Closed Mon.
Specialities: home-cooking.
Other points: credit cards accepted, bar, modern decor, terrace, pets allowed, car/lorry parking.
◀ ruins at Peyrusse-le-Roc; Décazeville: mine 'La Découverte'; grottes (caves) de Foissac.

LAPALME • Aude, 11480

🍽 LE CALYPSO
(Mme Rosie Guiraud) A9, services at Lapalme
☎ 68.45.65.00 [Fax] 68.45.65.03
Directions: A9 autoroute, accessible in both directions.
Languages spoken: German, English, Spanish, Italian.
Menu: 65 Frs.
Restaurant: breakfast from 7.00.
Specialities: home-cooking.
Other points: credit cards accepted, children's menu, modern decor, terrace, pets allowed, car/lorry parking.

🛏 LE CHANTECLAIR
(M. Yves Defromerie) Route Nationale 9, Les Cabanes de la Palme ☎ 68.48.15.03
Directions: RN 9, 2km from the Leucate exit going back towards Narbonne.
Menu: 55 to 140 Frs.
Accommodation: 120 to 190 Frs.

Restaurant: breakfast from 6.00. Lunch from 11.30 until 14.30. Dinner from 19.00 until 22.00. Closed Sat evening, Sun.
Specialities: regional menu, home-cooking.
Hotel: 7 rooms. Facilities: shower.
Other points: credit cards accepted, bar, children's menu, à la carte menu, traditional decor, terrace, pets allowed, car/lorry parking.
◁€ Sigean African reserve; château de Salses; Port la Nouvelle.

LAPANOUSE-DE-SEVERAC
Aveyron, 12150

🏠 **LES ROUTIERS**
(M. Roger Arnal) Route de Rodez
☎ 65.71.60.44
Directions: RN 88, in the centre of the village.
Menu: 50 to 60 Frs.
Accommodation: 80 to 120 Frs.
Restaurant: breakfast from 8.00. Lunch 12.00 to 15.00. Dinner 19.00 to 23.00. Closed Sun.
Specialities: tripoux, regional menu, home-cooking.
Hotel: 5 rooms. Facilities: shower, private bathroom.
Other points: bar, traditional decor, terrace, pets allowed.
◁€ lacs du Levézou; gorges of the Tarn; medieval château de Séverac; cave (cellar) de Roquefort; ski pistes 'Laguiole-Brameloup'.

LE LARDIN-SAINT-LAZARE
Dordogne, 24570

🏠 **LE RELAIS SAINT-LAZARE**
(M. Allen Westwood) Route Nationale 89
☎ 53.51.37.45
Directions: RN 89, between Périgueux (47km) and Brive-la-Gaillarde (20km).
Languages spoken: English, Italian.
Menu: 55 (wine included) to 65 Frs.
Accommodation: 120 to 160 Frs.
Restaurant: breakfast from 6.30. Lunch 12.00 to 14.30. Dinner 19.00 to 22.30. Closed Sun.
Specialities: home-cooking.
Hotel: 10 rooms.
Other points: bar, children's menu, traditional decor, pets allowed, car/lorry parking.
◁€ Montignac; Les Eyzies; Roc Saint-Christophe; Sarlat.

🏠 **LE VEZERE**
(Mme Marie-Claire Semprez) Route Nationale 89 ☎ 53.51.28.21
Directions: RN 89, the Périgueux/Brive-la-Gaillarde road.
Menu: 50 Frs (wine and coffee included) to 100 Frs.
Accommodation: 70 to 100 Frs.
Restaurant: breakfast from 5.00. Lunch 12.00 to 15.00. Dinner 19.00 to 24.00. Closed Sun.
Specialities: home-cooking.
Hotel: 6 rooms.
Other points: bar, children's menu, traditional decor, terrace, pets allowed, car/lorry parking.
◁€ 'Périgord noir'; the Dordogne and Vezère valleys.

LARUSCADE • Gironde, 33620

🍴 **LE CHAT HUANT**
(M. Ange Portela – SARL La Corogne) Route Nationale 10, Le Chauan ☎ 57.68.54.16
Directions: RN 10, the Bordeaux/Angoulême road.
Languages spoken: Spanish, Portuguese.
Menu: 55 Frs (wine and coffee included).
Restaurant: breakfast from 6.00.
Specialities: home-cooking.
Other points: credit cards accepted, bar, children's menu, traditional decor, terrace, pets allowed, car/lorry parking.

LAUSSEIGNAN-BARBASTE
Lot-et-Garonne, 47230

🍴 **LES PALMIERS**
(SNC Gineste & Fils) ☎ 53.65.55.02
Directions: RN 655, the Agen/Bayonne road.
Menu: 45 to 120 Frs 👞
Restaurant: breakfast from 7.00. Lunch 12.00 to 14.00. Dinner 19.30 to 21.15. Closed Sat (out of season), Mon evening (in season) and in Jan.
Specialities: paupiette de veau (grand prix d'honneur in the French 1992 championships), regional menu.
Other points: credit cards accepted, bar, children's menu, à la carte menu, lounge area, traditional decor, terrace, pets allowed, car/lorry parking.
◁€ moulin (windmill) des tours; Henri IV's chateau; Vianne: bastide (country house), verrerie (glass-works); la cave (wine-cellar) de Buzet; chocolate-making at Nérac.

LEDENON • Gard, 30210

🏠 **LE RELAIS DE LEDENON**
(M. Serge Kaszuba) Route Nationale 86
☎ 66.37.34.46
Directions: RN 86, the Avignon/Remoulins/Nîmes road.
Languages spoken: English, Spanish.
Menu: 60 Frs (coffee included).
Accommodation: 100 to 120 Frs.
Restaurant: breakfast from 6.00. Closed Sun.
Specialities: home-cooking.
Hotel: 7 rooms. Facilities: shower, private bathroom.
Other points: credit cards accepted, bar, children's menu, traditional decor, terrace, pets allowed, car/lorry parking.
◁€ Pont du Gard; Nîmes.

LIBOURNE • Gironde, 33500

🏠 **LE MOULIN BLANC**
(Mme Geneviève Fernandez) 132 avenue Georges-Clemenceau ☎ 57.25.06.27
Directions: RN 89, the Libourne/Périgueux road.
Languages spoken: Spanish, Italian.
Menu: 60 to 120 Frs.
Accommodation: 120 to 200 Frs.
Restaurant: breakfast from 7.30. Lunch from 12.00 until 15.00. Dinner from 19.00 until 21.30.

Specialities: couscous, paella, home-cooking.
Hotel: ☆ 10 rooms. Facilities: shower, private bathroom.
Other points: bar, children's menu, à la carte menu, lounge area, traditional decor, pets allowed, car/lorry parking.
⫷ *Bordeaux wine-growing region: Saint-Emilion (8km), Pomerol (3km), Fronsac (3km).*

LIGARDES • Gers, 32100

⇌ RELAIS CHEZ DUDULE
(M. Francis Dulong) Route d'Agen
☎ 62.28.85.76
Directions: RD 931, the Agen/Pau road.
Restaurant: breakfast from 7.30.
Specialities: regional menu, home-cooking.
Other points: credit cards accepted, bar, traditional decor, terrace, pets allowed, car/lorry parking.
⫷ *La Romieu; Seviac; Flardan; Condom.*

LIPOSTHEY • Landes, 40410

⇌ CHEZ ALINE
(Mme Aline Gros) ☎ 58.82.30.30
Directions: RN 10, exit 17.
Menu: 58 to 150 Frs.
Restaurant: breakfast from 7.30. Lunch from 12.00 until 14.00. Dinner from 19.30 until 21.00. Closed Sat, and from Christmas Day to mid-Jan.
Specialities: Landes dishes, home-cooking.
Other points: bar, children's menu, traditional decor, pets allowed, car/lorry parking.

LODEVE • Hérault, 34700

🛏 RELAIS DE LA CROIX
(M. Jean-Denis Roig) Cartels ☎ 67.44.00.72
Directions: RN 9.
Menu: 58 Frs.
Accommodation: 100 Frs.
Restaurant: breakfast from 7.00. Lunch 12.00 to 15.00. Dinner 19.30 to 22.00. Closed Sat and Sun.
Specialities: home-cooking.
Hotel: 5 rooms. Facilities: shower, private bathroom.
Other points: credit cards accepted, bar, lounge area, terrace, pets allowed, car/lorry parking.

🛏 RELAIS ESCALETTE
(M. Gilbert Cavalier) Route Nationale 9
☎ 67.44.01.14 [Fax] 67.44.43.93
Directions: RN 9.
Languages spoken: German, English, Italian.
Menu: 70 to 220 Frs.
Accommodation: 100 to 170 Frs.
Restaurant: breakfast from 4.00. Lunch from 12.00 until 13.30. Dinner from 19.00 until 22.00.
Specialities: boeuf Saint-Fulcran, grillade au feu de bois, canard aux olives, regional menu.
Hotel: 20 rooms. Facilities: shower.
Other points: credit cards accepted, bar, à la carte menu, lounge area, terrace, pets allowed, car/lorry parking.
⫷ *cirque de Navacelle and de Maureze; lac du Salagou; grottes (caves) de l'Abeil.*

LOMBEZ • Gers, 32220

🛏 LE RELAIS DES PYRENEES
(Mme Michelle Mula) Route de Samatan
☎ 62.62.32.11
Directions: the Auch/Toulouse/Tarbes road.
Languages spoken: Spanish.
Menu: 50 Frs (wine and coffee included) to 145 Frs.
Specialities: confits, magrets, foie gras, regional menu, home-cooking.
Hotel: 8 rooms.
Other points: credit cards accepted, bar, children's menu, à la carte menu, terrace, pets allowed, car/lorry parking.

LONS • Pyrénées-Atlantiques, 64149

⇌ LE MIDI–MINUIT
(M. Claude Prodocini) avenue Larregain
☎ 59.32.07.57
Directions: the Pau road.
Menu: 50 to 100 Frs.
Restaurant: breakfast from 6.30. Lunch from 11.30 until 15.00. Dinner from 19.30 until 23.00. Closed Sun, and in August.
Specialities: regional menu.
Other points: bar, à la carte menu, traditional decor, car/lorry parking.

LOURDES • Hautes-Pyrénées, 65100

⇌ LE MALLORY'S
(M. Serge and Claude Darrieutort) 21 avenue Alexandre-Marqui ☎ 62.94.19.41
Languages spoken: English, Italian.
Menu: 50 to 90 Frs.
Restaurant: breakfast from 6.30. Lunch from 12.00 until 14.30. Dinner from 19.00 until 21.00.
Specialities: foie gras, magrets, confits, garbure (thick soup), salade landaise, home-cooking.
Other points: credit cards accepted, bar, à la carte menu, terrace, car/lorry parking.
⫷ *Lourdes.*

LUBBON • Landes, 40240

🛏 CHEZ MAMY
(Mme Martine Laurens) ☎ 58.93.60.47
Directions: RD 933, between Casteljaloux and Mont-de-Marsan.
Languages spoken: Italian.
Menu: 55 Frs.
Accommodation: 60 Frs.
Restaurant: breakfast from 5.00. Lunch from 12.00 until 15.00. Dinner from 19.00 until 21.00. Closed Sat evening, and in Oct.
Specialities: foie gras, confits, cèpes, poulet farcie, regional menu, home-cooking.
Hotel: 8 rooms. Facilities: shower.
Other points: credit cards accepted, bar, children's menu, à la carte menu, traditional decor, pets allowed, car/lorry parking.
⫷ *Barbotan; old Nérac: chocolate-makers; Puydesseau.*

MAGNANAC · Haute-Garonne, 31340

⇌ CHEZ FRANCOISE
(Mme Françoise Rossi) ☎ 61.09.01.87
Directions: RN 630, between Montauban and
Castres.
Menu: 60 Frs.
Restaurant: dinner until 20.00. Closed Fri evening,
Sat evening, Sun, public holidays, last 2 weeks in Aug.
Specialities: home-cooking.
Hotel: 4 rooms. Facilities: shower, private bathroom.
Other points: credit cards accepted, bar, lounge
area, traditional decor, terrace, pets allowed,
car/lorry parking.

MARGUERITTES · Gard, 30320

🛏 LE RELAIS D'AVIGNON
(M. Yves Debrie) Route Nationale 86
☎ 66.26.02.20
Directions: Avignon.
Menu: 60 Frs.
Accommodation: 150 to 200 Frs.
Restaurant: breakfast from 7.00. Closed Sun.
Specialities: home-cooking.
Hotel: 15 rooms. Facilities: shower, private bathroom.
Other points: credit cards accepted, bar,
children's menu, à la carte menu, terrace, pets
allowed, car/lorry parking.

MARMANDE
Lot-et-Garonne, 47200

⇌ RESTAURANT LE MARINIER
(M. Antoine Florès) Pont-des-Sables, Coussan
☎ 53.93.60.37
Directions: RD 933, Marmande.
Languages spoken: English, Spanish, Italian.
Menu: 55 to 85 Frs.
Restaurant: breakfast from 6.00. Lunch from
12.00 until 14.00. Dinner from 19.30 until 22.00.
Closed Sat and Sun, and on 15th Aug.
Specialities: paella, couscous, foie gras, confit,
magret, regional menu, home-cooking.
Other points: bar, children's menu, lounge area,
terrace, pets allowed, car/lorry parking.
⟐ Marmande: basilica; canal du Midi.

MARSAN-AUBIET · Gers, 32270

⇌ RELAIS 124
(M. Fernand Castaing) ☎ 62.65.63.43
Directions: RN 124, the Toulouse/Auch road,
15km from Auch.
Languages spoken: English.
Menu: 57 Frs (wine included).
Restaurant: breakfast from 7.00. Lunch 11.30 to
15.00. Dinner 19.00 to 23.00. Closed Sat, Sun,
one week in Aug and one week at end of Dec.
Specialities: home-cooking.
Other points: credit cards accepted, bar,
children's menu, traditional decor, terrace, pets
allowed, car/lorry parking.

MARSAS · Gironde, 33620

⇌ LE TOURIN
(M. Daniel Leclerc) Route de Libourne
☎ 57.68.08.04
Directions: RN 10.
Menu: 48 Frs (wine included) to 80 Frs.
Restaurant: breakfast from 5.30. Dinner from
19.00 until 22.00.
Specialities: regional menu, home-cooking.
Other points: credit cards accepted, bar,
children's menu, à la carte menu, traditional decor,
terrace, pets allowed, car/lorry parking.
⟐ Blaye: citadel; vineyards: Saint-Emilion.

MARSEILLAN-PLAGE
Hérault, 34340

⇌ LE CREOLE
(M. Gilles Lepinette) 5 avenue de la
Méditerranée ☎ 67.21.98.25
Directions: Sète exit, towards Mèze.
Menu: 50 to 120 Frs.
Restaurant: restaurant situated 100m from the
beach. Breakfast from 9.30. Lunch 12.00 to 15.00.
Dinner 19.00 to 22.00. Closed Wed (out of season).
Specialities: regional menu, home-cooking.
Other points: credit cards accepted, bar, children's
menu, à la carte menu, pets allowed, car/lorry
parking.
⟐ Agde (Greek town) (6km); Minerve (medieval
town) (45km); Bouzigues: étang de Thau (15km);
Pézenas (Molière's medieval city) (20km).

MARVEJOLS · Lozère, 48100

🛏 HOTEL DE LA PAIX
(M. Jean-Jacques Bourguignon) 2 avenue
Brazza ☎ 66.32.10.17 [Fax] 66.32.34.93
Directions: RN 9.
Languages spoken: English, Spanish.
Restaurant: dinner until 21.00.
Hotel: 19 rooms.
Other points: bar.

MASSEUBE · Gers, 32140

⇌ CHEZ YVETTE
(Mme Yvette Beyries) Route Nationale 129
☎ 62.66.02.14
Directions: RN 129, Lamezan.
Menu: 50 Frs.
Restaurant: breakfast from 7.00. Lunch from
11.30 until 14.00. Closed Sun, and in Aug.
Specialities: home-cooking.
Other points: children's menu.

MAUBOURGUET
Hautes-Pyrénées, 65700

⇌ BAR RELAIS DES AUTOBUS
(Mme Nicole Dauba) 87 place de la
Libération ☎ 62.96.38.78
Menu: 35 to 165 Frs.

Restaurant: breakfast from 6.00. Lunch from 11.00 until 14.30. Dinner from 19.00 until 21.30.
Specialities: regional menu, home-cooking.
Other points: bar, children's menu, terrace, pets allowed, car/lorry parking.

MAVALEIX • Dordogne, 24800

☞ LES JARDINS DE LA TUILIERE
(Mme Suzette Deschamps) Route Nationale 21
☎ 53.52.03.85 [Fax] 53.62.54.44
Directions: RN 21, the Périgueux/Limoges road.
Languages spoken: English, Spanish.
Menu: 59 Frs to 130 Frs and.
Accommodation: 120 to 160 Frs.
Restaurant: breakfast from 6.00. Lunch from 11.30 until 15.00. Dinner from 19.00 until 22.00.
Specialities: Périgord dishes, confit, foie gras (to order), vins de pays, regional menu, home-cooking.
Hotel: 3 rooms. Facilities: shower, private bathroom.
Other points: credit cards accepted, bar, à la carte menu, traditional decor, modern decor, terrace, pets allowed, car/lorry parking.
◁€ grottes (caves) de Villars; Puiguilhem; Jumilhac-le-Grand; Sorges; Brantôme; reservoir at Miallet.

MAZEYROLLES • Dordogne, 24550

☞ L'AUBERGE D'ANAIS
(M. Xavier Belbis) Le Got ☎ 53.28.56.87
Directions: RD 710, between Fumel and Siorac.
Languages spoken: German, English, Spanish, Italian.
Menu: 50 Frs.
Restaurant: breakfast from 7.00. Lunch from 12.00 until 15.00. Dinner from 19.30 until 21.00.
Specialities: couscous, paella, chili con carne, home-cooking.
Other points: bar, à la carte menu, modern decor, terrace, pets allowed, car/lorry parking.
◁€ Belves; Monpazier; Les Eyzies; Sarlat; Dordogne valley.

MERCUS-GARRABET • Ariège, 09400

☞ LE CATHARE
(Mme Amélie Castellon) Route Nationale 20
☎ 61.05.68.09
Directions: RN 20, between Toulouse and Andorra.
Languages spoken: Spanish.
Menu: 55 (wine and coffee included)) 85 Frs.
Restaurant: breakfast from 7.00. Lunch from 12.00 until 15.00. Dinner from 19.00 until 21.00.
Specialities: regional menu, home-cooking.
Other points: credit cards accepted, bar, children's menu, à la carte menu, traditional decor, pets allowed, car/lorry parking.
◁€ château de Foix (6km); Montségur (15km).

MILLAU-LARZAC • Aveyron, 12230

☎ RELAIS ESPACE
(Mme Ginette Gineste) Aérodrôme Millau-Larzac ☎ 65.62.76.22 [Fax] 65.62.79.02

Directions: RN 9, the Clermont-Ferrand/Béziers road.
Languages spoken: English, Spanish.
Menu: 40 to 100 Frs.
Accommodation: 200 Frs.
Restaurant: breakfast from 6.00. Lunch from 11.15 until 15.00. Dinner from 18.30 until 21.30.
Specialities: terrine de foie gras, langue de boeuf sauce piquante, loup (bass) au basilic, regional menu, home-cooking.
Hotel: ☆ ☆ 10 rooms. Facilities: shower, private bathroom, television, telephone.
Other points: credit cards accepted, bar, children's menu, lounge area, modern decor, terrace, pets allowed, car/lorry parking.
◁€ gorges of the Tarn; cirque Navacelle; La Couvertoirade; Roquefort.

MIMIZAN • Landes, 40200

☎ HOTEL-RESTAURANT DUCOURT
(Mme Christine Kanitzer) 20 avenue de la Plage ☎ 58.82.44.98
Directions: RN 626, between Mimizan (town) and Mimizan-Plage.
Menu: 55 Frs.
Accommodation: 120 to 150 Frs.
Restaurant: breakfast from 7.00. Lunch from 12.00 until 15.00. Dinner from 19.00 until 22.00. Closed Sun (out of season).
Specialities: confit maison, choucroute, home-cooking.
Hotel: 18 rooms. Facilities: shower.
Other points: credit cards accepted, bar, children's menu, à la carte menu, traditional decor, terrace, pets allowed, car/lorry parking.
◁€ convent at Huchet; lac du Nord and lac des Landes; the Landes coast; Arcachon: Ecomusée at Marquèze.

☞ LE GRAIN DE SEL
(M. Michele Cassou) 28 avenue de la Plage
☎ 58.09.37.15
Languages spoken: English, Spanish.
Menu: 55 to 85 Frs.
Restaurant: breakfast from 7.30. Lunch from 12.00 until 15.00. Dinner from 19.00 until 22.00.
Specialities: confit de canard (48 Frs), brochette de coeur de canard (50 Frs), regional menu.
Other points: credit cards accepted, bar, à la carte menu, traditional decor, terrace, pets allowed, car/lorry parking.

MIRAMONT-D'ASTARAC
Gers, 32300

☎ LE RELAIS DES TROUETTES
(M. Frédéric Normand) Route Nationale 21
☎ 62.66.60.50
Directions: RN 21, the Agen/Auch/Tarbes road.
Languages spoken: English, Spanish.
Menu: 55 Frs (wine included) to 100 Frs.
Restaurant: breakfast from 6.00. Lunch from 12.00 until 14.00. Dinner from 19.30 until 22.30. Closed Sat, and end of Dec.
Specialities: home-cooking.

Hotel: 8 rooms. Facilities: shower.
Other points: bar, children's menu, traditional decor, terrace, pets allowed, car/lorry parking.
◀€ Auch (15km); Mirande (5km).

MIRAMONT-DE-GUYENNE
Lot-et-Garonne, 47800

🍴 LE RELAIS DE GUYENNE
(Mme Raymonde Rodes) Route de Paris, Saint-Pardoux-Isaac ☎ 53.93.20.76
[Fax] 53.20.91.95
Directions: CD 933, between Marmande and Périgueux.
Languages spoken: Spanish, Italian.
Menu: 55 to 80 Frs.
Accommodation: 150 to 230 Frs.
Restaurant: breakfast from 7.00. Lunch 11.00 to 14.30. Dinner 19.00 to 22.00. Closed Sat (out of season), and 3 weeks at beginning of Dec.
Specialities: fruits de mer, home-cooking.
Hotel: ☆ ☆ 8 rooms. Facilities: shower, private bathroom, television, telephone.
Other points: credit cards accepted, bar, children's menu, à la carte menu, lounge area, modern decor, car/lorry parking.
◀€ chateaux; the Dordogne; Duras; leisure lakes.

MOISSAC • Tarn-et-Garonne, 82200

🍴 RELAIS AUVERGNAT
(M. Jacques Ginisty) 31 boulevard Camille-Delthil ☎ 63.04.02.58
Directions: RN 927.
Languages spoken: English, Spanish.
Menu: 50 Frs ☜
Accommodation: 100 to 200 Frs.
Restaurant: breakfast from 6.30. Lunch 12.00 to 15.00. Dinner 19.30 to 22.00. Closed Sun afternoon.
Specialities: cassoulet, confit, grillades (grills), regional menu, home-cooking.
Hotel: ☆ 10 rooms. Facilities: shower, television.
Other points: credit cards accepted, bar, children's menu, à la carte menu, traditional decor, pets allowed, car parking.
◀€ sites de Boudou (viewing point); Montauban (30km): cathedral, museum; Larrazet (15km); Moissac: chateau, park.

LE MONASTIER • Lozère, 48100

🍴 LES AJUSTONS
(SARL Gibelin) Les Ajustons ☎ 66.32.70.35
Directions: RN 9, the Millau road.
Menu: 60 to 120 Frs.
Accommodation: 100 and 170 Frs.
Restaurant: breakfast from 7.30. Lunch 12.00 to 14.00. Dinner 19.30 to 21.00. Closed Sat, Sun, and in Jan or Feb.
Specialities: truite, tripoux auvergnat, regional menu, home-cooking.
Hotel: ☆ 18 rooms. Facilities: shower, private bathroom.
Other points: credit cards accepted, bar, à la carte

menu, traditional decor, pets allowed, car/lorry parking.
◀€ gorges of the Tarn; Aubrac plateau.

MONBEQUI • Tarn-et-Garonne, 82170

🍴 LE RELAIS D'AQUITAINE
(Mme Pascale Pares – SARL Le Bounty) Route Nationale 113 ☎ 63.65.53.62
Directions: RN 113, the Toulouse/Bordeaux road.
Languages spoken: English, Spanish.
Menu: 55 to 200 Frs.
Restaurant: breakfast from 5.00. Lunch from 11.30 until 15.00. Dinner from 19.00 until 22.00.
Specialities: home-cooking.
Other points: credit cards accepted, bar, children's menu, traditional decor, terrace, pets allowed, car/lorry parking.
◀€ Toulouse; Verdun-sur-Garonne; Montech: pool.

MONDAVEZAN
Haute-Garonne, 31220

🍴 LA FERMIERE
(Mme Alexine Ferrage) Route Nationale 117 ☎ 61.97.01.52
Directions: RN 117, the Toulouse/Saint-Gaudens road.
Languages spoken: Spanish.
Menu: 56 to 105 Frs.
Accommodation: 70 to 150 Frs.
Restaurant: breakfast from 6.00. Lunch from 11.00 until 14.00. Dinner from 19.00 until 22.00. Closed Sun, and last 2 weeks in Aug.
Specialities: confit de canard, cassoulet, regional menu, home-cooking.
Hotel: ☆ 21 rooms. Facilities: shower.
Other points: credit cards accepted, bar, à la carte menu, terrace, pets allowed, car/lorry parking.

MONT-DE-MARSAN • Landes, 40000

🍴 BAR DES SPORTS
(Mme Josiane Ledoux) place des Arènes ☎ 58.75.05.08
Languages spoken: Spanish.
Menu: 50 to 120 Frs.
Accommodation: 100 to 180 Frs.
Restaurant: breakfast from 6.30. Lunch 12.00 to 14.00. Dinner 19.30 to 22.00. Closed Sun.
Specialities: home-cooking.
Hotel: 22 rooms.
Other points: bar, pets allowed, car/lorry parking.

MONTAREN • Gard, 30700

🍴 LES ROUTIERS – Chez Régine
(Mme Régine Hangard) 7 route d'Alès ☎ 66.22.25.26
Directions: RN 981.
Restaurant: closed Sun.
Hotel: 9 rooms.
Other points: bar.

MONTECH • Tarn-et-Garonne, 82700

RELAIS DE L'AVENUE
(M. Georges Taupiac) 7 boulevard Lagal
☎ 63.64.72.26
Directions: RD 928, between Montauban and Auch.
Menu: 52 to 100 Frs.
Restaurant: breakfast from 7.00. Lunch from
11.30 until 14.00. Closed Sun, public holidays,
and 2 weeks from 20th Dec.
Specialities: regional menu, home-cooking.
Other points: à la carte menu, modern decor,
car/lorry parking.

MONTREAL • Aude, 11290

LE MALEPERE
(M. Gabriel François) Les Giscarels
☎ 68.76.29.43
Directions: RD 119, exit at Castelnaudary,
towards Limoux.
Languages spoken: English, Spanish.
Menu: 60 to 200 Frs.
Accommodation: 90 to 190 Frs.
Restaurant: breakfast from 7.00. Lunch 11.00 to
14.30. Dinner 19.00 to 22.00. Closed Sun.
Specialities: regional menu, home-cooking.
Hotel: 3 rooms. Facilities: shower, private
bathroom, television.
Other points: credit cards accepted, bar, children's
menu, à la carte menu, lounge area, traditional
decor, terrace, pets allowed, car/lorry parking.
◀ Carcassonne (15km); Catharist centre.

MONTREDON-DES-CORBIERES
Aude, 11100

LE STEPHANOIS
(M. Gilles Pasquet) Route Nationale 113
☎ 68.42.08.41 Fax 68.41.37.51
Directions: RN 113.
Languages spoken: Spanish.
Restaurant: breakfast from 4.00. Lunch 11.30 to
14.30. Dinner 19.00 to 24.00. Closed Sun.
Other points: bar, car/lorry parking.
◀ abbaye de Fontfroide (15km).

MONTVALENT • Lot, 46600

LA BERGERIE DE POULOT
(M. Marcel Magnier) Route Nationale 140,
Poulot ☎ 65.37.41.04
Directions: RN 140, between Brive-la-Gaillarde
and Rodez.
Menu: 55 (wine included) to 130 Frs.
Restaurant: breakfast from 6.00. Lunch from
11.00. Dinner until 22.00.
Specialities: Périgord dishes, regional menu, home-
cooking.
Other points: children's menu, à la carte menu,
traditional decor, terrace, pets allowed, car/lorry
parking.
◀ Rocamadour; Padirac; Gramat.

MOULEYDIER • Dordogne, 24520

RELAIS DU BARRAGE
(M. Patrick Delmas) Tuilières ☎ 53.63.47.56
Directions: RD 660, between Bergerac and Sarlat.
Languages spoken: English, Spanish.
Menu: 50 Frs (wine and coffee included).
Restaurant: breakfast from 7.00. Lunch from
12.00 until 14.00. Dinner from 19.30 until 23.00.
Closed Sat and Sun.
Specialities: home-cooking.
Other points: bar, children's menu, lounge area,
traditional decor, terrace, pets allowed, car/lorry
parking.
◀ dam; canal; the Dordogne.

MURET • Haute-Garonne, 31600

LE MARCLAN
(Mme Régine Soler) 22 bis rue de Marclan,
Zone Industrielle (Z.I.) de Marclan
☎ 61.56.82.93
Directions: RN 117, between Toulouse and Saint-
Gaudens.
Menu: 55 Frs (coffee included).
Restaurant: breakfast from 7.00. Lunch from 11.30
until 14.30. Closed Sat and Sun.
Specialities: soupe de poissons, home-cooking.
Other points: credit cards accepted, bar, modern
decor.

MUSSIDAN • Dordogne, 24400

LE PERIGORD
(Mme Annie Callens) 37 avenue Gambetta
☎ 53.81.05.85
Directions: RN 89, between Bordeaux and
Périgueux.
Menu: 50 to 150 Frs
Accommodation: 150 to 250 Frs.
Restaurant: breakfast from 7.00. Lunch from
12.00 until 14.30. Dinner from 19.30 until 22.00.
Closed 1st Nov.
Specialities: foie gras, cou d'oie (goose-neck) farci,
confit, ris de veau, magrets de canard, regional
menu, home-cooking.
Hotel: 6 rooms. Facilities: shower, private bathroom.
Other points: credit cards accepted, bar,
children's menu, à la carte menu, traditional decor,
terrace, pets allowed, car/lorry parking.
◀ château de Montréal; musée artisanal (crafts);
wine-cellars; caves; spring.

NARBONNE • Aude, 11100

LA CAILLE QUI CHANTE
(M. Alain Garcies) Montredon-des-Corbières
☎ 68.42.04.36 Fax 68.42.42.85
Directions: RN 113, exit at Narbonne Sud (South),
towards Carcassonne.
Languages spoken: English, Spanish, German.
Menu: 55 to 120 Frs.
Accommodation: 120 to 185 Frs.
Restaurant: breakfast from 4.00. Lunch from

12.00 until 15.00. Dinner from 18.30 until 24.00.
Specialities: grillades (grills), fruits de mer, paella, regional menu.
Hotel: ☆ ☆ 20 rooms. Facilities: shower, private bathroom, television, telephone.
Other points: credit cards accepted, bar, children's menu, à la carte menu, traditional decor, terrace, pets allowed, car/lorry parking.
◄€ *abbaye de Fontfroide; ranch offering 'promenades à cheval' (riding); Catharist chateau.*

🍽 LE NOVELTY
(Claude and Louis Strazzera) 33 avenue des Pyrénées ☎ 68.42.24.28 [Fax] 68.42.13.37
Languages spoken: English, Arabic, Spanish, Italian.
Menu: 53 to 95 Frs.
Accommodation: 80 to 175 Frs.
Restaurant: breakfast from 7.00. Lunch from 12.00 until 14.30. Dinner from 19.30 until 22.30.
Specialities: poulet à la narbonnaise, cassoulet, choucroute, paella, couscous (Thurs), regional menu, home-cooking.
Hotel: 21 rooms.
Other points: credit cards accepted, bar, à la carte menu, lounge area, pets allowed, car parking.
◄€ *cathedral; museums; ponds (étangs); beaches.*

🍽 RESTAURANT DES 2 MERS
(M. Franco Mattei) Route de la Nautique, Complexe Routier International
☎ 68.41.00.21
Directions: RN 9, exit at Narbonne Sud (South).
Languages spoken: English, Italian.
Menu: 56 to 68 Frs.
Restaurant: breakfast from 6.00. Dinner until 24.00. Closed Sat evening and Sun.
Specialities: poissons, viandes en sauce, home-cooking.
Other points: bar, children's menu, modern decor, terrace, pets allowed, car/lorry parking.
◄€ *abbaye de Fontfroide; route des Corbières; cathedral at Saint-Just; musée des vins.*

NEUVIC-SUR-L'ISLE
Dordogne, 24190

🍽 ESCALE DU BUT
(M. Jean-Luc Médard) Route Nationale 89, Le But ☎ 53.81.60.06
Directions: RN 89, between Bordeaux (195km) and Périgueux (30km).
Languages spoken: English, Spanish.
Menu: 53 Frs (wine and coffee included) to 80 Frs.
Restaurant: breakfast from 6.00.
Specialities: home-cooking.
Other points: credit cards accepted, bar, children's menu, à la carte menu, modern decor, terrace, pets allowed, car/lorry parking.
◄€ *Neuvic.*

NICOLE • Lot-et-Garonne, 47190

🏠 LE PLAISANCE
(M. Bernard Lambert) Route Nationale 113, Aiguillon ☎ 53.79.64.07
Directions: RN 113.

Menu: 51 to 100 Frs.
Accommodation: 80 to 100 Frs.
Restaurant: breakfast from 7.00. Lunch 12.00 to 14.00. Dinner 19.00 to 22.00. Closed Sat, Aug.
Specialities: confit, magret de canard, tête de veau ravigotte, regional menu.
Hotel: 6 rooms. Facilities: shower, television.
Other points: bar, children's menu, à la carte menu, modern decor, pets allowed, car/lorry parking.
◄€ *Lot and Garonne valleys; site du Pech de Berre.*

NIMES • Gard, 30900

🍽 L'AVONAGE
(M. Gabriel Finiels) Route de Générac, Camping du domaine de la Bastide
☎ 66.38.06.99
Menu: 60 to 100 Frs.
Restaurant: breakfast from 8.00. Closed Sun.
Specialities: escargots, gardiane de taureau, rouille, regional menu, home-cooking.
Other points: credit cards accepted, bar, children's menu, à la carte menu, modern decor, terrace, pets allowed, car/lorry parking.
◄€ *the Camargue; le Grau-du-Roi.*

ONET-LE-CHATEAU
Aveyron, 12850

🏠 LA ROCADE
(M. Francis Gayraud) La Roquette
☎ 65.67.10.44
Directions: RN 88, between Sévérac-le-Château and Millau.
Menu: 52 to 120 Frs 🍽
Accommodation: 120 to 200 Frs.
Restaurant: breakfast from 7.00. Lunch 12.00 to 14.00. Dinner 19.30 to 21.00. Closed Fri evening, Sat, 1st 2 weeks in July, 2 weeks from 24th Dec.
Specialities: confit de canard, civet (stew) d'oie (goose), tripoux, grillades au feu de bois (charcoal grills), regional menu.
Hotel: ☆ 14 rooms. Facilities: shower, private bathroom, television, telephone.
Other points: credit cards accepted, bar, children's menu, à la carte menu, lounge area, terrace, pets allowed, car/lorry parking.
◄€ *Conques; gorges of the Tarn; Rodez.*

🏠 LE CRYSTAL
(M. Yvan Dissac) route d'Espalion
☎ 65.74.91.49
Directions: CD 935, the Rodez/Clermont-Ferrand road.
Menu: 48 Frs.
Accommodation: 80 to 150 Frs.
Restaurant: breakfast from 7.00. Lunch 11.30 to 14.00. Dinner 19.00 to 21.00. Closed Sat, Sun, in Aug, and 1 week from Christmas Day.
Specialities: regional menu, home-cooking.
Hotel: 16 rooms. Facilities: shower.
Other points: credit cards accepted, bar, children's menu, traditional decor, terrace, pets allowed, car/lorry parking.
◄€ *Rodez; Conques; Bozouls; Espalion; gorges of the Tarn.*

ORTHEZ
Pyrénées-Atlantiques, 64300

LE RELAIS DE BAIGTS
(Mme Danièle Austruy) ☎ 59.65.32.42
Directions: RN 117.
Languages spoken: English, Spanish.
Hotel: 15 rooms.
Other points: bar, restaurant.

PAU
Pyrénées-Atlantiques, 64000

HOTEL DU BOIS LOUIS
(M. Jean-Marie Bareille) 18 avenue Gaston-
Lacoste ☎ 59.27.34.98
Directions: RN 117 and 134, Gare SNCF (station) –
Circuit automobile.
Menu: 55 to 120 Frs.
Accommodation: 85 to 120 Frs.
Restaurant: breakfast from 6.30. Closed Sat and
Sun, and 1st 2 weeks in Aug.
Specialities: confits, soupe de poissons, anguilles
(eels), couscous, regional menu, home-cooking.
Hotel: 7 rooms. Facilities: shower.
Other points: credit cards accepted, bar,
children's menu, à la carte menu, traditional decor,
pets allowed, car/lorry parking.
◄€ chateau; museum.

PAUILLAC • Gironde, 33250

LE YACHTING
(Mme Louisette Puyfourcat-Le-Fur) 12 port de
Plaisance, quai Léon-Ferrier ☎ 56.59.06.43
Directions: RD 2.
Menu: 44 to 133 Frs.
Accommodation: 120 to 280 Frs.
Restaurant: lunch from 12.00 until 14.00. Dinner
from 20.00 until 21.30. Closed Sat (in winter).
Specialities: entrecôte bordelaise, home-cooking.
Hotel: ☆ 16 rooms. Facilities: shower, private
bathroom.
Other points: bar, children's menu, à la carte
menu, traditional decor, terrace, pets allowed,
car/lorry parking.
◄€ numerous chateaux.

PERPIGNAN
Pyrénées-Orientales, 66000

LA CHAUMIERE
(M. Philippe Chevallier) avenue de Bruxelles,
Zone Industrielle (Z.I.) Saint-Charles
☎ 68.56.57.69
Languages spoken: English, Italian and Spanish.
Menu: 60 Frs.
Restaurant: breakfast from 6.30. Closed Sat
evening, Sun, and 15th July to 15th Aug.
Specialities: paella, grillades à la Plancha,
parillades, home-cooking.
Other points: credit cards accepted, bar, modern
decor, terrace, pets allowed, car/lorry parking.

PEYREHORADE • Landes, 40300

FINS GOURMETS
(M. Bernard Dupouy) rue du Fronton
☎ 58.73.00.68
Menu: 50 to 85 Frs.
Accommodation: 150 to 200 Frs.
Restaurant: breakfast from 8.00. Lunch 12.00 to
14.30. Dinner 18.00 to 22.00. Closed Sun.
Specialities: home-cooking.
Hotel: 6 rooms.
Other points: bar, children's menu, traditional
decor, terrace, pets allowed, car/lorry parking.

PEYRIAC-DE-MER • Aude, 11440

PORTE DE CORBIERES
(Mme Béatrice Vincent) Route Nationale 9
☎ 68.48.30.88
Directions: RN 9, opposite African reserve at Sigean.
Restaurant: lunch from 11.00 until 15.00. Dinner
from 18.00 until 23.30. Closed Sat evening, Sun.
Specialities: confit de canard, fruits de mer, home-
cooking.
Other points: bar, à la carte menu.

PIERREFITTE-NESTALAS
Hautes-Pyrénées, 65260

HOTEL BEL AIR
(Mme Eugénie Bellocq) 5 rue Lavoisier
☎ 62.92.75.22
Directions: RN 21, the Lourdes/Argelès road.
Languages spoken: Spanish.
Menu: 45 to 55 Frs.
Accommodation: 80 to 150 Frs.
Restaurant: breakfast from 7.00. Lunch from
12.00 until 14.30. Dinner from 19.30 until 21.30.
Closed 2 weeks in Oct and 1 week in Nov.
Specialities: home-cooking.
Hotel: 11 rooms. Facilities: shower.
Other points: bar, children's menu, lounge area,
modern decor, terrace, pets allowed, car parking.
◄€ grottes (caves) de Lourdes (20km); Cauteretz
(12km); Luz (12km); Danton-des-Aigles (3km).

PLAISANCE-DU-GERS • Gers, 32160

LA PERGOLA
(Mme Christiane Lagisquet) 11 allée des
Ormeaux ☎ 62.69.30.22
Directions: RN 646.
Menu: 55 to 150 Frs.
Accommodation: 80 to 230 Frs.
Restaurant: breakfast from 7.00. Lunch from
12.00 until 14.00. Dinner from 19.30 until 21.00.
Closed Sun, and 2 weeks from 24th Dec.
Specialities: foie gras, confit, magret, regional
menu, home-cooking.
Hotel: 10 rooms. Facilities: shower, television.
Other points: credit cards accepted, bar,
children's menu, à la carte menu, terrace, pets
allowed, car/lorry parking.
◄€ the Pyrenees and the ocean.

PORTIRAGNES · Hérault, 34420

🛏 LA VITARELLE
(M. Christophe Comandini) Route Nationale
112, La Vitarelle ☎ 67.90.88.90
Directions: RN 112, between Béziers and Sète.
Languages spoken: German, English, Spanish,
Italian.
Menu: 55 Frs (wine included) to 198 Frs.
Accommodation: 100 to 250 Frs.
Restaurant: breakfast from 6.45. Lunch from
11.45 until 15.00. Dinner from 18.45 until 22.00.
Closed Sun evening (out of season).
Specialities: paella, couscous, regional menu,
home-cooking.
Hotel: 28 rooms. Facilities: shower, private
bathroom, television, telephone.
Other points: credit cards accepted, bar,
children's menu, à la carte menu, lounge area,
terrace, pets allowed, car/lorry parking.
◀€ *Greco-Roman churches at Agde and Béziers;
les 9 écluses (locks) (unique in Europe); Cap d'Agde;
Sète; étang (pool) de Thau.*

POUSSAN · Hérault, 34560

☷ LE 7-SUR-SETE
(M. Paul Defaut) Route Nationale 113
☎ 67.78.33.29
Directions: between Sète and Béziers.
Languages spoken: English, Spanish.
Menu: 62 to 80 Frs.
Restaurant: breakfast from 6.00. Lunch from
12.00 until 15.00. Dinner from 19.00 until 23.00.
Specialities: regional menu, home-cooking.
Other points: credit cards accepted, bar,
children's menu, à la carte menu, modern decor,
pets allowed, car/lorry parking.
◀€ *Bouziques: oyster beds; Montpellier; the
Camargue.*

☷ LE LANDRY
(M. Siauvaud) Route Nationale 113
☎ 67.78.24.74
Directions: RN 113, A9 autoroute, Sète exit on
the right, Béziers, RN 113, Le Landry (2km).
Languages spoken: English, Spanish, Italian,
German.
Menu: 55 Frs.
Restaurant: dinner until 22.00. Closed Sat evening
and Sun evening.
Specialities: moules, seiches rouille (cuttlefish),
huîtres, home-cooking.
Other points: bar, à la carte menu, terrace, pets
allowed, car/lorry parking.
◀€ *the coast.*

PUJAUT · Gard, 30131

☷ LES GRAVIERES
(Mme Patricia Quiquemelle) Les Gravières,
Route de Bagnols-sur-Cèze ☎ 90.25.19.70
Directions: RN 580, Bagnols-sur-Cèze.
Restaurant: breakfast from 6.30. Lunch from

12.30 until 14.30. Dinner from 19.30 until 22.30.
Specialities: home-cooking.
Other points: credit cards accepted, bar, modern
decor, terrace, pets allowed, car/lorry parking.
◀€ *Pont du Gard; Avignon: Palais des Papes; Théâtre
Antique at Orange; Tavel vineyards; La Chartreuse.*

QUILLAN · Aude, 11500

☷ L'ESPAQUI
(M. Guy Gabens) 69 avenue de Carcassonne
☎ 68.20.03.51
Directions: RD 118, the Carcassonne/Perpignan
road.
Languages spoken: Spanish.
Menu: 60 to 110 Frs.
Restaurant: breakfast from 7.30. Lunch from
11.30 until 14.30. Dinner from 19.00 until 21.00.
Closed Mon evening, Sun evening, and the 1st
week of Jan.
Specialities: cassoulet, couscous (winter), paella,
regional menu, home-cooking.
Other points: bar, children's menu, à la carte
menu, traditional decor, terrace, pets allowed,
car/lorry parking.
◀€ *Catharist chateaux; dinosaur museum; musée du
chapeau (hats); gorges of Galamus and the Aguzau.*

REALMONT · Tarn, 81120

☷ LES ROUTIERS
(M. Richard Duarte) 27 boulevard Armengaud
☎ 63.55.65.44
Directions: RN 112, between Albi and Béziers.
Languages spoken: Spanish.
Menu: 55 to 85 Frs.
Restaurant: breakfast from 8.00. Lunch from
12.00 until 14.00. Dinner from 19.00 until 21.00.
Specialities: foie gras, magrets, regional menu.
Other points: credit cards accepted, bar, à la carte
menu, traditional decor, pets allowed, car/lorry
parking.
◀€ *Albi; Castres; barrage (dam) de la Bancalie.*

REBENACQ
Pyrénées-Atlantiques, 64260

☷ CHEZ PALU
(M. Alain Palu) place de la Mairie
☎ 59.05.54.11
Directions: RD 936, the Lourdes road.
Menu: 60 to 90 Frs.
Restaurant: breakfast from 7.00. Lunch from
10.00 until 15.00. Dinner from 19.00 until 15.00.
Closed Mon evening, Sun evening.
Specialities: garbure (thick soup), confits,
pipérade, fromage du pays, regional menu,
home-cooking.
Other points: credit cards accepted, bar,
children's menu, à la carte menu, lounge area,
traditional decor, terrace, pets allowed, car/lorry
parking.
◀€ *Ossau valley; ancient church; Spanish frontier.*

REMOULINS • Gard, 30210

🍴 AUBERGE LES PLATANES
(M. Gérard Reynaud) Castillon du Gard, Les
Croisées ☎ 66.37.10.69 [Fax] 66.37.34.03
Directions: RN 86.
Languages spoken: English, Spanish.
Menu: 55 to 110 Frs 🍲
Accommodation: 130 to 350 Frs.
Restaurant: dinner until 22.00.
Specialities: lamelles (slices) de Saint-Jacques
(scallops) en aigre-doux, rouille d'encornets (seafood)
camargueuse, potée du pêcheur aux fruits de mer (to
order), taureau sauvage, aiguillettes de canard au
beurre d'estragon, regional menu.
Hotel: ✿ ✿ 35 rooms. Facilities: shower, private
bathroom, television, telephone.
Other points: credit cards accepted, bar,
children's menu, à la carte menu, lounge area,
terrace, pets allowed, car/lorry parking.

🍴 LE CALAO
(Mme Béatrice Boutin) Route de Beaucaire
☎ 66.37.25.33
Directions: RD 986, exit at Remoulins towards
Beaucaire.
Menu: 55 Frs.
Accommodation: 150 to 200 Frs.
Restaurant: breakfast from 6.00. Dinner from
19.30 until 21.30. Closed Sun.
Specialities: pied paquet, soupe de poissons,
regional menu.
Hotel: 5 rooms. Facilities: shower, private bathroom.
Other points: credit cards accepted, bar, children's
menu, à la carte menu, lounge area, traditional
decor, terrace, pets allowed, car/lorry parking.
◁€ *Pont du Gard; Beaucaire-le-Château; Les
Saintes-Marie; the Camargue.*

LA REOLE • Gironde, 33190

🍴 LE FLAUTAT
(M. Jean-Paul Daldoss) Route Nationale 113,
Le Flautat ☎ 56.71.00.37
Directions: RN 113.
Languages spoken: English.
Menu: 50 Frs (wine included).
Restaurant: breakfast from 6.00. Lunch from
11.00 until 15.00. Dinner from 19.00 until 22.00.
Closed Sat, Sun and public holidays.
Specialities: home-cooking.
Other points: credit cards accepted, bar, children's
menu, modern decor, pets allowed, car/lorry parking.
◁€ *La Réole.*

RIBERAC • Dordogne, 24600

🍴 BAR RESTAURANT LAKANAL
(M. Jean-Marie Lagarde) 1 avenue Lakanal
☎ 53.90.04.77
Directions: the Angoulême/Agen road.
Languages spoken: English.
Menu: 50 to 80 Frs.
Restaurant: breakfast from 9.00. Lunch 12.00 to
15.00. Dinner 17.00 to 22.00. Closed Thurs.

Specialities: Périgord dishes, home-cooking.
Other points: bar, children's menu, à la carte
menu, traditional decor, terrace, pets allowed,
car/lorry parking.
◁€ *Brantôme; grotte (cave) at Villars; Dordogne
valley.*

RIEUPEYROUX • Aveyron, 12240

🍴 CHEZ PASCAL
(M. Claude Bou) rue de l'Hom
☎ 65.65.51.13
Directions: RD 605, between Rodez (38km) and
Villefranche-de-Rouergue (23km).
Menu: 60 to 130 Frs.
Accommodation: 95 to 210 Frs.
Restaurant: breakfast from 7.00. Lunch 12.00 to
14.00. Dinner 19.00 to 21.00. Closed Sun evening
(out of season), and 25th Sept to 20th Oct.
Specialities: tripoux, confits, magrets, regional menu.
Hotel: ✿ 14 rooms. Facilities: shower, private
bathroom, television, telephone.
Other points: credit cards accepted, bar, children's
menu, à la carte menu, lounge area, modern decor,
terrace, pets allowed, car/lorry parking.
◁€ *chateau de Belcastel (15km); château du Bosc;
grottes (caves) at Foissac (30km); viaduct at Le Viaur
(30km); Rodez: cathedral (38km); Albi; gorges of
the Tarn.*

RIEUTORT-DE-RANDON
Lozère, 48700

🍴 RELAIS DE LA POSTE
(Mme Annie Magne) place de la Poste
☎ 66.47.34.67
Directions: RN 106, between Saint-Chély-
d'Apcher and Mende.
Menu: 55 to 70 Frs.
Restaurant: breakfast from 6.30. Lunch from
11.00 until 14.00. Closed Sat and Sun.
Specialities: home-cooking.
Other points: bar.

RISCLE • Gers, 32400

🍴 RELAIS DE L'AUBERGE
(Mme Elisabeth Portes) place de la Mairie
☎ 62.69.70.49
Directions: RD 135.
Accommodation: 65 to 80 Frs.
Restaurant: closed Sun, and in Oct.
Hotel: ✿ 10 rooms.
Other points: bar, pets allowed, car/lorry parking.
◁€ *cave de Saint-Mont; tour of Thermes
d'Armagnac; foie gras cannery.*

LA RIVIERE • Gironde, 33126

🍴 LA RIVIERE
(Mme Laurence Cazenave) Route
Départementale 670 ☎ 57.24.94.26
Directions: RD 670, between Libourne and Saint-
André-de-Cubzac.

Languages spoken: English.
Menu: 55 Frs (wine included) to 75 Frs.
Restaurant: breakfast from 6.30. Lunch from 11.30 until 15.00. Dinner from 19.00 until 23.00.
Specialities: home-cooking.
Other points: credit cards accepted, bar, children's menu, traditional decor, terrace, pets allowed, car/lorry parking.
◀ Fronsac; the Bordeaux vineyards.

ROCAMADOUR · Lot, 46500

🏨 HOTEL DES VOYAGEURS
(Mme Simone Lasfargues) place de la Gare
☎ 65.33.63.19
Directions: between Brive-la-Gaillarde and Rodez.
Menu: 55 to 135 Frs.
Accommodation: 105 to 200 Frs.
Restaurant: breakfast from 7.00. Lunch from 12.00 until 14.00. Dinner from 19.00 until 21.00. Closed Sat (from Oct to March), and 2 weeks in Oct.
Specialities: omelette aux noix, home-cooking.
Hotel: 9 rooms. Facilities: shower, private bathroom, telephone.
Other points: credit cards accepted, bar, lounge area, traditional decor, terrace, pets allowed, car/lorry parking.
◀ Rocamadour; Padirac; cave.

LA ROCHE-CHALAIS
Dordogne, 24490

🍴 RELAIS DU MIDI
(M. Michel Visier) 32 avenue du Stade
☎ 53.91.43.65
Menu: 55 Frs (wine included) to 75 Frs.
Restaurant: breakfast from 7.00.
Specialities: home-cooking.
Other points: bar, children's menu, traditional decor, pets allowed, car/lorry parking.
◀ Aubeterre; Saint-Aulaye; Riberac.

ROQUEFORT-DES-CORBIERES
Aude, 11540

🍴 RELAIS DES COTES DE ROQUEFORT
(M. René Carbonnel) Route Nationale 9
☎ 68.48.45.51 Fax 68.48.32.88
Directions: RN 9.
Languages spoken: German and Spanish.
Menu: 55 to 85 Frs.
Restaurant: breakfast from 7.00. Lunch from 11.30 until 15.00. Dinner from 19.00 until 22.00. Closed Sun (out of season).
Other points: bar, car/lorry parking.

ROUFFIGNAC-DE-SIGOULES
Dordogne, 24240

🍴 LA TAVERNE ALSACIENNE
(Mme Francine Thomann) La Tabarline
☎ 53.58.84.13
Directions: between Marmande and Bergerac.

Languages spoken: German.
Menu: 50 to 120 Frs 🍽
Restaurant: lunch 11.30 to 15.00. Dinner 19.00 to 23.00.
Specialities: Périgord dishes: cuisse de canard confit, pommes sarladaises aux cèpes, regional menu, home-cooking.
Other points: credit cards accepted, bar, children's menu, à la carte menu, lounge area, traditional decor, terrace, pets allowed, car/lorry parking.
◀ Bergerac (8km); Mont-Basillac (6km); vineyards; château de la Bridoire at Rouffignac.

ROUFFILLAC-DE-CARLUX
Dordogne, 24370

🏨 AUX POISSONS FRAIS
(M. Jean-Noël Cayre) ☎ 53.29.70.24
Fax 53.31.16.36
Directions: RD 703, between Sarlat and Souillac.
Languages spoken: English.
Menu: 70 to 220 Frs.
Accommodation: 240 to 365 Frs.
Restaurant: breakfast from 8.00. Lunch 12.30 to 14.00. Dinner 19.30 to 21.00. Closed in Oct.
Specialities: confit de canard, cou d'oie farci (stuffed goose-neck), tête de veau ravigotte, large choice of desserts on Sun and public holidays, regional menu, home-cooking.
Hotel: ☆ ☆ 18 rooms. Facilities: shower, private bathroom, television, telephone.
Other points: credit cards accepted, bar, à la carte menu, lounge area, traditional decor, terrace, pets allowed, car/lorry parking.
◀ grottes (caves) de Lascaux; Rocamadour; Padirac; Cognac; Les Eyzies; Sarlat; manoir d'Eyrignac.

SAINT-ANTOINE-DE-BREUILH
Dordogne, 24230

🍴 CAFE DE FRANCE
(M. Marc Manjon) Route Départementale 936
☎ 53.24.78.97
Directions: RD 936, between Bergerac and Libourne.
Languages spoken: English, Spanish.
Menu: 55 Frs (wine included) to 65 Frs.
Restaurant: breakfast from 7.00. Lunch 12.00 to 14.30. Dinner 19.00 to 21.00. Closed Sun.
Specialities: home-cooking.
Other points: bar, children's menu, traditional decor, pets allowed, car/lorry parking.
◀ Bergerac vineyards; Saint-Emilion.

SAINT-AUBIN-DE-BLAYE
Gironde, 33820

🍴 LE RELAIS DE ROUBISQUE
(M. Olivier Devesa) Route Nationale 137
☎ 57.64.72.62
Directions: RN 137, the Bordeaux/Saintes/Royan road.
Languages spoken: English, Spanish.
Menu: 59 Frs (wine and coffee included).

Restaurant: breakfast from 7.00. Lunch 11.30 to 14.30. Dinner 19.00 to 22.00. Closed Sun.
Specialities: plateau de fruits de mer, regional menu, home-cooking.
Other points: bar, children's menu, traditional decor, terrace, pets allowed, car/lorry parking.
◁€ *centrale (power station) de Blaye.*

SAINT-CERE • Lot, 46400

🚗 HOTEL RESTAURANT DU QUERCY
(Mme Colette Gibbe) 21 avenue Anatole-de-Monzie ☎ 65.38.04.83
Directions: between Gramat and Rocamadour.
Menu: 52 to 180 Frs.
Accommodation: 130 to 200 Frs.
Restaurant: breakfast from 7.00. Lunch from 12.00 until 14.00. Dinner from 19.00 until 21.00. Closed Fri afternoon (out of season).
Specialities: salade de gésiers, confit de canard forestier, foie gras, regional menu, home-cooking.
Hotel: 10 rooms. Facilities: shower.
Other points: credit cards accepted, bar, children's menu, à la carte menu, modern decor, terrace, pets allowed, car parking.
◁€ *châteaux de Lurçat, Castelnau and Montal; grottes (caves) de Padirac (gouffre); Saint-Céré: old town.*

SAINT-CHELY-D'APCHER
Lozère, 48200

🚗 LE BARCELONE
(Mme Monique Vitré) 33 avenue de la Gare ☎ 66.31.01.22
Directions: RN 9, Montpellier or Clermont-Ferrand.
Menu: 55 Frs.
Accommodation: 100 to 130 Frs.
Restaurant: breakfast from 9.00. Lunch from 12.00 until 13.30. Dinner from 19.30 until 21.00. Closed Sun evening (out of season).
Specialities: home-cooking.
Hotel: 5 rooms. Facilities: shower, private bathroom.
Other points: credit cards accepted, bar, pets allowed, car/lorry parking.
◁€ *Garabit viaduct; gorges of the Tarn; parc des loups du Gévaudan; les bisons de La Margeride; Lozère region.*

SAINT-FELIX-LAURAGAIS
Haute-Garonne, 31540

🚗 LE GRILLON
(Mme Aliette Bonnes) Route de Castelnaudary, Revel ☎ 61.27.65.27
Directions: RN 622, between Toulouse and Castelnaudary.
Menu: 70 Frs.
Accommodation: 150 to 200 Frs.
Restaurant: breakfast from 7.00. Lunch from 12.00 until 14.00. Closed Sun, public holidays and last 2 weeks in Aug.
Specialities: cassoulet au confit de canard, couscous, regional menu, home-cooking.

Hotel: 5 rooms. Facilities: shower.
Other points: credit cards accepted, bar, modern decor, pets allowed, car/lorry parking.
◁€ *montagne noire; lac de Saint-Féréol; village de cuivres (copper); Carcassonne.*

SAINT-GEORGES-DE-MONTCLARD • Dordogne, 24140

🍽 LE BON COIN
(Mme Catherine Malnatti) Le Bourg
☎ 53.82.98.47
Directions: RD 21, between Périgueux and Bergerac.
Menu: 54 to 110 Frs.
Accommodation: 100 to 140 Frs.
Restaurant: breakfast from 6.30. Lunch from 12.00 until 14.00. Dinner from 19.00 until 21.00. Closed Sat and Sun evening.
Specialities: regional menu, home-cooking.
Hotel: 4 rooms. Facilities: shower, private bathroom.
Other points: bar, à la carte menu, traditional decor, pets allowed, car/lorry parking.
◁€ *grottes (caves) de Lascaux (30km); grottes de Grand-Roc (30km); Les Eyzies (30km).*

SAINT-GERMAIN-D'ESTEUIL
Gironde, 33340

🍽 LE RELAIS
(M. André Destruel) Route Nationale 215
☎ 56.73.06.28
Directions: RN 215, the Bordeaux/Le Verdon road.
Menu: 55 to 82 Frs.
Restaurant: breakfast from 7.00. Lunch 12.00 to 15.00. Dinner 19.00 to 21.00. Closed Sun.
Specialities: magrets, confits, gambas, home-cooking.
Other points: bar, children's menu, à la carte menu, traditional decor, terrace, pets allowed, car/lorry parking.
◁€ *Pauillac; Le Verdon; Hourtin: lakes; vineyards; extensive beaches.*

SAINT-GERMAIN-DU-BEL-AIR
Lot, 46310

🍽 CAFE DE FRANCE
(Mme Mélina Francoual) Le Bourg
☎ 65.31.06.99
Directions: RD 23.
Restaurant: closed Sun.
Other points: bar.

SAINT-GILLES • Gard, 30800

🍽 LE MIRADOR
(M. Alain Martin) Route de Montpellier, Route Nationale 572 ☎ 66.87.31.20
Directions: RN 572.
Languages spoken: English, Italian.
Restaurant: breakfast from 6.30. Lunch from 11.30 until 14.30. Dinner from 19.00 until 20.30.
Specialities: regional menu, home-cooking.

Other points: credit cards accepted, bar, children's menu, à la carte menu, modern decor, terrace, pets allowed, car/lorry parking.
◄€ *the Camargue; Nîmes; Arles.*

SAINT-JULIEN-LES-ROSIERS
Gard, 30340

🍴 **LE MISTRAL**
(M. José Garcia) Route de Saint-Ambroix
☎ 66.86.15.29
Directions: RD 904.
Languages spoken: Spanish.
Accommodation: 100 to 150 Frs.
Restaurant: dinner until 22.00.
Specialities: tripoux, paella, rouille du pêcheur, regional menu, home-cooking.
Hotel: 15 rooms. Facilities: shower.
Other points: bar, children's menu, à la carte menu, terrace, pets allowed, car/lorry parking.
◄€ *grottes Cocalières (20km); grottes Trabuc (20km); Pont du Gard (40km).*

SAINT-LON-LES-MINES
Landes, 40300

🍴 **HOTEL DU FRONTON**
(M. Daniel Laffitte) Au Bourg ☎ 58.57.80.45
Directions: RN 117, between Dax and Peyrehorade.
Languages spoken: Spanish.
Accommodation: 130 to 200 Frs.
Restaurant: breakfast from 7.00. Lunch from 12.00 until 14.00. Dinner from 19.00 until 21.00. Closed Fri evening, Sat lunch, and in Feb.
Specialities: foie gras, confits, magrets, regional menu, home-cooking.
Hotel: ☆ 10 rooms. Facilities: telephone.
Other points: credit cards accepted, bar, children's menu, à la carte menu, lounge area, traditional decor, terrace, pets allowed, car/lorry parking.
◄€ *château de Peyrehorade; hot springs at Dax.*

SAINT-MARTIAL-D'ARTENSET
Dordogne, 24700

🍴 **LA HALTE 24**
(Mme Caroline Trouillet) Route Nationale 89
☎ 53.81.85.34
Directions: RN 89, the Périgueux/Bordeaux road.
Languages spoken: English, Italian.
Menu: 50 Frs (wine included).
Restaurant: breakfast from 5.00.
Specialities: home-cooking.
Other points: credit cards accepted, traditional decor, terrace, pets allowed, car/lorry parking.
◄€ *Mussidan (11km); vallée de l'Isle; Bergerac: vineyards.*

SAINT-NAUPHARY
Tarn-et-Garonne, 82370

🍴 **LES ROUTIERS**
(M. Patrick Monruffet) ☎ 63.67.85.09
Directions: RD 999, between Albi and Castres.

Languages spoken: English.
Menu: 50 Frs (coffee included) to 62 Frs.
Accommodation: 80 to 130 Frs.
Restaurant: breakfast from 7.00. Lunch from 12.00 until 14.00. Closed Sat, Sun, and in Aug.
Specialities: confits, home-cooking.
Hotel: 11 rooms. Facilities: shower, private bathroom.
Other points: bar, children's menu, modern decor, terrace, car/lorry parking.
◄€ *Saint-Antonin-Noble-Val; gorges of the Tarn.*

SAINT-NAZAIRE • Gard, 30200

🍴 **LES TERAILLES**
(Mme Menu) Route Nationale 86
☎ 66.89.66.14
Directions: RN 86.
Restaurant: closed Sat afternoon, and in Sept.
Hotel: ☆ 12 rooms.
Other points: bar.

SAINT-PARDOUX-ISAAC
Lot-et-Garonne, 47800

🍴 **LE BOSQUET – Chez Milord**
(M. Jean-Pierre Saby) Route de Bergerac
☎ 53.93.49.59
Directions: RD 933, between Bayonne and Limoges.
Languages spoken: Spanish.
Menu: 55 Frs (wine included) to 115 Frs.
Accommodation: 100 to 130 Frs.
Restaurant: breakfast from 5.30. Lunch from 11.30 until 15.00. Dinner from 19.30 until 23.00.
Specialities: regional menu, home-cooking.
Hotel: 7 rooms.
Other points: credit cards accepted, bar, children's menu, à la carte menu, traditional decor, pets allowed, car/lorry parking.
◄€ *châteaux de Duras and de Lauzun; Eymet; musée de la préhistoire; Miramont-de-Guyenne.*

SAINT-PAUL-CAP-DE-JOUX
Tarn, 81220

🍴 **LES GLYCINES**
(M. Claude Peyrard) rue Philippe-Pinel
☎ 63.70.61.37
Directions: RN 112, between Montauban and Toulouse.
Menu: 60 Frs (wine included).
Restaurant: closed Tues.
Specialities: home-cooking.
Other points: bar, children's menu, traditional decor, terrace, pets allowed, car/lorry parking.

SAINT-PAUL-DE-LOUBRESSAC
Lot, 46170

🍴 **RELAIS DE LA MADELEINE**
(M. Bernard Devianne) Route Nationale 20
☎ 65.21.98.08
Directions: 100m from the RN 20 on RD 83 bis towards La Madeleine.

Languages spoken: English (Spanish in summer).
Menu: 55 to 120 Frs 🍽
Accommodation: 135 to 240 Frs.
Restaurant: breakfast from 7.30. Lunch from 12.00 until 13.45. Dinner from 19.30 until 21.00. Closed Sat all year, Sun (out of season), 1 week in early Nov and 2 weeks at Christmas.
Specialities: Quercy dishes: foie gras, confit, magret, regional menu, home-cooking.
Hotel: ☆ 15 rooms. Facilities: shower, private bathroom, television, telephone.
Other points: credit cards accepted, bar, children's menu, à la carte menu, terrace, pets allowed, car/lorry parking.

SAINT-PAUL-LES-DAX
Landes, 40190

🍴 **LE VIEUX TACHOIRE**
(M. Jean-Luc Belin) 1049 avenue du Maréchal-Foch ☎ 58.91.61.00
Directions: the Dax road.
Languages spoken: English, Spanish.
Menu: 55 to 85 Frs.
Restaurant: breakfast from 6.00. Dinner from 19.00 until 22.00. Closed Sun evening, and last week of Dec to 1st Jan.
Specialities: confit de canard, jambon de canard, poule au pot, regional menu, home-cooking.
Other points: credit cards accepted, bar, children's menu, à la carte menu, lounge area, modern decor, terrace, pets allowed, car/lorry parking.
◀ lake and sea.

SAINT-PERDON • Landes, 40090

🏠 **LE RELAIS DE LA LANDE**
(Mme Christiane Labarrière) ☎ 58.75.08.25
Directions: between Mont-de-Marsan and Dax.
Languages spoken: English, Spanish.
Menu: 60 to 120 Frs.
Accommodation: 140 to 250 Frs.
Restaurant: breakfast from 7.30. Lunch from 12.00 until 14.00. Dinner from 17.30 until 21.30. Closed Sat ou Sun (out of season).
Specialities: confits, magrets, gambas, foie gras, jambon de Bayonne, regional menu, home-cooking.
Hotel: ☆ 10 rooms. Facilities: shower, private bathroom, television, telephone.
Other points: credit cards accepted, bar, children's menu, à la carte menu, modern decor, terrace, pets allowed, car/lorry parking.
◀ Mont-de-Marsan: museum, amphitheatre, animal park.

SAINT-PEY-D'ARMENS
Gironde, 33330

🍴 **RELAIS DE GASCOGNE**
(M. Eric Samson) Route Départementale 936 ☎ 57.47.15.02
Directions: RD 936, the Bergerac road.
Languages spoken: English.

Menu: 53 to 110 Frs.
Restaurant: breakfast from 6.00. Lunch from 11.30 until 14.30. Dinner from 19.30 until 22.00. Closed Sun (out of season).
Specialities: grillades, entrecôte, côte bordelaise, magret, regional menu, home-cooking.
Other points: credit cards accepted, bar, children's menu, à la carte menu, lounge area, modern decor, terrace, pets allowed, car/lorry parking.
◀ Saint-Emilion; wine route; excavations.

SAINT-PRIVAT-DES-VIEUX
Gard, 30340

🏠 **L'ESCALE**
(Mme Ginette Calcat) 59 route de Bagnols ☎ 66.30.49.76
Directions: RD 216, between Alès and Bagnols-sur-Cèze.
Languages spoken: English.
Menu: 55 to 80 Frs.
Accommodation: 90 to 160 Frs.
Restaurant: breakfast from 5.00. Lunch from 12.00 until 14.00. Dinner from 20.00 until 23.00.
Specialities: home-cooking.
Hotel: 8 rooms. Facilities: shower.
Other points: credit cards accepted, bar, lounge area, terrace, pets allowed, car/lorry parking.
◀ Bambouseraie; mine témoin (mining exhibition) at Alès.

SAINT-ROME-DE-CERNON
Aveyron, 12490

🏠 **LE RELAIS DU CERNON**
(M. Marc Belloli) avenue de Millau ☎ 65.62.33.56
Directions: RD 999, the Millau/Saint-Affrique/Albi road.
Menu: 60 to 100 Frs.
Accommodation: 120 to 140 Frs.
Restaurant: breakfast from 7.00. Lunch from 11.30 until 15.00. Dinner from 19.00 until 22.00.
Specialities: truite au roquefort, écrevisses à l'américaine, truite aux amandes, entrecôte au roquefort, regional menu, home-cooking.
Hotel: 6 rooms.
Other points: credit cards accepted, bar, children's menu, à la carte menu, lounge area, traditional decor, terrace, pets allowed, car/lorry parking.
◀ gorges of the Tarn; caves (cellars) de Roquefort.

SAINT-VINCENT-DE-PAUL
Landes, 40990

🍴 **AUX PLATANES**
(M. Roger Vicente) ☎ 58.73.90.13
Directions: RN 124.
Languages spoken: Spanish.
Restaurant: closed Sun.
Other points: bar.

SAINTE-LIVRADE-SUR-LOT
Lot-et-Garonne, 47110

AU BON ACCUEIL
(M. Cougouille) route de Villeneuve
☎ 58.01.02.34
Directions: RN 111.
Restaurant: closed Sun evening, and 1 week at Christmas.
Hotel: ☆ 10 rooms.
Other points: bar.

SAINTE-MARIE-DE-GOSSE
Landes, 40390

LES ROUTIERS
(M. Marc Deloube) Route Nationale 117
☎ 59.56.32.02 [Fax] 59.56.36.06
Directions: RN 117, between Bayonne and Pau.
Languages spoken: English, Spanish.
Menu: 50 to 120 Frs
Accommodation: 120 to 180 Frs.
Restaurant: breakfast from 6.00. Lunch from 12.00 until 14.30. Dinner from 19.30 until 22.00. Closed Fri evening and Sat (out of season), and from mid-Oct to mid-Nov.
Specialities: confits, foie gras, poissons régionaux (in season), salade landaise, foie en terrine et foie frais, regional menu, home-cooking.
Hotel: ☆ 15 rooms. Facilities: shower, private bathroom, telephone.
Other points: credit cards accepted, bar, children's menu, à la carte menu, lounge area, traditional decor, terrace, pets allowed, car/lorry parking.
Landes and Basque coasts; caves; abbeys.

SAINTE-MARTHE
Lot-et-Garonne, 47430

LE RELAIS DU PONT DE L'AVANCE
(M. Hervé Pouchet) Route Nationale 933
☎ 53.20.63.39
Directions: RN 933, 200m from the toll (péage) exit at Marmande.
Menu: 50 to 70 Frs
Restaurant: breakfast from 6.00. Lunch from 11.00 until 15.00. Dinner from 18.00 until 22.00. Closed Sun.
Specialities: home-cooking.
Other points: credit cards accepted, bar, children's menu, pets allowed, car/lorry parking.

SAINTE-TERRE · Gironde, 33350

CHEZ REGIS
(M. Jacques Astarie) avenue du Général-de-Gaulle ☎ 57.47.16.21
Directions: the Libourne/Bergerac road.
Accommodation: 100 to 120 Frs.
Restaurant: dinner from 19.00 until 21.00. Closed Mon, in Oct and in Jan.
Specialities: lamproie (lamprey), anguilles (eels),

cèpes (flat mushrooms), regional menu.
Hotel: 6 rooms. Facilities: shower.
Other points: credit cards accepted, bar, children's menu, à la carte menu, traditional decor, terrace, pets allowed, car/lorry parking.
Saint-Emilion (5km).

SALSES
Pyrénées-Orientales, 66600

LE CASANOVA
(M. Alain Commes) Route Nationale 9, Planal de Salses ☎ 84.73.11.18
Directions: between Narbonne and Perpignan.
Languages spoken: Spanish.
Menu: 55 Frs.
Restaurant: lunch from 10.30 until 15.00. Dinner from 18.30 until 22.00. Closed Sun evening.
Specialities: tripes catalanes, boles de picoulat, regional menu, home-cooking.
Other points: credit cards accepted, children's menu, à la carte menu, terrace, car/lorry parking.
château de Salses; Perpignan; Le Perthus.

SARLAT · Dordogne, 24200

CAFETERIA DU PONTET
(M. Jean-Pierre Bouy) Route de Bergerac
☎ 53.31.05.36 [Fax] 53.04.72.32
Directions: RN 21, the Bergerac road.
Languages spoken: English, Spanish.
Menu: 35 to 50 Frs.
Restaurant: breakfast from 7.30. Lunch from 11.00 until 15.00. Dinner from 19.00 until 22.00. Closed New Year's Eve and New Year's Day.
Specialities: gibiers (game), sanglier (boar), magret sauce au poivre, regional menu, home-cooking.
Other points: credit cards accepted, bar, children's menu, lounge area, modern decor, terrace, pets allowed, car/lorry parking.
Sarlat; Rocamadour; gouffre de Padirac; Castelnaud; Les Eyzies; grottes de Lascaux.

LA SAUVETAT-SUR-LEDE
Lot-et-Garonne, 47150

LA RENAISSANCE
(M. Louis Le Gall) Le Bourg ☎ 53.41.94.50
Directions: RD 676, the Limoges/Paris road.
Languages spoken: English.
Menu: 58 Frs (with wine and coffee included) to 120 Frs.
Accommodation: 100 to 150 Frs.
Restaurant: breakfast from 8.00. Lunch from 12.00 until 15.00. Dinner from 19.00 until 22.00. Closed Mon.
Specialities: home-cooking.
Hotel: 7 rooms. Facilities: shower, private bathroom.
Other points: bar, children's menu, à la carte menu, lounge area, traditional decor, terrace, pets allowed, car/lorry parking.
ville neuve (new town); Montflanquin.

SAUVETERRE-DE-GUYENNE
Gironde, 33540

🛏 **HOTEL DE GUYENNE**
(M. Jean-Paul Daldoss) Route de Libourne, Pringis ☎ 56.71.54.92
Directions: on the Libourne road.
Languages spoken: English.
Menu: 65 to 120 Frs.
Accommodation: 100 to 160 Frs.
Restaurant: lunch from 11.00 until 15.00. Dinner from 19.00 until 23.00.
Specialities: escargots à la Bordelaise, magret, foie gras, lamproie (lamprey), regional menu, home-cooking.
Hotel: ☆ 15 rooms. Facilities: shower, private bathroom, telephone.
Other points: credit cards accepted, bar, à la carte menu, terrace, pets allowed, car/lorry parking.

SEILH • Haute-Garonne, 31840

🍴 **LES ROUTIERS**
(Mme Nelly Gouyou) Les Tricheries
☎ 61.59.90.17
Directions: Blagnac or Grenoble.
Menu: 55 to 120 Frs.
Restaurant: breakfast from 6.30. Dinner from 18.30 until 20.30.
Specialities: cassoulet, daube, pot au feu, home-cooking.
Other points: bar, children's menu, car/lorry parking.

SERRES-CASTET
Pyrénées-Atlantiques, 64121

🛏 **LES ROUTIERS**
(M. Léon Salis) ☎ 59.33.91.06
Directions: RN 134, the Bordeaux road.
Languages spoken: Spanish.
Menu: 50 Frs.
Accommodation: 60 Frs.
Restaurant: breakfast from 7.00. Closed Sat, Sun, and in Aug.
Specialities: Béarn dishes, regional menu, home-cooking.
Hotel: 5 rooms. Facilities: shower.
Other points: bar, children's menu, à la carte menu, lounge area, traditional decor, terrace, car/lorry parking.
◁ *Pau: museum, chateau; Lourdes.*

SETE • Hérault, 34200

🍴 **LA REGENCE – Les Isles**
(Mme Savita Barthe) 1 place de Lille
☎ 67.74.32.92
Directions: RN 108, on the Montpellier road, at the entrance to the port.
Menu: 65 Frs (wine included).
Restaurant: breakfast from 8.30. Meals from 9.00 until 16.00. and from 19.00 until 23.00. Closed

Sun (occasionally), and from 28th July to 15th Aug.
Specialities: moules farcies, paella, encornets farcis (seafood), poulet au curry, couscous, regional menu.
Other points: bar, children's menu, à la carte menu, traditional decor, terrace, pets allowed, car/lorry parking.
◁ *the sea; pool (étang); mountains; grave of George Brassens.*

🍴 **LE PAVILLON**
(Mme Marie France Petitfils) 23 route de Montpellier ☎ 67.48.62.53
Directions: RN 112, Sète centre, in the port area.
Languages spoken: German, English.
Menu: 55 Frs.
Restaurant: breakfast from 6.00. Lunch from 12.00 until 15.00. Dinner from 19.30 until 22.00. Closed Sat afternoon and Sun.
Specialities: soupe de poisson, moules et encornets farcis (seafood), regional menu, home-cooking.
Other points: credit cards accepted, bar, traditional decor, pets allowed, car/lorry parking.
◁ *Sète; Marseillan (étang de Thau); Bouzigues; Cap d'Agde; Hérault gorges.*

🍴 **RESTO ROUTIER – La Péniche**
(Mme Pâquerette Dupuy) 1 quai des Moulins
☎ 67.48.64.13
Directions: RN 108; as you reach Sète, coming from Montpellier.
Languages spoken: English, Spanish.
Menu: 57 to 95 Frs.
Restaurant: breakfast from 9.30. Lunch from 12.00 until 14.00. Dinner from 19.00 until 22.30. Closed Sat lunch.
Specialities: rouille sétoise, bourride sétoise, coquelet aux écrevisses, moules, regional menu, home-cooking.
Other points: credit cards accepted, children's menu, modern decor, pets allowed, car/lorry parking.
◁ *Mont Saint-Clair; espace Georges-Brassens.*

SEYCHES • Lot-et-Garonne, 47350

🛏 **AU BON ACCUEIL**
(Mme Marie Laliette) ☎ 53.83.60.10
Directions: CD 933, between Marmande and Périgueux.
Menu: 48 Frs (wine included).
Accommodation: 90 to 120 Frs.
Restaurant: breakfast from 8.00. Lunch 12.00 to 14.00. Dinner 19.30 to 22.00. Closed Sat.
Specialities: home-cooking.
Hotel: 5 rooms.
Other points: bar, traditional decor, pets allowed, car/lorry parking.
◁ *Marmande (15km); Miramont-de-Guyenne (7km).*

SOTURAC • Lot, 46700

🍴 **LA TABLE AUX AMIS**
(Mme Bernadette Bessou) Route Départementale 911 ☎ 53.40.97.78
Directions: RD 911, between Cahors and Fumel.

Menu: 55 Frs (wine included) to 90 Frs.
Restaurant: breakfast from 7.00. Lunch from 11.30 until 15.00. Dinner from 19.00 until 22.00. Closed Mon evening, and 2 weeks in Feb.
Specialities: poule au pot, raviolis frais, mique, home-cooking.
Other points: bar, children's menu, traditional decor, terrace, pets allowed, car/lorry parking.
◀€ *Fumel; Duravel.*

SOUAL • Tarn, 81580

🛏 LA MAIZOU
(M. Jean-Marie Lemaire) 12 Grand'Rue
☎ 63.75.52.24
Directions: RN 126.
Menu: 58 to 160 Frs.
Accommodation: 90 to 140 Frs.
Restaurant: breakfast from 7.00. Lunch 12.00 to 14.00. Dinner 19.30 to 21.30. Closed Tues and Sun evening.
Specialities: confit, cassoulet, magrets de canard, regional menu, home-cooking.
Hotel: 6 rooms. Facilities: shower, private bathroom.
Other points: credit cards accepted, bar, children's menu, à la carte menu, lounge area, traditional decor, terrace, pets allowed, car/lorry parking.
◀€ *Durfort (village of copper); Revel.*

SOUILLAC • Lot, 46200

🍽 RELAIS DE L'ESCALE
(M. Alain Fage) 39 avenue Louis-Jean-Malvy
☎ 65.37.82.65
Directions: RN 20.
Restaurant: closed Sun.
Other points: bar.

SOUMOULOU
Pyrénées-Atlantiques, 64420

🛏 HOTEL-RESTAURANT BEARNAIS
(Mme Anne-Marie Delroise) 5 rue des Platanes ☎ 59.04.60.45
Directions: between Tarbes and Lourdes.
Menu: 47 to 65 Frs.
Accommodation: 80 to 100 Frs.
Restaurant: breakfast from 6.00. Lunch 11.00 to 16.00. Dinner 18.00 to 22.00. Closed Sat, and 3 weeks in Aug.
Specialities: confit de canard, poissons, regional menu, home-cooking.
Hotel: 6 rooms.
Other points: bar, children's menu, modern decor, terrace, pets allowed, car/lorry parking.
◀€ *grottes (caves) de Betharan; Lourdes; Pau: chateau; the Pyrenees.*

TARBES • Hautes-Pyrénées, 65000

🍽 LE CLAUZIER
(M. Jean-Marc Noë) 10 place Germain-Claverie ☎ 62.93.18.57

Menu: 45 Frs (wine included).
Restaurant: breakfast from 7.00. Closed Sun.
Specialities: home-cooking.
Other points: credit cards accepted, bar, children's menu, traditional decor, pets allowed, car/lorry parking.
◀€ *Lourdes (30km).*

🍽 LE RELAIS DES PYRENEES
(M. Jean-Louis Perez and Jacques Duvin) Autoport des Pyrénées, Boulevard Kennedy
☎ 62.93.26.06 [Fax] 62.93.28.88
Directions: the Bayonne/Toulouse road, via boulevard périphérique.
Languages spoken: Spanish.
Menu: 50 to 90 Frs.
Restaurant: breakfast from 6.30. Lunch from 11.45 until 14.15. Dinner from 19.30 until 21.30. Closed Sat evening and Sun (except groups).
Specialities: tripes, cassoulet, confits, couscous, home-cooking.
Other points: credit cards accepted, bar, children's menu, à la carte menu, lounge area, modern decor, pets allowed, car/lorry parking.
◀€ *Lourdes; ski resorts; mountains; lakes.*

🛏 LE VICTOR HUGO
(Mme Patricia Jouanlong) 52 rue Victor-Hugo
☎ 62.93.36.71
Directions: RN 117, Gare SNCF.
Languages spoken: English, Spanish.
Menu: 30 to 95 Frs.
Accommodation: 70 to 120 Frs.
Restaurant: breakfast from 7.00. Lunch 11.00 to 15.00. Dinner 18.00 to 21.30. Closed Sun.
Specialities: confit de canard maison, magret de canard, gambas flambées, moules marinières, brochettes, regional menu, home-cooking.
Hotel: 8 rooms.
Other points: bar, children's menu, à la carte menu, lounge area, pets allowed, car parking.
◀€ *Lourdes; La Mongie and Cauterets (ski); grottes (caves) de Bétharam; le 'donjon des aigles'.*

TARNOS • Landes, 40220

🍽 LA MADRAGUE
(M. Jean-Pierre Aregay) Route de la Barre
☎ 59.64.93.04
Menu: 55 Frs (wine and coffee included) to 110 Frs.
Restaurant: breakfast from 6.00. Lunch from 12.00 until 14.00. Dinner from 19.00 until 23.00. Closed Sun evenings from May to Nov, and Sat and Sun from Nov to May.
Specialities: soupe de poisson, paella, regional menu, home-cooking.
Other points: credit cards accepted, à la carte menu, terrace, pets allowed, car/lorry parking.
◀€ *Biarritz; Hendaye; Spain (30km).*

LE TEMPLE-SUR-LOT
Lot-et-Garonne, 47110

🛏 LE VAL DU LOT
(M. Lionel Hutrel) Gouneau ☎ 53.84.90.26

Directions: RD 911, the Villeneuve-sur-Lot/
Bordeaux/Agen/Bergerac road.
Languages spoken: English.
Menu: 47 Frs to 120 Frs.
Accommodation: 100 to 120 Frs.
Restaurant: breakfast from 7.00. Lunch 12.00 to
14.30. Dinner 19.00 to 22.00. Closed Sat (out of
season), and from mid-Aug to mid-Sept.
Specialities: confits, magrets, regional menu,
home-cooking.
Hotel: 5 rooms. Facilities: shower.
Other points: credit cards accepted, bar,
children's menu, à la carte menu, lounge area,
traditional decor, terrace, pets allowed, car/lorry
parking.
◀€ *naval base; abbaye des automates (automata);
musée du pruneau (prunes/plums), caves
(wine-cellars) de Buzet.*

THENON • Dordogne, 24210

🚗 **CHEZ SERGE – LES TOURNISSOUS**
(M. Serge Leymarie) Les Tournissous
☎ 53.05.20.31
Directions: RN 89, between Brive-la-Gaillarde
and Périgueux.
Languages spoken: English, Portuguese.
Menu: 40 to 76 Frs.
Accommodation: 90 to 180 Frs.
Restaurant: breakfast from 4.00.
Specialities: foie gras, confit de canard, entrecôte,
home-cooking.
Hotel: 12 rooms. Facilities: shower, private
bathroom, television, telephone.
Other points: credit cards accepted, bar,
children's menu, à la carte menu, lounge area,
traditional decor, terrace, pets allowed, car/lorry
parking.
◀€ *grottes de Lascaux (15km); Sarlat (40km).*

TOCANE-SAINT-APRE
Dordogne, 24350

🍴 **LE CAPITOLE**
(M. Xavier Clauzel) ☎ 53.90.71.01
Directions: the Brantôme/Périgueux/Riberac road.
Languages spoken: Spanish.
Menu: 55 Frs (wine included) to 130 Frs.
Restaurant: breakfast from 7.00. Lunch from
12.00 until 15.00. Dinner from 19.00 until 22.30.
Specialities: home-cooking.
Other points: bar, children's menu, à la carte
menu, lounge area, traditional decor, terrace, pets
allowed, car/lorry parking.
◀€ *Brantôme; Bourdeille; the Dordogne.*

TOULOUSE • Haute-Garonne, 31300

🍴 **LE PROGRES**
(M. Félix Ober) 185 route de Bayonne
☎ 61.49.22.75
Directions: RN 124, Auch.
Menu: 60 to 220 Frs.

Restaurant: breakfast from 7.00. Lunch from
12.00 until 14.00. Dinner from 19.00 until 22.00.
Closed Sun, and in Aug.
Specialities: regional menu.
Other points: credit cards accepted, bar, à la carte
menu, traditional decor.
◀€ *Toulouse.*

TREBES • Aude, 11800

🏨 **LE RELAIS DES CAPUCINS**
(M. Gilbert Laffont) 34 route de Narbonne
☎ 68.78.70.07
Directions: RN 113, 2km from the Carcassonne
Est (East) exit, towards Narbonne.
Languages spoken: English, Spanish.
Menu: 60 Frs (wine included).
Accommodation: 90 to 130 Frs.
Restaurant: breakfast from 6.00. Lunch from
11.30 until 15.00. Dinner from 19.00 until 22.00.
Closed Sat, Sun, one week in July and 1 week from
Christmas Day.
Specialities: cassoulet au confit, couscous, regional
menu, home-cooking.
Hotel: 11 rooms.
Other points: credit cards accepted, bar,
children's menu, traditional decor, pets allowed,
car/lorry parking.
◀€ *Carcassonne; Catharist chateaux.*

TRIE-SUR-BAISE
Hautes-Pyrénées, 65220

🍴 **CAFE-RESTAURANT DE LA PAIX**
(M. Jacky Cenac) 37 rue des Monts-de-
Bigorre ☎ 62.35.61.11
Directions: RD 632.
Languages spoken: Spanish.
Menu: 55 Frs (wine included).
Restaurant: breakfast from 7.00. Lunch from
10.00 until 15.00. Dinner from 19.30 until 22.00.
Closed Wed afternoon (after 3pm).
Specialities: home-cooking.
Other points: credit cards accepted, bar,
children's menu, traditional decor, car/lorry
parking.
◀€ *Lourdes.*

VALENCE-SUR-BAISE • Gers, 32310

🍴 **RESTAURANT LADOUCH**
(Mme Ginette Ladouch) place de l'Hôtel-de-
Ville ☎ 62.28.50.45
Directions: RD 930, between Auch and Condom.

VALERGUES • Hérault, 34130

🍴 **RELAIS DE VALERGUES**
(M. Claude Bernabé) Route Nationale 113
☎ 67.86.75.27
Directions: RN 113.
Languages spoken: Spanish.

Restaurant: dinner until 23.00. Closed Sun, Dec.
Other points: bar, car/lorry parking.

VENSAC • Gironde, 33590

🍴 RESTAURANT CHEZ NICOLE
(Mme Nicole Figerou) 24 Grand'Rue
☎ 56.09.44.05
Menu: 60 to 160 Frs.
Accommodation: 120 Frs.
Restaurant: breakfast from 8.00. Lunch from
12.00 until 14.00. Dinner from 19.00 until 21.00.
Closed Mon (out of season).
Specialities: foie gras, confits maison, cèpes,
regional menu, home-cooking.
Hotel: 5 rooms. Facilities: shower.
Other points: credit cards accepted, bar,
children's menu, à la carte menu, modern decor,
terrace, pets allowed, car/lorry parking.
◁€ windmill; chateaux.

VIC-EN-BIGORRE
Hautes-Pyrénées, 65500

🍴 LE RANCH
(M. Bernard Griffon) Route de Rabastens-
de-Bigorre ☎ 62.96.72.32
Directions: the Auch road.
Menu: 55 to 120 Frs.
Restaurant: breakfast from 7.00. Lunch from
12.00 until 15.00. Dinner from 20.00 until 22.00.
Closed Sat, and in Oct.
Specialities: regional menu, home-cooking.
Other points: credit cards accepted, bar,
children's menu, à la carte menu, terrace, pets
allowed, car/lorry parking.
◁€ Lourdes; the Pyrenees.

VIC-LE-FESQ • Gard, 30260

🍴 RELAIS DE LA NOUVELLE
(M. Hubert Tani) ☎ 66.77.82.81
Directions: between Montpellier and Alès.
Menu: 60 Frs.
Restaurant: breakfast from 6.00. Lunch 11.00 to
14.00. Dinner 19.00 to 20.30. Closed Sat evening,
Sun and public holidays (out of season).
Specialities: regional menu, home-cooking.
Other points: credit cards accepted, bar, à la carte
menu, traditional decor, terrace, pets allowed,
car/lorry parking.
◁€ gateway to the Cévennes; caves (wine-cellars);
museums.

VILLEFRANCHE-DE-ROUERGUE
Aveyron, 12200

🍴 RELAIS DES CABRIERES
(M. Alain Toulouse) Route de Montauban
☎ 65.81.16.99
Directions: RD 926, the Montauban/Toulouse road.
Menu: 45 to 60 Frs.

Restaurant: breakfast from 8.00. Lunch from
11.00 until 15.00. Closed Sun.
Specialities: tripes, tripoux, home-cooking.
Other points: bar, traditional decor, pets allowed,
car/lorry parking.
◁€ grottes (caves) de Foisac; Villefranche: bastide
(country house); chateau (ruins) at Najac.

VILLENEUVE-D'AVEYRON
Aveyron, 12260

🍴 AUBERGE DE LA TOUR –
Chez Rosy et Francis
(Mme Rose-Mary Scudier-Laval) Faubourg
Saint-Roch ☎ 65.81.75.62
Directions: in the suburb of Saint-Roch.
Menu: 50 to 140 Frs.
Restaurant: breakfast from 7.00. Lunch from
11.30 until 14.00. Dinner from 19.00 until 20.30.
Closed Sat, and 2 weeks in Aug.
Specialities: home-cooking.
Other points: credit cards accepted, bar,
children's menu, à la carte menu, traditional decor,
pets allowed, car/lorry parking.

VILLENEUVE-DE-RIVIERE
Haute-Garonne, 31800

🍴 L'ESCALE
(M. Gérard Valentin) Route Nationale 117
☎ 61.89.39.05
Directions: RN 117, between Toulouse and Irun
(Spanish border).
Languages spoken: Spanish.
Menu: 50 to 70 Frs.
Accommodation: 100 to 150 Frs.
Restaurant: breakfast from 5.15. Lunch 11.00 to
14.30. Dinner 18.30 to 22.30. Closed Sun.
Specialities: confits de canard, foie gras mi-cuit,
regional menu, home-cooking.
Hotel: 9 rooms. Facilities: shower, television.
Other points: credit cards accepted, bar,
children's menu, à la carte menu, traditional decor,
terrace, pets allowed, car/lorry parking.
◁€ Luchon; Lourdes; the Pyrenees.

VILLENEUVE-SUR-LOT
Lot-et-Garonne, 47300

🍴 RELAIS DE GASCOGNE
(M. Alain Guiraud) 31 avenue du Général-
Leclerc ☎ 53.70.06.48
Directions: RN 21, Agen.
Languages spoken: Spanish.
Menu: 54 to 110 Frs.
Accommodation: 100 to 140 Frs.
Restaurant: lunch 11.45 to 14.00. Dinner 19.00
to 22.00. Closed Sun (except bookings).
Specialities: Gascon dishes, regional menu.
Hotel: 8 rooms. Facilities: shower.
Other points: credit cards accepted, bar,
children's menu, à la carte menu, traditional decor,
pets allowed, car/lorry parking.

VILLETELLE • Hérault, 34400

BOUQUET RESTAURATION
(Bouquet SA) A9, services at Ambrusson Nord
☎ 67.71.70.70 [Fax] 67.71.70.71
Directions: A9, between Nîmes and Montpellier.
Languages spoken: English, Spanish, Italian.

Menu: 64 Frs.
Restaurant: breakfast from 6.00.
Specialities: boeuf gardiane, seiche (cuttlefish)
provençale, regional menu.
Other points: credit cards accepted, children's
menu, lounge area, modern decor, terrace.
◁≡ *Ambrusson; Gallo-Roman bridge.*

SOUTH-EAST FRANCE

The following *départements* are included in this chapter:

Ain (01)
Alpes-de-Haute-Provence (04)
Alpes Maritimes (06)
Ardèche (07)
Bouches-du-Rhône (13)
Drôme (26)
Haute-Savoie (74)

Hautes Alpes (05)
Isère (38)
Loire (42)
Rhône (69)
Savoie (73)
Var (83)
Vaucluse (84)

L'ALBENC • Isère, 38470

AUBERGE DU VERCORS
(Mme Claudette Torri) place Jean-Vinay
☎ 76.64.75.17
Directions: RN 92, the Grenoble and Valence road.
Restaurant: breakfast from 6.30. Lunch from
12.00 until 14.00. Dinner from 19.00 until 21.00.
Closed Sun, and the 1st week of Aug.
Specialities: home-cooking.
Other points: bar, modern decor, pets allowed,
car/lorry parking.
◁≡ *Le Vercors; wine-cellars at Choranche; Voiron:
La Grande Chartreuse.*

ALBON • Drôme, 26140

RELAIS DE LA TOUR D'ALBON
(M. Camille Bertrand) Route Nationale 7
☎ 75.03.11.22
Directions: RN 7, either Chanas Sud (South) exit
or Valence Nord (North) exit.
Languages spoken: English.
Menu: 60 Frs.
Accommodation: 130 to 200 Frs.
Restaurant: breakfast from 5.30. Lunch from
11.00 until 15.00. Dinner from 19.00 until 22.30.
Closed Sun (except to order).
Specialities: home-cooking.
Hotel: 13 rooms. Facilities: shower.
Other points: credit cards accepted, bar,
children's menu, lounge area, modern decor, pets
allowed, car/lorry parking.
◁≡ *Auterive: palais idéal du Facteur Cheval (fantasy*

*shell palace); Peaugres: safari park; tour d'Albon;
cave (wine-cellar) de Saint-Donat.*

ALIXAN • Drôme, 26300

HOTEL ALPES PROVENCE
(M. Jean-Claude Bocaud) Aire de Bayanne
☎ 75.47.02.84 [Fax] 75.47.11.72
Directions: RN 532, Valence Nord (North) exit,
towards Grenoble.
Languages spoken: German, English.
Menu: 58 to 200 Frs.
Accommodation: 140 to 300 Frs.
Restaurant: breakfast served from 6.00. Lunch
12.00 to 14.00. Dinner 19.30 to 21.30.
Specialities: regional menu.
Hotel: ☆ ☆ 22 rooms. Facilities: shower, private
bathroom, television, telephone.
Other points: bar, children's menu, à la carte
menu, traditional decor, terrace, pets allowed,
car/lorry parking.
◁≡ *Romans: musée de la chaussure (shoes);
Auterive: palais du Facteur Cheval; excursions into
Le Vercors; Upie: jardin des oiseaux (bird garden).*

ALLEX • Drôme, 26400

LE DAUPHINOIS
(M. Marcel Pisano) Quartier de la Butte
☎ 75.62.61.69
Directions: RN 7 and RD 93, between Fiancey
and Crest.
Menu: 55 to 60 Frs.

Restaurant: breakfast from 6.30. Lunch from 12.00 until 13.30.
Specialities: home-cooking.
Other points: credit cards accepted, bar, traditional decor, terrace, pets allowed, car/lorry parking.
◁€ *site des Rainières; Le Vercors (60km); Auterive: palais idéal du Facteur Cheval (60km); aquarium and bird gardens.*

AMBERIEU-EN-BUGEY • Ain, 01500

⇌ LE RELAIS DU BUGEY-HUBERT – Chez Denise
(Mme Denise Hubert) 84 avenue Jules-Pellaudin ☎ 74.38.10.27
Directions: RN 504.
Restaurant: dinner until 24.00. Closed Sun, Aug.
Other points: bar.

AMPUIS • Rhône, 69420

🍴 AUX PORTES DE PROVENCE
(M. Maurice Terpend) Route Nationale 86, Les Allées ☎ 74.56.10.31 [Fax] 74.56.19.10
Directions: RN 86, Nîmes.
Accommodation: 80 to 150 Frs.
Restaurant: breakfast from 7.00. Lunch 12.00 to 14.30. Dinner 19.00 to 22.00. Closed Wed.
Specialities: home-cooking.
Hotel: 9 rooms. Facilities: shower.
Other points: credit cards accepted, bar, children's menu, lounge area, pets allowed, car/lorry parking.
◁€ *Peaugres: safari park.*

APT • Vaucluse, 84400

⇌ LE RELAIS DU LAC
(M. Yvon Jean) Route Nationale 100 ☎ 90.74.01.10
Directions: RN 100, the Apt/Avignon road.
Languages spoken: English.
Menu: 60 Frs.
Restaurant: breakfast from 7.00.
Specialities: home-cooking.
Other points: credit cards accepted, bar, terrace, pets allowed, car/lorry parking.

L'ARBRESLE • Rhône, 69210

⇌ RELAIS DES ROUTIERS
(Mme Marie-Antoinette Durix-Michaud) 91 rue Gabriel-Péri ☎ 74.01.05.81
Directions: RN 89, Clermont-Ferrand.
Menu: 55 Frs.
Restaurant: breakfast from 6.00. Closed Sat afternoon and Sun.
Specialities: home-cooking.
Other points: pets allowed.

LES ARCS-SUR-ARGENS • Var, 83460

🍴 HOTEL DE L'AVENIR
(Mme Marie-Jeanne Hortal) rue Jean-Jaurès ☎ 94.73.30.58

Menu: 55 to 73 Frs.
Accommodation: 80 to 130 Frs.
Restaurant: lunch from 12.00 until 14.30. Dinner from 19.00 until 21.30.
Hotel: 9 rooms.
Other points: bar, car/lorry parking.

L'ARGENTIERE-LA-BESSEE
Hautes Alpes, 05120

🍴 RESTAURANT DE LA MAIRIE
(M. Yves Sabater) 32 avenue Charles-de-Gaulle ☎ 92.23.10.36
Directions: RN 94, between Gap and Briançon.
Menu: 55 to 85 Frs.
Accommodation: 150 Frs.
Restaurant: breakfast from 6.00. Meals from 11.30 until 22.00. Closed Sun.
Specialities: home-cooking.
Hotel: 8 rooms. Facilities: shower.
Other points: bar, children's menu, à la carte menu, traditional decor, terrace, pets allowed.

ARLES
Bouches-du-Rhône, 13200

🍴 LE RELAIS DU PASSAGE A NIVEAU
(Antoine and Laurence Pech-Faure) Route de Tarascon, 31 avenue de la Libération ☎ 90.96.06.64
Directions: RN 113.
Languages spoken: German, English, Spanish, Italian.
Restaurant: closed Sun.
Hotel: 8 rooms.
Other points: bar.

ASTET • Ardèche, 07330

⇌ LE RELAIS DE LA SOURCE DE L'ARDECHE
(Mme Anne-Marie Soulet) Col de la Chavade ☎ 75.87.20.91
Menu: 52 Frs.
Restaurant: breakfast from 6.00.
Specialities: home-cooking.
Other points: bar.

AUBIGNAS • Ardèche, 07400

🍴 CAFE TABAC DE LA GARE
(Mlle Elisabeth Borne) Quartier de la Gare ☎ 75.52.43.89
Directions: RN 102, between Montélimar and Le Puy-en-Velay.
Languages spoken: English, Spanish.
Menu: 55 to 65 Frs.
Accommodation: 75 to 200 Frs.
Restaurant: breakfast from 6.30. Lunch from 11.30 until 14.30. Dinner from 19.00 until 21.00. Closed Sun (out of season).
Specialities: regional menu, home-cooking.
Hotel: 5 rooms. Facilities: shower, private bathroom.
Other points: credit cards accepted, bar, lounge

area, terrace, pets allowed, car/lorry parking.
◀€ *gorges of the Ardèche; Ardèche canoe trips; Vallon-Pont-d'Arc; Vals-les-Bains (thermal resort).*

AVIGNON • Vaucluse, 84140

🚇 RELAIS D'AVIGNON
(M. Daniel and Laurent Savry) La Petite
Castelette, Montfavet ☎ 90.84.18.28
[Fax] 90.84.17.60
Directions: RN 7, exit at Avignon Sud (South).
Restaurant: breakfast from 5.00. Lunch from
11.00 until 15.00. Dinner from 19.00 until 24.00.
Specialities: toro à la gardiane, regional menu.
Hotel: ☆ ☆ 19 rooms. Facilities: shower, private
bathroom, television, telephone.
Other points: credit cards accepted, bar, children's
menu, à la carte menu, lounge area, modern decor,
terrace, pets allowed, car/lorry parking.
◀€ *Avignon; Saint-Rémy; Les Baux-de-Provence; Pont du Gard; Nîmes; Arles; the Camargue.*

BAIX • Ardèche, 07210

🍴 RESTAURANT MA CAMPAGNE
(Mme Nara Arsac) Quartier des Lilas
☎ 75.85.80.26
Menu: 50 Frs.
Restaurant: closed Sun.
Specialities: home-cooking.
Other points: modern decor, terrace, pets
allowed, car/lorry parking.

BALAN-LA-VALBONNE • Ain, 01360

🚇 LE FRONT DE BANDIERE
(M. André Voussatiouk-Koval) Route de Balan
☎ 78.06.35.61
Menu: 53 Frs.
Accommodation: 80 to 100 Frs.
Restaurant: lunch from 11.45 until 15.00. Dinner
from 19.45 until 22.00.
Specialities: home-cooking.
Hotel: 10 rooms. Facilities: shower.
Other points: bar, traditional decor, terrace, pets
allowed, car/lorry parking.
◀€ *Pérouges: medieval city; Port-Galan.*

BARCELONNETTE
Alpes-de-Haute-Provence, 04400

🚇 LES SEOLANES
(M. Hubert Maure) Les Thuiles
☎ 92.81.07.37
Directions: Gap.
Languages spoken: English, Italian.
Menu: 68 to 120 Frs.
Accommodation: 110 to 200 Frs.
Restaurant: breakfast from 7.00. Lunch from
12.00 until 13.30. Closed 1 day per week (out of
season), and in Jan.
Specialities: raviolles, home-cooking.
Hotel: 6 rooms. Facilities: shower.

Other points: credit cards accepted, bar,
children's menu, traditional decor, terrace, pets
allowed, car/lorry parking.
◀€ *vallée de l'Ubaye: fort; musée de Barcelonnette; parc national de Mercantour.*

LA BARQUE
Bouches-du-Rhône, 13710

🍴 LE RELAIS DES 4 CHEMINS
(M. Girardi – SARL Lauvir) ☎ 42.58.60.03
Menu: 58 Frs.
Restaurant: breakfast from 4.00. Lunch from
11.30 until 14.00. Closed Sat and Sun.
Specialities: regional menu, home-cooking.
Other points: credit cards accepted, bar, terrace,
car/lorry parking.

BEAUCROISSANT • Isère, 38140

🍴 LES ROUTIERS DU CHAMP-DE-FOIRE
(Mme Marie-Thérèse Blain) Le Bain
☎ 76.91.05.17
Directions: RD 159.
Menu: 55 to 60 Frs.
Restaurant: lunch from 11.00 until 14.30. Dinner
from 19.00 until 21.00. Closed Sun, 2 weeks in
May and 2 weeks in Oct.
Specialities: couscous, poulet aux écrevisses and
rognons à la portugaise, home-cooking.
Other points: bar, traditional decor, terrace, pets
allowed, car/lorry parking.
◀€ *couvent (convent) at La Chartreuse (30km); distillery (10km).*

LE BEAUSSET • Var, 83330

🍴 LE RESTAURANT DE L'AERODROME DU CASTELLET
(Mme Marie-France Gautier) Route Nationale 8
☎ 94.90.71.48
Languages spoken: English, Portuguese.
Restaurant: lunch from 11.30 until 15.00. Closed
Sat, and in Aug.
Specialities: couscous, aïoli, home-cooking.
Other points: bar, children's menu.

BELIGNIEUX • Ain, 01360

🍴 BAR-RESTAURANT JATHANIEL
(M. Jacques Jarrier) Route Nationale 84,
La Grande Dangereuse ☎ 78.06.32.64
Directions: RN 84, the Lyon/Geneva road.
Languages spoken: English.
Menu: 62 to 110 Frs.
Restaurant: breakfast from 7.30. Lunch from
11.45 until 14.00. Dinner from 19.00 until 21.00.
Closed Sun, and 1 week at Christmas.
Specialities: home-cooking.
Other points: credit cards accepted, bar,
children's menu, traditional decor, terrace,
car/lorry parking.
◀€ *Pérouges: medieval city; Meximieux.*

BELLEVILLE • Rhône, 69220

≋ RESTAURANT BELLERIVE
(M. Lucien Pages) 6 avenue du Port
☎ 74.66.33.82 [Fax] 74.66.39.81
Directions: RD 17, exit Belleville, towards Châtillon.
Menu: 56 to 99 Frs.
Restaurant: breakfast from 8.00. Lunch from 12.00 until 15.00. Dinner from 19.00 until 22.30. Closed Sun evening (from Oct to March).
Specialities: fritures (whitebait) de Saône, grenouilles, coq au vin, regional menu, home-cooking.
Other points: bar, à la carte menu, modern decor, pets allowed, car/lorry parking.
❦ Villars: bird park; museums; Beaujolais wine-cellars; Roche de Solutré; Pérouge: medieval village.

BELLEY • Ain, 01300

≋ RESTAURANT DE LA GARE
(Mme Elisabeth Bavu) avenue de la Gare
☎ 79.81.06.60
Directions: RN 504.
Languages spoken: Italian.
Menu: 40 Frs.
Accommodation: 80 to 150 Frs.
Restaurant: breakfast from 6.30. Lunch from 12.00 until 14.00. Dinner from 20.00 until 22.00 Closed last 2 weeks in Dec.
Specialities: gibiers (game), poissons, grenouilles, escargots, regional menu, home-cooking.
Hotel: 5 rooms.
Other points: bar, lounge area, terrace, pets allowed, car/lorry parking.

BELLIGNAT • Ain, 01810

≋ LA BONNE AUBERGE – Les Routiers
(M. Michel Detouillon) 11 avenue Oyonnax
☎ 74.77.24.18
Directions: RN 840, exit Saint-Martin-du-Frêne, towards Lyon/Nantua.
Menu: 55 Frs (wine and coffee included).
Restaurant: breakfast from 6.00. Lunch from 12.00 until 13.30. Dinner from 19.30 until 20.00. Closed Sun, and in Aug.
Specialities: regional menu, home-cooking.
Hotel: 4 rooms. Facilities: shower, telephone.
Other points: bar, children's menu, traditional decor, pets allowed, car/lorry parking.

BERRE L'ETANG
Bouches-du-Rhône, 13130

≋ RESTAURANT L'ENTENTE
(Mme Marie-Thérèse Le Guennec) Route du Moulin Vieux ☎ 42.85.37.44
Directions: RN 113, Marseille.
Languages spoken: German, English.
Menu: 50 Frs (wine included).
Restaurant: breakfast from 6.30. Lunch from 11.00 until 18.00. Closed Sat, Sun, and in Aug.
Specialities: home-cooking.
Other points: traditional decor, car/lorry parking.

BEVENAIS • Isère, 38690

⊟ LE RELAIS DE MI-PLAINE
(M. Michel Fernandez) Route Nationale 85, Mi-Plaine ☎ 76.93.21.03
Directions: RN 85, the Lyon/Grenoble road.
Languages spoken: Spanish.
Menu: 59 to 75 Frs.
Accommodation: 180 to 200 Frs.
Restaurant: breakfast from 6.30. Lunch from 11.30 until 15.00. Dinner from 19.00 until 22.00.
Specialities: home-cooking.
Hotel: 10 rooms. Facilities: shower, private bathroom, television, telephone.
Other points: credit cards accepted, bar, children's menu, lounge area, modern decor, terrace, pets allowed, car/lorry parking.
❦ Berlioz museum; Voiron; La Grande Chartreuse.

BLYES • Ain, 01150

≋ AUBERGE DE BLYES
(M. Patrice Astier) 'La Plaine de l'Ain'
☎ 74.61.50.15
Directions: exit Pérouges/Lagnieu.
Languages spoken: English.
Menu: 60 to 138 Frs.
Restaurant: breakfast from 7.00. Lunch 11.30 to 14.30. Dinner 19.00 to 21.00. Closed Sat and Sun.
Specialities: Périgord dishes, regional menu, home-cooking.
Other points: credit cards accepted, bar, children's menu, à la carte menu, lounge area, modern decor, terrace, pets allowed, car/lorry parking.
❦ Pérouges: medieval city; grottes (caves) de La Balme; Cerdon (wines); centrale (power station) at Le Bugey.

BOEN-SUR-LIGNON • Loire, 42130

≋ LES ROUTIERS – Chez Pen et Gérard
(Mme Pénélope Adams) 83 rue de Lyon
☎ 77.24.44.76 [Fax] 77.97.31.25
Directions: RN 89, between Feurs and Clermont-Ferrand.
Languages spoken: English, German.
Menu: 55 Frs (wine and coffee included).
Restaurant: breakfast from 6.00. Lunch 11.30 to 14.30. Dinner 19.00 to 21.00. Closed Sun.
Specialities: home-cooking.
Other points: bar, children's menu, modern decor, pets allowed, car/lorry parking.
❦ Montrond-les-Bains.

BOLLENE • Vaucluse, 84500

⊟ LE RELAIS DE LA CROISIERE
(M. Serge Bacon) Route Nationale 7,
La Croisière ☎ 90.30.08.53
[Fax] 90.30.08.53
Directions: RN 7, exit at Bollène, towards Orange.
Languages spoken: English.
Menu: 56 Frs.
Accommodation: 100 to 180 Frs.

Restaurant: breakfast from 4.30. Lunch from 11.30 until 14.30. Dinner from 19.00 until 21.30. Closed Sat evening and Sun.
Specialities: home-cooking.
Hotel: 15 rooms.
Other points: credit cards accepted, bar, children's menu, traditional decor, pets allowed, car/lorry parking.
◁ gorges of the Ardèche; Orange; Avignon.

BONSON • Loire, 42160

🍴 **RESTAURANT DES SPORTS**
(M. Alain Chazelle) 14 avenue de Saint-Rambert ☎ 77.55.20.12
Directions: RN 198, between Andrézieu and Bouthéon or Saint-Just and Saint-Rambert.
Languages spoken: English.
Menu: 50 to 200 Frs.
Accommodation: 100 to 130 Frs.
Restaurant: breakfast from 7.00. Lunch 12.00 to 14.30. Dinner 19.00 to 20.30. Closed Sun, Aug.
Specialities: home-cooking.
Hotel: ☆ 7 rooms. Facilities: shower, television.
Other points: credit cards accepted, bar, children's menu, pets allowed, car/lorry parking.
◁ Bonson: chapel; musée de Saint-Rambert; Saint-Etienne.

BOUC-BEL-AIR
Bouches-du-Rhône, 13320

🍴 **AUBERGE DES MURIERS**
(M. Frédéric Dhilly) Plan Marseillais
☎ 42.22.08.04
Directions: RN 8, between Marseille and Aix.
Menu: 58 Frs.
Accommodation: 100 to 120 Frs.
Restaurant: breakfast from 5.30. Lunch from 11.30 until 14.30. Dinner from 19.30 until 21.00. Closed Sat and Sun in summer.
Specialities: regional menu, home-cooking.
Hotel: 12 rooms. Facilities: shower, television.
Other points: bar, traditional decor, terrace, pets allowed, car parking.

🍴 **LES ROUTIERS DE LA MALLE**
(M. Jean-Louis Zanon) La Malle
☎ 42.22.08.84
Directions: RN 8.
Menu: 50 Frs.
Restaurant: breakfast from 6.00. Closed Sat, Sun.
Specialities: Provençal dishes, home-cooking.
Other points: bar, pets allowed, car/lorry parking.

BOUGE-CHAMBALUD • Isère, 38150

🍴 **LA FONTAINE DU VERNAY**
(Mme Françoise Nivelle) ☎ 74.84.15.18
Directions: between Chanas and Grenoble.
Languages spoken: German, English.
Menu: 68 to 110 Frs.
Accommodation: 150 Frs.
Restaurant: breakfast from 7.00. Lunch 12.00 to 15.00. Dinner 19.00 to 21.00. Closed Wed.

Specialities: regional menu, home-cooking.
Hotel: 6 rooms.
Other points: credit cards accepted, bar, children's menu, traditional decor, terrace, pets allowed, car/lorry parking.
◁ Assieu: musée animalier; Auterive: palais idéal du Facteur Cheval; distillery; Moiroud; Beaurepaire; Peaugres: safari park.

BOURG-ARGENTAL • Loire, 42220

🍴 **LE PERRON**
(M. Georges Tardy) Route Nationale 82
☎ 77.39.62.65
Directions: RN 82, between Saint-Etienne and Valence.
Languages spoken: English.
Menu: 58 to 85 Frs.
Restaurant: breakfast from 8.00. Lunch from 11.00 until 14.30. Dinner from 18.00 until 21.30. Closed Mon evening (Mon all day, out of season).
Specialities: regional menu, home-cooking.
Other points: credit cards accepted, bar, children's menu, à la carte menu, modern decor, terrace, pets allowed, car/lorry parking.
◁ Peaugres: safari park; Saint-Julien-Molin-Molette: artists' village; Annonay: musée des Frères (brothers) Montgolfier.

BOURG-DE-PEAGE • Drôme, 26300

🍴 **RELAIS ROUTIER DU VERCORS SARL**
L'Ecancière ☎ 75.48.83.44
Directions: RN 532, between Pizançon and Saint-Nazaire-en-Royan.
Menu: 60 Frs.
Restaurant: breakfast from 5.00. Lunch 11.45 to 14.00. Dinner 19.30 to 22.00. Closed Sun.
Specialities: home-cooking.
Other points: credit cards accepted, bar, traditional decor, pets allowed, car/lorry parking.
◁ Le Vercors.

BOURGOIN-JALLIEU • Isère, 38300

🍴 **RELAIS DE LA MAISON BLANCHE**
(M. André Piloz) Route Nationale 85, Nivolas-Vermelle ☎ 74.27.92.86
Directions: RN 85, exit Bourgoin, towards Grenoble.
Menu: 60 Frs.
Restaurant: breakfast from 5.00. Lunch from 11.15 until 14.00. Closed Sat, Sun, 3 weeks in Aug and 1 week at Christmas.
Specialities: home-cooking.
Other points: bar, à la carte menu, traditional decor, pets allowed, car/lorry parking.
◁ lac de Charavines; the Alps.

LE BREUIL • Rhône, 69620

🍴 **CAFE DE L'ESPERANCE**
(M. Marc Thivin) Le Gélicain, Route Nationale 485 ☎ 74.71.64.82
Directions: RD 485, between Lyon and Charolles.

Languages spoken: English, Spanish.
Menu: 55 to 125 Frs.
Restaurant: breakfast from 6.30. Lunch from
12.00 until 13.30. Closed Mon.
Specialities: home-cooking.
Other points: credit cards accepted, bar,
children's menu, traditional decor, terrace, pets
allowed, car parking.
◁€ Beaujolais wine-cellars; route des Pierres
Dorées; le bois d'Oingt; Lyon.

BRIANCON • Hautes Alpes, 05100

⊨ LA LANTERNE
(M. René Parisot) Chamandrin
☎ 92.21.12.33
Directions: RN 94, the Gap road.
Languages spoken: German, English, Spanish.
Menu: 65 Frs.
Restaurant: breakfast from 9.00. Lunch from
11.00 until 14.00. Dinner from 18.00 until 21.30.
Specialities: home-cooking.
Other points: credit cards accepted, bar,
children's menu, à la carte menu, modern decor,
terrace, pets allowed, car/lorry parking.
◁€ Briançon: old town; forts built by Vauban.

CANNES-LA BOCCA
Alpes Maritimes, 06150

⊨ CAVE DE LA ROUBINE
(Mme Jeanine Canton) 40 avenue de la
Roubine ☎ 93.47.77.10
Menu: 52 Frs.
Restaurant: breakfast from 7.00. Dinner until
22.00. Closed Sun.
Other points: bar, terrace, car parking.

⊟ LE PEROU
(M. Patrick Toriti) Zone Industrielle (Z.I.)
La Fayère ☎ 93.48.03.72
Directions: La Bocca Ouest.
Menu: 59 Frs.
Restaurant: closed Sun.
Specialities: regional menu, home-cooking.
Other points: credit cards accepted, modern
decor, pets allowed, car/lorry parking.
◁€ beaches and hinterland.

LE CANNET-DES-MAURES
Var, 83340

⊨ AUBERGE LES QUATRE VENTS
(Mme Antonia Iannella) Route Nationale 7
☎ 94.60.96.41
Directions: RN 7, exit Le Luc, towards Vidauban.
Languages spoken: Spanish, Italian.
Restaurant: breakfast from 5.00. Lunch from
11.30 until 17.00. Dinner from 18.30.
Specialities: home-cooking.
Other points: credit cards accepted, bar, pets
allowed, car parking.
◁€ Var plain and hinterland; village des tortues
(tortoises).

CARNOULES • Var, 83660

⊟ CHEZ DOUDOU
(M. Adrien Piasco) 20 rue Pierre-Sémard
☎ 94.28.33.15
Directions: RN 97, between Toulon and Nice via
Le Luc.
Languages spoken: Italian.
Menu: 53 to 170 Frs.
Accommodation: 100 Frs.
Restaurant: breakfast from 6.15. Lunch 11.30 to
14.00. Dinner 19.30 to 21.00. Closed Sat, and
2 weeks in Sept.
Specialities: Provençal dishes, home-cooking.
Hotel: 5 rooms.
Other points: credit cards accepted, bar,
children's menu, à la carte menu, modern decor,
terrace, pets allowed, car/lorry parking.

CARPENTRAS • Vaucluse, 84200

⊨ RESTAURANT DU MARCHE GARE
(M. Bernard Gil) Route de Velleron
☎ 90.63.19.00
Directions: RN 538.
Languages spoken: Spanish.
Menu: 58 Frs (wine included) 🍷
Restaurant: breakfast from 5.00. Lunch 12.00 to
14.30. Dinner 19.00 to 20.30. Closed Sun.
Specialities: home-cooking.
Other points: credit cards accepted, bar, modern
decor, pets allowed, car/lorry parking.
◁€ Mont-Ventoux; Fontaine-de-Vaucluse; Gordes.

LE CASTELLET • Var, 83330

⊨ See LE BEAUSSET

CAZAN • Bouches-du-Rhône, 13116

⊨ L'ESCALIER, RN 7.
(M. Alexandre Ghigo) Route Nationale 7
☎ 90.59.13.15
Directions: RN 7.
Restaurant: closed Sun.
Specialities: tripes provençales, chili con carne,
manchons de canard confits, andouillet à la ficelle,
darne de saumon.
Other points: bar.

CHAMPAGNEUX • Savoie, 73240

⊨ RELAIS DES TROIS PROVINCES –
Chez Nicole
(Mme Nicole Curtillat) La Tuilière
☎ 76.31.86.97
Directions: RN 516, between Yenne and Saint-
Genix-sur-Guiers.
Menu: 55 Frs.
Restaurant: breakfast from 6.00. Lunch from
11.30 until 14.00. Closed Sat.
Specialities: fondue savoyarde, fondue
bourguignonne, home-cooking.

Other points: bar, modern decor, pets allowed, car/lorry parking.
❧ *château de Montfleury; musée d'Aoste (Gallo-Roman); Glandieu: waterfall.*

LA CHAPELLE • Savoie, 73220

🍴 **LE VORNAY**
(M. Jean-Marc Fedezyszyn) Route Nationale 6
☎ 79.36.12.05
Directions: RN 6, Chambéry or Grenoble/Turin.
Languages spoken: English, Italian.
Menu: 64 Frs (drink included) to 84 Frs.
Specialities: regional menu, home-cooking.
Other points: open 24 hours, credit cards accepted, bar, children's menu, à la carte menu, lounge area, modern decor, terrace, pets allowed, car/lorry parking.
❧ *La Maurienne valley; ski resorts.*

CHARMES-SUR-L'HERBASSE
Drôme, 26260

🍴 **RELAIS DU CABARET NEUF**
(M. Michel Dreveton) Le Cabaret Neuf
☎ 75.45.65.65
Directions: RD 538, Romans.
Menu: 55 to 115 Frs.
Restaurant: breakfast from 7.00. Lunch from 12.00 until 14.00. Dinner from 19.00 until 20.00. Closed Tues, and from 15th Sept to 15th Oct.
Specialities: cuisses de grenouilles, gambas au whisky, home-cooking.
Other points: bar, pets allowed, car/lorry parking.
❧ *musée de Madagascar; Auterive: palais idéal du Facteur Cheval (fantasy shell palace).*

CHARVIEU-CHAVAGNEU
Isère, 38230

🍴 **BAR-RESTAURANT DE LA LECHERE**
(M. Paul Maunand) Route de Lyon,
La Léchère ☎ 72.46.04.89
Directions: Route de Lyon.
Menu: 62 Frs (wine and coffee included) to 110 Frs.
Restaurant: breakfast from 6.30. Lunch 11.30 to 14.30. Dinner 19.00 to 21.00. Closed Sat and Sun.
Specialities: grenouilles, fritures, home-cooking.
Other points: credit cards accepted, bar, children's menu, modern decor, terrace, pets allowed, car/lorry parking.
❧ *Crémieu: medieval city; grotte (cave) de La Balme.*

CHASSE-SUR-RHONE
Isère, 38670

🍴 **CENTRAL BAR – Chez Babeth**
(Mme Elisabeth Marotte) 5 rue Pasteur
☎ 78.73.10.82
Directions: the Lyon/Valence road.
Menu: 60 Frs.
Restaurant: breakfast from 6.00. Lunch from 11.30 until 14.30. Dinner from 19.00 until 22.00. Closed Sat afternoon, Sun and public holidays.

Specialities: couscous, cassoulet, choucroute, home-cooking.
Other points: credit cards accepted, bar, children's menu, à la carte menu, traditional decor, pets allowed, car/lorry parking.
❧ *Vienne: ancient city.*

CHATEAUNEUF-DE-GADAGNE
Vaucluse, 84470

🍴 **RESTAURANT DU MARCHE**
(M. Claude Micheletti) place du Marché
☎ 90.22.41.14
Languages spoken: Spanish.
Restaurant: breakfast from 6.30. Closed Sun.
Other points: bar, car/lorry parking.

CHATEAUNEUF-LES-MARTIGUES
Bouches-du-Rhône, 13220

🍴 **L'OASIS**
(M. Thierry Dichard) Route Nationale 568
☎ 42.79.88.35
Directions: RN 568, between Martigues and Fos.
Menu: 55 Frs.
Restaurant: breakfast from 6.00. Lunch from 11.00 until 14.00. Dinner from 19.00 until 21.00. Closed Fri afternoon, Sat and Sun.
Specialities: bouillabaisse, paella, home-cooking.
Other points: bar, lorry parking.

CHATTE • Isère, 38160

🍴 **LE SIROCCO**
(M. Maurice Moyroud) Quartier Saint-Ferréol
☎ 76.64.43.41 [Fax] 76.64.45.95
Directions: RN 92, between Romans and Grenoble.
Menu: 60 Frs.
Restaurant: breakfast from 6.00. Lunch from 11.30 until 14.00. Closed Sat afternoon, Sun, 1st 2 weeks in Aug and 1 week at Christmas.
Specialities: home-cooking.
Other points: credit cards accepted, bar, terrace, pets allowed, car/lorry parking.
❧ *jardin ferroviaire (railways); abbaye de Saint-Antoine; 'Royans-Vercors' paddle-boat.*

CHAUFFAYER • Hautes Alpes, 05800

🏨 **TOURISME HOTEL**
(M. Robert Reynaud) Route Nationale 85
☎ 92.55.22.74
Directions: RN 85.
Languages spoken: English.
Menu: 65 Frs.
Accommodation: 100 to 165 Frs.
Restaurant: breakfast from 6.00. Lunch from 11.00 until 15.00. Dinner from 19.15 until 22.00. Closed 10 days in June and 2 weeks in Sept.
Specialities: regional menu, home-cooking.
Hotel: 10 rooms. Facilities: shower.
Other points: credit cards accepted, bar, children's menu, à la carte menu, traditional decor, terrace, pets allowed, car/lorry parking.

CHORGES • Hautes Alpes, 05230

🛏 HOTEL DES ALPES
(M. Roger Mauduech) avenue de la Gare
☎ 92.50.60.08
Directions: RN 94, the Gap/Briançon road.
Menu: 55 to 85 Frs.
Accommodation: 140 to 260 Frs.
Restaurant: breakfast from 7.30. Lunch from
12.00 until 13.00. Dinner from 19.30 until 21.00.
Closed from 1st Oct to 11th Nov.
Specialities: salade caturige, gratin dauphinois,
gigot pré-Alpes, terrine maison, regional menu.
Hotel: ☆ 16 rooms. Facilities: shower, television,
telephone.
Other points: credit cards accepted, bar,
children's menu, à la carte menu, traditional decor,
terrace, pets allowed, car/lorry parking.
◖€ *ancient village; church; barrage (dam) and lac
de Serre-Ponçon; baie Saint-Michel; montagne de
Chorges; forest walks.*

LA CLUSE • Ain, 01460

🍴 AU PETIT BAR
(M. Jean Dufour) 1 rue du Lyonnais
☎ 74.76.03.57
Directions: RN 79 and 84.
Menu: 55 Frs.
Restaurant: breakfast from 4.00. Closed Sun, Aug.
Specialities: home-cooking.
Other points: bar.

COGOLIN • Var, 83310

🍴 AUBERGE DU GISCLET
(Mme Nicole Vialenc) Route Nationale 98
☎ 94.56.40.39
Directions: RN 98.
Menu: 60 to 75 Frs.
Restaurant: breakfast from 8.00. Closed Sun.
Specialities: home-cooking.
Other points: credit cards accepted, children's
menu, traditional decor, terrace, pets allowed,
car/lorry parking.
◖€ *Saint-Tropez.*

CORMORANCHE-SUR-SAONE
Ain, 01290

🍴 AUBERGE CHEZ LA MERE MARTINET
(Mme Geneviève Martinet) Le Bourg
☎ 85.36.20.40 [Fax] 85.31.77.19
Directions: RN 6, Crêches-sur-Saône, 1st left at
the lights.
Languages spoken: German, English, Spanish.
Menu: 68 to 220 Frs 🍽
Accommodation: 180 Frs.
Restaurant: lunch from 12.00 until 14.00. Dinner
from 19.30 until 21.00. Closed Tues evening,
Wed, and from 15th Aug to 15th Sept.
Specialities: saucisson chaud à la beaujolaise,
suprême de volaille, grenouilles fraiches, regional
menu, home-cooking.

Hotel: ☆ ☆ 7 rooms. Facilities: shower,
television, telephone.
Other points: credit cards accepted, bar,
children's menu, à la carte menu, traditional decor,
terrace, pets allowed, car parking.
◖€ *Bey: church; mont du Beaujolais; roche de
Solutré; circuit Lamartine; musée hypomobile de
Vannas (9km); Macon/Beaujolais mountains.*

CORPS • Isère, 38970

🛏 RESTAURANT DU TILLEUL
(M. Claude Jourdan) rue des Fossés
☎ 76.30.00.43
Directions: RN 85, between Grenoble and Gap.
Languages spoken: German, English.
Menu: 70 to 145 Frs 🍽
Accommodation: 180 to 310 Frs.
Restaurant: breakfast from 7.00. Lunch from
12.00 until 14.00. Dinner from 19.00 until 21.00.
Closed in Nov and the 1st 2 weeks in Dec.
Specialities: gratin dauphinois, civet de porcelet,
poulet aux écrevisses, regional menu, home-cooking.
Hotel: ☆ ☆ 10 rooms. Facilities: shower, private
bathroom, television, telephone.
Other points: credit cards accepted, bar, à la carte
menu, modern decor, terrace, pets allowed, car/
lorry parking.
◖€ *barrage (dam) de Sautel; sanctuaire de La Salette.*

LA COUCOURDE • Drôme, 26740

🍴 LES MARRONNIERS
(M. Thierry Jan) Route Nationale 7
☎ 75.90.02.35
Directions: RN 7.
Languages spoken: English.
Menu: 60 Frs.
Restaurant: breakfast from 5.00. Lunch from
11.00 until 15.00. Dinner from 18.30 until 23.00.
Closed Sun (out of season).
Specialities: home-cooking.
Other points: credit cards accepted, bar,
children's menu, traditional decor, terrace, pets
allowed, car/lorry parking.

🍴 RELAIS DES ROCHES
(M. Yvon Larsonnier) Route Nationale 7
☎ 75.53.70.02
Menu: 55 Frs.
Restaurant: breakfast from 4.00. Meals from 11.00.
Specialities: home-cooking.
Other points: credit cards accepted, bar,
children's menu, traditional decor, terrace, pets
allowed, car/lorry parking.

COURTHEZON • Vaucluse, 84350

🍴 LE RELAIS DU SOLEIL
(Mme Chantal Ponzo) Route Nationale 7
☎ 90.70.74.36
Directions: RN 7, between Orange and Avignon.
Languages spoken: English, Spanish, Italian.
Menu: 56 Frs.
Restaurant: breakfast from 6.00. Lunch from

11.30 until 15.30. Dinner from 18.30 until 22.30. Closed Sat and Sun.
Specialities: regional menu, home-cooking.
Other points: credit cards accepted, bar, terrace, pets allowed, car/lorry parking.
◁ *Orange: Théâtre Antique; Fontaine-de-Vaucluse; Montmirail: lace-making; wine route.*

CREST • Drôme, 26400

≕ LE CHAMP-DE-MARS
(M. Bernard Genthon) 8 place de la Liberté
☎ 75.40.61.06
Languages spoken: German.
Restaurant: breakfast from 6.00. Lunch from 12.00 until 14.00. Dinner from 19.00 onwards.
Specialities: home-cooking.
Other points: credit cards accepted, bar, modern decor.
◁ *Crest: old town, tower.*

LA CROIX-VALMER • Var, 83420

ᕦ LA CIGALE
(M. Eric Korhel) Route Départementale 559
☎ 94.79.60.41
Directions: RD 559, between La Foux/Cavalaire.
Menu: 65 Frs.
Accommodation: full board and half board.
Restaurant: lunch from 12.00 until 14.30. Dinner from 19.30 until 21.00. Closed Sat (out of season), and Christmas to New Year.
Specialities: bouillabaisse façon pêcheur, bourride véritable, daurade royale, chapon farci, home-cooking.
Hotel: 7 rooms.
Other points: credit cards accepted, bar, children's menu, à la carte menu, modern decor, pets allowed, car/lorry parking.

CRUAS • Ardèche, 07350

≕ RELAIS ROUTIER
(Mme Sylvie Madeira) La Devière
☎ 75.51.41.12
Directions: RN 86.
Menu: 50 to 130 Frs.
Restaurant: breakfast from 6.00. Lunch from 10.00 until 17.00. Dinner from 17.00 until 23.00.
Specialities: home-cooking.
Other points: bar, children's menu, traditional decor, pets allowed, car/lorry parking.
◁ *medieval chateaux; church; nuclear power station.*

CUZIEU • Loire, 42330

ᕦ RESTAURANT DE LA MAIRIE
(Mme Janine Dard) Route Nationale 82, Le Bourg ☎ 77.54.88.21 [Fax] 77.54.42.07
Directions: RN 82, coming from Saint-Etienne, exit at Veauche.
Languages spoken: German, English, Spanish, Italian.
Menu: 60 Frs.

Accommodation: 120 to 180 Frs.
Restaurant: breakfast from 6.00. Lunch from 11.00 until 15.00. Dinner from 18.00 until 23.00. Closed Sat afternoon, Sun, and in Aug.
Specialities: regional menu, home-cooking.
Hotel: 12 rooms. Facilities: shower, private bathroom, television.
Other points: credit cards accepted, bar, lounge area, modern decor, terrace, pets allowed, car/lorry parking.
◁ *barrages (dams) de Villerest and Grangent-sur-la-Loire; Mont-Pilat; Saint-Romain-le-Puy: priory; la Bâtie d'Urfé; musée de la mine (mining).*

DARDILLY • Rhône, 69570

ᕫ AUBERGE POLONAISE : CRACOVIE
(M. Jean-Jacques Sadeski) 22 Route Nationale 7
☎ 78.48.01.39
Directions: old RN 7.
Languages spoken: English, Italian, Polish.
Menu: 60 Frs.
Accommodation: 110 to 130 Frs.
Restaurant: lunch from 11.30 until 14.00. Dinner from 19.00 until 21.30. Closed Sun.
Specialities: Polish dishes, home-cooking.
Hotel: 8 rooms.
Other points: credit cards accepted, bar, children's menu, à la carte menu, pets allowed, car/lorry parking.
◁ *Marcy-l'Etoile: musée nationale de la Poupée (dolls); Courzier: wildlife park (eagles).*

ᕫ LE CHENE ROND
(M. Emile Lagoutte) 87 Route Nationale 7
☎ 78.87.15.48
Directions: RN 7, the Lyon/Roanne road.
Menu: 56 Frs.
Accommodation: 55 to 110 Frs.
Restaurant: breakfast from 6.30. Lunch from 12.00 until 13.30. Closed Sat afternoon, Sun, public holidays, and in Aug.
Specialities: home-cooking.
Hotel: 6 rooms. Facilities: shower.
Other points: bar, car/lorry parking.

≕ LE RELAIS DE LA BASCULE
(M. Roger Martins) Porte de Lyon, Route Nationale 6 ☎ 78.35.56.30
Directions: RN 6, 23km after the toll at Villefranche-sur-Saône.
Languages spoken: Italian and Portuguese.
Menu: 60 Frs.
Restaurant: breakfast from 6.00. Lunch 12.00 to 14.30. Dinner 19.00 to 22.00. Closed Sat, Sun, Aug.
Specialities: home-cooking.
Other points: credit cards accepted, bar, traditional decor, pets allowed, car/lorry parking.
◁ *Lyon (Gallic capital): museums, monuments, parc de la Tête d'Or, basilicas.*

DOMANCY • Haute-Savoie, 74700

≕ AUBERGE DE L'ETRAZ
(Mme Viviane Fivel-Demoret) Route Nationale 205, L'Etraz ☎ 50.93.90.86

Directions: RN 205, Mont Blanc.
Languages spoken: English.
Menu: 60 Frs.
Restaurant: breakfast from 9.00. Dinner from 18.00 until 3.00. Closed one week at Christmas.
Specialities: Norman dishes, regional menu.
Other points: bar, children's menu, à la carte menu, traditional decor, terrace, pets allowed, car/lorry parking.

DONZERE • Drôme, 26290

🍴 LA MARGELLE FLEURIE
(M. Claude Jeannaux) Route Nationale 7
☎ 75.51.75.11
Languages spoken: German, English.
Accommodation: 95 to 115 Frs.
Restaurant: breakfast from 5.00. Lunch from 11.30 until 14.00. Dinner from 19.00 until 22.00. Closed 25th Dec and 1st Jan.
Specialities: Savoy dishes, home-cooking.
Hotel: 9 rooms. Facilities: shower.
Other points: credit cards accepted, bar, children's menu, à la carte menu, modern decor, terrace, pets allowed, car/lorry parking.
◀ gorges of the Ardèche; Pierrelatte.

🍴 RELAIS DE DONZERE
(M. Jean Bertrand) Route Nationale 7
☎ 75.51.64.58 [Fax] 75.51.56.78
Directions: RN 7.
Languages spoken: German, Spanish, and Italian.
Accommodation: 95 to 115.
Restaurant: closed 1 week from 25th Dec.
Specialities: poulet aux écrevisses, waterzooi (Belgian speciality), home-cooking.
Hotel: 9 rooms. Facilities: shower, private bathroom.
Other points: credit cards accepted, bar, children's menu, lounge area, traditional decor, terrace, pets allowed, car/lorry parking.
◀ the Ardèche region.

🍴 RELAIS LE BOLO
(M. Martial Da Fonseca) Route Nationale 7
☎ 75.51.61.48 [Fax] 75.51.57.54
Directions: RN 7, exit Montélimar Sud (South).
Languages spoken: English, Spanish, Portuguese.
Menu: 60 Frs.
Accommodation: 100 to 200 Frs.
Hotel: ☆ 24 rooms. Facilities: shower, private bathroom.
Other points: facilities open 24 hours, credit cards accepted, bar, terrace, car/lorry parking.

DRAGUIGNAN • Var, 83300

🍴 LE PENALTY
(M. Guy Chabrand) 1 avenue de la 1ère Armée ☎ 94.68.11.28
Directions: in the Saint-Léger quarter.
Menu: 55 to 65 Frs.
Restaurant: breakfast from 5.30. Lunch from 12.00 until 14.00. Dinner from 19.00 until 20.00. Closed Sun and public holidays.
Specialities: regional menu, home-cooking.
Other points: bar, traditional decor, pets allowed, car/lorry parking.

ECULLY • Rhône, 69130

🍴 LES ROUTIERS
(Mme Sylvie Taillandier) 30 route de Paris
☎ 78.34.01.40
Directions: RN 7, between Tarare and Roanne, the Lyon exit.
Menu: 47 to 75 Frs.
Restaurant: breakfast from 7.00. Lunch from 11.30 until 14.00. Closed Sat, Sun, and in Aug.
Specialities: home-cooking.
Other points: credit cards accepted, bar, traditional decor, pets allowed.
◀ Lyon: château de la Poupée.

EYGUIANS • Hautes Alpes, 05300

🍴 HOTEL DE LA GARE
(Mme Michelle Robert) ☎ 92.66.20.08
Directions: RN 75, exit A51, 20km north of Sisteron.
Menu: 60 to 90 Frs ☞
Accommodation: 100 to 210 Frs.
Restaurant: breakfast from 6.00. Lunch from 12.00 until 14.00. Dinner from 20.00 until 21.30. Closed Sat (out of season), and in Jan.
Specialities: gigot d'agneau de pays, pieds et paquets (mutton tripe and trotters), daube, gratin dauphinois, regional menu, home-cooking.
Hotel: ☆ 15 rooms. Facilities: shower, private bathroom, television, telephone.
Other points: credit cards accepted, bar, children's menu, à la carte menu, modern decor, terrace, pets allowed, car/lorry parking.
◀ gorges of the Méouge; Prieuré (priory) de Saint-André; Sisteron: citadel; Orpierre: Provençal village (7km).

FEISSONS-SUR-ISERE
Savoie, 73260

🍴 LE RELAIS ROUTIERS
(M. Michel Ruffier) ☎ 79.22.50.97
Directions: RN 90, between Albertville and Moutiers, exit 36.
Menu: 58 Frs.
Restaurant: breakfast from 5.45. Lunch from 11.45 until 14.15. Closed Sat afternoon, Sun, last 2 weeks in Aug and 1 week at Christmas.
Specialities: home-cooking.
Other points: credit cards accepted, bar, children's menu, modern decor, terrace, pets allowed, car/lorry parking.
◀ 'circuit de la Tarentaise'.

FELINES • Ardèche, 07340

🍴 LE RELAIS DE LA REMISE
(M. Jean-Jacques Goichot) La Remise
☎ 75.34.82.22
Directions: RN 82, the Annonay/Saint-Etienne/Le Puy-en-Velay road.
Menu: 58 Frs.
Accommodation: 125 to 140 Frs.
Restaurant: breakfast from 5.30. Lunch from

11.00 until 14.00. Dinner from 19.00 until 21.00. Closed Sat and Sun.
Specialities: home-cooking.
Hotel: 3 rooms. Facilities: shower, private bathroom.
Other points: bar, children's menu, traditional decor, terrace, pets allowed, car/lorry parking.
⁅ *Peaugres: safari park.*

FEURS • Loire, 42110

≒ LE FARFADET
(André Dubesset) 72 rue de Verdun
☎ 77.26.47.74
Directions: RN 82, between Saint-Etienne and Roanne.
Menu: 55 to 99 Frs.
Restaurant: breakfast from 8.00. Lunch 10.00 to 15.00. Dinner 18.00 to 22.00. Closed Sun evening, Mon, 2 weeks in Feb and 2 weeks in Oct.
Specialities: home-cooking.
Other points: credit cards accepted, bar, children's menu, à la carte menu, modern decor, pets allowed, car/lorry parking.
⁅ *musée du chapeau (hats) at Chazelles; reserve for birds of prey (volerie des rapaces) at Macilly-le-Châtel; musée de la poupée (dolls) at Montbison; Gallo-Roman museum.*

FIANCEY • Drôme, 26250

⊟ ROUVEYROL
(M. Roland Rouveyrol) Route Nationale 7
☎ 75.61.62.06
Directions: RN 7, exit Valence Sud (South), towards Montélimar.
Menu: 55 to 60 Frs.
Accommodation: 100 to 140 Frs.
Restaurant: breakfast from 5.30. Lunch from 12.00 until 14.30. Dinner from 19.30 until 22.30. Closed Sun, last 2 weeks in Aug, and last week in Dec.
Specialities: home-cooking.
Hotel: 13 rooms.
Other points: credit cards accepted, bar, children's menu, lounge area, modern decor, terrace, pets allowed, car/lorry parking.
⁅ *palais idéal du Facteur Cheval (fantasy shell palace); tour (tower) de Crest; Le Vercors.*

FIANCEY-LIVRON • Drôme, 26250

⊟ RELAIS DU SUD-EST
(M. Joseph Pandolfo) Route Nationale 7
☎ 75.61.61.19
Directions: RN 7, Valence South.
Languages spoken: English.
Menu: 60 to 75 Frs.
Accommodation: 90 to 130 Frs.
Restaurant: breakfast from 5.00. Lunch 11.30 to 15.00. Dinner 18.30 to 23.00. Closed Sat afternoon and Sun.
Specialities: home-cooking.
Hotel: 9 rooms.
Other points: credit cards accepted, bar,

children's menu, à la carte menu, traditional decor, terrace, pets allowed, car/lorry parking.
⁅ *Diois; Le Vercors; the Ardèche region.*

FLAVIAC • Ardèche, 07000

⊟ LES ROUTIERS
(M. Didier Garayt) place Emile-Crémière
☎ 75.65.77.57
Directions: RN 104, exit Loriol, towards Aubenas.
Menu: 52 to 80 Frs.
Accommodation: 110 to 220 Frs.
Restaurant: breakfast from 6.30. Dinner until 21.00. Closed Sun, and from 15th Sept to 15th Oct.
Specialities: rognons au madère, home-cooking.
Hotel: 8 rooms. Facilities: shower, private bathroom.
Other points: credit cards accepted, bar, children's menu, à la carte menu, car/lorry parking.
⁅ *gorges of the Ardèche (55km); Eyrieux valley (20km).*

FOS-SUR-MER
Bouches-du-Rhône, 13270

≒ LE MOULIN
(M. Jean-Bernard Lefèbvre) place du Cavaou
☎ 42.05.48.38 / 42.05.30.01
[Fax] 42.05.42.10
Directions: crossroads at Ma Campagne, towards Les Plages.
Languages spoken: English.
Restaurant: dinner until 22.00.
Other points: bar.

⊟ LE RELAIS DE LA FOSSETTE
(Investiland) Route Nationale 113
☎ 42.05.30.01 [Fax] 42.05.42.10
Directions: RN 113, the Arles/Marseille road.
Menu: 65 to 99 Frs.
Accommodation: 99 Frs.
Restaurant: breakfast from 6.00. Lunch from 11.30 until 15.00. Dinner from 18.00 until 24.00. Closed Sat and Sun.
Specialities: gardiane, confits, home-cooking.
Hotel: ☆ 40 rooms
Other points: credit cards accepted, children's menu, à la carte menu, pets allowed, car/lorry parking.

⊟ MA CAMPAGNE – SARL LE TRIDENT
(M. Bernard Silhol) 50 avenue Jean-Jaurès
☎ 42.05.01.66 [Fax] 42.05.53.67
Directions: the Arles/Marseille expressway.
Languages spoken: English, Spanish, Italian.
Menu: 50 to 98 Frs.
Accommodation: 100 to 150 Frs.
Restaurant: breakfast from 6.00. Lunch 11.00 to 15.00. Dinner 19.00 to 22.00. Closed Sun.
Specialities: poissons, regional menu, home-cooking.
Hotel: 25 rooms. Facilities: shower.
Other points: credit cards accepted, bar, children's menu, à la carte menu, lounge area, traditional decor, terrace, pets allowed, car/lorry parking.
⁅ *the Camargue.*

FREJUS • Var, 83600

🏠 **LES TROIS CHENES**
(Mme Monique Laurent) Route de Cannes
☎ 94.53.20.08
Directions: RN 7, exit 38 at Fréjus, towards Cannes.
Languages spoken: German, English, Italian.
Menu: 65 Frs.
Accommodation: 200 to 260 Frs.
Restaurant: breakfast from 7.00. Lunch from
12.00 until 15.00. Dinner from 19.00 until 22.00.
Specialities: bouillabaisse, paella, bourride,
regional menu, home-cooking.
Hotel: ☆ 29 rooms. Facilities: shower, private
bathroom, television.
Other points: credit cards accepted, bar, à la carte
menu, traditional decor, terrace, car/lorry parking.
◄ *Indochina memorial; gorges of the Verdon;
lakes at Saint-Cassien; grotte (cave) de Saint-
Cezaire; Cannes.*

GAP • Hautes Alpes, 05000

🍴 **LE BOCAGE**
(M. Vincent Médili) 39 avenue d'Embrun
☎ 92.51.03.67
Languages spoken: Italian.
Menu: 55 Frs.
Restaurant: breakfast from 4.00. Lunch from
11.30 until 14.30. Closed Sun, 1st 2 weeks in Aug
and 1 week at Christmas.
Specialities: home-cooking.
Other points: credit cards accepted, bar,
children's menu, modern decor, terrace, pets
allowed, car/lorry parking.
◄ *barrage (dam) de Serre-Ponçon; Saint-Véran;
Corps; Notre-Dame-de-la-Salette; Route Napoléon.*

🍴 **RESTAURANT ALPES-DAUPHINE**
(Mme Micheline Argelas) La Descente
☎ 92.51.47.15
Directions: RN 85, exit at Gap Nord (North).
Languages spoken: some German, English.
Menu: 58 to 120 Frs.
Restaurant: breakfast from 6.30. Lunch from
11.00 until 15.00. Dinner from 19.00 until 21.30.
Closed Mon evening (out of season).
Specialities: regional menu, home-cooking.
Other points: credit cards accepted, bar,
children's menu, à la carte menu, terrace, pets
allowed, car/lorry parking.

GENAY • Rhône, 69730

🏠 **LA PETITE RIVE**
(SARL Fegotome) Zone Industrielle Nord
(Z.I.), Chemin de Halage ☎ 78.91.34.02
Directions: A 46.
Languages spoken: English.
Menu: 60 to 115 Frs.
Accommodation: 135 Frs.
Restaurant: breakfast from 6.30. Lunch from
12.00 until 14.30. Dinner from 19.00 until 21.30.
Specialities: regional menu, home-cooking.
Hotel: ☆ 8 rooms. Facilities: shower, private

bathroom, television, telephone.
Other points: credit cards accepted, bar,
children's menu, à la carte menu, modern decor,
terrace, pets allowed, car/lorry parking.
◄ *Rochetaillée: musée de l'automobile; Ars; Lyon.*

GRANGES-LES-VALENCE
Ardèche, 07500

🍴 **LE RELAIS DE CRUSSOL**
(M. Gilbert Bridon) avenue Sadi-Carnot,
Les Freydières ☎ 75.41.40.10
Directions: RN 86, between Valence and La Voulte.
Menu: 54 Frs.
Restaurant: breakfast from 6.00. Closed Sun (out
of season).
Specialities: pizza, home-cooking.
Other points: credit cards accepted, bar, à la carte
menu, terrace, pets allowed, car/lorry parking.
◄ *château Crussol: caves; museum; Soyons.*

GRENOBLE • Isère, 38000

🍴 **LE CATALPA**
(Mme Denise Brisset) 8 boulevard de
l'Esplanade ☎ 76.47.38.03
Directions: Grenoble Bastille.
Languages spoken: Italian.
Menu: 62 Frs (wine and coffee included).
Restaurant: breakfast from 7.00. Lunch from
12.00 until 15.00. Dinner from 19.00 until 24.00.
Closed Sun afternoon.
Specialities: gratin dauphinois, regional menu,
home-cooking.
Other points: credit cards accepted, bar, à la carte
menu, modern decor, terrace, pets allowed, car/
lorry parking.
◄ *Bastille; le musée dauphinois (museum of the
Dauphinée region); old Grenoble; fortifications.*

GRIMAUD • Var, 83310

🍴 **LE RESTAUROUTE**
(M. Bernard Gentile) Route Nationale 98,
Saint-Pons-les-Mûres ☎ 94.56.03.75
Directions: RN 98, Saint-Tropez.
Languages spoken: English, Italian.
Menu: 65 Frs.
Restaurant: breakfast from 6.00. Lunch from
12.00 until 14.00. Dinner from 19.00 until 21.45.
Closed Sun, and in Dec.
Specialities: bouillabaisse, paella, home-cooking.
Other points: credit cards accepted, bar,
children's menu, à la carte menu, terrace, pets
allowed, car/lorry parking.
◄ *Port-Grimaud (1km); Saint-Tropez (6km);
Cogolin: musée Raimu, manufacture of pipes and
carpets (6km).*

GUEREINS • Ain, 01090

🍴 **LA CROISEE**
(M. Michel Manains) La Croisée
☎ 74.66.14.93

Directions: RD 17, Belleville, towards Châtillon.
Menu: 58 to 103 Frs.
Restaurant: breakfast from 6.15. Lunch from
11.00 until 15.00. Dinner from 19.00 until 21.30.
Closed Tues evening, Sun evening, 3 weeks in Aug.
Specialities: grenouilles, home-cooking.
Other points: credit cards accepted, bar,
children's menu, à la carte menu, modern decor,
pets allowed, car/lorry parking.
◀ the Beaujolais region; Pérouges: medieval city;
Dombes.

GUILLESTRE
Hautes Alpes, 05600

🍴 **HOTEL DE LA GARE**
(SNC Lacour) Montdauphin Gare (station)
☎ 92.45.03.08 Fax 92.45.40.09
Directions: RN 94.
Languages spoken: English.
Menu: 60 to 170 Frs 🍽
Accommodation: 140 to 330 Frs.
Restaurant: breakfast from 7.00. Lunch from
12.00 until 13.45. Dinner from 19.00 until 21.00.
Closed Sat (May and June and Sept to Dec).
Specialities: truites aux morilles, filet de boeuf
grillé, côte d'agneau, regional menu.
Hotel: ☆ ☆ 30 rooms. Facilities: shower, private
bathroom, television.
Other points: credit cards accepted, bar, children's
menu, à la carte menu, lounge area, modern decor,
terrace, pets allowed, car/lorry parking.
◀ Montdauphin-Fort; la vallée du Queyras; le col
d'Izoard; Saint-Véran.

HEYRIEUX • Isère, 38540

🍴 **LE GLOBE TROTTER**
(Mme Henriette Meslati) 1 place Jules-Ferry
☎ 78.40.00.29
Directions: on the bypass Est (East), the Lyon/
Grenoble/Chambéry autoroute.
Languages spoken: English.
Menu: 60 Frs (wine and coffee included) to 85 Frs.
Accommodation: 120 to 150 Frs.
Restaurant: breakfast from 6.15. Lunch 11.30 to
14.30. Dinner 19.00 to 22.00. Closed Sun.
Specialities: regional menu, home-cooking.
Hotel: 10 rooms. Facilities: shower.
Other points: credit cards accepted, bar, children's
menu, modern decor, terrace, car/lorry parking.
◀ Lyon region; Eurespo.

L'HOPITAL-SOUS-ROCHEFORT
Loire, 42130

🍴 **CHEZ SYLVIANNE ET JEANNOT**
(M. Jean Devanne) Route Nationale 89, Boën-
sur-Lignon ☎ 77.24.55.52
Directions: RN 89.
Languages spoken: English.
Restaurant: dinner until 23.00.
Other points: bar, car/lorry parking.

L'ISLE-D'ABEAU • Isère, 38080

🍴 **L'ARCHE DE L'ISLE D'ABEAU**
(M. Guy Lapierre.) A43, services at l'Isle
d'Abeau (accessible in both directions)
☎ 74.27.10.14 Fax 74.27.01.45
Other points: credit cards and foreign currency
accepted.

JAMEYZIEU • Isère, 38230

🍴 **RESTAURANT DU PONT –**
Chez Yvonne et Jacky
(Mme Yvonne Besançon) 57 route de Lyon
☎ 78.32.56.41
Directions: RN6, between Lyon and Crémieu.
Menu: 60 Frs.
Restaurant: breakfast from 8.00. Lunch from
11.30 until 15.30. Closed Mon afternoon.
Specialities: home-cooking.
Other points: bar, children's menu, modern
decor, terrace, pets allowed, car/lorry parking.
◀ Le Bugey: centrale électrique (power station);
Crémieu: medieval city.

JARRIE • Isère, 38560

🍴 **LE RELAIS DU PONT**
(M. André Nucci) Champ-sur-Drac
☎ 76.68.85.38
Directions: RN 85, between Grenoble and Briançon.
Languages spoken: Italian.
Menu: 48 to 60 Frs.
Restaurant: breakfast from 6.00. Lunch from
11.30 until 14.00. Dinner from 19.00 until 21.00.
Closed Sat evening and Sun evening.
Specialities: home-cooking.
Other points: bar, modern decor, terrace, pets
allowed, car/lorry parking.
◀ Le Vercors; Vizille; Le Bourg-d'Oisans.

JOYEUSE • Ardèche, 07260

🍴 **LES CEVENNES**
(Mme Colette Reynouard) Rosières
☎ 75.39.52.07
Directions: Loriol.
Menu: 60 to 100 Frs.
Accommodation: 120 to 140 Frs.
Restaurant: breakfast from 7.00. Lunch 12.00 to
14.00. Dinner 20.00 to 22.00. Closed 2 weeks in Oct.
Specialities: home-cooking.
Hotel: ☆ 14 rooms.
Other points: credit cards accepted, bar,
children's menu, à la carte menu, traditional decor,
terrace, pets allowed, car parking.
◀ Vallon-Pont d'Arc; gorges of the Ardèche;
grottes (caves) Cocalières; Orgnac.

LABEGUDE • Ardèche, 07200

🍴 **RELAIS DE LA POSTE**
(M. Maurice Teyssier) 64 Route Nationale
☎ 75.37.40.25

Directions: RN 102.
Menu: 55 to 75 Frs.
Accommodation: 100 to 150 Frs.
Restaurant: breakfast from 6.30. Lunch from 12.00 until 13.30. Dinner from 19.00 until 21.00. Closed Sun (out of season), and in Sept.
Specialities: home-cooking.
Hotel: 12 rooms. Facilities: shower, private bathroom.
Other points: bar, traditional decor, terrace, pets allowed, car parking.
❧ *Aven d'Orgnac; lac d'Issarlès.*

LALEVADE-D'ARDECHE
Ardèche, 07380

🏠 **L'ESCHALLIER**
(M. José Ferraro) 31 place de la Gare
☎ 75.94.17.23
Directions: RN 102, between Aubenas and Le Puy-en-Velay.
Languages spoken: German, English.
Menu: 55 (wine and coffee included) to 120 Frs.
Accommodation: 95 to 190 Frs.
Restaurant: breakfast from 8.00. Lunch from 10.30 until 15.00. Dinner from 18.30 until 21.00. Closed Sat evening, Sun.
Specialities: home-cooking.
Hotel: ☆ 8 rooms. Facilities: shower.
Other points: credit cards accepted, bar, children's menu, à la carte menu, traditional decor, terrace, pets allowed, car/lorry parking.
❧ *parc de Vals.*

LAMBESC
Bouches-du-Rhône, 13410

🍴 **LE RELAIS DE LA GARE**
(Mme Germaine Lansac) boulevard des Coopératives ☎ 42.92.97.60
Directions: RN 7.
Languages spoken: Italian.
Restaurant: closed Sun.
Other points: bar.

LAMOTTE-DU-RHONE
Vaucluse, 84840

🏠 **LE RELAIS DU RHONE**
(Mme Elise Ruat) Quartier Santi
☎ 90.30.41.89
Directions: RN 994, Pont-Saint-Esprit.
Languages spoken: German, English.
Menu: 50 Frs.
Accommodation: 50 Frs.
Restaurant: breakfast from 6.00. Lunch from 12.00 until 14.00. Dinner from 19.00 until 21.00. Closed from Sat 3pm to Mon 6am.
Specialities: home-cooking.
Hotel: 5 rooms. Facilities: shower.
Other points: credit cards accepted, bar, modern decor, terrace, pets allowed, car/lorry parking.
❧ *gorges of the Ardèche (13km); Pont-Saint-Esprit.*

LANCON-DE-PROVENCE
Bouches-du-Rhône, 13680

🏠 **AUBERGE DU MOULIN**
(Mme Monique Eymard) Route Nationale 113
☎ 90.42.71.14
Directions: RN 113, between Salon-de-Provence and Marseille.
Menu: 55 Frs.
Accommodation: 100 Frs.
Restaurant: breakfast from 5.30. Lunch 11.30 to 15.00. Dinner 19.00 to 21.00. Closed Sun.
Specialities: regional menu, home-cooking.
Hotel: 6 rooms. Facilities: shower.
Other points: credit cards accepted, bar, children's menu, à la carte menu, terrace, pets allowed, car/lorry parking.
❧ *château Cempeni; zoo at La Barben; musée Grévin (wax figures).*

🍴 **L'ARCHE DE LANCON-DE-PROVENCE**
(M. Marcel Prioul) A7, services at Lançon-de-Provence (accessible in both directions)
☎ 90.42.88.88 [Fax] 90.42.83.60
Other points: credit cards accepted, facilities open 24 hours.

🏠 **LE RELAIS DES FOURCHES**
(M. Bruno Calderone) Quartier des Ferrages, Route Nationale 113 ☎ 90.42.71.21
Directions: RN 113.
Menu: 60 to 75 Frs.
Accommodation: 100 Frs.
Restaurant: breakfast from 6.30. Closed Sun and public holidays.
Specialities: paella, couscous, regional menu, home-cooking.
Hotel: 3 rooms. Facilities: shower, private bathroom.
Other points: credit cards accepted, bar, traditional decor, terrace, pets allowed, car/lorry parking.
❧ *Salon-de-Provence; Arles; l'Etang de Berre.*

LEYMENT • Ain, 01150

🏠 **LE RELAIS DE LA GARE**
(M. Marcel Bessière) 34 rue de la Gare
☎ 74.34.94.30
Directions: RN 84.
Restaurant: closed Tues afternoon, Wed afternoon, and from 22nd Dec to 2nd Jan.
Hotel: 7 rooms.
Other points: bar.

LIGNANE • Bouches-du-Rhône, 13540

🍴 **LE RELAIS DE LIGNANE**
(M. Christian Mondin) Route Nationale 7
☎ 42.92.51.15
Directions: RN 7, the Aix-en-Provence/Avignon/ Salon road.
Menu: 55 to 65 Frs ✍
Restaurant: breakfast from 6.00. Lunch from 11.00 until 14.30. Dinner from 19.00 until 23.00. Closed Sun, and in mid-Aug.
Specialities: pieds et paquets (mutton tripe and

trotters), boeuf en daube, alouettes sans tête (beef or veal strips), civet de porcellet, regional menu, home-cooking.
Other points: bar, traditional decor, terrace, car/lorry parking.
◄€ *Aix-en-Provence; La Barben: chateau; Lauris.*

LIVRON • Drôme, 26250

🏠 **AUBERGE RELAIS MACAMP**
(Mme Josiane Vocanson) Route Nationale 7, Fiancey ☎ 75.61.73.91
Directions: RN 7.
Restaurant: breakfast from 6.30. Closed Sun, and in Aug.
Specialities: regional menu, home-cooking.
Hotel: 17 rooms. Facilities: shower, private bathroom, television.
Other points: credit cards accepted, bar, children's menu, lounge area, traditional decor, terrace, pets allowed, car/lorry parking.
◄€ *the Ardèche region; Le Vercors.*

LA LONDE-DES-MAURES
Var, 83250

🍴 **LE PETIT BOIS**
(Mme Yvette Bouvier) Route de Maramar
☎ 94.66.80.12
Menu: 55 Frs.
Restaurant: breakfast from 7.00.
Other points: bar, lorry parking.

LORIOL • Drôme, 26270

🍴 **LE RELAIS DE SAINT-PAUL**
(M. Jacques Plessis) Route Nationale 7
☎ 75.61.76.31
Directions: RN 7.
Menu: 58 Frs.
Restaurant: breakfast from 6.00. Lunch from 11.30 until 14.30. Dinner from 19.00 until 21.30. Closed Sun (out of season).
Specialities: home-cooking.
Other points: credit cards accepted, bar, children's menu, à la carte menu, modern decor, terrace, pets allowed, car/lorry parking.

LYON • Rhône, 69002

🍴 **LES ROUTIERS**
(M. Pierre Sala) 21 quai Perrache
☎ 78.37.75.86
Directions: via Fourvière tunnel, towards Perrache.
Menu: 65 Frs (wine included).
Restaurant: breakfast from 7.00. Lunch from 12.00 until 15.00. Dinner from 19.30 until 24.00. Closed Sat, Sun, and in Aug.
Specialities: home-cooking.
Other points: children's menu, modern decor, pets allowed, car/lorry parking.
◄€ *Lyon.*

MARCILLY-LE-CHATEL
Loire, 42130

🍴 **RELAIS DU CHATEL**
(Mme Josianne Béal) Le Bourg
☎ 77.97.44.36
Directions: RD 8, between Boën and Montbrison.
Menu: 55 to 75 Frs.
Restaurant: breakfast from 7.00. Lunch from 12.00 until 14.00. Dinner from 19.00 until 21.00. Closed last 2 weeks in Aug.
Specialities: home-cooking.
Other points: bar, children's menu, à la carte menu, traditional decor, terrace, pets allowed, car/lorry parking.
◄€ *château de Sainte-Anne (volerie du Forez); la Bâtie d'Urfé.*

MARSEILLE
Bouches-du-Rhône, 13016

🍴 **BAR DE LA GARE D'ARENC**
(M. Philippe Chiaramonte) 25 rue d'Anthoine
☎ 91.91.23.07
Languages spoken: English, Italian.
Menu: 45 Frs.
Restaurant: breakfast from 5.00. Closed Sat, Sun.
Other points: bar, car parking.

🍴 **LE RELAIS DES AMIS**
(M. Raymond Servière) 110 boulevard de Paris ☎ 91.62.60.76
Directions: RN 8.
Menu: 35 Frs (choice of 8 main courses).
Restaurant: breakfast from 5.00. Closed Sat, Sun, and in Aug.
Specialities: regional menu, home-cooking.
Other points: bar, à la carte menu, traditional decor, pets allowed, car/lorry parking.
◄€ *Marseille.*

MARTIGUES
Bouches-du-Rhône, 13500

🍴 **RELAIS ROUTIER LES COPAINS**
(Mme Marcelle Sodano) Zone Industrielle (Z.I.) Croix-Saintes ☎ 42.49.36.57
Languages spoken: Italian.
Menu: 50 Frs.
Restaurant: breakfast from 6.00. Lunch from 12.00. Dinner from 19.00.
Other points: bar, car/lorry parking.

MEGEVE • Haute-Savoie, 74120

🏠 **CHALET DES FLEURS**
(M. Georges Roussel) Pont d'Arbon
☎ 50.21.21.46
Directions: RN 212, from Sallanches, first building on the left as you enter Megève.
Languages spoken: English.
Menu: 87 to 18 Frs 🍽
Accommodation: 150 to 270 Frs.

Restaurant: breakfast from 7.00. Lunch from 12.00 until 14.30. Dinner from 19.30 until 22.00. Closed from Apr to mid-June, and from Oct to mid-Dec.
Specialities: truite à la crème et aux amandes, escalope normande garnie, quenelles (meatballs) de brochet à la crème, foie gras des Landes à l'Armagnac, regional menu, home-cooking.
Hotel: ✫ ✫ 25 rooms. Facilities: shower, private bathroom, television.
Other points: credit cards accepted, bar, à la carte menu, lounge area, terrace, pets allowed, car/lorry parking.
◁᷂ Mont-Blanc; Mont d'Arbois; Rochebrune; Le Jaillet; gorges of the Arlly; numerous lakes.

MEGEVETTE
Haute-Savoie, 74490

🍴 **AUBERGE DE MEGEVELLE**
(M. Thierry Balandras) Le Bourg
☎ 50.35.76.71 [Fax] 50.35.73.12
Directions: RD 922, 'autoroute blanche', Findrol exit.
Languages spoken: German, English, Spanish.
Menu: 65 to 150 Frs.
Accommodation: 210 to 300 Frs.
Restaurant: breakfast from 7.00. Lunch from 12.00 until 14.00. Dinner from 19.00 until 22.30.
Specialities: tartiflette, écrevisses, féra (salmon) du Lac Léman, regional menu, home-cooking.
Hotel: ✫ ✫ 7 rooms. Facilities: shower, private bathroom, television, telephone.
Other points: credit cards accepted, bar, children's menu, lounge area, modern decor, terrace, pets allowed, car/lorry parking.
◁᷂ grottes (caves) de Mégèvette; moulin à eau (water-mill); lac de Vallon; Duriss valley; ski resort.

MENTON
Alpes Maritimes, 06500

🍴 **RAPID BAR**
(M. Alexandre Pérucchini) 63 avenue Cernuschi ☎ 93.35.93.69
Directions: Route de Sainte-Agnès.
Languages spoken: English, Italian.
Restaurant: breakfast from 7.00. Lunch from 12.00 until 14.30.
Specialities: home-cooking.
Other points: bar, modern decor, terrace, pets allowed, car/lorry parking.

MEYTHET • Haute-Savoie, 74960

🏨 **LE RELAIS**
(M. Claude Gallay) 22 route de Frangy
☎ 50.22.02.93
Accommodation: 120 to 150 Frs.
Restaurant: dinner until 22.00. Closed Sun, 1 week at Christmas, and in May.
Hotel: 17 rooms.
Other points: bar.

MEYZIEU • Rhône, 69330

🍴 **LE RELAIS DE L'INDUSTRIE – PMU**
(M. Gérard Dumont) 104 rue de la République, Les Plantées ☎ 78.31.78.31
Directions: RD 517, Lyon.
Menu: 62 Frs (wine and coffee included).
Restaurant: breakfast from 6.30. Lunch from 11.30 until 15.00. Dinner from 19.00 until 21.30. Closed Sun afternoon.
Specialities: couscous, paella, choucroute (Friday), home-cooking.
Other points: credit cards accepted, bar, modern decor, terrace, pets allowed, car/lorry parking.

MEZEL
Alpes-de-Haute-Provence, 04270

🏨 **HOTEL-RESTAURANT DE LA PLACE**
(Mme Christiane Sarracanie et Fils) place Victor-Arnaux ☎ 92.35.58.10
Directions: RN 85, between Digne and Nice.
Languages spoken: English, Spanish.
Menu: 65 to 110 Frs.
Accommodation: 135 to 210 Frs.
Restaurant: breakfast from 6.30. Lunch 12.00 to 14.00. Dinner 19.30 to 21.00. Closed Mon (out of season), and from 15th Dec to 15th Jan.
Specialities: civet de porcelet, écrevisses provençales, regional menu, home-cooking.
Hotel: 11 rooms. Facilities: shower, private bathroom.
Other points: credit cards accepted, bar, children's menu, à la carte menu, lounge area, traditional decor, terrace, pets allowed, car/lorry parking.
◁᷂ gorges of the Verdon; Col d'Allos; lac de Sainte-Croix; geological storehouse.

MEZERIAT • Ain, 01660

🍴 **RELAIS DE MEZERIAT**
(M. Alain Darbon) Les Pigots ☎ 74.30.25.87
Directions: RN 79, A40 autoroute, exit Mâcon Est (East), towards the town (bourg).
Menu: 68 to 148 Frs.
Restaurant: breakfast from 6.30. Lunch 12.00 to 14.30. Dinner 19.00 to 22.30. Closed Sun, Aug.
Specialities: grenouilles, poulet à la crème, fricassé de volaille à la crème, regional menu.
Other points: credit cards accepted, bar, children's menu, à la carte menu, traditional decor, terrace, pets allowed, car/lorry parking.

MIONNAY • Ain, 01390

🍴 **LE RELAIS BRESSAN**
(Monique Millet and Christian Desmaris) Route Nationale 83 ☎ 78.91.05.23
Directions: RN 83, Les Echets exit.
Menu: 58 Frs (plat du jour from 42 Frs).
Restaurant: breakfast from 5.00. Lunch 11.00 to 15.00. Dinner 19.00 to 20.30. Closed Sat, Sun, 3 weeks in Aug and one week in winter.

233

Specialities: home-cooking.
Other points: credit cards accepted, lounge area, traditional decor, terrace, pets allowed, car/lorry parking.
◀€ *Pérouges; parc des oiseaux (bird park) at Villars-les-Dombes; musée du camion (HGVs) at Villars; musée de l'automobile at Rochetaillée.*

MIRABEAU • Vaucluse, 84120

🏨 RELAIS DE LA DILIGENCE
(M. Alain Michel) Route Nationale 96
☎ 90.77.00.90 [Fax] 90.77.05.10
Directions: RN 96, the Manosque/Sisteron road.
Languages spoken: English, Italian.
Accommodation: 80 to 100 Frs.
Restaurant: breakfast from 5.00.
Specialities: paella, couscous, bouillabaisse, cassoulet, home-cooking.
Hotel: 5 rooms. Facilities: shower, private bathroom, television, telephone.
Other points: credit cards accepted, bar, children's menu, lounge area, traditional decor, terrace, pets allowed, car/lorry parking.
◀€ *chateaux at Mirabeau and Peyrolles; la Tour d'Aigues.*

MODANE • Savoie, 73500

🏨 LA CROIX DU SUD
(M. Bernard Mestrallet) La Praz
☎ 79.05.34.47
Directions: RN 6, Fréjus tunnel.
Languages spoken: English, Italian.
Menu: 60 Frs.
Accommodation: 120 Frs.
Restaurant: breakfast from 7.00. Lunch 12.00 to 14.00. Dinner 19.00 to 24.30. Closed Sun, Aug.
Specialities: home-cooking.
Hotel: 6 rooms. Facilities: shower.
Other points: credit cards accepted, bar, children's menu, terrace, pets allowed, car/lorry parking.
◀€ *parc national de la Vanoise; col du Mont-Cenis; col du Liseran.*

MOIDIEU-DETOURBE • Isère, 38440

🍴 CHEZ DEDE
(M. André Seigle) ☎ 74.58.13.02
Directions: RD 502, the Vienne/Grenoble road.
Menu: 60 Frs.
Restaurant: breakfast from 5.00. Lunch 11.00 to 14.00. Dinner 19.00 to 21.30. Closed Sat afternoon, Sun afternoon, 2 weeks in Aug, 1 week at Christmas.
Specialities: home-cooking.
Other points: bar, car/lorry parking.

MOIRANS • Isère, 38430

🍴 LE RELAIS DU VIADUC
(M. Fernand Barral-Poulat) 4 route de Grenoble ☎ 76.35.31.01
Directions: RN 85, the Lyon/Grenoble road.
Menu: 55 Frs.
Accommodation: 70 Frs.

Restaurant: breakfast from 6.00. Lunch 11.30 to 15.00. Dinner 19.30 to 22.00. Closed Sat and Sun.
Specialities: home-cooking.
Other points: credit cards accepted, bar, children's menu, modern decor, terrace, pets allowed, car/lorry parking.
◀€ *lakes; dams; grottes (caves) de Sassenage; Chartreuse liqueur cellars.*

MONTAUROUX • Var, 83440

🏨 LE RELAIS DU LAC
(Nicole and Jean Hernandez) Route Nationale 562 ☎ 94.76.43.65 [Fax] 94.47.60.13
Directions: RN 562, between Grasse and Draguignan.
Languages spoken: English, Spanish.
Restaurant: dinner until 23.00.
Specialities: paella, couscous.
Hotel: ✩ ✩ 37 rooms.
Other points: bar, children's menu, terrace, car/lorry parking.

MONTBRISON • Loire, 42600

🏨 LE RELAIS DE LA GARE
(M. Jean-Pierre Gacon) 2 place de la Gare
☎ 77.58.30.33
Menu: 60 to 110 Frs.
Accommodation: 99 to 120 Frs.
Restaurant: breakfast from 6.30. Dinner until 22.00. Closed Sun, and in Aug.
Specialities: home-cooking.
Hotel: 8 rooms. Facilities: shower, private bathroom, telephone.
Other points: bar, children's menu, terrace, pets allowed, car/lorry parking.

MONTFAVET • Vaucluse, 84140

🏨 RELAIS DE BONPAS
(M. Alain Laugier) Route Nationale 7
☎ 90.23.07.01
Directions: RN 7, between Avignon and Marseille, exit Avignon Sud (South).
Languages spoken: English, Spanish.
Menu: 63 to 100 Frs.
Accommodation: 95 to 120 Frs.
Restaurant: breakfast from 6.00. Lunch from 11.30 until 14.30. Dinner from 19.00 until 23.00.
Specialities: home-cooking.
Hotel: ✩ 15 rooms. Facilities: shower.
Other points: credit cards accepted, bar, à la carte menu, modern decor, terrace, pets allowed, car/lorry parking.
◀€ *Fontaine-de-Vaucluse; Avignon; Les Baux-de-Provence; the Lubéron and Camargue regions; Saint-Rémy-de-Provence.*

🏨 See also AVIGNON

MONTFERRAT • Isère, 38620

🍴 LE PRESSOIR
(M. Gérard Coffinhal) Le Bourg
☎ 76.32.31.82

Directions: RN 75, between Bourg-en-Bresse and Grenoble.
Menu: 45 to 120 Frs.
Restaurant: breakfast from 8.00. Lunch from 12.00 until 14.30. Dinner from 19.00 until 21.00. Closed Sun evening and Mon.
Specialities: regional menu, home-cooking.
Other points: credit cards accepted, bar, children's menu, modern decor, terrace, pets allowed, car/lorry parking.
◁€ *lacs de Paladru and de Charavines; Walibi: leisure park (15km).*

MONTFORT
Alpes-de-Haute-Provence, 04600

☲ **LE RELAIS FLEURI DE MONTFORT**
(M. Robert Estournet) Route Nationale 96
☎ 92.64.11.91
Directions: RN 96, between Peyruis and Saint-Auban.
Menu: 65 Frs.
Restaurant: breakfast from 7.00. Lunch from 11.30 until 15.00. Dinner from 19.00 until 22.00. Closed Sun evening.
Specialities: home-cooking.
Other points: credit cards accepted, bar, children's menu, à la carte menu, terrace, pets allowed, car/lorry parking.
◁€ *pénitents des Mées; station de Lurs.*

MONTROND-LES-BAINS
Loire, 42210

☲ **BAR-RESTAURANT LE 82**
(M. Patrice Pereira) 37 route de Roanne
☎ 77.54.89.88
Directions: RN 82, the Saint-Etienne/Roanne road.
Languages spoken: English, Spanish, Portuguese.
Menu: 58 Frs.
Restaurant: breakfast from 6.00. Lunch from 11.30 until 15.00. Dinner from 19.00 until 23.00.
Specialities: home-cooking.
Other points: credit cards accepted, bar, children's menu, modern decor, terrace, pets allowed, car/lorry parking.
◁€ *casino at Montrond; thermal spring.*

☲ **LES OMBRELLES**
(M. Laurent Thouant) Route Nationale 82, Meylieu ☎ 77.54.52.44
Directions: RN 82, between Saint-Etienne and Clermont-Ferrand.
Languages spoken: English.
Menu: 57 Frs.
Restaurant: breakfast from 4.00. Lunch 11.45 to 15.00. Dinner 19.00 to 21.30. Closed Sat, Sun, mid-Apr to mid-May, and one week at Christmas.
Specialities: cuisses de grenouilles (in July/Aug), home-cooking.
Other points: credit cards accepted, bar, children's menu, traditional decor, terrace, pets allowed, car/lorry parking.
◁€ *château de Montrond.*

MORANCE · Rhône, 69480

🍽 **RESTAURANT DE LA MAIRIE**
(M. Rémy Dorier) Le Bourg ☎ 78.43.60.82
Directions: RD 100, the Anse/Larbresle/Feurs road.
Accommodation: 120 to 150 Frs.
Restaurant: breakfast from 7.00. Lunch from 11.30 until 14.30. Dinner from 19.00 until 21.00.
Specialities: home-cooking.
Hotel: 5 rooms.
Other points: bar, children's menu, lounge area, modern decor, terrace, pets allowed, car/lorry parking.
◁€ *Beaujolais wine circuit; Villefranche-sur-Saône.*

MORNANT · Rhône, 69440

☲ **LE RELAIS DE BELLEVUE**
(M. Patrick Coupard) Route Départementale 42, Bellevue ☎ 78.81.22.26
Directions: RD 42, between Brignais and Rive-de-Gier.
Languages spoken: Spanish.
Menu: 58 to 150 Frs.
Restaurant: breakfast from 6.30. Lunch from 11.30 until 15.00. Dinner from 19.00 until 22.00. Closed 1st Sun of each month, and in Aug.
Specialities: poulet aux écrevisses, loup (bass) à l'américaine, regional menu.
Other points: credit cards accepted, bar, children's menu, à la carte menu, modern decor, pets allowed, car/lorry parking.
◁€ *Mornant; monts du Lyonnais.*

MORNAS · Vaucluse, 84420

☲ **L'ARCHE DE MORNAS**
(M. Stéphane Brun) A7, services at Mornas Village, (accessible in Lyon/Marseille direction) ☎ 90.37.03.09 [Fax] 90.37.05.29
Other points: credit cards and foreign currency accepted, facilities open 24 hours.

☲ **LA CASCADE**
(Mme Jeanne Bretagnolle) Route Nationale 7
☎ 90.37.02.67
Directions: RN 7, the Avignon road.
Languages spoken: Spanish.
Menu: 60 Frs.
Restaurant: breakfast from 5.00. Lunch from 11.30 until 14.30. Dinner from 19.00 until 22.30. Closed Sat, Sun and 3 weeks in Aug.
Other points: credit cards accepted, bar, pets allowed, car/lorry parking.
◁€ *Mornas: medieval chateau.*

LE MUY · Var, 83490

🍽 **LA CHAUMIERE**
(M. Claude Brunasso-Cattarello) Quartier de la Gare (near station), Route Nationale 7
☎ 94.45.10.81
Directions: RN 7.
Languages spoken: Italian.
Menu: 55 Frs.

Accommodation: 110 (half board) to 160 Frs (full board).
Restaurant: lunch from 11.45 until 14.30. Dinner from 19.00 until 21.30. Closed Sun.
Hotel: 7 rooms.
Other points: bar.

MYANS • Savoie, 73800

L'ARCHE DE CHAMBERY GRANIER.
(M. Thierry Sauvage) A41, services at Granier (accessible in both directions)
☎ 79.28.24.70 Fax 79.28.22.77
Other points: credit cards and foreign currency accepted.

NANTUA • Ain, 01130

LE MALOUIN
(M. Michel Garel) 11 rue du Docteur-Mercie
☎ 74.75.22.75
Directions: Bourg-Genève.
Menu: 57 to 110 Frs.
Restaurant: breakfast from 7.00. Lunch 11.00 to 14.30. Dinner 19.30 to 22.00. Closed Mon, Aug.
Specialities: fruits de mer, galette bretonne, regional menu, home-cooking.
Other points: credit cards taken, bar, children's menu, à la carte menu, traditional decor, car/lorry parking.
◁ lac de Nantua; grottes (caves) de Cerdon; Le Bugey: centrale électrique (power station); Le Poizat.

NEAUX • Loire, 42470

CHEZ GINOU
(Mme Geneviève Ducreux) Route Nationale 7 – La Croix ☎ 77.62.70.32
Directions: RN 7, between Lyon and Roanne.
Menu: 55 to 60 Frs.
Restaurant: breakfast from 5.00. Lunch from 11.00 until 14.30. Dinner from 19.00 until 21.30. Closed Mon afternoon, Sun, and in Aug.
Specialities: home-cooking.
Other points: credit cards accepted, bar, children's menu, traditional decor, terrace, pets allowed, car/lorry parking.
◁ Loire: gorges and chateaux.

NOVES • Bouches-du-Rhône, 13550

RELAIS DE LA BASSAQUE
(M. Joseph Masi) Route Nationale 7
☎ 90.94.26.84
Directions: RN 7.
Languages spoken: Italian.
Restaurant: closed Sun.
Other points: bar.

NOYAREY • Isère, 38360

AU BON ACCUEIL
(M. Jean-Claude Compe) rue du Maupas
☎ 76.53.95.61
Directions: RN 532, the Grenoble/Valence road.

Languages spoken: German, Spanish, Italian.
Menu: 61 to 85 Frs.
Accommodation: 90 to 140 Frs.
Restaurant: breakfast from 5.30. Lunch from 11.30 until 14.00. Closed Sat and Sun.
Specialities: home-cooking.
Hotel: 11 rooms. Facilities: shower.
Other points: bar, children's menu, traditional decor, terrace, pets allowed, car/lorry parking.
◁ Le Vercors; La Chartreuse massif.

ORANGE • Vaucluse, 84100

LA FINE FOURCHETTE ORANGEOISE
(M. Joseph Delhorme) Route Nationale 7, Pont-de-l'Aygues ☎ 90.51.76.35
Directions: RN 7, Nord (North) exit.
Languages spoken: Italian.
Menu: 50 Frs.
Restaurant: breakfast from 8.00. Dinner until 24.00. Closed Mon afternoon and Tues (out of season).
Specialities: charolais (beef), regional menu, home-cooking.
Other points: credit cards accepted, bar, children's menu, à la carte menu, modern decor, terrace, pets allowed, car/lorry parking.

ORGON • Bouches-du-Rhône, 13660

AU BEC FIN
(Mme Arlette Sault) Route Nationale 7
☎ 90.73.00.49
Directions: RN 7, between Aix-en-Provence and Marseille.
Languages spoken: Spanish, Italian.
Menu: 55 Frs.
Restaurant: breakfast from 5.00. Lunch from 11.30 until 15.00. Dinner from 19.00 until 23.00. Closed Sat evening, Sun.
Specialities: couscous, paella, gratin du chef, regional menu, home-cooking.
Other points: credit cards accepted, bar, children's menu, à la carte menu, lounge area, traditional decor, terrace, car/lorry parking.
◁ Les Baux-de-Provence; Gordes; Fontaine-de-Vaucluse.

BRASSERIE BELLEVUE
(M. Jean-Louis Gros) Route Nationale 7
☎ 90.73.00.24 Fax 90.73.08.70
Directions: RN 7, the Marseille/Lyon road.
Menu: 55 to 95 Frs.
Restaurant: breakfast from 6.00. Lunch from 11.30 until 15.30. Dinner from 18.30.
Specialities: Provençal dishes, regional menu, home-cooking.
Other points: credit cards accepted, bar, children's menu, à la carte menu, terrace, pets allowed, car/lorry parking.
◁ Les Baux-de-Provence; the Lubéron region.

RELAIS DES FUMADES
(M. Jean Etcheverry) ☎ 90.73.00.81
Fax 90.73.30.69
Directions: RN 7, between Avignon and Aix-en-Provence.

Languages spoken: German, English, Italian, Spanish.
Menu: 57 to 70 Frs.
Accommodation: 110 to 150 Frs.
Restaurant: breakfast from 6.00. Lunch from 12.00 until 14.00. Dinner from 19.30 until 24.00.
Specialities: home-cooking.
Hotel: ☆ 11 rooms. Facilities: shower.
Other points: credit cards accepted, bar, lounge area, traditional decor, terrace, pets allowed, car/lorry parking.
◀€ Saint-Rémy-de-Provence; Salon; Gordes; Fontaine-de-Vaucluse.

ORLIENAS • Rhône, 69530

⇛ BAR-RESTAURANT CHEZ CHAPELLE
(Mme Annie Chapelle) Les 7 Chemins
☎ 78.05.21.54
Directions: RN 86, the Lyon/Saint-Etienne road.
Menu: 57 Frs.
Restaurant: breakfast from 5.30. Lunch from 12.00 until 15.00. Closed Sat and Sun.
Specialities: cuisses de grenouilles, couscous, paella, home-cooking.
Other points: bar, modern decor, terrace, pets allowed, car/lorry parking.
◀€ Lyon: aqueducts, wine-cellars of côteau du Lyonnais, with tasting (caveau de dégustation), at Millery and Taluyers.

LA PACAUDIERE • Loire, 42310

⇛ LE RELAIS DU LAC
(M. Marcel Vernay) Route Nationale 7
☎ 77.64.36.08
Directions: RN 7, the Roanne/Paris road, at Pacaudière Nord (North).
Menu: 59 Frs.
Accommodation: 60 to 100 Frs.
Restaurant: breakfast from 5.00. Lunch from 11.30 until 15.00. Dinner from 19.00 until 24.00. Closed Sat evening, Sun lunch, and in Aug.
Specialities: regional menu, home-cooking.
Hotel: 3 rooms. Facilities: shower.
Other points: credit cards taken, bar, children's menu, traditional decor, pets allowed, car/lorry parking.
◀€ Petit Douvre; La Pacaudière; Le Crozet: medieval village.

PAJAY • Isère, 38260

🏠 MA PETITE AUBERGE
(Mme Huguette Vivier) La Côte Saint-André
☎ 74.54.26.06
Directions: RD 73.
Languages spoken: German, English.
Menu: 55 to 120 Frs ☜
Accommodation: 80 to 150 Frs.
Restaurant: breakfast from 6.00. Lunch 12.00 to 14.00. Dinner 19.00 to 21.00. Closed 1st 2 wks Sept.
Specialities: grenouilles, lotte (monkfish) à l'américaine, gratin dauphinois, regional menu.
Hotel: 7 rooms. Facilities: shower, private bathroom, television.

Other points: bar, children's menu, à la carte menu, lounge area, traditional decor, terrace, pets allowed, car/lorry parking.
◀€ Côte Saint-André; Berlioz museum; route du tabac; Auterive: palais idéal du Facteur Cheval; Voiron: la Chartreuse.

PARIGNY-LE-COTEAU • Loire, 42120

🏠 RELAIS LE PARIGNY
(Mme Christine Favre) Route Nationale 7, Le Bas-de-Rhins ☎ 77.62.06.18
Directions: RN 7.
Menu: 55 Frs.
Accommodation: 90 to 120 Frs.
Restaurant: breakfast from 6.00. Lunch from 11.30 until 14.30. Dinner from 19.00 until 21.30. Closed Sat afternoon, Sun and 1st 2 weeks in Aug.
Specialities: home-cooking.
Hotel: 7 rooms. Facilities: shower.
Other points: bar, children's menu, traditional decor, pets allowed, car/lorry parking.

PERTUIS • Vaucluse, 84120

⇛ LE VICTOR HUGO
(M. Jacky Chalot) 143 boulevard Victor-Hugo
☎ 90.79.12.29
Directions: on the Cavaillon road.
Languages spoken: English, Italian.
Menu: 55 Frs.
Restaurant: breakfast from 6.30. Lunch from 11.30 until 15.00. Closed Sat evening and Sun.
Specialities: home-cooking.
Other points: bar, children's menu, traditional decor, terrace, pets allowed, car/lorry parking.
◀€ châteaux d'Ansouis, de Lourmarin and de la Tour-d'Aigues; étang (pond) de la Bonde.

PIERRELATTE • Drôme, 26700

🏠 LE RELAIS DES COTES DU RHONE
(M. Laurent Ouamed) Quartier des Blâches, Route Nationale 7 Sud ☎ 75.04.04.21
Directions: RN 7.
Languages spoken: English.
Menu: 60 Frs.
Accommodation: 120 to 150 Frs.
Restaurant: breakfast from 5.00. Lunch 11.30 to 14.30. Dinner 19.00 to 23.00. Closed Sun.
Specialities: couscous, paella, choucroute, cassoulet, home-cooking.
Hotel: 6 rooms. Facilities: shower.
Other points: credit cards accepted, bar, children's menu, lounge area, modern decor, terrace, pets allowed, car/lorry parking.
◀€ gorges of the Ardèche; Le Tricastin: centrale (nuclear centre).

PIOLENC • Vaucluse, 84420

⇛ LE COMMERCE
(M. Roger Sambucini) place Cours-Corsin
☎ 90.29.60.14 [Fax] 90.29.60.14

Directions: RN 7.
Languages spoken: English.
Menu: 56 to 120 Frs 🍽
Restaurant: breakfast from 7.00. Lunch 12.00 to 14.00. Dinner 19.00 to 21.00. Closed Wed, Dec.
Specialities: filet de boeuf aux morilles, poulet, écrevisses, pieds et paquets (mutton tripe and trotters), galantine de canard, home-cooking.
Other points: credit cards taken, bar, à la carte menu, modern decor, terrace, pets allowed, car parking.
◁€ *Orange: arc de triomphe (5km); Avignon: Palais des Papes, pont Saint-Bénézet.*

LA POINTE-DE-BLAUSASC
Alpes Maritimes, 06440

=€ **LE RELAIS CAMPAGNARD**
(Mme Lannoy) ☎ 93.91.13.14
Languages spoken: English.
Menu: 58 Frs.
Restaurant: breakfast from 6.00. Lunch 11.30 to 14.30. Dinner 19.00 to 20.00. Closed Sun.
Specialities: home-cooking.
Other points: credit cards accepted, bar, terrace, pets allowed, car/lorry parking.

PONT-D'AIN • Ain, 01160

=€ **RESTAURANT DE LA GARE –
LE CRISNO**
(M. Christian Sanchez) 56 rue Saint-Exupéry
☎ 74.39.01.22 [Fax] 74.39.18.48
Menu: 60 to 90 Frs.
Restaurant: breakfast from 6.00. Lunch from 11.30 until 15.00. Dinner from 19.00 until 23.00.
Other points: credit cards taken, bar, children's menu, modern decor, pets allowed, car/lorry parking.
◁€ *Cerdon; château d'Ambronay; Le Bugey: centrale électrique (power station).*

PONT-DE-CHERUY • Isère, 38230

🛏 **LE ROUTIER**
(M. Bernard Demonet) 30 rue Giffard
☎ 78.32.20.02
Directions: RN 517, the Loyettes road.
Languages spoken: Italian.
Menu: 60 Frs (wine and coffee included).
Accommodation: 100 to 180 Frs.
Restaurant: breakfast from 5.00.
Specialities: home-cooking.
Hotel: 30 rooms. Facilities: shower.
Other points: credit cards accepted, bar, à la carte menu, lounge area, modern decor, terrace, pets allowed, car/lorry parking.
◁€ *Cremieu; Le Bugey.*

PONT-DE-L'ISERE • Drôme, 26600

=€ **L'ARCHE DE VALENCE – LATITUDE 45**
(M. Philippe Vaché) A7, services at Latitude 45, accessible in Orange/Lyon directions
☎ 75.84.50.37 [Fax] 75.84.79.09
Other points: credit cards / foreign currency accepted.

PONTCHARRA • Isère, 38530

=€ **RELAIS DU PONT DE LA GACHE**
(M. Jean-Pierre Rubatat) La Gache
☎ 76.97.30.08
Directions: RN 90, between Grenoble and Chambéry.
Languages spoken: English, Italian.
Menu: 60 to 65 Frs.
Restaurant: breakfast from 6.30. Lunch from 11.00 until 15.00. Dinner from 19.00 until 22.00. Closed Sat and the last 2 weeks in Aug.
Specialities: gratin dauphinois à la crème, regional menu, home-cooking.
Other points: credit cards accepted, modern decor, terrace, pets allowed, car/lorry parking.
◁€ *La Chartreuse massif.*

LE PONTET • Vaucluse, 84130

🛏 **L'OSERAIE**
(M. Guy Cherpin) Quartier de l'Oseraie, Route Nationale 7 ☎ 90.31.04.55
Directions: RN 7.
Menu: 60 Frs.
Accommodation: 100 to 120 Frs.
Restaurant: breakfast from 6.30. Lunch 12.00 to 14.00. Dinner 19.30 to 21.00. Closed Sat, Sun, Aug.
Specialities: home-cooking.
Hotel: 5 rooms. Facilities: shower.
Other points: credit cards accepted, bar, lounge area, traditional decor, terrace, pets allowed, car/lorry parking.
◁€ *Avignon.*

=€ **LA CROIX VERTE**
(M. Guy Prat) Route de Lyon ☎ 90.86.39.56
Directions: RN 7, Avignon North.
Menu: 60 to 75 Frs.
Restaurant: breakfast from 6.30. Lunch from 12.00 until 14.00. Dinner from 19.30 until 23.00.
Specialities: couscous, regional menu.
Other points: credit cards accepted, bar, à la carte menu, terrace, pets allowed, car/lorry parking.
◁€ *Avignon: Palais des Papes; Fontaine-de-Vaucluse; Pont du Gard.*

POURRIERES • Var, 83910

=€ **SARL LE LORRAINE-PROVENCE**
(M. Magne) Route Nationale 7
☎ 94.78.41.28
Directions: RN 7, between Aix and Saint-Maximin.
Menu: 59 to 70 Frs.
Restaurant: breakfast from 6.00. Closed Sun.
Specialities: home-cooking.
Other points: credit cards accepted, bar, children's menu, à la carte menu, modern decor, terrace, pets allowed, car/lorry parking.
◁€ *Sainte-Victoire; Saint-Maximin basilica.*

LE POUZIN • Ardèche, 07250

🛏 **LES ROUTIERS**
(Mme Juliette Vialatte) 64 rue Olivier-de-Serres ☎ 75.63.83.45

Directions: between Loriol and Privas.
Menu: 55 to 65 Frs.
Restaurant: breakfast from 7.00. Lunch 12.00 to 14.00. Dinner 19.00 to 20.30. Closed Sun, Aug.
Specialities: home-cooking.
Hotel: 5 rooms.
Other points: bar, children's menu, modern decor.
◀ the Ardèche region.

PRIVAS • Ardèche, 07000

LA RENAISSANCE
(M. Jean-Pierre Monteil) place du Champ-de-Mars ☎ 75.64.21.60
Directions: RN 104, between Pouzin and Aubenas.
Menu: 50 Frs.
Restaurant: breakfast from 7.30. Lunch 11.15 to 14.00. Dinner 19.15 to 20.30. Closed Sun, Aug.
Specialities: home-cooking.
Other points: bar.

PUYRICARD
Bouches-du-Rhône, 13540

LE TOURANGEAU
(Mme Danielle Roccia) Route Nationale 7, La Petite Calale ☎ 42.21.60.65
Directions: RN 7.
Languages spoken: Italian.
Restaurant: closed Sun, and in Aug.
Hotel: 14 rooms.
Other points: bar.

RENAGE • Isère, 38140

LE CLOS JUVIN
(M. Jean Ségui) Chemin du Gua
☎ 76.91.11.40
Directions: RN 520, the Lyon/Grenoble road.
Languages spoken: German, English, Italian.
Menu: 60 to 120 Frs.
Restaurant: breakfast from 8.30. Lunch from 11.45 until 14.30. Dinner from 19.00 until 22.00. Closed Sat lunch and Sun evening.
Specialities: regional menu, home-cooking.
Other points: credit cards accepted, bar, children's menu, à la carte menu, lounge area, traditional decor, terrace, pets allowed, car/lorry parking.
◀ Le Vercors; Renage: chapelle de la Grande Fabrique.

REYRIEUX • Ain, 01600

RESTAURANT DE LA GARE
(Mme Yvonne Ortiz) rue de la Gare
☎ 74.00.03.04
Directions: RD 933, between Neuville and Trévoux.
Languages spoken: Spanish and a little English.
Menu: 65 Frs (wine and coffee incl.); Sun 80–140 Frs.
Restaurant: breakfast from 7.00. Lunch from 11.00 until 15.30. Dinner from 19.00 until 21.00. Closed Sun (out of season).
Specialities: grenouilles fraiches, home-cooking.
Other points: credit cards accepted, bar,

children's menu, traditional decor, terrace, pets allowed, car/lorry parking.
◀ Ars: basilica; Trévoux and Pérouges: medieval cities.

RIVE-DE-GIER-LA-MADELEINE
Loire, 42800

RESTAURANT LE BARBECUE
(Mme Marie-Claude Gonon) 70 rue des Martyrs de la Résistance ☎ 77.75.59.70
Directions: RN 88, the Lyon/Saint-Etienne road.
Menu: 55 to 110 Frs.
Restaurant: breakfast from 7.00. Lunch from 11.45 until 14.30. Dinner from 19.00 until 21.00. Closed Mon afternoon (out of season).
Specialities: cuisses de grenouilles, fritures (whitebait), regional menu, home-cooking.
Other points: bar, children's menu, à la carte menu, lounge area, modern decor, terrace, pets allowed, car parking.
◀ zoo at Saint-Martin-la-Plaine; la Chartreuse de Sainte-Croix-en-Jarez; le Mont-Pilat.

ROCHE-LA-MOLIERE
Loire, 42230

LE FLORENCE
(M. Michel Bruyas) 3 rue des Carrières
☎ 77.90.58.41
Directions: between Roche-la-Molière and Saint-Genest-Lerpt.
Menu: 49 Frs.
Restaurant: lunch from 12.00 until 14.00. Dinner from 19.00 until 23.00. Closed Sun, and in Aug.
Specialities: Italian dishes, home-cooking.
Other points: à la carte menu.

ROCHEMAURE • Ardèche, 07400

RELAIS DE LA CONDAMINE
(Mme Josiane Sicoit) ☎ 75.52.96.26
Directions: RN 86, the Lyon/Marseille road.
Menu: 48 Frs.
Restaurant: breakfast from 6.00. Lunch 11.00 to 14.00. Dinner 19.00 to 20.30. Closed Sun.
Specialities: home-cooking.
Other points: terrace, pets allowed, car/lorry parking.

ROCHETAILLEE • Isère, 38520

HOTEL BELLEDONNE
(Mme Mireille Esposito) ☎ 76.80.07.04
Directions: RD 91, between Briançon and l'Alpe-d'Huez.
Menu: 65 to 110 Frs
Accommodation: 110 to 300 Frs.
Restaurant: breakfast from 6.30. Lunch from 12.00 until 13.30. Dinner from 19.30 until 21.00. Closed Sat and Sun (out of season).
Specialities: regional specialities to order, home-cooking.
Hotel: ✪ 21 rooms. Facilities: shower.
Other points: credit cards accepted, bar, à la carte

menu, modern decor, terrace, pets allowed, car/lorry parking.
◁€ *various ski resorts (stations de ski), incl. l'Alpe-d'Huez, from 3–50km.*

LA ROQUE-D'ANTHERON
Bouches-du-Rhône, 13640

🍽 **AU RELAIS FLEURI**
(M. Guy Auguste) Hameau de Saint-Christophe ☎ 42.50.20.24
Directions: CD 543 and 561, at the intersection of CD 561 and 543.
Languages spoken: English, German, Italian.
Menu: 55 to 80 Frs.
Accommodation: 120 to 150 Frs.
Restaurant: breakfast from 7.00. Lunch from 12.00 until 14.00. Dinner from 19.30 until 22.00.
Specialities: home-cooking.
Hotel: 9 rooms. Facilities: shower.
Other points: credit cards accepted, bar, children's menu, à la carte menu, traditional decor, terrace, pets allowed, car/lorry parking.
◁€ *the Lubéron region; château de Lourmarin.*

ROUSSET • Bouches-du-Rhône, 13790

🍽 **LA BEGUDE**
(Mme Rosine Barneoud) Route Nationale 7
☎ 42.29.09.82
Directions: RN 7, between Aix and Saint-Maximin.
Languages spoken: English, Italian.
Menu: 60 Frs.
Restaurant: breakfast from 6.00. Lunch from 11.30. Dinner from 18.30. Closed Sun.
Specialities: home-cooking.
Other points: credit cards accepted, children's menu, modern decor, terrace, pets allowed, car/lorry parking.

SABLONNIERES • Isère, 38460

🍽 **BAR-RESTAURANT DE LA PLACE**
(Mme Noelle Mailler) ☎ 74.92.80.19
Directions: RD 522 and 517.
Menu: 55 (75 Frs on Sun).
Restaurant: breakfast from 6.30. Lunch 12.00 to 14.30. Dinner 19.30 to 21.00. Closed Sat, Aug.
Specialities: home-cooking.
Other points: bar.

SAILLANS • Drôme, 26340

🍽 **LE NATIONAL – PMU**
(Mme Jeanine Chauvet) Grande Rue
☎ 75.21.51.33
Directions: RN 93, between Crest and Gap.
Menu: 60 to 80 Frs.
Accommodation: 120 to 180 Frs.
Restaurant: breakfast from 8.00. Lunch from 12.30 until 14.00. Dinner from 19.30 until 21.00. Closed Wed, and 5 weeks in Sept/Oct.
Specialities: gigot d'agneau, daube provençale, gratin dauphinois, regional menu, home-cooking.

Hotel: 6 rooms. Facilities: shower.
Other points: bar, children's menu, traditional decor, terrace, pets allowed, car/lorry parking.
◁€ *Drôme valley; 11thC church; Le Vercors.*

SAINT-BONNET-LES-OULES
Loire, 42330

🍽 **LE GORDON**
(Mme Marie-Thérèse Munier) Lapra
☎ 77.94.93.30
Menu: 50 to 100 Frs.
Restaurant: breakfast from 9.00. Lunch from 12.00 until 14.00. Dinner from 18.30 until 21.30.
Specialities: lapin au whisky, home-cooking.
Other points: credit cards accepted, bar, children's menu, modern decor, terrace, pets allowed, car/lorry parking.
◁€ *musée ferme agricole (farming).*

SAINT-CHAMOND • Loire, 42400

🍽 **AUBERGE DES SAULES**
(M. Jean-Michel Maillot) 39 route de la Varizelle ☎ 77.22.10.43
Directions: the Lyon/Saint-Etienne road.
Languages spoken: English.
Menu: 55 to 110 Frs.
Restaurant: breakfast from 8.00. Lunch from 11.30 until 14.30.
Specialities: home-cooking.
Other points: bar, children's menu, modern decor, car/lorry parking.
◁€ *Saint-Etienne.*

SAINT-CLAIR-DU-RHONE
Isère, 38370

🍽 **LE RELAIS FLEURI**
(M. Tonino Tognoloni) 3 rue du Commandant-l'Herminier ☎ 74.56.43.12
Directions: RN 516.
Languages spoken: Italian.
Restaurant: closed one week in Aug.
Hotel: 7 rooms.
Other points: bar, car/lorry parking, facilities open 24 hours.

SAINT-CYR-DE-FAVIERES
Loire, 42132

🍽 **RELAIS ALSACIEN**
(M. Marcel Terrier) ☎ 77.64.81.01
Directions: RN 7, the Paris/Lyon road.
Restaurant: breakfast from 6.00. Lunch 11.30 to 14.30. Dinner 19.30 to 22.00. Closed Sat, Sun, July.
Specialities: home-cooking.
Other points: bar, traditional decor, terrace, pets allowed, car/lorry parking.
◁€ *dam at Villerest.*

🍽 **RELAIS ROUTIERS LAGOUTTE**
(M. Yves Jonard) L'Hôpital-sur-Rhins
☎ 77.64.80.13

Directions: from the autoroute, exit at L'Hôpital-sur-Rhins.
Languages spoken: English.
Menu: 52 to 130 Frs.
Accommodation: 95 Frs (per person).
Restaurant: breakfast from 5.00. Lunch from 12.00 until 15.00. Dinner from 19.00 until 22.00. Closed Sat, and in Aug.
Specialities: regional menu.
Hotel: 3 rooms.
Other points: credit cards accepted, bar, lounge area, traditional decor, pets allowed, car/lorry parking.
◁€ *dam at Villerest.*

SAINT-CYR-SUR-MENTHON
Ain, 01380

≕ **SARL LE SAINT-CYR**
(M. Allek) Route Nationale 79, Le Logis
☎ 85.36.30.69
Directions: RN 79.
Languages spoken: English.
Menu: 50 to 55 Frs.
Restaurant: breakfast from 6.00. Lunch from 11.30 until 14.30. Dinner from 19.00 until 23.00.
Specialities: couscous.
Other points: bar, lorry parking.

SAINT-CYR-SUR-MER • Var, 83270

≕ **MICKEY RESTO**
(M. Christian Reverberi) 20 rue d'Arquier
☎ 94.26.49.98
Directions: on the Bandol road.
Menu: 45 to 85 Frs.
Restaurant: lunch 12.00 to 14.00. Dinner 19.15 to 24.00. Closed Sun, and from 20th Dec to 3rd Jan.
Specialities: couscous, daube, tripes, regional menu, home-cooking.
Other points: credit cards accepted, children's menu, à la carte menu, traditional decor, pets allowed, car/lorry parking.

SAINT-ETIENNE • Loire, 42000

≕ **LE MISTRAL**
(Mme Martine Gante) 4 rue Jean-Neyret
☎ 77.32.95.39
Directions: RN 82, Douanes/Marché de gros (customs/wholesale market).
Languages spoken: Spanish.
Menu: 55 Frs (wine and coffee included).
Restaurant: breakfast from 6.00. Lunch 12.00 to 15.00. Dinner 19.30 to 22.00. Closed Sat, Sun, Aug.
Specialities: couscous, pizza, home-cooking.
Other points: bar, traditional decor, pets allowed, car/lorry parking.

≕ **LE POISSON ROUGE**
(Mme Monique Coquard) 134 rue Florent-Evrard ☎ 77.81.30.52
Directions: near the western bypass (la rocade).
Menu: 52 Frs (wine and coffee included) to 89 Frs.

Restaurant: breakfast from 8.30. Lunch from 11.30 until 14.30. Dinner from 19.00 until 21.00. Closed Sun and 2 weeks in Aug.
Specialities: regional menu, home-cooking.
Other points: credit cards accepted, bar, children's menu, modern decor, terrace, car/lorry parking.
◁€ *musée de la mine (mining); le Mont-Pilat (ski piste); zoo at Saint-Martin-de-la-Plaine.*

SAINT-FIRMIN • Hautes Alpes, 05800

🏠 **LA TRINITE**
(M. Gérard Marletta) Route Nationale 85 (Route Napoléon) ☎ 92.55.21.64
Directions: RN 85, between Grenoble and Gap.
Menu: 60 to 150 Frs.
Accommodation: 130 to 220 Frs.
Restaurant: breakfast from 6.00. Lunch from 12.00. Dinner until 23.00
Specialities: oreille d'ane, magret de canard, regional menu, home-cooking.
Hotel: ☆ 12 rooms. Facilities: shower, private bathroom.
Other points: credit cards accepted, bar, children's menu, à la carte menu, modern decor, terrace, pets allowed, car/lorry parking.
◁€ *vallée de Valgodemard; Notre-Dame-de-la-Salette.*

SAINT-GENIX-SUR-GUIERS
Savoie, 73240

≕ **AUBERGE MA CAMPAGNE**
(Mme Reine Ailloud) Hameau de Joudin
☎ 76.31.80.19
Directions: RD 916, Le Pont-de-Beauvoisin.
Menu: 55 to 110 Frs.
Restaurant: breakfast from 7.00. Lunch from 11.00 until 15.00. Dinner from 19.00 until 21.00. Closed Sat, and Sept and Oct.
Specialities: grenouilles, home-cooking.
Other points: bar, à la carte menu, traditional decor, terrace, pets allowed, car/lorry parking.
◁€ *château de Montfleury-sur-Auressieux; musée d'Aoste; abbaye en Chartreuse.*

SAINT-HILAIRE-DU-ROSIER
Isère, 38840

🏠 **LE RELAIS – Chez Tony**
(M. Tony Lopez) ☎ 76.64.53.84
Directions: RN 92, between Saint-Marcellin and Romans.
Languages spoken: German, Spanish.
Menu: 55 to 98 Frs.
Accommodation: 100 to 160 Frs.
Restaurant: breakfast from 7.00. Lunch from 12.00 until 14.00. Dinner from 19.00 until 22.00. Closed Sat, Sun, and in Sept.
Hotel: 5 rooms. Facilities: shower, private bathroom.
Other points: bar, children's menu, à la carte menu, modern decor, terrace, car/lorry parking.
◁€ *Le Vercors.*

SAINT-JEAN-DE-CHEVELU
Savoie, 73170

🚌 LES QUATRE CHEMINS
(M. Jean Rubod) 'Les Quatre Chemins'
☎ 79.36.80.06 [Fax] 79.36.78.07
Directions: RN 504, between Lyon and Chambéry.
Languages spoken: English.
Menu: 62 to 120 Frs.
Accommodation: 110 to 190 Frs.
Restaurant: breakfast from 4.00. Lunch from 11.30 until 14.15. Dinner from 19.00 until 22.30. Closed Sat evening, Sun.
Specialities: home-cooking.
Hotel: 10 rooms. Facilities: shower, private bathroom.
Other points: credit cards accepted, bar, children's menu, lounge area, traditional decor, pets allowed, car/lorry parking.
◀ *abbaye de Hautecombe (12km); cru Jongieux wine-cellars.*

SAINT-JEAN-DE-MAURIENNE
Savoie, 73300

🚌 BAR-RESTAURANT RELAIS ROUTIERS
(Mme Angèle Dompnier) place du Champ-de-Foire ☎ 79.64.12.03
Directions: RN 6.
Languages spoken: Italian.
Menu: 50 to 150 Frs 🍽
Restaurant: breakfast from 7.00. Lunch 11.30 to 14.00. Dinner 19.00 to 22.00. Closed Sun.
Specialities: home-cooking.
Other points: bar, children's menu, traditional decor, terrace, pets allowed, car/lorry parking.
◀ *La Maurienne and surrounding resorts.*

SAINT-JUST-DE-CLAIX
Isère, 38680

🚌 BAR-RESTAURANT LE DAUPHINOIS
(Mme Arlette Doncques) in the village
☎ 75.47.55.25
Directions: RN 532, the Valence/Grenoble road.
Languages spoken: German, English.
Menu: 55 Frs.
Restaurant: breakfast from 6.00. Lunch from 11.30 until 15.00. Dinner from 19.00 until 21.00.
Specialities: home-cooking.
Other points: bar, children's menu, modern decor, pets allowed, car/lorry parking.
◀ *grottes (caves) de Choranche and de Thaïs; Le Vercors.*

SAINT-LAURENT-DU-VAR
Alpes Maritimes, 06700

AU COUP DE FUSIL
(M. Eugène Bagi – SARL Florèje) boulevard Pierre-et-Marie-Curie, Zone Industrielle (Z.I.) secteur B ☎ 93.31.60.55
Languages spoken: Italian.

Menu: 60 to 80 Frs.
Restaurant: breakfast from 6.30. Lunch 11.30 to 15.00. Closed Sun, public holidays, and in Aug.
Specialities: regional menu, home-cooking.
Other points: children's menu, à la carte menu, modern decor, pets allowed, car/lorry parking.
◀ *Nice; Cannes.*

🚌 LE RELAIS ROUTIER
(Mme Torrente) allée des Cableurs, Zone Industrielle (Z.I.) secteur B ☎ 93.31.26.47
Languages spoken: German, English, Spanish.
Menu: 57 Frs.
Restaurant: lunch from 12.00 until 14.00. Dinner from 19.00 until 21.30. Closed Sun.
Specialities: paella, couscous, cassoulet, home-cooking.
Other points: bar, car/lorry parking.

SAINT-MARCEL-DE-FELINES
Loire, 42122

🚌 LA REVOUTE
(M. Didier Rey) La Revoute ☎ 77.64.61.60
Directions: RN 82, between Roanne and Saint-Etienne.
Languages spoken: English.
Menu: 56 to 118 Frs.
Restaurant: breakfast from 7.30. Lunch 11.45 to 14.00. Dinner 19.00 to 21.00. Closed Mon evening, and in June.
Specialities: home-cooking.
Other points: credit cards accepted, bar, modern decor, terrace, pets allowed, car/lorry parking.
◀ *château de Saint-Marcel-de-Félines; barrage (dam) at Villerest; banks of the Loire.*

SAINT-MARCEL-LES-VALENCE
Drôme, 26320

🚌 LA PRAIRIE
(M. Michel Montusclat – SARL La Prairie) 8 rue de la Liberté ☎ 75.58.70.38
Directions: RN 532, between Valence and Romans.
Menu: 55 to 110 Frs.
Restaurant: breakfast from 7.00. Closed in Aug.
Specialities: poissons, regional menu, home-cooking.
Other points: credit cards accepted, bar, children's menu, à la carte menu, terrace, pets allowed, car/lorry parking.

SAINT-MARTIN-DE-CLELLES
Isère, 38930

🚌 MON REGAL
(Mme Monique Flandin) Route Nationale 75
☎ 76.34.42.84
Directions: RN 75.
Restaurant: dinner until 21.00. Closed every evening from Nov to Feb.
Specialities: home-cooking.
Other points: children's menu, à la carte menu, terrace, car/lorry parking.

SAINT-MARTIN-DE-CRAU
Bouches-du-Rhône, 13310

⊟ LA CABANE BAMBOU
(Jacques Giraud et Fils) Route Nationale 113
☎ 90.58.67.25
Directions: RN 113, between Salon and Arles.
Languages spoken: English, Spanish, Italian.
Restaurant: closed Sun (out of season).
Specialities: daube de toro, regional menu.
Hotel: 10 rooms.
Other points: credit cards accepted, bar, à la carte menu, terrace, pets allowed, car/lorry parking, facilities open 24 hours.
⋐ the Camargue; Les Baux-de-Provence; Saint-Rémy-de-Provence; la plaine de la Crau.

⋑ LE RELAIS DES SPORTS
(M. Daniel Nivaggioli) La Dynamite
☎ 90.47.05.24
Languages spoken: Spanish, Italian.
Menu: 50 Frs.
Restaurant: breakfast from 6.00. Closed in Aug.
Other points: bar, à la carte menu, lorry parking.

⊟ RESTAURANT DE LA GARE
(M. Pascal Selva) Route de la Dynamite
☎ 90.47.05.18
Directions: in the station area.
Menu: 52 Frs.
Accommodation: 100 Frs.
Restaurant: breakfast from 5.30. Lunch from 11.30 until 14.30. Closed Sun.
Hotel: 7 rooms.
Other points: bar, car/lorry parking.

SAINT-PAUL-LE-JEUNE
Ardèche, 07460

⋑ RELAIS DE CHEYRES
(Mme Marie-Thérése Vernede) Banne
☎ 75.39.30.09
Directions: RD 104.
Restaurant: breakfast from 8.00. Closed Sun.
Specialities: escargots, regional menu, home-cooking.
Other points: bar, children's menu, traditional decor, terrace, car/lorry parking.
⋐ grottes (caves) Cocalières; Vallon-Pont-d'Arc; Orgnac; gorges de l'Ardèche.

SAINT-RAPHAEL
Var, 83700

⊟ BEL AZUR
(M. Robert Magnani) 247 boulevard de Provence ☎ 94.95.14.08
Languages spoken: Italian.
Menu: 60 to 140 Frs ⌣
Accommodation: 180 to 250 Frs.
Restaurant: breakfast from 7.00. Lunch from 12.00 until 14.00. Dinner from 19.00 until 21.30. Closed Sat, Sun evening (out of season), and from 24th Dec to 4th Jan.

Specialities: bouillabaisse, aïoli, paella, marmite du pêcheur, soupe de poissons maison, home-cooking.
Hotel: ☆ 20 rooms. Facilities: shower, private bathroom, telephone.
Other points: credit cards accepted, children's menu, à la carte menu, traditional decor, pets allowed, car/lorry parking.
⋐ gorges of the Verdon and the Loup; Roman remains; Fréjus: Roman arena.

SAINT-ROMAIN-LA-MOTTE
Loire, 42640

⋑ AU BON ACCUEIL
(Mme Lucienne Galichon) Les Baraques, Saint-Germain-Lespinasse ☎ 77.70.12.03
Directions: RN 7, the Paris/Roanne road.
Menu: 60 to 80 Frs.
Accommodation: 72 to 176 Frs.
Restaurant: breakfast from 5.00. Lunch from 11.00 until 15.00. Dinner from 19.00 until 22.30. Closed Sat afternoon, Sun afternoon, and in Sept.
Specialities: grenouilles (in summer), fritures (whitebait), home-cooking.
Hotel: 3 rooms. Facilities: shower.
Other points: credit cards accepted, traditional decor, pets allowed, car/lorry parking.
⋐ lac de Villeré; barrage (dam) de La Toiche.

SAINTE-FOY-L'ARGENTIERE
Rhône, 69610

⋑ AUBERGE DE LA PLACE –
Chez Nadine et Christian
(Mme Nadine Aimé) 49 Grande Rue
☎ 74.70.00.51
Directions: RN 89, the main Lyon/Clermont-Ferrand road.
Languages spoken: English, Italian.
Menu: 50 to 63 Frs.
Restaurant: breakfast from 6.30. Lunch 11.00 to 15.00. Dinner 19.00 to 21.00. Closed Sat.
Specialities: home-cooking.
Other points: bar, children's menu, traditional decor, terrace, pets allowed, car/lorry parking.
⋐ wildlife park at Courzier; millinery museum at Chazelle-sur-Lyon; mining museum at Saint-Pierre-de-la-Palud.

SAINTE-FOY-LES-LYON
Rhône, 69110

⋑ AU REVEIL MATIN
(Mme Michèle Lely) 66 route de la Libération
☎ 78.59.03.05
Menu: 55 to 60 Frs.
Restaurant: breakfast from 6.00. Lunch 11.00 to 15.00. Closed Sat afternoon, Sun, and in Aug.
Specialities: home-cooking.
Other points: credit cards accepted, bar, terrace, pets allowed, car/lorry parking.
⋐ Beaunart aqueducts.

SALAISE-SUR-SANNE • Isère, 38150

⌁ RELAIS DE LA SANNE
(M. Marc Giraud) Route Nationale 7
☎ 74.86.37.91
Directions: RN 7, the Lyon/Valence road, Chanas exit.
Languages spoken: German, English.
Menu: 62 to 88 Frs.
Restaurant: breakfast from 6.00. Lunch from 11.45 until 14.30. Dinner from 19.15 until 22.30. Closed Sun.
Specialities: grenouilles, truites, home-cooking.
Other points: credit cards accepted, bar, children's menu, à la carte menu, lounge area, modern decor, terrace, pets allowed, car/lorry parking.
◖ *Peaugres: safari park; musée animalier à Ville-sous-Anjou.*

SALON-DE-PROVENCE
Bouches-du-Rhône, 13300

⌁ RESTAURANT LA JAUFFRETTE
(M. Claude Cachon) Route Nationale 113, La Jauffrette ☎ 90.53.20.19
Directions: RN 113, the Marseille road.
Menu: 51 Frs.
Restaurant: breakfast from 6.30. Closed Sat, Sun, and in Aug.
Specialities: home-cooking.
Other points: bar, car/lorry parking.
◖ *Saint-Rémy; Les Baux-de-Provence.*

SARCEY • Rhône, 69490

⌁ RELAIS DES MARRONNIERS
(M. Patrick Parisi) place de l'Eglise
☎ 74.26.86.65
Directions: RN 7, between L'Arbresle and Tarare.
Languages spoken: English.
Menu: 50 to 80 Frs.
Restaurant: breakfast from 6.00. Lunch from 12.00 until 13.30. Closed Wed afternoon.
Specialities: home-cooking.
Other points: bar, modern decor, pets allowed, car parking.
◖ *the Beaujolais region.*

SAULCE • Drôme, 26270

⌁ LE DISQUE BLEU
(M. Jacques Brillo) Quartier des Blâches, Cliousclat ☎ 75.63.00.08 Fax 75.63.13.45
Directions: RN 7 and RD 26, autoroute exits at Loriol and Montélimar Nord (North).
Menu: 60 Frs.
Accommodation: 60 to 80 Frs.
Restaurant: closed Sun.
Specialities: home-cooking.
Hotel: 8 rooms.
Other points: credit cards accepted, bar, children's menu, à la carte menu, pets allowed, car/lorry parking.

LES SAUVAGES • Rhône, 69170

⌁ HOTEL SAINT-PIERRE
(M. Jean Gouttenoire) ☎ 74.89.10.49
Directions: RD 8.
Accommodation: 80 to 220 Frs.
Restaurant: lunch from 12.00 until 13.30. Dinner from 19.00 until 20.30. Closed Wed, beginning of Sept and one week at Christmas.
Specialities: grenouilles, home-cooking.
Hotel: 7 rooms. Facilities: shower, private bathroom.
Other points: credit cards accepted, bar, traditional decor, car/lorry parking.
◖ *Notre-Dame-de-Rohe; le lac des Sapins.*

SENAS • Bouches-du-Rhône, 13560

⌁ L'ETAPE
(SNC Veyrier Frères) Route Nationale 7
☎ 90.59.22.81
Menu: 54 Frs.
Restaurant: breakfast from 6.00. Closed Sat and Sun.
Specialities: home-cooking.
Other points: credit cards accepted, à la carte menu, pets allowed, car/lorry parking.

SERVAS • Ain, 01000

⌁ LE RELAIS POSTILLON – Chez Marcelle
(M. Kaddour Lastab) Route Nationale 83
☎ 74.52.79.10
Directions: RN 83.
Menu: 57 Frs (wine and coffee included).
Accommodation: 100 to 120 Frs.
Restaurant: breakfast from 6.00. Lunch from 11.30 until 14.00. Dinner from 19.00 until 21.30. Closed Sat evening and Sun.
Specialities: home-cooking.
Hotel: 5 rooms. Facilities: private bathroom.
Other points: credit cards accepted, bar, children's menu, modern decor, pets allowed, car/lorry parking.
◖ *Villard-les-Dombe: bird park; Gourg: église de Brou.*

LA SEYNE-SUR-MER • Var, 83500

⌁ RELAIS DE BREGAILLON
(M. Robert Montesino) Route de Toulon
☎ 94.94.86.56
Directions: Route de Toulon.
Languages spoken: English, Italian and Spanish.
Accommodation: (half board and full board only).
Restaurant: breakfast from 6.00. Closed Sun.
Specialities: canard aux olives, paella, couscous, regional menu, home-cooking.
Hotel: 9 rooms.
Other points: credit cards accepted, bar, traditional decor, terrace, pets allowed, car/lorry parking.
◖ *the port; the beaches.*

SEYNOD • Haute-Savoie, 74600

RELAIS SAINTE-CATHERINE
(M. Lucien Zerbola) 181 route d'Aix
☎ 50.69.00.86 [Fax] 50.52.07.49
Directions: RN 201, exit Annecy Sud (South),
towards Chambéry.
Languages spoken: German, English.
Menu: 60 to 100 Frs.
Accommodation: 120 to 160 Frs.
Restaurant: breakfast from 6.00. Lunch from
12.00 until 13.30. Dinner from 19.30 until 21.00.
Closed Sat and Sun, and in Aug.
Specialities: steack aux morilles, fondue
savoyarde, cuisses de grenouilles, regional menu,
home-cooking.
Hotel: ☆ 10 rooms. Facilities: shower, private
bathroom.
Other points: credit cards accepted, bar, à la carte
menu, lounge area, terrace, car/lorry parking.
◀ lac d'Annecy; Albertville; Chamonix; gorge du
Fier; Mont-Blanc; chateaux.

SIGOTTIER • Hautes Alpes, 05700

PONT LA BARQUE
(M. Claude Faizende) Pont La Barque
☎ 92.67.04.15
Directions: RN 75.
Languages spoken: Italian.
Menu: 60 to 100 Frs.
Restaurant: breakfast from 7.00. Lunch 11.00 to
15.00. Dinner 19.00 to 22.00. Closed Sun (out of
season), and from 25th Dec to 7th Jan.
Specialities: gibiers (game), home-cooking.
Other points: credit cards accepted, bar, à la carte
menu, traditional decor, terrace, pets allowed, car/
lorry parking.

SISTERON
Alpes-de-Haute-Provence, 04200

LE CHALET DE L'EUROPE
(M. Jean-Marie Estèves) 1 allée des Romarins
☎ 92.61.26.55 [Fax] 92.61.26.55
Directions: in the 'parc d'activité de Sisteron'.
Menu: 65 Frs.
Restaurant: breakfast from 5.00. Lunch from
11.30 until 15.00. Dinner from 19.30 until 22.00.
Closed Sat evening and Sun.
Specialities: regional menu, home-cooking.
Other points: credit cards accepted, bar, children's
menu, terrace, pets allowed, car/lorry parking.

SURY-LE-COMTAL • Loire, 42450

RESTAURANT DE LA TERRASSE
(Mme Georgette Cote) rue Jordan
☎ 77.30.81.38
Directions: RD 8, between Saint-Etienne and
Montbrison.
Menu: 55 Frs.
Restaurant: breakfast from 7.00. Lunch from

11.45 until 15.00. Dinner from 19.00 until 21.00.
Closed Sun, and the week of 15th Aug.
Specialities: home-cooking.
Other points: credit cards accepted, bar,
children's menu, modern decor, car/lorry parking.
◀ medieval chateau and church; foire (fair) de
Saint-André.

TARARE • Rhône, 69170

LE PROVENCAL
(Mme Anne-Marie Bidot) 8 avenue Edouard-
Hérriot ☎ 74.63.33.64
Directions: RN 7, Roanne.
Menu: 51 Frs.
Restaurant: breakfast from 5.00. Lunch from
11.30 until 14.00. Dinner from 19.00 until 20.00.
Closed Sat afternoon, Sun and public holidays.
Specialities: home-cooking.

LE TEIL • Ardèche, 07400

AU BON COIN
(Mme Marie Gineste) 11 rue Henri-Barbusse
☎ 75.49.02.61
Directions: RN 86.
Restaurant: closed in Aug.
Other points: bar.

L'ETAPE
(M. Christophe Vantouroux) 40 avenue Paul-
Langevin ☎ 75.49.09.19
Directions: RN 86.
Languages spoken: German, English.
Menu: 55 Frs.
Accommodation: 100 to 120 Frs.
Restaurant: breakfast from 6.30. Lunch from
11.30 until 14.00. Dinner from 19.00 until 21.30.
Specialities: boeuf bourguignon, couscous, home-
cooking.
Hotel: 7 rooms.
Other points: bar, children's menu, traditional
decor, pets allowed, car/lorry parking.
◀ gorges of the Ardèche; Drôme chateaux.

TERNAY • Rhône, 69360

LE GAULOIS
(M. Jean-Pierre Coursat) 2 rue Saint-Nicolas
☎ 78.73.07.34
Directions: CD 12, exit Chasse-sur-Rhône,
towards Saint-Symphorien-d'Ozon.
Languages spoken: English.
Menu: 55 to 175 Frs.
Restaurant: breakfast from 6.00. Lunch from
12.00 until 14.30. Dinner from 19.00 until 22.00.
Closed Sun evening, and in Aug.
Specialities: oeufs pochés aux escargots, fricassé
de faisan (pheasant) à la moutarde de Meaux,
coquelet aux morilles, home-cooking.
Other points: credit cards accepted, bar,
children's menu, à la carte menu, traditional decor,
terrace, pets allowed, car/lorry parking.
◀ Vienne: Roman city (15km).

THOISSEY • Ain, 01140

🍴 LE RIVAGE
(Mme Véronique Panchot) Le Port
☎ 74.04.01.66
Directions: between Belleville-sur-Saône and Bourg-en-Bresse.
Languages spoken: Spanish.
Menu: 56 Frs (wine and coffee included) to 140 Frs.
Accommodation: 160 to 200 Frs.
Restaurant: breakfast from 8.00. Lunch from 11.30 until 14.30. Dinner from 19.30 until 23.30
Specialities: grenouilles, regional menu, home-cooking.
Hotel: 8 rooms. Facilities: shower, private bathroom.
Other points: credit cards accepted, bar, children's menu, à la carte menu, lounge area, modern decor, terrace, pets allowed, car/lorry parking.
◀ *Ars: animal park at Romanèche-Thorins; Beaujolais circuit.*

THONES • Haute-Savoie, 74230

🍴 L'HERMITAGE
(M. Pierre Bonnet) avenue du Vieux-Pont
☎ 50.02.00.31
Directions: RN 509.
Languages spoken: English.
Menu: 60 to 160 Frs 🍽
Accommodation: 120 to 200 Frs.
Restaurant: breakfast from 7.00. Lunch 12.00 to 14.00. Dinner 19.00 to 21.00. Closed 1st week of May, and from 20th Oct to 15th Nov.
Specialities: papillote de saumon, feuilleté d'escargots, foie gras, magrets, pithiviers de Saint-Jacques, poularde landaise, sole belle meunière, fricassé de canette, regional menu, home-cooking.
Hotel: ☆ 45 rooms. Facilities: shower, private bathroom, television, telephone.
Other points: credit cards accepted, bar, children's menu, à la carte menu, lounge area, traditional decor, terrace, car/lorry parking.
◀ *col des Aravis; ski resorts; museum.*

TIGNIEU • Isère, 38230

🍴 AUBERGE DES CHARMILLES
(Mme Josiane Renon) 71 route de Bourgoin
☎ 78.32.23.57
Directions: RD 18.
Menu: 52 to 110 Frs (plat du jour 35 Frs).
Restaurant: breakfast from 7.00. Lunch from 12.00 until 14.30. Closed Sun afternoon.
Specialities: grenouilles, gratin dauphinois, home-cooking.
Other points: bar, children's menu, à la carte menu.

TOULON • Var, 83000

🍴 RESTAURANT DE L'ESCAILLON
(M. Bernard Lemaire) 2 rue Chateaubriand
☎ 94.24.21.02
Directions: RN 8, the Toulon/Marseille road.
Menu: 58 Frs (¼ bottle of wine included).
Restaurant: breakfast from 6.00. Lunch from 12.00 until 14.00. Dinner from 19.30 until

21.00. Closed last 2 weeks of Aug.
Specialities: home-cooking.
Other points: credit cards accepted, bar, traditional decor, pets allowed, car/lorry parking.

LA TOUR-DU-PIN • Isère, 38110

🍴 CHEZ BABETH
(Mme Elisabeth Rostaing)
Saint-Didier-de-la-Tour ☎ 74.97.15.87
Directions: RN 6, between La Tour-du-Pin and Les Abrets, on the main road.
Menu: 58 to 98 Frs 🍽
Restaurant: breakfast from 5.30. Lunch from 12.00 until 14.00. Dinner from 19.00 until 21.00. Closed Sun evening.
Specialities: grenouilles, home-cooking.
Other points: credit cards accepted, bar, à la carte menu, modern decor, terrace, car/lorry parking.
◀ *Walibi: leisure park; lac de Charavines; medieval cities of Saint-Chef and Crémieu.*

TRETS • Bouches-du-Rhône, 13530

🍴 L'AERODROME
(M. Pascal Seclet – SARL MAS) Route Nationale 7 ☎ 42.61.48.26
Directions: RN 7.
Languages spoken: English, Spanish, Italian.
Menu: 60 Frs.
Restaurant: closed Sat evening, Sun, public holidays and the following day.
Specialities: regional menu, home-cooking.
Other points: credit cards accepted, bar, lounge area, terrace, pets allowed, car/lorry parking, facilities open 24 hours.
◀ *basilica at Saint-Maximin; cooperative wine-cellars.*

TULLINS-FURES • Isère, 38210

🍴 RESTAURANT DU CENTRE
(Mme Monique Duclos) 110 boulevard Michel-Perret ☎ 76.07.93.08
Directions: RN 92, the Grenoble/Valence road.
Languages spoken: English.
Menu: 55 Frs (wine and coffee included).
Restaurant: breakfast from 8.00. Lunch from 12.00 until 14.30. Dinner from 19.00 until 24.00. Closed Wed afternoon.
Specialities: (to order) regional menu, home-cooking.
Other points: bar, traditional decor, pets allowed, car/lorry parking.
◀ *Grenoble; Le Vercors; La Chartreuse massif.*

VALLEIRY • Haute-Savoie, 74520

🍴 L'ARCHE DE BELLEGARDE-VALLEIRY
(M. Yannick Lebret) A40, services at Valleiry Nord ☎ 50.04.27.27 [Fax] 50.04.29.05
Directions: A40, accessible in both directions.
Restaurant: open 6.00 until 22.00.
Other points: credit cards and foreign currency accepted.

VAUX-EN-BUGEY • Ain, 01150

⊨ LE RAMEQUIN
(Mme Michelle Gallon) Route Nationale 75
☎ 74.35.95.09
Directions: RN 75, the Grenoble road.
Restaurant: breakfast from 6.00. Lunch from
11.45 until 14.30. Dinner from 19.15 until 21.30.
Closed Sat, Sun, 2 weeks in Aug and 2 weeks in
Dec.
Specialities: home-cooking.
Other points: credit cards accepted, bar, terrace,
pets allowed, car/lorry parking.

VENISSIEUX • Rhône, 69200

⊨ LES ROUTIERS
(M. Hervé Ligier) 66 boulevard Joliot-Curie
☎ 78.76.49.94
Directions: the Saint-Etienne/Marseille road.
Languages spoken: Spanish.
Menu: 66 Frs (wine and coffee included).
Restaurant: breakfast from 6.00. Lunch from
11.30 until 15.00. Dinner from 19.00 until 21.00.
Closed Sat, Sun, and in Aug.
Specialities: home-cooking.
Other points: bar, modern decor, terrace, pets
allowed, car parking.

VEYRINS-THUELLIN
Isère, 38630

⊨ L'OUSTRAL
(M. Raymond Belingheri) Le Bourg
☎ 74.33.94.27
Directions: RN 75, Bourg Grenoble.
Languages spoken: English, Italian.
Menu: 55 to 110 Frs.
Accommodation: 130 to 170 Frs.
Restaurant: breakfast from 6.30. Lunch from
12.00 until 14.30. Dinner from 19.00 until 22.00.
Closed 1st 2 weeks in Oct.
Specialities: regional menu, home-cooking.
Hotel: ☆ 9 rooms. Facilities: shower.
Other points: bar, children's menu, à la carte
menu, modern decor, terrace, car/lorry parking.
⫷ *Walibi: leisure park; centrale nucléaire (nuclear
power station) at Crest-Malville.*

VILLARS-SUR-VAR
Alpes Maritimes, 06710

⊨ AUBERGE ALP' AZUR
(M. Maurice Sécula) Gare de Villars-sur-Var,
Route Nationale 202 ☎ 93.05.78.44
Directions: RN 202, the Nice/Digne/Grenoble
road.
Languages spoken: English, Italian.
Menu: 65 to 200 Frs.
Restaurant: breakfast from 6.00
Specialities: regional menu, home-cooking.
Other points: credit cards accepted, bar, terrace,
pets allowed, car/lorry parking.

VILLEFRANCHE-SUR-SAONE
Rhône, 69400

⊨ LE RELAIS CALADOIS
(M. Denis Gimaret) 300 rue Joseph-Léon-
Jacquemaire ☎ 74.60.69.88
Directions: RN 6, Mâcon.
Languages spoken: English, Spanish.
Restaurant: breakfast from 5.30. Lunch from
11.30 until 15.00. Dinner from 19.00 until 22.30.
Closed Sat, Sun, and in Aug.
Specialities: regional menu, home-cooking.
Other points: credit cards accepted, bar, lounge
area, modern decor, terrace, pets allowed, car/
lorry parking.
⫷ *caveaux (vaults) du Beaujolais.*

VILLENEUVE
Alpes-de-Haute-Provence, 04180

🛏 CHEZ ROGER
(SARL Pierre Curri) Route Nationale 96
☎ 92.78.42.47
Directions: RN 96, between Aix and Sisteron.
Menu: 60 Frs.
Accommodation: 100 Frs.
Restaurant: breakfast from 5.00. Closed Sun,
2 weeks at end of Aug and 2 weeks at Christmas.
Specialities: home-cooking.
Hotel: 7 rooms. Facilities: shower, private bathroom.
Other points: credit cards accepted, bar, lounge
area, traditional decor, terrace, pets allowed, car/
lorry parking.
⫷ *Manosque region; Sisteron; the Lubéron; gorges
of the Verdon.*

VILLEURBANNE • Rhône, 69100

⊨ CHEZ NICOLE
(Mme Nicole Grass) 165 rue Jean-Voillot
☎ 72.37.52.00
Directions: the Paris/Geneva road.
Restaurant: lunch from 11.00 until 14.00. Closed
mid-Aug.
Specialities: home-cooking.
Other points: bar, modern decor, pets allowed,
car/lorry parking.

VINEZAC • Ardèche, 07110

⊨ AUBERGE DES COTES
(M. Serge Zagar) Les Côtes ☎ 75.36.80.10
Directions: RD 104, between Aubenas and Alès.
Menu: 70 to 120 Frs.
Accommodation: 100 to 135 Frs.
Restaurant: breakfast from 6.00. Lunch from
12.00 until 14.00. Dinner from 19.00 until 20.00.
Closed Sat, Sun, and in Sept.
Specialities: home-cooking.
Hotel: 3 rooms. Facilities: shower.
Other points: credit cards accepted, bar,
traditional decor, pets allowed, car/lorry parking.
⫷ *Vinezac; Balazuc.*

INDEX OF PLACE NAMES

Membership Application Form
Britannia Rescue
FREEPOST
Huddersfield
HD1 1WP

BLOCK LETTERS PLEASE

SURNAME ➤_____ INITIALS ➤ _____ TITLE (Mr/Mrs/Miss/Ms) ➤ _____

ADDRESS ➤ _____

_____ POSTCODE ➤ _____ TEL NO ➤ _____

Cover commences from midnight of date of our receipt of this application form or later if you specify here ➤

COMPLETE SECTIONS A OR B, AND C TOGETHER WITH METHOD OF PAYMENT DETAILS.

A ANNUAL RATES applicable to 31.12.95 or later review date.	Single Vehicle	✓ Tick	Two Vehicles	✓ Tick
SUPERSTART	£26.50		£53.00	
RESCUE PLUS	£30.00		£45.00	
STANDARD	£57.25		£85.90	
COMPREHENSIVE	£75.70		£116.00	
DELUXE	£92.50		£141.50	
Optional extra PERSONAL COVER (with Free Card for Spouse/Domestic Partner Please tick ☐			£18.50	
JOINING FEE (waived if payment made by Direct Debit or Continuous Credit Card Authority)			£10.00	
ENTER TOTAL COST OF TICKED OPTIONS		➤	£	

Note: ANNUAL RATE is a single payment, providing 12 months cover.

B MONTHLY PREMIUMS (Direct Debit Only)	Single Vehicle	✓ Tick	Two Vehicles	✓ Tick
STANDARD	£5.75		£8.60	
COMPREHENSIVE	£7.60		£11.60	
DELUXE	£9.25		£14.15	
Optional extra PERSONAL COVER (with Free Card for Spouse/Domestic Partner Please tick ☐			£1.85	
ENTER TOTAL COST OF TICKED OPTIONS		➤	£	

Note: MONTHLY PREMIUMS are continuous payments available only by DIRECT DEBIT until cancelled by either party and are subject to amendments from time to time. Members are given prior notice of any change of payment.
CAR GRILLE BADGE (inc. VAT and P&P) £5.50 payment by cheque only ☐   Additional vehicles – details on request.

C 1st CAR DETAILS	Reg No ▼	Year New ▼	Make ▼	Model ▼
2nd CAR DETAILS	Reg No ▼	Year New ▼	Make ▼	Model ▼

The above rates include Insurance Premium Tax at 2.5% and are applicable only to vehicles under 2.5 tonnes/2,540 kilos gross vehicle weight.
I wish to apply for membership of Britannia Rescue and I certify that the vehicle(s) to be covered is/are fully roadworthy and in normal use and is/are insured and kept at my home address here given. I agree to abide by the Terms and Conditions of Britannia Rescue. **ALL MEMBERS MUST SIGN.**

SIGNATURE ➤ [_____]   DATE ➤ [_____]

METHODS OF PAYMENT

1. TRANSCASH ➤   Complete Transcash forms from the Post Office, make payable to Britannia Recovery Ltd., Girobank Account No 3006980. Please enclose receipt with application form. Standard Transcash fee will be payable.

2. CHEQUE/P.O. ➤   Make payable to Britannia Recovery Ltd.   Cheque/P.O [_____]

3. CREDIT CARD ➤   Please debit my   ACCESS ☐   VISA ☐   (please tick)

Card No [_|_|_|_|_|_|_|_|_|_|_|_|_|_|_|_|_]   Card Expiry Date [_____]

4. CONTINUOUS CREDIT CARD AUTHORITY ➤ Sign here only if you wish to authorise automatic renewal by credit card:
I authorise Britannia Recovery Ltd. until further written notice, to charge my Access/Visa card account with unspecified amounts in respect of my annual Britannia Rescue membership.

SIGNATURE ➤ [_____]   DATE ➤ [_____]

5. DIRECT DEBIT ➤   Please complete the direct debit mandate overleaf.

As part of our service, Britannia Rescue will send you information about valuable offers especially negotiated for members. If you prefer not to receive this information, please tick here. ☐

The Direct Debit Guarantee

This Guarantee is offered by all Banks and Building Societies that take part in the Direct Debit Scheme. The efficiency and security of the Scheme is monitored and protected by your own Bank or Building Society.

If the amounts to be paid or the payment dates change, you will be told of this in advance by at least 30 days as agreed.

If an error is made by us or your Bank/Building Society, you are guaranteed a full and immediate refund from your branch of the amount paid.

You can cancel a Direct Debit at any time, by writing to your Bank or Building Society. Please also send a copy of your letter to us.

BRITANNIA RESCUE

Instruction to your Bank or Building Society to pay Direct Debits.

Please fill in the whole form and send it to: Britannia Recovery Ltd, Freepost (no stamp required) Huddersfield HD1 1WP

1. Names and full address of your Bank or Building Society Branch

To: The Manger

_____ Bank or Building Society

Address _____

Postcode _____

2. Names(s) of Account holder(s)

_____

3. Branch sort code
(from the top right hand corner of your cheque)

[__] - [__] - [__]

Direct Debit

Originators Identification Number

9	1	2	9	3	0

4. Bank or Building Society Account number

5. Britannia Recovery Ltd. reference number (for office use only)

6. Instructions to your Bank or Building Society
Please pay Britannia Recovery Ltd. Direct Debit from the account detailed on this Instruction subject to the safeguards assured by The Direct Debit Guarantee.

Signature(s)

_____

Date

Banks and Building Societies may not accept Direct Debit instructions for some types of account.

CLUB BON VIVEUR
The Ultimate Dining Scheme!

CLUB BON VIVEUR is an exciting British nationwide scheme for diners, operated by *Les Routiers*, through which you are invited to rediscover the *Joie de Vivre* in hundreds of restaurants throughout Britain, offering more than 23 types of international cuisine!

As a *Club Bon Viveur* cardholder, you are entitled to a range of substantial discounts and benefits, including reductions of up to 50% on food bills (subject to individual restaurants' restrictions), when dining with one or more guests. You can use your card as often as you wish, in any of the establishments listed in the *Joie de Vivre* Directory. The Directory will be sent to you with your Members' Pack, when you join.

Membership of *Club Bon Viveur* costs just £30 per annum, which can very quickly be recouped through discounts.

MEMBERSHIP BENEFITS INCLUDE:

- Discounted food prices when dining out
- The *Joie de Vivre* Directory for easy reference
- Discounts on purchases of *Les Routiers* guidebooks and publications
- Other promotional offers

To apply for your *Club Bon Viveur* membership, simply complete the application form (overleaf) and return it with your payment of £30 to:

The Club Secretary
CLUB BON VIVEUR
25 Vanston Place
London SW6 1AZ

Your personal invitation . . .

To: Club Bon Viveur
25 Vanston Place, London SW6 1AZ
Telephone: 0171 385 6644 Fax: 0171 385 7136

Please enrol me in the Club Bon Viveur
National Dining Scheme, at an annual
subscription of £30.00 inc. VAT.
PLEASE COMPLETE IN BLOCK CAPITALS

Mr/Mrs/Ms/Miss

Forename

Surname

Address
Postcode

Telephone

Profession

THE ABOVE INFORMATION WILL BE KEPT IN THE STRICTEST
CONFIDENCE AND USED FOR INTERNAL PURPOSES ONLY.

I enclose my cheque for £30.00 inc. VAT, made payable to
Club Bon Viveur
Or
Charge my Access/Visa/Mastercard/Amex No.

Expiry Date

IF YOU ARE INTRODUCING A NEW MEMBER,
PLEASE COMPLETE YOUR DETAILS BELOW

Restaurant Name

Postcode

OR

Cardmember Name

Membership No.

Postcode